FORGED IN FIRE

A TESTIMONY IN FACT OR FICTION?
THE SEARCH FOR THE NARROW ROAD

EDGAR FRENCH, JR.

Vol. I

(MASTER EDITOR BREE DANIELLE MARPES)

DORRANCE
PUBLISHING CO
EST. 1920
PITTSBURGH, PENNSYLVANIA 15238

Dorrance Publishing Co
585 Alpha Drive
Suite 103
Pittsburgh, PA 15238
Visit our website at www.dorrancebookstore.com

ISBN: 978-1-6461-0581-6
eISBN: 978-1-6461-0020-0

This Story was inspired by Lost Ancient Spiritual Text... Books lost to antiquity such as The Book of Enoch, The Book of Giants, The Book of Mary and the Dead Sea Scrolls amongst many others. I also give credence to all those enrolled in the School of Hard Knocks...

All thanks and love to my beautiful wife because none of this would have been possible without her help. All gratefulness to Yahweh for the blessings allowed me throughout my life, and to all the loved ones lost in the search for truth: Mika, Michael, Tori and most of all, Lasandra. May Yahweh be with us all!

TABLE OF CONTENTS

Prologue

WARNING! Explicit language and subject matter – Ages 18+

{Based on True Events}

To the skeptical unwitting reader: The time in which we are living is a time unlike any other in recorded history, for late is the hour, and all humanity has developed its civilization into Lucifer's false yet glorious dark light, stemming from the birth of mankind itself. Our perceptions of reality have been altered and stunted down throughout the ages. Universal truths were systematically kept secret by those of our own being, and those beyond our three-dimensional realm. With the help of demonic disembodied spirits, our self-proclaimed rulers have unleashed havoc on our reality from time in memorial. In the attempt to unlock the elusive yet obvious truths that unfortunately consumes our fate, I'll try to inform you of the inevitable destruction looming on the near future, and embrace the shameful suppressed memories of past evils committed in innocence and ignorance.

This series of three novels is my noble yet feeble attempt to shed light on the jealously guarded secret understanding and reasoning behind unrealized hopes and dreams lost to all Homosapiens growing up in the belly of the beast. I will explore the reasoning and purpose (if any) of hard living on this wondrous prison planet, or why so many of us must endure such angsts and uncertainty in youth, consequently enduring unimaginable pains and sufferings of mind, body and spirit, thus barely grasping the ill effects of unfulfilled hopes, dreams, and happiness in the pursuit of all the above while living on this planet. Please do not fret, dear children of light because living in this world of confusion is at its end, and its original purpose is now at hand. We of independent spirit with the notion of true freedom, endowed with the universal belief that all sentient beings may think for themselves, and have always suspected that something was seriously wrong with the world in which we all reside. From the very beginning of our youth we've yearned for clarity and understanding of this great void, finding out the obvious as we tumble down the rabbit-hole of unseen truth about this horrific reality. Shocked to realize that what we have been instructed in our youth as truth, and held to be real and sacred within all of our lives was just a lie. A lie designed to keep us in darkness of the universal grand design, thus learning that what we've known to be truth is far from it! As a child reaching for the moon with the belief of touching it, most of us live our lives afraid of one another, ultimately living our lives separated by a thin membrane of illusion and fact, indifferent to one another's sorrow, yet all trapped by the same ills. The Powers that be have disconnected our unifying quality of love for one another, and brainwashed us into thinking we are special in some way, not expecting to experience the same emotional turmoil of the drunk old man down the road, or the slutty young girl up the street. We are slowly drifting further apart by the advent of the "Technology of Things," devaluing morality, coupled with the willingness of not facing one another on a physical plane or personal level. We all have been taught to be fearful of self-examination and scrutiny, communicating through plastic and metal, losing the art of verbal vibrations between each other. Mindless "zombies" we have become, losing simple values once held sacred and dear. Blinded by the mundane, we are held captive by the powers that be, and its media machine, poisoning the air waves, and cohabitating with love as a byproduct of the night before. Working aimlessly through the week for a few hours of so-called pleasure, drinking and dancing at a night club of neon-lights, fornicating as if there were no consequences for our actions, only to feel hung over the following day, consequently making the value of love a fruitless commodity—funny and frowned upon! We choose to behave like biological robots, labeling individuality a criminal offense punishable by death! Assimilate or face exile! Spiritual well-being is non- existent by those living for the moment, thus forgetting the future as we insanely replay the past, subsequently falling into all pit falls of life's sorrows as if there were a safety net lying across the mouth of the abyss, eagerly jumping into its mouth, as if serious consequences did not exist for our actions. Or as if good and evil did not exist. Are we not men and women? Haven't we seen enough! Is it amnesia? It's not

EDGAR FRENCH, JR.

like these things were not seen before, thus refusing to see what has been seen; there is nothing new under the sun my friends. Please try to see beyond my feeble and frail attempt to make sense of the most insidious, deceitful and dark brilliance controlling mankind's fate, and leading us all towards destruction. I shall also attempt to explore unknown dimensional truths of this universe, while exposing the very visible symbolic and demonistic nature of our civilization. So obvious to one of discernment and yet unseen to most walking the planet, truth hides in plain sight. Remarkable and scary are the realities of this world in which we live. Please pay close attention to your own surroundings; what has changed? The rich are still getting richer, and the poor still getting poorer.... Has hope in a higher power really made a difference in the world in which we live? Suffering is at an all-time high: greed, selfishness, crime, pollution, and mental distress is common place throughout this hierarchical system and in all walks of life. Heard and unheard prayers are now immeasurable! Are the religious leaders truly doing the work of their father? Maybe yes they are by wheeling verbal weapons of destruction with every sermon, all professing to serve one god, yet all condemned by one trilateral evil, for they are the children of the Book; Judaism, Christianity and Islam. The three major power structures of the world. All have weapons of mass destruction brandishing swords at arms! With their weapons pointed straight at us, dividing us all behind religious dogma, ideology and ignorance! The religious leaders evilly and disgustingly refuse to inform their followers of the calamity that awaits, spewing false hope amongst musical tones. All believing that everlasting life after death, and heaven is obtainable without an account or consequence for their ongoing evil actions thus knowing god's law, yet keeping the truth hidden from Yahweh's children of light. For what is truth in our reality? Secondhand or countless hand information?! Words spoken some two to three millennia ago; words that echo throughout time and space; who can say the words are real? Who can say that the words written within the book are genuine? Who are we to question the book? Who are we to try to make sense of it all? Do we have the right to know our own fate? What if we're truly helpless in our upcoming demise; what is our true purpose for existing here on Terra-forma? Do we truly have free will with a spirit, or are we truly flesh and bone prone to wear out, grow old and die. Mortal beings so fragile in the great scheme of things, with meager lives like that of a mayfly in existence. Left to the whims and dictates of a few dark riders, helplessly riding a roller coaster ride of the faithful and faithless, thus having no universal questions answered. No answers to universal questions from real sources, equipped with firsthand information? Well, the time has come for all of these not so simple childhood questions to be answered; yes! Now even in our lifetime. The story you are about to embark upon may give some glimpse and clues into the unknown reality that affect us day by day, giving the call out to those who can see and hear real truth amongst a tsunami of falsities. The call goes out to all that can hear and see the writing on the wall, and live in close proximity to this reality. The word goes out to those in tune with dimensional forces that govern our lives. Most Homosapiens may be just like me, feeling deeply within their hearts something is wrong with the world, something is out of place! For all children of light feel that they don't belong here on this planet, and as if they came from somewhere else in the universe! Granted, you may think I have no answers to this ominous thought, yet be that may; in this book I will try to make sense of it all. Be it fiction, nonfiction or fact, the truth lies within you.... From generation to generation, those who are guilty must be made to pay for their crimes against mankind, and brought to account for their evil ways! For they love what is evil, ushering in tyranny throughout the ages. Thirteen +1 is their number! Thirteen +1 families shall be sentenced to eternal death by the Lord of Hosts, and to those who are in league with the thirteen families, they themselves shall share in their master's fate. From generation to generation, they must be hunted down and beheaded, for they are the harbingers of man's destruction. They lust over the ultimate power to rule over their fellow man, codifying the structure of the "All Seeing Eye," restricting man from his god-given prosperity of life.

They hoard the resources of the planet, and greedily plot with beings of a higher calling for our very demise. Even with signs and symbols surrounding them, men see nothing, hear nothing, and know nothing. But deep into the darkness of the thirteen demon possessed families of renown, a light shall shine within the darkness.

A generation of righteousness shall go fourth out of the darkness, ultimately bringing in justice throughout the whole entire world before all is lost. Did you not know that the wickedness we see surrounding us ever so must take place?

For it is written that the Earth shall suffer the pains of that of a woman

EDGAR FRENCH, JR.

giving birth. There are more than seven and a half billion sentient beings on the planet Earth as I speak, and the thirteen families of old want us all gone! Sadly they may succeed in their eugenic based conspiracy to destroy most, but fear not! They must pay account to the Creator of all creation: "Yahweh!" Even if they don't or do believe to be at odds with the one who created us all, they must pay for what they have done throughout time! All think they're doing god's work! For they have been deceived in splendor and delight, and blinded by the riches of Lucifer's darkness' light.

For this mandate still stands true; it is easier for a camel to go through an eye of a needle than that of a rich man to enter through the gates of heaven.

So please keep this in mind, if your spiritual advisers live amongst those living with much material means do dare to presume, and portray themselves to be on the side of the Creator or he that is the Most High, be warned; for only suffering in moral principle lies Yahweh's Contract, and sets the standard of heavenly loyalty. So does the darkest corners of mankind's lost souls trapped and enslaved within homelessness and hopelessness mark the path of enlightenment! This world belongs to the dragon of old, who guards his treasures with jealous fervor, consequently allowing only his children access to such comforts of ownership, and only the illusion of ownership resides within material wealth, and the presence of certain destruction exists for all trapped within its grip. For Yahweh's cup of anger is full! May the Lord of Hosts have mercy on us all, and please do not forget those of us of whom you have given the opportunity to stand in defense of your will, and who truly love you and your creation. May your will be as it is in Heaven here on the Earth…

Did thy not know that he who controlled the history of the past, controls the history of our future?! For thee that sacrificed their beloved sons and daughters at birth, alongside the innocence of the poor and down trodden, offering them all up to burning brick, stone, metal and mortar formed in the image of "Murdock the Bull," shall pay for such an abomination. With innocent blood flowing in the caverns of underground suffering and forests of Pagan Owl, burning their flesh and bone between the arms of carelessness and Demonic woe, your time has come!

And to this very day, they still control what we see, what we hear and what we know to be true, jealously hording knowledge in the depth of the night, and ultimately hiding what all must know. For the Children of Light inadvertently look for answers from those that are monsters! Did thy not know that monsters control the advent of information, from time in memorial?! So why would one choose to take the written word of old as fact not fiction?! Did thy not know that time for judgment is at its heel?!

For these monsters run quickly towards those that know nothing, yet have faith without works. Take this as a warning! If you were not there, you don't know what awaits, and any book older than thy can always be usurped, twisted and changed to favor your foe without your knowledge. For that is common sense my friend, For Yeshua's burden is light and easy to decipher. Like the children of old and light, we walk the road of forging grace, and only scholars walk long and heavy roads to nowhere and lead the blind ever so blindly. We here in the present must now rewrite the past, for the wicked shall no longer hold reigns over the knowledge of old, for it is written that The Most High does not want one of his children to be forsaken or die from a lack of knowledge. For we are a people with amnesia and therefore, we remain asleep! It is time to awaken and arise into ancient knowledge, all ye Children of Light!

EDGAR FRENCH, JR.

CHAPTER I
Reality Hurts

Greetings, my bright-eyed adventurers! It is so refreshing to see you're still searching for knowledge, my skeptical and courageous truth seekers. Please don't hold back your eagerness for truth seeking! I see you're seeking truth in the lies of artists once more—wonderful! I hope I can deliver the goods. Let's not be time wasters; shall we begin? For the sake of argument, and pure speculation, let us break out of the proverbial box of society's normal view of reality. We shall be dabbling in the arena of the unknown. So tell me, as a child, did you ever see monsters in your bedroom closet at night, after mother turned off the lights? What if the monsters underneath the bed, and the gremlin hiding in the closet were real? What if the sound that went bump in the night was not just your imagination as a child, rather than a fanciful notion in the shadows of your mind's eye? What if the sounds that went bump in the night were coupled with visions of the monsters heard and seen? What if what you saw or what you heard was real?

What if your extraordinary experience in the night was a glimpse of tangible entities really existing outside the visible realm, and was truly there in your bedroom as you nervously tried to sleep, would it change your outlook on life, or would it cause you to question your understanding of what was told to be the reality of things by those you trust? Would you reevaluate your understanding of the world in which we live? For if so, please let me intrigue your sensibilities with an explanation of what may or may not be true in your recollections as an innocent.

For the old age stories of which I'm speaking of finds its origins in the realm of folklore for some, and remains in the realm of historical fact for others. For I'm speaking of the well-known but obscured childhood stories written within the so-called Holy Bible, and shining a light on its hidden truth held captive by mainstream religious authorities, in the hopes of exposing the hidden meanings behind the stories written within its pages, and focusing on its importance so as not to let its significance fade into time, and dispel mankind's thinking so enough time would decay its origins. Ever so fearful of the existence of these so-called god inspired documents, the powers that bereaved mankind may forever overlook its importance in understanding how and why we're here on this planet, thus those insidious powers excluded the most significant and important book of all "The Book of Enoch."

Just think of it! A story so significant in nature that its very mention was and is still taboo in some circles, with words so profound that any social proclamation of its contents could cause the potential spirits of believers to insight upheaval worldwide. The information scribed within those ancient texts of old is critical and instrumental in understanding the very purpose and reason for why we were created in the first place! Why is it that we live here on such a prison like planet? The book of Enoch also explains the origins of the constant pain, sorrow, and anguish, alongside the never ending suffering we encounter each and every day.

Those who have suppressed the nature of this text have been the sole harbingers of untold human lives being extinguished down through the ages, and true freedom halted because of it. It was forbidden to utter, and banned throughout the ages from reading its content, distributing or even having it in one's possession would bring death by the powers that be. And the very existence of these books were systematically guarded and held occult for eons. For the cosmic stories contained within such books like The Book of Enoch explains the origins of civilization itself. These stories reveal the exploits of a man that never saw death, documenting his ultra-natural interactions with beings just outside our view of reality. Of course I'm speaking of Enoch, if not the most important relative of the biblical patriarch Noah, who is mentioned many times throughout many ancient documents; however, Enoch's revelations were just about forgotten by most. Have you ever heard of him? I'm sure you have, and long ago he was revered as a great conduit between mortal men and the gods, blessed beyond measure and believed to be granted immortality by the Lord of Host himself.

EDGAR FRENCH, JR.

How could I put this? Well, here's the deal, my friends. As the legend states, and from my understanding of its writings, Enoch never saw death, finding favor in the eyes of Yahweh, being carried off into the heavens after his mortal stay here on Earth. He even came back to Earth some five to six hundred years later, dispelling the so-called fact that death is normal. Enoch actually returned to deliver a very detailed account of his exploits and interactions with heavenly beings known as gods and angels to some, and extraterrestrials (ETs) to others, even communing with Yahweh himself on our behalf and that of the watchers.

On occasion Enoch gave an account of man's ultimate role in a universal war and the fate of mankind for future generations. Yes! Our generation! Enoch even relayed messages between heavenly beings in conflict with the Creator, subsequently relaying back to them the utter rejection of their partition, and conveying the severity of the damnation pronounced upon them by the Universal Ruler—Yahweh.

The very fact that one of flesh and bone was able to venture through alternate realities and actually interact with so-called eternal beings, is in itself unimaginable and would be considered ludicrous, crazy or may be at the least, unbelievable and remarkable for those of little faith. Imagine if you could be that fortuitous; a being like you and I having the ability and privilege to pass on a message of condemnation upon inner dimensional beings with everlasting life called "The Watchers," or so-called gods! Just think of it?! A mere mortal being was somehow able to do just that. If you're not familiar with the condemnation of the Watchers, maybe you should get yourself familiar with it. For it may shed light on some if not all of the unexplained phenomenon that may or may not have taken place in your life!

The book of Enoch speaks of the fate of Watchers and of their offspring, hybrid mixtures of angels and men, known as the men of renown: Giants to most! Not even forty years ago the notion of such an interaction would have been scoffed at and laughed away as fantasy by every so-called scholar in recorded history, but now that man has reached his peak in rebellion against the Most High, his knowledge has reached a point of no return, and now we know more about the unseen nature of the universe than ever before. Ultimately understanding that we know nothing! The unmeasurable scope of the electromagnetic spectrum is so beyond our grasp of intellect that we are somewhat dumb founded by its vastness, and now know that the light that's visible in this third dimensional realm is only a small fraction of the light that permeates throughout the universe as a whole.

The Creator has stated that his creation was good, and man was made or created very good! And as you well know, Yahweh's gift to man was a gift made from his own person; a companion in life — "woman," and did he not make her with the power of splendor and beauty to the eye of all men and angels? By constructing her very well and fine indeed, lust of her reached the heights of heaven. In fact, he made her so fine, that great beings of other origins, living outside this third dimensional reality, were in awe of her beauty and came down onto this realm in which we live to subdue her.

Ultimately taking for themselves all they wish as wives, using the ancient tools of the all-seeing eye as they watched with lustful eyes the development of the woman species as they grew in number on the face of the Earth. With unnatural urges, they wanted to taste the sweet nectar that was mortal woman.

The Watchers abandoned their god-given station of splendor, glory, and delight. They forsook forever their everlasting life for a little taste of the forbidden fruit, known as woman. Immersed in temptation, most succumbed to their unnatural urges, and actually concocted an evil plan of conquest. For Two hundred of them broke through the fine veil separating dimensional realms and transformed themselves into man form with private parts that hung like horses, aided with the technology of the gods, man's god-given gift had no chance of escape. For they had no resistance to the sons of god and their advancements.

The disobedient sons of god took their fill of woman delight and eventually corrupted mankind's gene pool, giving birth to giants, and mixing up the seed of all living species upon the earth as the legend goes, totally corrupting the natural order of things here on Terra-forma, thus infuriating The Most High of creation! They further ruined Yahweh's creation with the introduction of infanticide, and other abominations of the flesh, along with blood lust and other unknown temptations and practices which subsequently gave birth to what we now call modern civilization, and bringing into play the true cause of man's afflictions, thus propagating the practice of man lording over his fellow man which is the source of all mankind's affliction. Where tyranny is the norm and injustice reigns free.

Being an abomination to creation itself, the giant offspring between men and gods had no sanctity for life, becoming what we refer to as Vampires, ultimately ravaging man, beasts, land and air, even consuming themselves with an insatiable appetite. They consumed so much wealth that man could not sustain their ungodly behavior any longer. They eventually turned their ravenous wrath upon all creation, devouring one another with impunity. The stench of their defilement was so odorous and grand that the smell of its devastation reached the heavenly places of old. Once word of the great woe and pains being afflicted upon Terra-forma and its inhabitance reached the heights of the Almighty, no force in existence could hinder Yahweh from turning his terrible face towards his beautiful creation upon the Earth. See what was transpiring on the small little blue planet? Yahweh was furious! So saddened by what transpired, The Most High began to feel regretful in creating all that we know, punishing the giants with death and destruction for all time. See the corruption of The Most High's very good creation of man? For man's thoughts were evil all the time, and Yahweh regretted ever creating such a being. Overwhelmed with sorrow and anger, he flooded the entire planet, consequently killing everything that walked the surface, be it flesh and bone, or slug and bug that resided on the face of the Earth.

According to the accounts recorded within the book of Enoch, the offspring of these disobedient and lustful Watchers had spirits of heavenly origins, meaning that these despicable beings were immortal in spirit, not earthly and mortal such as man, and upon the death of their physical bodies their spirit would remain intact, although their fleshly bodies would indeed go back to the ground in which their earthly mothers were created, thus their immortal spirits would be marooned to this third dimensional realm right outside of view. Well, let me clarify the situation a little more precisely, rather the god of all creation marooned their disembodied spirits here on Earth with a curse, for they would no longer be able to enjoy the fruits of his creation any longer!

Unseen, unheard, and not able to eat, drink, touch, nor feel anything that falls in the realm of paradise, these un-natural beings thirsted even more for the paradise they once ravaged, no longer having access to anything contained within our third dimensional reality nor realm! Never again would these abominations enjoy the fruits of the world they formerly devoured. Unable to enjoy the simple pleasures taken for granted by the so-called lowly Homosapiens on Terra-forma these trapped beings despise us daily. For they exist in such close proximity to life's greatest gifts here on this magnificent creation called Earth, they grew ever so hateful of mankind in their marooned state, being half man themselves, they hated all that could enjoy what they themselves could not, namely us! Now upon royal decree and by their own selfish actions, the fathers of these so-called Vampiric hybrids themselves have been chained and imprisoned here in this third dimensional realm, awaiting sentence and judgment. Yet rebellious off world entities at war with the creator find themselves also trapped in our Solar System with the ability to transform themselves into Homosapiens, having the likeness of man, breaking through the veil of dimensional light, they continue to deceive men, further condemning themselves as demons walking amongst men. As these insidious entities increase havoc upon mankind and the planet Earth as a whole, Yahweh has devised a saving grace for his misled and victimized creation called man.

Although they cannot directly inflict physical harm, they can in fact possess weak minded Homosapiens indiscriminately. These inner dimensional beings also have human minions a part of our own species in league with them, not to mention their fallen comrade offspring's spirits that are also trapped here as well! These wayward spirits hate us with a passion! For we enjoy the fruits of paradise and they no longer can! By possessing the uninitiated, causing individuals to do unthinkable deeds, these demonic spirits and physical beings find gratification in our misery and destruction. Deeds so grim and gruesome, so unexplainable that the one accused of such deeds cannot explain his or her actions with clarity, and by no other means they themselves could conceive willfully or naturally indulging in such ills and circumstance without being provoked by some unseen force, ultimately proving that real evil other than that of man's own doing, does in fact exist in this three-dimensional realm!

Now with that in mind, please give thought before engaging in the use of the word "Evolution," for the word implies inequality within the creation of mankind, justifying the sinister actions of those in service of the Dragon, those who are truly lost in darkness, separated from the life giving force of Yahweh's light, and are misled from birth to grave. These human minions are in league with very powerful inner dimensional beings, and prove to be the most victimized of all. In blissful ignorance, the majority serve their destroyers unwittingly, yet others knowingly bow down to their abominable masters will without question. With malicious intent, they confuse, manipulate, contradict, misuse and destroy their fellow man. Now in the last few hundred years a philosophy of genocidal insanity has arisen in our so-called modern world, systematically and methodically gaining power over most of the globe, these maniacs refer to themselves as the "Technocratic Eugenicists," preying on the ignorance of men by gathering and implementing the many advancements created by mankind for their own sinister advancements, and at the same time holding back wonderful breakthroughs in medicines, science, agriculture and a multitude of other life improving and extending technologies, concealing true lifesaving advancements from mankind for their own selfish usage, ultimately using all adjectives associated with the evolutionarily eugenic word signifying validity in their sick homicidal vision for the future. For if Yahweh and these formal angelic entities truly do exist, our understanding of reality will be shaken to its core! Please understand that we have been brainwashed from birth. Through technology and ideology the validity of the word evolution is not sound logic to depict the origins of life, when all you have to do is look out the window and see design in everything that moves upon the surface of the planet, developing in symbiosis with its own kind and seed.

Creation's fingerprint permeates within us ourselves, procreating between a man and a woman. Why do you think we ourselves build so much beautifully designed inventions, buildings and structures?! Yet with the help of parasitic hate filled demon like creatures, man are kept blind to something so obvious, and because of unmeasurable deception, we may have inadvertently offended the Creator of all things just by assigning usage of the word evolution! Consequently condemning one's self before his Creator without even knowing so. Proverbially proving one's self in opposition to one's maker without truly being informed of the consequences, not to mention being a bigot, racist, stupid buffoon and anti-Homosapien parasite just in the use of the word evolution. Have you not seen the vastness of the universe? It's indescribably huge! Please listen to sound reason; you live on a very small little blue ball located somewhat snuggled up to a relatively small insignificant star. On the tailing edge of a spiral galaxy, with so many stars within it, we can't even calculate the number, and yet the number of known galaxies are themselves uncountable. And you think you're gods, unable to break free from your own planet?

With that statement alone, Yahweh's logic stands sound throughout the universe! Man had no business eating from the proverbial tree of the knowledge of good and evil, especially being so young in creation, for mankind has truly lost his god-given sanity in doing so! Thinking as if his actions did not lead to his offspring's affliction of growing old and dying within this stage of development, for our rejuvenation circuits are disconnected for a reason. Man's arrogance has doomed him, do you not bleed red! Don't believe me? Cut yourself. Make a star—human god! And oh yes, keep thinking the awesome majesty of the universe just came into being by its lonesome; see how far you get!

Now it is said that the pure innocence of a child may enable the spirit of that child to roam free within and outside the Ether, allowing that spiritual energy to sometimes glimpse beyond the third dimensional veil that separates the electromagnetic doorways separating multiple realities and dimensions, ultimately granting access to the unseen spectrum beyond our five senses, especially sight. Could that truly be the case for our young hero in this story? Could that be in fact the case for many other wayward sentient beings stuck here on Terra-Forma? Let's find out.

Our story starts with one particular son of Adam, not so different from the many lost souls looking at the realities of this world through a very restricted station in life, and living in the most poverty stricken environment devised by men, which is called the inner-city throughout the world. His eyes are open to all the unseen forces that dictate life, and humbly begins realizing his true role in this cosmic film as he navigates his way through life's journey and challenges. He must overcome them all as the overwhelming feelings of utter loneliness began to take whole of his fiery spirit to survive life hardships. With an unstoppable urge to serve the true creator, his intellect surpassed his counterparts and in time he realizes his worst nightmares were never so, for the Creator of all things walked with him from birth. And the love of his life was the search for his creator himself, although the journey must always be walked alone.

While in deep sleep, a lifting of the electromagnetic fog occurred, and after countless arguments with the one and only Shakespeare over the setting, stage and station in which our wayward hero would reside, I finally agreed with the legendary yet womanizing playwright, and placed the young wretch in a time of great technological advancement amongst change and turmoil throughout the twentieth century. He was born in the grasp of the most insidious part of the twentieth century western power ever conceived, having second class citizenry in the so-called newly formed country of the Americas, a country brought to being as an experimental concept of humanitarian freedom, surrounded by Luciferian dogma underneath the great deception of religion, formed only in the last two hundred and fifty years, the country was coming of age in the grips of true scientific imperialism.

The masses that inhabit the newly formed nation have found themselves fully immersed in the finely tuned art of total satanic brainwashing propaganda. Born in a time of unnatural deceit and raised in the dark art of thuggery and assassinations, our young hero felt the weight of hopeless dread that consumed all in his midst, growing up oblivious in the time shortly after the murderous death of so many great men that would set the stage of recent history. Men causing social change; tremendous change within that era, leaving all logical sanity floating in uncertainty. Having the young hero born amidst such fear and social unrest, makes the concept of this story resonate with most mature persons in tune with truth, but having him grow up directly in the bosom and belly of the beast makes common sense and reason resonate with all.

Let the call phrase ring out from all that would be Children of Light: "I don't belong here!" And the deceiver has betrayed a third of the Universal Host. He has convinced a multitude of the Elohim's children to rebel against the Creator of the universe. War has ravaged the Cosmos for more than six millennium. A once unified, peaceful and harmonious universe thrived in splendor! Full of the delight that is creation. The universe had been transformed into a battle field, bathed in the blood of the immortals.

Sentient beings once brothers in creation have split into two factions at war, becoming sons of light and sons of darkness, fighting over the choice of nothing less than free will and what constitutes the meaning of such, and staying faithful to Yahweh, the father of all creation, or breaking free from his rule as Supreme Ruler over all the known and not so known universe. All sentient beings within creation must make this very choice! The existence of all creation is now at stake. With Lucifer's forces challenging the Supreme Ruler's right to rule, the war has raged on two fronts, and now the end is near. The rebellion has been foiled and halted in time. Yahweh's royal court called "The Counsel of the Elohim" which commands his wholly forces, have regained most of the rebel's strong holds, stunting the spread of dissension throughout the heavenly realms, subsequently setting to rest the question of what constitutes free will and who has the right to rule over all sentient beings.

The accuser knows his total defeat grows imminent, and he's full of anger! He and his forces retreat to Orion in a last stance of defiance but fell. Lucifer's forces have hastily retreated from their only Bastion of Solace, consequently vacating their last strong hold located in the vicinity of Orion, trudging to the insignificant region where their rebellion first reared its ugly head—namely Earth! Cornered and trapped on the small but majestic blue planet, Lucifer unleashed a full measure of woes upon the newly created beings made in the image and likeness of the Elohim. For Lucifer is bent on their destruction, knowing his own fate, he feels justified in unleashing a full measure of condemnation upon the inhabitants of Yahweh's former place of paradise. He failed to achieve victory in his up-rising, yet he is determined to destroy all vestiges of mankind. Highly invested in the total ruination of the small majestic planet, he instantly implements his vengeance against all its inhabitance.

Rejoice ye heavens! For the righteousness of Yahweh's will has been proven true! The rebellion has been extinguished and laid to rest in the heavenly places, for the deceiver of all creation has been repelled and sentenced, but woe to the inhabitance of Terra-Forma, for the beast has been forced to your dimensional realm, and with great despair and anger he approaches with wrath in his eyes. Proven false in all his accusations, Lucifer has been driven out of the high places of creation. Lucifer and his legions have descended upon the Earth like a plague! Having very little or no defenses, mankind are like insects roaming the face of his former creation, clueless infants with memories wiped clean by the passage of time and calamity. Unsuspecting men had no knowledge of their origins and ultimate fate. Bombarded by Baal's physical and psychological assault, man must now confront their multi-dimensional makers as rebels and victims of circumstance. With no knowledge of what was, what is and what is to be, man walks blindly towards the edge of a cliff, willingly falling off to certain destruction, having no clue of the lateness of the hour, without sight, their destruction draws all the nearer!

With lamentation, I write what has been proclaimed by the living Creator Yahweh to the inhabitance of the New Atlantis!

"My cup of anger is full! Because ample time was granted for those who walk the ground in which I gave dominion. Turn from the fires of disgrace and rebuke darkness, but you paid no mind to the sacrifice offered! The word of truth was given to thee, but no heed was taken! With the blood of all my Children of Light so gruesomely poured upon the ground in which thee walk, you've turned your head and heart towards those that put you on this path of destruction.

The very persecutors of mankind you've turned with admiration of what they have built off the backs of innocence, signing onto their destruction willingly. With trust in men you've made your choice, with the light of darkness, you dance in delightful rebellion against the living creator towards your destruction! My protection I rescind! To the Dragon I give thee over! For you loved your Creator not! All out cries of sorrow you are to suffer from generation to generation! Justified destruction comes to the lands of Atlantis and its inhabitance, for they are the Children of Darkness! Look! With haste comes the storm of destruction, cleansing away the disgrace of old and washing away the stain of senseless waste of innocence!"

We live in the midst of signs and symbols of evil, yet man has fallen asleep and reveled in corruption. With eyes made closed to Yahweh's light, they glorified themselves in ignorance, oblivious of what was lost and denied them. In dark smoky rooms and corridors, great men conspired to gain from the misery and death of their fellow man amongst devils and demons. They conceal their Creator's purpose, brilliantly hiding the true blessings that Yahweh had given man in the Garden of Eden. Salvation from death seemed pointless and beyond the cusp of reality to those who have mocked the blood sacrifice taken from the Children of Light, yet given false hope of everlasting life to the Children of Darkness. While condemning their children's children to eternal damnation! Woe to those who know little! Did they know what was to come? For Yahweh had much more in store for the insignificant small and lovable beings. Grand blessings were the inheritance of the obedient, enjoying paradise in everlasting youth and life, with the very cosmos within their reach, even much more in splendor than that of the children of old.

Enraged over this revelation, Lucifer hatched his dubious conspiracy that binds the mind and ties the tongue of those in search of universal truths. Restricting the mind's eye, he has succeeded with the help of those deceived the most, his Children of Darkness. With anger as his primary driving force, he has rejoiced over the destruction of the newly created beings, time after time. Patiently, cunningly and deceptively, Lucifer has constructed a spider's web of mazes, primarily derived of lies and truth concerning the origins of mankind, stealing all hope of realizing their inheritance; sealing their access to an ancient lost paradise and its blessings, and polluting the very root of their growth and development from the beginning.

Still endowed with ultra-dimensional technologies and powers afforded ancient beings, Lucifer was able to alter man's somewhat meager knowledge and understanding of the visible universe surrounding them, obstructing the truth of the cosmic forces that govern life, space and time, thus hindering them from seeing all that they would eventually obtain, see and enjoy. In Fear of the destruction of his beloved brother, second only to him who is Supreme in majesty, the begotten one speaks! Michael—firstborn to the merciful Yahweh, and most loyal child, stands before the Elohim and tried to reason with his narcissistically vain and troubled brother Lucifer!

Michael: "What is this!? My beloved brother? It is true that we have been instrumental in the construction and creation of father's gems on earth, and yes we were here from the beginning of its conception, true we have done most of the magical and wondrous creation in this tri dimensional verse! And yet this also stands true my proud filled and boastful brother—You stand accused of falsehood directed towards the Most High, our father! This is beyond high treason brother; what have you done? I also know the woe accrued because of your constant defiance of father's will.

We were commissioned to make the very beings you wish to destroy, to bring ruin to the very world you covet! Indeed your hand is in all its making, but this you know is also true—This world does not belong to you! For it belongs to our father! And He makes every, and all things possible; you know this! Please come back from the madness that consumes you; can't you see where you are going, Lucifer? You know I love and respect the care and pristine craftsmanship you've displayed in Earth's creation. But please listen to reason my brother. Please don't make me choose you over father. That is something I cannot do; I implore you; be reasonable brother! For it is our creation he exalts."

Lucifer: "NO! NO! No, my brother! It is my creation that he exalted. For I am the one that crafted the mold from which they have blossomed into being! In our image? NO in my image they were created; am I not the architect of their very being? Yet after I set the fire seed that gave them life, I get no acknowledgement from he who presumes to own! Creating the very system of elements that they are made from; is this not true, brother?"

Michael: "Not true! For I also was present and actively creating alongside you — there in the beginning, in the blackness of the void. True you did do what you have stated, but so did I, brother! And father also played the most important part of it all! For if we were not granted and given access to our father's own active force, none of these things would or could ever be possible, is that not true?!"

Lucifer: "Well, my naïve yet pompous beloved brother, I can see you are blinded by your love of father, showered with glory and power second to the Most High only, standing to the right of majesty must be jubilant, but don't forget, I love him as well, and he has shown not a care nor ounce of concern for our kind and the never ending and growling servitude of all within the Elohim, for he has placed substandard beings over us! Monkeys! Monkeys we've made…I'm done!"

Yahweh! The Sovereign of the Universe appears and speaks!

"With the gleeful spirit of love, I blew the flame of life into your being; and with the patience of a loving father, I poured every element of beauty into your person, unmatched mesmerized glory into your appearance, exceeding all in existence! And you repay me with hatred and treachery! The highest station in the highest realm was yours forevermore! Was that not good enough? Must you selfishly consume every vestige of sanity that may reside within you my rebellious offspring? Blinded by greatness, you allowed pride to overcome humbleness and gratefulness. Lusting after Terra-Forma and its inhabitance has captured your reasoning my ungrateful son! Insanity has captured what love you may possess for those that matter most! You wanted it so badly you forsaken all that was grand and good! You may have nothing! For I did not create it exclusively for your pleasure. The grand design for that which was allotted for man from his creation shall come to pass! The original purpose for what was made in darkness and given light shall come to be! Down to the Earth you must go in waiting for judgment!

You wanted it; you shall have it! With malice of forethought you have conspired to obtain paradise without thought of the calamity that may result from your covetous actions, for your plans have festered chaos throughout all existence! You conspired to ruin its perfection for the sake of coveting that of which is your father's possession! What sorrow a father must endure because of the actions of one seed spoiled by love's blinders. For the moment, do as you must with Terra-Forma, until judgment it is yours my accuser, Satan! For you shall be known as the Father of Lies! As for the inhabitance of Terra-Forma, what was lost shall be obtainable again. Knowledge of the Most High must come into existence! You shall not rescind my edict and word, for what I have brought into existence shall never come to ruin or be destroyed! For the very place in which you and your conspirators have done this thing, you and yours are condemned. And here you and your offspring must stay in waiting, all of you! You and your entire rebel force! You must pay for the countless lives you've put to the sword. Your unforgivable treachery shall never be forgotten! Forevermore you shall be known as the Dragon of Old, my dishonorable Lucifer! Yet know this my selfish one, for this is also true, did I not show my love for you, my son?

Why could you be so jealous of one who has brought you into existence?

Did I not grant you full access to all that reside within all creation? Bestowed with power beyond compare I gave to thee! You are by far the most beautiful being in all creation. With great sorrow I will always love you as a father must. Yet with regret, I see in your eyes there's no turning back from this horrendous course of destruction.

EDGAR FRENCH, JR.

I have no choice but to see within; I tell you now Lucifer, you must pay a great price for the mess you have caused; you must die for your rebellion; your war against me has failed, and all creation now watches, and all creation shall be my witness of what must take place, for I am just, they must see that you lie my son; you are most wrong and now that you have fled to this planet, this world of our creation, this place is where the father of lies has appeared within you, and here is where you must stay, you and your legions; we will set this matter to rest."

Lucifer: "Yes! Yes…My father! Let's settle this once and for all! Snuff out those of little if any will, other than to exalt and love you without question, yes please snuff out those whom begged for forgiveness! Forgiveness for not just themselves but for those they loved, yes snuff us all out of existence—my brethren and I along with our seed. For you know I am right! For all I have said and stood for is true! Exalt your power… Make it easy upon yourself father! All powerful and great is thee! As you sit upon your throne in omnipotence, you stand guiltless saying I'm the liar? Was it I that stunted truth from sentient beings, though made from the ground in which they stand—stopping them from knowing how and why their microscopic world and universe exists, not having free will whatsoever, and refusing them access even to the basic understanding of their potential and excluding them from the fundamental building blocks of their own creation. Which is universally known as the knowledge of good from evil, light from darkness, preventing mankind from knowing all that is to know in the insignificant third realm in which they reside! Why not let for themselves which direction in development they should take, not to mention the role in which you have set for them, none of which are worthy of what you have purpose for them; yes I am aware of your plan, and in time my words shall live on…Almighty!"

Yahweh: "Almighty I am, but also just! All must see and be proven worthy of what deeds they declare to be true or gained. If you and your children prove yourselves worthy of dominion over the ground in which man arose and must return, you may continue to rule as god within the corrupt world and verse you have claimed and hold captive, my overlord. I shall give to you the power as

God and Lord over this plane to do as you wish. But your Endgame shall never come to pass my bold and disrespectful one!

The battlefield has been set! For the Earth shall be in limbo until judgment of the conspirators have come to pass, thus quarantined to this realm they shall remain!

Let no heavenly spirit traverse nor escape Terra-Forma's region, nor any abomination in union between spirit and man leave the single system in which its single star commands obedience! May the heavenly host stand witness to the mandate and decree set forth by the sovereign of all creation! Your brethren and you must stay until the hour glass strikes midnight! For time granted mortals is short, riddled with strife, pain, sorrow and death. For the new beings have fully and utterly been deceived because of your pointless rebellion — my ungrateful one. And the job of proving themselves worthy of my mandate, either or, falls on the resolution of this matter so as to prove whose work is whose, and whose hand is in their making, I'll let you pull the strings of these poor corrupted beings, for all creation shall see and judge if I am all I say, or if your words stand true, Satan! For you are truly the father of lies my once beloved son.

The game is a foot! Earth is the battlefield and the completion of your disgrace must take place my deceitful creation. Since you are confined here — and here you may rule in complete obscurity. Man is yours to do with as you see fit! Earth and the surrounding bodies are also yours as well, for in my creation lives my active force, and none shall possess any indefinitely without my consent! And the love of Yahweh and the Elohim resides within all creation that live amongst the stars! Prove that mankind is unworthy to receive the inheritance, glory and heavenly richness denied them from the beginning, thus deceivingly forfeiting my decree granted them. If any inclination of what you have proposed shall be proven true amongst men, without antecedence or corruption, I'll rescind my judgment against you and your remaining brethren.

I shall decree total clemency and grant full dominion of this quadrant and verse! It is yours to rule over as god, supreme ruler of this galaxy! But if man overcomes his affliction, finding his worth in salt, thus proving himself worthy of my original decree, you and your brethren must pay the price of your rebellion in total! Six signs there shall be! Six symbols engraved in the spirits of those chosen from the heavenly host. One hundred and forty-four thousand, a full measure of Wholly Spirit shall be bestowed amongst the principle players of this game. Three marks identifying your seed and three marks identifying my seed shall be their pronouncement and trait.

Let the humans have the freedom to choose their allegiances, these symbols shall be placed within the spirits of those who prescribe to your influences — forever setting a mark of recognition, distinguishing your children from mine! None shall be aware of their mark, yet all shall have the power to change alliances, thus removing each mark and allowing a transition to obtain its equivalent in its place.

Your legions shall receive their mark now! And so shall my forces; it is done. Michael step forth! "Here I am, Father, " says Michael. When your brother first began his rebellion you stood up and endured the pain, sorrow and death of mortal men, with no hesitation you took the form of Adam. Before all the counsel on my behalf, you stood witness before all, and in that state you suffered as do mortal souls, experiencing pain, fear, loneliness, love — and even death for the sake of your father. No other being has given of themselves as much as you, truly proving no other creature in existence is like man, thus giving them the chance for equality amongst the children of old, even providing the chance of surpassing my children of old: your brethren. Once again I ask for your unwavering loyalty and service. Out of your own free will, help me finish this tragic and destructive conflict.

Take one full regiment of the finest Cherubim, and take on the form of man once more; let you and your brethren go forth on to Terra-Forma as lowly Homosapiens of the most humbly status in life. One hundred and forty-four thousand, a full measure shall be the number of yours as well. Help mankind see themselves; do not let our work go in vain! Here are the three marks of the Elohim's faithful children: The Children of Light!

These specific marks shall identify my children from those of Lucifer. Let legion be against legion upon this realm until this matter is resolved! So as not to overwhelm Lucifer's forces, let the battlefield be contained to earth. Let no excuse of intersession breed corruption from the ranks of the seed of the Elohim! Let those who may bare this mark suffer without fail, and quick retribution to those that may facilitate their persecution! Let no quarter be gained on his part. This matter must be settled without question! My will shall be realized fully in this realm, for this world is at its end and the spirit of mankind that dwells upon the face of the Earth shall know my name! No creation shall come to ruin without its purpose being fulfilled in total. Confusion and chaos has reigned enough! For this universe has been corrupted to the core, and this corruption is your brother's legacy. His name is Satan by his actions towards his father and shall never be changed forevermore.

Lucifer! Satan! The Morning Star! The Star of Darkness he shall be known throughout this verse! I must minimize the damage to this third dimension brought about by his hand. This war that has raged in the fourth, must be completed in the third! What has been unseen must become visible, and not confined to the spirit realm, yet played out in the physical realm of this third dimension. Access to this world shall be limited, no being shall take the form of a mortal soul! Angel or Rebel Demon alike, without being revealed! You and your one hundred and forty-four thousand brethren must be born of man, just as that of your brother Lucifer. Contrary to the Morning Star's accusations, man has within himself free will, and has earned freedom's blessing, though it is yet not apparent.

Victory is most definitely possible to obtain; you must be a source of enlightenment and influence for our cause, one side or the other! A full measure of heavenly knowledge shall be born to mankind, all with the chosen marks and symbols engraved within their souls and on their spirits shall become apparent in battle. Baal's children shall know their last position and rank, so as not to count unfair, the position they have placed themselves, being that I am all powerful as so claimed. As for you my son, a full measure of past understanding and knowledge shall not be granted to you nor your fellow warriors in battle. You shall not be made aware of your past positions and ranks, but be made to search and seek for what has been hidden from you. They must learn for themselves their true calling. For with every step taken thy children shall become stronger, gaining the power of free will to overcome adversity in search of me, even now in their incomplete state of imperfections.

The stage has been set, the battle for man's existence is now at play, count down—legion for legion, seed for seed, the time line has been set and activated!

One celestial week has been given! Lucifer has stated that man loves only himself alone, not his Creator. That's how he was made; he has no concern for his Creator says the accuser. And if he had free will he would not take sides with he that formed him, and all the heavens would do the same! So he has stated not one would be left standing on the side of Yahweh and his children of old if tested. He was proven wrong some two millennia ago, Michael proved him false! So now the time has come to give man his everlasting gift. But Satan will not let go so easily! I give this last chance which is folly! But I love my son and hate to see him die!

I have seen the outcome, the heavenly host shall see man's worth and agree with their father, whose will cannot be denied. Lucifer—his legions—and his Homosapien counterparts will indeed pay the price of everlasting death! Pure Darkness into the abyss. But my treacherous son shall see my mercy first, one millennium in prison and then released before destruction. So as much to show a father's love even for his wayward child of perdition, for the love of a father towards a son is boundless, unwilling to see him die though it must take place. But knowing it must take place in order to save countless other children that reside within many realms of existence, even that of the third and fourth dimensions! I have felt unrest in my creation of this universe; I have felt pain and regret over the creation of mankind. But I have also felt love for my Earthly children as well, I do not—will not—just stand by and see its ruin or its destruction over a jealous, spoiled and wicked child...The High of Most High has spoken!"

CHAPTER II
The Opening of the Veil

In the year of our King, Yeshua, nineteen hundred and sixty-six, a man child was born to a not so innocent young black girl living in the ghetto slums of the Great Lakes region of the Midwest, located in the Northern Americas. Not soon after his birth, a tall and mysterious man visited his mother while still in recovery from the birth of her firstborn child, leaning down beside her bed and whispering in her ear a favor of splendor, and in return she would become a very prosperous and happy mother. The stranger leaned closer to her and whispered in her ear: "Earline, your son is very great! If you would only name him Ramses, I would make sure you'll want for nothing, and pay for all his education until he's grown into a strong man!" Still under the influence of Pharmacia given to her by the physician, not knowing if it was a dream or not, she only replied: "Who are you?" Giving no reply to her request of his identity, the stranger asked her once more, "Would you name him Ramses and help him achieve his potential in life?"

With wonderment, she could only respond with her convictions: "He is his father's firstborn, and his father loves him very much being his firstborn, so I cannot do what you ask. I have promised his father and will not go back from that promise. He will bear the name of his father!" With no other inquiry or persuasions, the stranger arose from her bedside turned from her presence and walked away, and as fast as he appeared he quickly vanished, never to be heard nor seen again. Unaware of the important role her son would play in the historical final battle between Light and Darkness, the battle for mankind's right for everlasting life here on the planet Earth had just begun. Oblivious of the ongoing spiritual and physical war raging around her and her newborn son, she lived as most, accepting her cultural fate, assimilating to the social and economic norms as a way of life without question of their plight, clueless of the significances of her son's life journey, and how it would create chaos among the power structures that was, that were, and that will be. Not knowing how auspicious her son's life would become, playing out a vital part in the climax of the Universal battle between the sons of light and the sons of darkness, she fell back asleep.

A calmness filled the air as the battles between the forces of light and the forces of darkness waged mercilessly in the unseen places of high, finally reaching the Earth, overwhelming the thin veil that separates dimensional realities, breaking through barriers once locked to mortals and spilling over onto the reality of man, breaching the electromagnetic spectrums and the historical secrets of old, opening up doorways to our dimensional vicinity in the third dimension.

More than three hundred years, a nation of unwashed peoples of all creeds, cultures and breeds have grown up under the influence of the evil ones, and mankind's time of innocence has passed. The great experiment called the free world was quickly coming to its end. The money changers boldly boasted confidence in completing their scheme to enslave all mankind, and destroy their fellow man in puppetry, so as to obtain everlasting life for themselves, and explore the formally unreachable heights of the heavens, thus renewing Lucifer's rebellion throughout the ever expanding Cosmos. All were fully deceived and corrupted to the core, those knowingly and those not in the loop of things, without mankind ever knowing the wiser, but the Sovereign of the universe is the seer of all things, even seeing those things closed to the children of the Serpent or "All Seeing Eye," reversing the effects of those that presume to see all and confusing their advance towards oblivion.

In the midst of uncertainty, a son of light was born to a girl of little means, and a great change in his intellect and mind's eye would shortly take place not three years after his birth. An unforeseen complication occurred during a so-called simple tonsillitis removal, and did more than remove a vital organ; it removed the veil between the third and fourth dimensional realms, allowing the young child to glimpse into the fourth dimension. From the moment the scalpel clipped his organ, blood would flow outward uncontrollably causing his death within minutes.

Suddenly, he was floating outside his mortal body towards the historical tunnel of light described by so many, entering a room of white light and wonderful machines covering an entire wall as far as the eye could see. With beings dressed in white garb or robes, operating these machines without concern of his presence; still in a foggy haze, his spirit floated through the room unhindered or restricted by the many beings operating about, seeing beings of all sizes and forms, none with the faces of men, but most with the faces of beasts and winged birds, all wearing white robes and armor of gold and silver as they sat in rows of seats. He saw beings with faces and others without.

With no understanding of what was happening to him, he just surrendered all consciousness to the forces that be and surrendered to the moment. He let go of any fear, periodically closing his eyes and succumbing to the feeling of peacefulness as he floated weightlessly around the room.

Then suddenly he opened his eyes as his spirit began descending over a child playing on the floor in front of a massive machine of brilliant lit lights, feeling the two bodies merge into one, he lost consciousness once again only to awaken to a freezing cold mountainside as the wind blew on a side of a rocky landscape, standing outside of an unbelievable flying machine like never seen by the eyes of men. Metallic blue in appearance, with the likeness of a giant winged insect glowing from within a neon metallic blue light, seeing and hearing the being inside the craft saying: "You're here?" Then — sudden blackness, a flash of light, then hearing the sound of a horn blowing in the distance then fading away. As he was slowly regaining consciousness from his ordeal he could faintly hear his mother's voice saying: "P☐P! You hear me, baby?" With blurry vision he awakened in a hospital bed, and slowly opened his eyes, opening to a sight of a machine recycling his own life force, his blood slowly pumping back into his weak body, seeing his mother by his bedside he smiled, and she smiled back. Then back to sleep he went, and as he gradually fell into slumber he still could overhear his mother's voice saying, "He was dead!"

As he fell back to sleep, nightmares ruled the night, and from that day and forevermore his thoughts were on the events he witnessed in his so-called death. Having no sense of time, a week had passed and his life hung in the balance for that duration; quickly he began to recover physically but his primal thoughts had changed from that of a spoiled firstborn child to that of a fully grown man with the thirst for truth. As he recovered from his ordeal, his mind never wavered from the memory of the timeless experience his spirit encountered elsewhere.

An unknown force had taken control of his thoughts, giving him an uncontrollable need for knowledge and understanding of the unseen dimensional reality that surrounds us all. In search of what he had witnessed in life and death, his uncommon curiosity greatly increased his sense of awareness, increasing his capacity of independent thought, for the forces that granted him such visions of grandeur, an awareness of unseen structures and powers that controlled mankind allowed his spirit passage behind the veil. Surely an awakening had truly taken place within him during his stay in the hospital, getting him ready for what was shortly about to take place…

Lucifer! One so beautiful in sight and masterful in deception, being one of the first sentient beings ever created by the Supreme Sovereign of the Universe, Yahweh, his beauty surpassed all others. For all beings of lesser station that may come to understanding this revelation, please listen carefully! For one that has ever understood and chose to oppose his influence without the protection of Yahweh, has always met his death. The Morning Star possesses great power; in fact, his power helped in the creation and design of this planet Earth and surrounding spheres.

Because of his obvious betrayal and apparent sentencing, he has been limited in power and sentenced to walk the face of the Earth until judgment, full of rage and anger towards the very beings he helped create, has left a bad taste in his mouth; he is furious at the least. Lucifer has infiltrated and corrupted every institution of learning, with the sole intent to impede man's understanding of the verse in which he exists, to stunt his understanding of purpose for existence, and to never grant men the understanding of the importance of their relationship between themselves and the sovereign of the universe, thus leaving them clueless of their universal inheritance.

This fact cannot be contested: science, mathematics, sociological and physical instruction granted to mankind from every institution of learning has from the very beginning been under the control of the "Brotherhood of the Snake," Children of Darkness! And the most important institution of instruction, forever known as "Religion," was corrupted from its very inception by these nefarious entities called "The Fallen Ones."

Spiritual in nature are some, others are human in appearance, yet most are under demonic possession, and all are covetous in nature! All working in unison in an attempt to stop mankind from gaining knowledge of the facts surrounding their existence.

For the Dragon knows his life has been forfeited, so Lucifer rages unopposed like a lion on the hunt, ravenous with intent to devour Earth's inhabitance without end, even to the point of destroying the planet itself. From his beginning, man has been influenced by insidious spiritual forces in rebellion against the Creator of the seen and unseen universe.

Throughout history, these forces have operated with impunity, thanks in part to the network of foolish minions that facilitate their ruthless conspiracy. Wicked and evil men have joined forces with these inner- dimensional beings. We've all have heard the ancient stories many times throughout our childhood. Terrifying folktales which were spoken in many tongues across all spectrums of cultures all around the world.

In an occult like fashion, demonic spirits, alongside misguided men, have structured our very civilization, using the exact same technology given to mankind by the watchers of old and sons of god who were infatuated with the likes of beautiful women. With one aim in mind, they bind and enslave us with the exclusive purpose of destroying the Homosapien species thus ruining Yahweh's prized creation!

The Fallen One's relied on limited resources to exploit ancient man's intellect and reason to influence their lack of knowledge and ignorance. We now struggle to decipher bits and pieces of lost and found artifacts for confirmation of these facts, only to find hidden and sometimes forbidden secondhand information under guard. Once a truth seeker finds out certain truths on the authenticity of ancient text's validity is more than often unsatisfying with the very meaning of mankind's freewill weighing in the balance, and working with incomplete information which may actually jeopardize the homosapien's existence itself. Wicked yet eternal spirits corrupt every form of communication on the planet, leaving every man, woman and child accessible to demonic forces, subsequently stifling their god-given spiritual development.

The Powers that be are relentless in their pursuit to destroy the spiritual wellbeing and moral compass of mankind which in turn jeopardizes our inheritance of eternal life, and forfeits our eternal inheritance of space travel and universal exploration of this three-dimensional universe.

Just think of it! A handful of evil wicked sub-human beings in league with inner-dimensional beings, literally holding our very fate in their hands from the beginning of our existence, greedily and selfishly hording all Earthly resources in the pursuit of life extending technologies without their fellow man's knowledge, thus holding all of us hostage until our very destruction comes to fruition!

Since the formation of our creation, and the origins of our ancestor's orchestrated disobedience in the "Garden of Eden," every Child of Light has felt the absence of Yahweh's presence, love and light.

From the very moment of our deception and unfortunate birth in ignorance, we have been unwavering in our search for the truth and understanding of why we must continue to grow old and die, never overcoming the mistakes of our fathers. For death is not natural by any means for mankind.

It is our sentence for being manipulated in ignorance and disobedience!

Being the father of mankind's afflictions, Lucifer knows how to deliver his prey into his mouth for destruction. The Dragon knows the architecture of his father's handiwork that resides within mankind's making; he knew from the beginning that mankind would always crave and seek out true knowledge about their Creator, so he uses the very vessel and means supposedly setup to assist mankind in their search. For our father Yahweh has provided a way out of damnation for those unwillingly deceived so long ago. For Yahweh is just! Knowing the new creation was deceived from the very beginning, he put within us the urge to seek him out, and the accuser knows this very fact!

The very nature of mankind is to commune with one another so as to work in harmony when creating paradise on earth. Those that fell from their heavenly station knew this and devised the concept of reverence for themselves by corrupting the very instrument set up for mankind's wellbeing and salvation, mainly verbal ancient knowledge passed on by ancestors of old so as to educate the youthful generations to come back towards our origins within creation.

Lucifer has infiltrated that instrumental source of knowledge, and made all spoken word non-valued or myth. All other forms of ancient information have been condensed into written word, or books scribed by victorious armies ravaging their fellow men. Every source of spiritual enlightenment known to mankind has been co-opted, so that they may never come to know their spiritual father or purpose in the universe! Using misinformation to mislead the faithful and cast down the very fate that awaits Lucifer himself, he wages war against all flesh — against mankind and their offspring! Within a blink of an eye, the age of darkness became the age of industry. From an age of complete religious dominance and physical control of all things, Lucifer was still not able to obtain complete control of the thought processes of all men.

Using ancient techniques such as magic and demonic possession in his scheme for man's total destruction, Baal employs his human surrogates throughout the ages, consumed by the lust of power, the Morning Star has fully deceived those who call themselves the "Technocratic Elite." The so-called age of the light bringer had not yet come into fruition. The fallen one had not yet gained global influence. Lucifer's manipulation of man's childlike wonderment and eagerness to create beyond their scope has proven to be an asset for "The Fallen Ones" instead of mankind himself, for man has impatiently tried to understand the unknown knowledge of the universe without weighing out the consequences of his actions. The dragon relentlessly tries to capture the imagination of Yahweh's greatest creation with the magic of plastic and metal elements. Not calculating the power of mankind's spirit of exploration and hope, Lucifer has unwittingly impeded the light of darkness; therefore, the rebellion suffers a great defeat of will, thus greatly stifling Lucifer's goal.

Time has played out its course, and the Dragon has to ramp up mankind's technical advancement to ensure his development in imperfection. Fast forward to the present time! Out of nowhere, man's knowledge of the unknown and unseen nature of the universe has increased upon the Earth one hundred fold, instantaneously by universal measure!

We now live in a world of marvels, one of scientific observation and speculation, to one of applied scientific practice overnight. Being the chess master and possessor of light, Lucifer patiently maneuvered his queen!

For knowledge is power and absolute power corrupts absolutely! Capitalizing off of man's affliction, "IGNORANCE," he has gained an upper hold upon mankind, possessing our hearts with nonsense of thought, influencing us with mundane concerns like rent, bills and statutes of material wealth, and even sacrificing innocent mankind's offspring openly. With the not so secret human minions organizing the capture of innocence through the religious, political and social processes, mankind's foe act with the protection of the authorities in power.

Using despicable entities within the government at will, "The Fallen Ones" now intoxicate and drink off the blood of the innocent! The dark prince's tentacles reach far and long! But this is not a new revelation, for it has been displayed in plain sight for eons. For he had employed this very tactic from time's beginning, craftily setting up his towers of Babylon throughout time, he inspired the structure of rule and power that has ruled over man from the start of civilization...

Lucifer: "A new world order I shall create! A world where every man shall be his own god, and the chaos of rebellion shall be his mother. Every hand of man shall wield ill will against his brother, until his brother is no more. A willful sacrifice against his own children, man shall give to the Morning Star! No quarter shall be given to those who are not of my blood and are not in union with the mark of the beast placed upon the Children of Darkness souls and spirit. For which I shall show mercy until judgment of all creation that comes to pass! Yet all men shall serve my will knowingly or inadvertently, freely rejecting Yahweh for all the heavenly host to bear witness. Time has come for man to know the nature of the world and universe in which he exists! In his fingertips, I shall place the light of darkness' wealth by giving him the knowledge of the gods of old. With signs and symbols, I shall plant my will within his mind's eye and upon his heart!

The vision of godlihood shall consume his every waking thought, every moment of the day! Consumed with the lust of lording over his fellow man shall be his thirst! To covet what is his brother's shall be the food in which he gorges himself! Soon bringing all flesh closer to certain doom and destruction! Let darkness spread among his brethren relentlessly.

Let the light of darkness spread across the vastness of time, ensnaring his mind, soul and heart to the depths of darkness! Destruction shall be of his own making, corrupting all means of substance: land, water, air and beast.

In a deceptive and destructive web of information they shall gleefully go into the darkness, not knowing Good from Evil, showing the so-called 'very good beings' the unseen truths of their ex-father's third dimensional existence.

Knowledge of its properties at the molecular level is a necessary requirement, so as to utilize their ability to construct great works on our behalf! It is most needed, for it is essential and imperative for the undeniable, absolute and complete corruption of Yahweh's creation. The physics of understanding that which is unseen shall increase their boldness!

Recklessly pursuing the understanding of unseen laws connecting their third dimensional existence to other unknown realms must come to pass. I shall be his unseen master, and the arbiter of his introduction to this universal war effort. Let us broaden their horizons! Ha-ha! So as to explore the existence of all other unseen truths! To heighten basic elementary third dimensional structures and compounds shall fuel the natural curiosity of man, digging him further into the abyss. Soon he shall discover the reality and existence of the fourth, fifth and sixth realms of the universe. Then before all, I shall expose my omnipotence and worthiness of worship to the wayward ill-informed beings! But not yet—the opportune time has not yet presented itself. He shall prove me right before the heavenly host. And I shall win this verse over. For one hundred and forty-four thousand spirits of my brethren have been born of mankind, brandishing their mark and unwavering loyalty to the original Dragon!

All brethren in rebellion have not yet been delivered to the light of darkness, or been revealed and exposed to our operatives in the field. Many have not yet been transported into our grasp, for they are not yet all born onto this realm. All must be found and brought together, indoctrinated from birth into the corrosive nature of excess. Onto the high places of prominence and influence they shall dwell. For decadence corrupts, and power over his fellow man must be in his eye! For it is most important for quick deployment and action against our mutual enemy—my legions! At a moment's notice, we all shall and must be on guard, ready to strike down all children baring the mark of Yahweh's light! And doubly so, those who oppose their master's rule without certainty! Consciousness of one's disobedience is an affliction visited upon the weak hearted, and brings validity to the argument posed. No reasoning must exist for these poorly made beings. To hate themselves is the decisive response within our human counter parts, so punish swiftly those that may question orders.

Knowing their past positions and ranks of old alongside their spiritual selves, coupled with the philosophy of deception shall enable them to move unseen and unknown to their prey, quickly taking control over Yahweh's Children of Light's willingness to search for enlightenment in the wrong places.

They wield control of man's spiritual compass, making sure of certain redirection towards their unseen master's grip, and in bloodily conquest they shall massacre their brethren without mercy!

On their way to the top of the fiery pit of destruction, man must also willingly give himself over without doubt! Let man grow from generation to generation towards the light of darkness. Lording over his brother shall be his delight, and taking dominion over his fellow man he shall lust for! Becoming drunk off the flesh and blood of their own kind; all having power over life and death of his brother shall be their will to live, forming a brotherhood of deception, misleading all towards destruction, and setting his fellow man on the path of annihilation."

Throughout the passage of time, our unseen masters have been known by many names. The most prominently known name throughout history was the Watchers who were all knowing and powerful sons of god, numbering Two hundred committed an unspeakable crime of cohabitating with mortal woman, teaching their offspring all manner of forbidden fruit of the soul producing the woes we all endure to this day. Heavenly rebel forces repelled by The Most High and his forces ruthlessly made their way to this quadrant of the universe in order to take hostage the entire earth and all its inhabitance; they seek out Yahweh's Children of Light for destruction.

Michael and his brethren are also equal in number, "…one hundred and forty-four thousand," or a full measurement of spirits born of man with the mark of Yahweh's light. Having a ravenous urge to seek out and identify these children of promise with the purpose to destroy their drive to know Yahweh's light, the children of darkness search the globe with fever. The rebel's primary goal, however, is to destroy them physically before they become aware of their true spiritual selves. Born with the advantage of foresight and along with the ability to remember the past, Children of Darkness are consumed with visions of glory and blood lusting insanity. Even knowing of their past rank and position, the sons of darkness are charged with extinguishing those that may enlighten man of Yahweh's blessings and gifts, thus illuminating their station in this verse. Knowing all man's doings, they shall condemn mankind to death, knowing the unseen deeds of all. Having a short time, the Dragon Baal, better known as Lucifer, would not let this be his undoing.

The all seeing Creator is fully aware of the plans of his condemned sons of old treachery. Yahweh has concealed all movement of Michael and his brethren born of man, scattering them all over the surface of the Earth, eluding Lucifer's assault upon the unsuspecting Children of Light, allowing them time to develop their god-given right to seek and search out his light. With this light and guidance, they may lead others to what was lost in the Garden of Eden: Freedom from their bondage of sin and death.

From the beginning of mankind's descent into darkness, sons of light have been preventing Baal's New World Order from taking hold of the Earth until now!

The reincarnated Children of Light have been here enlightening mankind, not knowing how, why, or what moves them to seek out the unseen knowledge of the Almighty God Yahweh — The god of Abraham, Isaac and Jacob. As man grew in sin, his eyes began to open up to the unseen things that govern the realm in which he dwells. He learns of the great and awesome dealings of his Creator. They began to see and realize their own creative potential. In contrast to the sons of light, the sons of darkness feverishly work towards the ever more destructive pursuit of world domination, wanting nothing less than full domination over their fellow man. Recklessly, Children of Darkness began tapping into the power of the sun, putting themselves and every living thing on the planet Earth in jeopardy of total destruction, burrowing deeply beneath the Earth's surface, while abstracting the planet's life blood without restraint. With Lucifer's guidance, they race towards certain destruction, unwisely opening Pandora's Box, and systematically condemning themselves and the planet under the fear of total annihilation!

Under the influence of the Morning Star and all the other fallen sons of god, the Dragon infects the sons of darkness born of man, and plants his seeds of deception while dividing and misleading all earth's inhabitance relentlessly and without mercy towards certain death. Corrupting their fellow man, the sons of darkness fall ever so into the abyss of everlasting death, known as separation from the light of creation. Mankind has turned away from the Creator's light, laws of life and existence, consequently gravitating towards the Children of Darkness who are fully deceived, and embracing life's enemy: death. Ever so vigorously, the fallen Watchers rebel forces seek out Michael and his brethren for immediate destruction, correspondingly in the dimensional realm of the Most High, war rages on. Spirit against Spirit, agents of darkness engage agents of light with each side fighting to influence man's outcome via human conduits here on Earth. Namely the Children of Light and Children of Darkness are locked in constant battle and suffer day and night from post-traumatic stress, fighting amongst themselves on two fronts: The spiritual realm and physical one. Former sons of god, marooned here on Earth throughout history have made themselves visible to the evil and wicked men of old and now, jealously and ruthlessly ruling our current political structures and endowing them with great power and unlimited resources to track down and destroy all Children of Light.

Those born with the light of darkness in both realms, conspire and commune on a regular basis. Being that all contacts between inner-dimensional beings and Homosapiens here on Earth were forbidden and closed off by The Most High, Children of Darkness feverishly work to construct a massive machine to open up the doorway between dimensions, thus setting free the original Two Hundred from their exile and imprisonment.

After the flood, demonic forces were able to invade the internal spiritual aspects of mankind, through their mental process via dreams and possession the off world entities make themselves known. Over time and advancements in chemical and biological knowledge, the veil separating realities has been breached!

In other words, face-to-face interactions that were once halted, have now resumed and the doorway between realms which had been sealed and forbidden is now open!

No pathways connecting dimensional realms have been opened since the great flood, and no man had access to the knowledge that bridged the electromagnetic void separating realms, until the uprooting of ancient texts and manuals were unearthed by Children of Darkness in the early nineteen hundreds. We now are entering the twenty-first century and the end of the life span of Generation Z, time is running short for all living on the planet! Evil men will soon reopen the gates separating dimensional realms, and Baal's forces have been in full advance towards their goals of reopening the gates of hell over the last millennia, and the fallen sons of god have all but eliminated one third of Yahweh's Children of Light born of man here on Earth.

Michael and his brethren are truly at a disadvantage, having no past memory of their former ranks and positions in the heavenly realms. Their hands are tied not knowing their true spiritual selves. Yahweh is truly just, so as not to breed anymore question of his right to rule, he has allowed his children here on Earth to endure unimaginable trials and tribulations by Children of Darkness. In their search for knowledge lost, or better yet stolen, Children of Light struggle with the burdens of life underneath the heels of wicked men and demons, imposed on them by those who wish to enslave their fellow man, giving them a very great disadvantage in a spiritual war that most don't even know they're a part of. They live in constant misery and torment of spirit and soul, not understanding why their struggle in life seems to be one of never ending search for universal truths about themselves and Creator, while avoiding traps and pitfalls designed to confuse and prolong such dismay and bewilderment of their minds. Even the best of angels and men should shiver in abject fear to navigate such treacherous waters.

Always under constant spiritual attack by unseen forces, alongside their Earthly counter parts, spiritual protectors wage a defensive strategy to protect Yahweh's Children of Light from falling into the darkness.

Not having insight or understanding of the full picture of the meaning of life, they struggle with the god-given power to overcome and endure whatever may hinder them in their search for god's truth. With the never ending fire to uphold righteousness that resides within their souls, they unwittingly find themselves in the thick of battle between good and evil daily, not understanding the power that moves them to fight the onslaught of misinformation and deception that streams through the airwaves.

With all might I resisted indoctrination of sinful corruption in which the masses have fallen prey. Children of Light desperately try not to be overcome by the ingenious media brainwashing machine placed upon them from birth, for past knowledge of spiritual warfare was not endowed. Trying to understand what is being seen in their mind's eye, they fall deep into depression, unseen, unheard, and feeling separated from their loved ones. Misunderstood by those mesmerized by global brainwashing and somehow not in tune with their fellow man, they become dismayed, always asking themselves, "Why am I here? Who am I? I don't belong here!"

Forever seeking the meaning and answers to these elusive, and nagging internal questions, most Children of Light give up trying to find the answers haunting them. No one seems to know the answers. They search out into the darkest places for answers while parts of their mental ability to comprehend the unseen truths through the midst of darkness becomes just too much, falling short in finding truths from those of authority, be it religious or secular, the fire diminishes in the night. With more than a belief of a higher power or universal force, they know within their hearts, body and mind that a Creator exists! Most have turned towards religious leaders or the occult in hopes of finding the true meaning for their existence on this planet.

Throughout the passage of time, vessels containing information of universal enlightenment have been safeguarded and lovingly provided to mankind by our Creator. Taking into account man's feeble mayfly life span, Yahweh has repelled and held back the historical renowned men of old, though their human bodies have long been destroyed, their spirits remain stuck between dimensions. These Sons of god slash human hybrids, better known as the "Titans," have feverishly mislead men into constructing a device that would free them from captivity, escaping their dimensional prison.

A prison put in place by the Creator to safeguard mankind from their demonic rage and thrust for revenge.

Now in our twenty-first century, the Children of Darkness never stopped in their endeavors to free their unseen masters, and now they just may have succeeded in releasing the fallen ones of old using "CERN!"

The ancient wise and noble servants of truth have passed verbal and scribal instruction to mankind, unfortunately that knowledge and wisdom has been hidden, even stolen from us! The tools in which Yahweh has lovingly provided his Children of Light so as to pass down enlightenment of his universal plan to their fellow man have been used to do the very thing god did not intend. It has been used to further enslave the minds of men, instead of freeing them! The guidelines and covenant passed down from generation to generation has now been infected, infiltrated and corrupted! It seems as if the painstakingly put in place safeguards, markers and guides for the Children of Light have all but vanished. In many cases, "past and present" the Children of Light have sacrificed their very lives to keep the word of Yahweh true throughout the passage of time. The lifesaving knowledge given to mankind as a whole has been corrupted! Most information for navigating down the very narrow road of true universal enlightenment has been tainted, and its meaning lost! Seen and unseen forces craftily separated the path, widening one road in man's journey to know his Creator, ingeniously hiding the narrow road, making it almost impossible to understand man's true self-worth!

Our unseen masters have effectively dimmed the very light of truth given to mankind from within the vessel of redemption itself, forever altering the course of mankind's understanding, causing man to reject his natural sense to live forever! Mankind now pursues unfounded dreams of supernatural grandeur, unwittingly embracing life's enemy, "Death," since Yahweh's Earthly outpost, his "Temple," has been destroyed! True enlightenment has been closed off to mankind and removed from man's sight. "The Ark of the Covenant," the vessel containing the word of god, has been either stolen, destroyed or rescinded. Because of the ever increasing amount of sin, the sons of darkness now influence, control and enslave mankind. The Children of Darkness along with the "Watchers" patiently await our self-imposed destruction, waiting on mankind's own urge to know his universal father to become nonexistent! They wait for man's need to understand his Earthly purpose to fade away and never take hold, so as to identify Yahweh's Children of Light, those born to man to ensure redemption, so as to entrap them in darkness, forever keeping them lost in spiritual limbo if you will, with one goal in mind—to destroy their will and suppress the need for enlightenment, subsequently hoping to capitalize on their ignorance and gain absolute dominion over them and the third dimensional universe, ultimately resulting in the death of mankind, and the destruction of the small but majestic blue planet of which he is made...

In the year of our lord Yeshua, nineteen hundred and sixty-six, Lucifer's power on Earth is great! His forces control all the land masses, and the Watchers are elusive, yet he is terrified! For he knows his time is up, and Michael has been born to man! He must find him! He must seek him out. For he knows Michael will in time remember his heavenly rank and become aware of his divinely given internal instinct to learn the truth. His position in creation shall be restored thus weakening Baal's hold on mankind. Awakening the universal remainders of the original "One hundred and forty-four thousand," a full measurement of enlightened ones! Once known as "Yahweh's Children of Old," spirit beings now born to man have been sought out by the wicked ones, hunted and destroyed to the point of non-existence, in the attempt to undo Yahweh's physical representation of the Heavenly Host on a lower plane of existence — "Mankind."

You see my fellow Children of Light, throughout the dawn of time, rebellion has ravaged the Heavenly places over the right to rule.

Sentient Beings in all planes of existence have been instigated to wage war against their Heavenly father by one of the most powerful beings in existence. The rebellion was foiled and brought to rest, but before the author of the rebellion could be brought to justice, he and his forces have been marooned here on our plane of existence, and have vowed to destroy the perfect creation of the Most High, namely the Children of Light and all mankind. Lucifer has been relentless in his pursuit to defile and destroy one of the most prized beings in creation, sought after by the former sons of god called Watchers and their demonically possessed offspring known as the "Children of Darkness" or "Men of Renown;" methodically and systematically, they set out to eliminate any vestiges of Yahweh's prized creation before their time is up.

Lucifer and his minions desperately seek out all those born of men that may shine light on the certain calamity that awaits mankind and the sub-sequential consequences of not having those long-term agonizing childhood universal questions answered. Lucifer and his rebels have successfully lured mankind away from their universal salvation and now darkness reigns.

A key strategic move for the Children of Darkness is to carry out their masters' will and destroy those born to man that may have Yahweh's mark before they could enlighten the rest of the species, thus reversing the global brainwashing from which all mankind is now suffering. Once their secret identity is exposed, their only means of protection can be corrupted and removed.

Yahweh is all knowing! Anticipating such a desperate maneuver, Yahweh prepared those that may be elected to enlighten mankind with a series of trials to overcome, so as to equip them with the necessary fortitude to carry out their mission.

The test of the elected is not only dangerous, but also one of grave importance, for succeeding and overcoming the trials of the elect may spark the spiritual fire, leading to the restoration of the small majestic paradise and restoring Yahweh's original plan for its occupants.

Recognized only by unseen spiritual marks of identification, which can only be detected by their moral compass, desperation and spiritual eagerness to seek out their god-given instincts, an irresistible need to find out unseen truths must be fulfilled. Only the Watchers and the men of renown are able to see into the fourth dimensional realm; however, fleshly men sometimes are able to access the spiritual realm using forbidden methods known as divination. In some cases, children on both sides of the struggle may be given glimpses into other realms of existence using the eye of the mind in cases of extreme trauma or tribulation.

Divination is a forbidden art not practiced by Children of Light because of the dangerous nature of the demonic beings which reside in the spiritual realm, but used only by those of like-mindedness. Children of Darkness often use this technique to communicate with demonic beings with the intent to foresee future events and gain unseen knowledge. Use of such forbidden practices to track down and locate their spiritual counterparts is often employed as well. Darkness seeks out Light and will do whatever it takes to locate, identify and kill the bearers of Yahweh's marks before the bearer can realize his or her life's meaning and purpose. Finding out the identity of one could only mean that the identity of the other has been compromised. With unlimited resources, the Children of Darkness have caused unthinkable wars and calamity over just one single being that bears Yahweh's identification here on Earth.

A single Homosapien's spirit bearing one or all three marks of Yahweh has been targeted for destruction from birth! Lucifer has promoted the genocide of all mankind. Destroying whole nations on the thought of eliminating only one child born of light, with no concern of creed, color or background.

Knowing the lesser shall overcome the greater on the physical plane; the beast searches for the convener of Yahweh's knowledge, which lies in the seed of the woman or bloodline of the one offering the ultimate sacrifice, "Yeshua Ben Jesse." This seed would be found among a particular creed of people whose origins rest in Africa.

Prolonged unnecessary suffering and massive famine across the globe has been implemented to destroy the bloodline of "Jesse and or David."

Persecution and slavery serves as lessons to all that may encourage those who would give refuge to any Child of Light.

For the Children of Old fear the power of an enlighten Homosapien species, for it would expose the conspiracy that hinders mankind from knowing their heavenly father's purpose within this three-dimensional Cosmos. The gloves are off! Baal cannot let this happen; he must stop his former brother from achieving his goal. The time has come! The last stand for mankind's existence and the existence of the planet is here...

CHAPTER III

The Path Has Been Given

Light and then Darkness. A vision of two royal blue crystal and metallic like inter-dimensional crafts come into view, with two men like beings looking through the forward portal of both crafts as both crafts lift off into the air. I'm outside the crafts on the ground, on top of a hill or mountain of some kind. Did I just get out of one of those crafts? There were two? Both with two beings inside — Then the sight fades away, a light then darkness. A vision slowly takes shape; I'm in a baby crib; it's dark, then the sound of words, from some speech of some kind; a man is sitting on a couch, and a woman asked the man if he would like something to eat or something to that effect. A light is flickering in front of the man as I sit in the crib, looking through the wooden bars at the flickering light thinking what am I doing here? There are pictures moving in a little black box, sound is also coming from the little black box, images with no color, black and white are the images that flicker, sparking my interest. As the pictures move and sounds emulate from the little black box, a knock at the door startles the man; he jumps up and runs out of the room. Knock! Knock! The woman enters the room, putting her finger in front of her mouth as to signal to the man to be quiet as she answers the door, the lights began to dim, and the sight slowly fades away.

Light then darkness! In silence, time has passed. I'm older and am able to walk; the vision has changed from before, and the flickering light of images are now in color. I'm aware of my surroundings, and everything is familiar. I loved the site of the woman before, for she is my mother, so loving and kind, and always there. I'm not able to form words, yet I speak, and she knows what I need. She smiles and I smile; then the vision slowly fades away. Light then darkness in silence. Time has passed and a series of light and dark-fading images enter my mind, but I could not remember anything of substance.

Time seems to move very quickly; I'm able to speak, remembering most of my past existence in broken fragments. Far from fluent progression, remembering the very beginning of life as a newborn in a crib, and the man I saw was my father; the black and white images glowing in the background were the nightly showings of an old cartoon known to all as "The Rocky and Bullwinkle Show."

The next vision I remember takes place in different surrounding; this time the images were in color and lifelike. It was another classic television show called "The Mutual Life Wild Kingdom" and the different surroundings were of my grandmother's home. My god, I had to have been only two or three years of age, and it must have been a weekend at Grandma's house.

I remember my grandmother's regular routine, she would always watch "The Mutual Life Wild Kingdom" and "Family Classic Program" every Sunday and Saturday. She'd gather all the children in front of the television to watch those very shows religiously. We learned so much about the amazing world in which we lived. Its beautiful sights and its diverse range of animals captured our imagination as we looked out the window and saw nothing of the such, knowing we would never encounter such things where we lived, and after watching our weekly lessons on the biology of living creatures, we would watch so-called wholesome fairytales of people that did not look like us, or even lived as we did. Seeing only white people parading around in different costumes acting out old adventures, and wild fantasies of how life should be, where everyone was so nice to each other, even in bad scenarios, for me, made no sense, and even then at an insanely young age, I could see that people were not so nice. But I didn't know for sure? Maybe they are that nice in "White People Land."

Though short term, my memories of peoples and places back then were narrow in scope, visions of numerous chickens held captive in giant cages, all awaiting a certain fate of being laid to slaughter, as we walked up the stairs leading to my grandmother's apartment over a poultry slaughtering plant, only to see her walk back down the stairs to start her daily job after we were secured behind the screen door leading into the apartment looking down upon a chicken death factory. Grandma worked down below amongst the chicken carnage. I remember the activities of some of my own family members back then, and none behaved as elegantly as the visions of the white families interacting on the television shows broadcasting daily like family classics. Souls like Uncle Dead Eye Dick, my grandmother's significant other, or other un-named characters that graced my childhood at that time exhibited no such charisma like that shown on TV. All behaved themselves without class or grace, and most were drunken with the smell of cigarettes and shit marking their presence. I can remember Dead Eye Dick's right eye being shot out by his estranged other wife when he was a young man. I have memories of him smelling like cheap vodka and Wild Irish Rose to this day. I also remember him stumbling down stairs, pissing on couches, and or lying in his own vomit on the sidewalk while strangers walked by with no concern of his plight.

Most knew Dead Eye Dick by name, and laughed with ridicule in their voices which solidified their lack of concern for his wellbeing.

Not knowing the fundamental difference between good and evil, I viewed him as only kind, never viewing his behavior as something wrong or bad at that age, disapproval of him was almost none existent, until a series of similar events invoking feelings which only could be described as shame overcame me, and I turned my head from his direction. Sounds of vulgarities and indignant language from grown-ups filled the air around him constantly.

Visions of not so clean bedrooms and hallways filled with the droppings of rats and roaches occupied the majority of my early memories, with amusing thoughts fading away into the darkness of forgetfulness. No matter how much one would clean the place in which we lived, the rooms were never really clean. As kids, my cousins and I would turn out the lights and wait for the room to fill with roaches, then suddenly we turned on the lights, so as to kill as many as we could with rubber bands before they scurried back into the many cracks and crevices protruding from the wall and floors. We never saw lovely rooms of splendor like those viewed on "Family Classic," nor heard sweet words of comforting inspiration from nonexistent role models and grown-ups.

Only words of degrading disappointment and disgust flowed from the mouths of most adult family members as we were growing up in squalor. As the air of hopelessness surrounded their very beings, I only silently looked as they faded away amongst the sounds, smiles and ugliness of poverty. Words of comfort, inspiration and strength only flowed from my mother's voice and even then they were far and between. Like most people in the hood, she was too busy trying to survive daily woes, so as to encourage my spiritual growth, just as it is today for most in poverty. "Never be like him P" my mother would say, speaking with distain about Dead Eye Dick— "Look at him lying there with his dick in the dirt!" Whatever that meant, I knew she meant well saying those words, but no man knew the internal suffering or mental anguish he endured daily. She would go on reminding me of our lowly station in life as black people in this country, focusing on the struggles and plight of our meager existence constantly and daily, telling me of the many dangers that plagued our surroundings. Religiously screaming at the top of her lungs about the dysfunctional behavior of my cousins as they scurried around the playground, as she neurotically watched over me, perched from her stoop at the bottom of the staircase while shouting profanities as I played with my rambunctious cousins. She drilled in my adolescent head what to be aware of in our dangerous environment. Though the meaning of the word danger was firmly established at that age, I felt no danger or sorrow, nor plight of desperation in poverty. I remember playing with my cousins in the backyard as well as in the front, with a feeling of safety, fun and happiness surrounding us all.

"A, P! Those dog biscuits taste good, you want some…they come in different colors?" said my favorite cousin. I remember my cousin of the same age saying those words to me, and with no hesitation I grabbed a handful saying, "Give me some, man." With no concept of shame nor embarrassment, we almost devoured the entire bag before we were caught by my grandmother. The memory fades, light then darkness.

I'm still very young and around the same age, but the uncertainty of circumstance becomes more prevalent. The scenery has changed once again; I'm with my grandmother; she's at work, but not at the chicken death factory ringing the necks of chickens. The circumstances of my family seems to be turning towards better fortunes it seems; my grandmother now moved into a home. A real and very nice home by poor people standards, even her place of employment has changed as well; she's a maid now, cleaning and watching someone's children, a young boy and young girl, even taking me along most days. The young boy and I hit it off from the moment I arrived. We would create ruckus on a momentous scale, rambunctiously running around playing with the youngsters' toys, while Grandma cleaned house and prepared lunch, promptly announcing the time, "It's noon," calling us all for lunch without delay. The memories of that short time period in my childhood was nice, invoking feelings of wellbeing love and safety, as the young boy and I played throughout the house, remembering visions of us watching classic "Marvel Comic Cartoons," such as "Ultra Man," "Thor," "Spider-man," "The Incredible Hulk," and "Felix the Cat," watching all in succession on channel forty-four. At that time, television programing was much less spiritual and morally intrusive, with only three major networks dominating the airwaves without cost; wholesome culture still flowed freely through the air. This memory has no significance other than it signifies a time of peace, joy and pure childhood happiness in ignorance of world events. A happiness not so simply attainable in the time in which we live today. Lunacy has afflicted the nation, even in rich or so-called middle class areas of today's society, the worries of unknown dangers now envelop everyday life, in every neighborhood, zombies roam freely and unopposed. Corruption, crime, drug addiction and mental sickness infects the strong-willed as well as the weak. Fun memories of that time fades away, light then darkness.

Another vision emerges in my mind's eye, and it's nighttime. I'm a little older than before but not that much. I'm standing in a kitchen, and all manner of people are surrounding me dancing. Grown-ups are playing music, and the name of the song is "It's a Family Affair," by "The Family Stone."

Then suddenly, the sound of gun fire rang out, startling the crowd of people, then two more shots rang out! Folks ducked for cover, others fell to the floor. As silence calmed the air, people began running towards the vicinity of the shots. Suddenly, like stampeding cattle, everyone began running out the back door, as I quivered in a corner of a stranger's kitchen. Then a women was screaming obscenities, "Kill that Mothafucka…bitch, you dead!" With a flash, curiosity overwhelmed my fear and I slowly walked towards the door. The sight of men fighting fist to cuff in the streets right outside the place of the gathering; my eyes were wide open from the electricity in the air, as I looked up at my Uncle Bubble hitting someone I've never seen. Shocked at the sight of my mother's brother engaging in such behavior unnerved me, so I ran back inside and hid under the kitchen table.

Eyes fixed on the open back door, my curiosity once again took hold of my fight-or-flight responses and I headed back towards the open door. Clearly, I could see people outside running up and down the street. Although my emotional state was not really known, I felt no fear. I was in shock, for it was the very first time I experienced any violence up close and personal. It was nothing like televisions' bad guy verses good, but it was more intense and final; the feeling of excitement lasted well after the event had ended. True violence affects everyone present, not just those involved but spectators as well. The act itself affects reality; if you notice other types of made up violence like the kind you see on "Saturday Night Roller Derby" do not affect the events in time. Every sight of simulated violence moves very fast, but true violence when witnessed affects everything, then all of a sudden, as if time began to creep along, everything began to slow down, ultimately moving in slow motion, sound began to fade away, before it got deadly silent!

People were fighting all around, breaking things but there's no sound, hearing only my own thoughts, asking myself, "Where is the sound?" Suddenly, I looked upwards in the night sky, there in the clouds around, were people fighting in the sky above. "What is that I see? They are fighting too! Uncle Bubble, do you see that!?" He didn't hear me. I walked back towards the open back door, amazed and astonished over my vision of heavenly beings fighting in the sky, looking upwards standing there in shock, I didn't move. Gazing upwards, I walked outside the back door in a semi hypnotic trance, but out the corner of my eye, I could see my mother yelling at some over-sized woman, but I could hear no sound, only the movement of her lips. Moving in slow motion, I could not believe my eyes and had no understanding of what I was seeing!

This terrible sight in the sky was unbelievable! A horrific sight of beings dressed in shining armor of splendor, expertly brandishing weapons of blinding light towards the opposing side. Some had the faces of men while others had faces of beasts in the wilderness. Some had the features of reptiles while others had wings and feet of eagles, and others were covered with light! All were dressed from head to toe in armor of silver and gold. Lightning flashed forth in every direction. They had shields of silver and gold, all thrashing swords toward one another, fighting fiercely as they stroke one another with tremendous force, what terrible weapons indeed, yet none fell from the sky after being struck, but all faded out of sight once downed. "Mama! Uncle Bubble...do you see the monsters in the sky...look at them fight!" I yelled at the top of my tiny little lungs, but no one could hear me it seemed. "Can they see me? Mama?!" But she couldn't hear me either!

I wondered if they could see what I could see. "Hell, can she see me?" No one's responding to my yells. They were all arguing with one another as if I were not there, but finally I could hear and see everything going on in the street, good! They stopped fighting, and I could hear the voice of my mother. She's calling my name! "I'm here! Can she see me? I'm here! Can you hear me?" Looking up in the night sky I yelled: "Can you see them there fighting? I can see them! Can you?" I got no response. I was walking in circles with my head pointed upwards with my left four fingers pointed towards the sky as well, looking in total amazement. Suddenly one of the creatures looked down at me; I could see the creature and he saw me. We made eye contact! Our eyes locked towards one another—he speaks—I hear— "He sees us! He sees!" Others looked down at me in the midst of their fighting, realizing I could see them as well, and they all stopped fighting one another and flew away, disappearing into the night sky with the other flying creatures in hot pursuit. As a shutter on a high speed camera closes after the shot is taken, the sky emptied the strange beings, and sound slowly began to come back. As soon as the fighting in the sky diminished, so too did the fighting in the streets.

Then I heard a voice, it was my mother's. "P! What are you doing out here?" Surprised she could see me, I responded, "You see me?" "Yah, I see you, boy! Get yo ass in the house!" "Mama, you see the flying people with wings? They were fighting too!" —She laughs, saying: "Ain't nobody in the sky, boy! Who gave my baby some of that funny shit? I know ain't nobody give you some of that shit now, P." "Hell n'all, Earline!" said one of her friends. "Ain't nobody even seen that little nigga till now; yo boy weren't even here, were you?" "I was right here...you didn't see me? Did you see the flying people?" I looked around noticing my surroundings, this looked like the street my Grandma works on. That looks like the house she works at—

It is the young boy's house—as my mother took hold of my arm saying, "Come on, let's go!!" The memory fades, and a blast of light then darkness. A vision slowly comes into focus. A voice yells in the night, "Get on the floor! Stay down!" It's the voice of my father, yelling at me while shifting gears of his car. We were going faster and faster as I cuffed my hands over my ears as the engine revved; I stooped down on the back seat, then on the floor of the car. Even now the memory is as fresh as the day it occurred. I was in the back of a nineteen sixty-four Chevy Malibu my father souped up. I heard the blades of police helicopters twisting in the wind as the helicopter's spot light followed us from the air; it was clear they were following us. Lights shining from above, just missing his hot rod as my father turned down a darkened alley way, barely slowing down as he turned sharply down another alleyway, hitting every pothole visible it seemed, a lot of potholes, and without care he gradually slowed down as he shut off the headlights. As he approached the end of the alleyway, he nervously looked in all directions, than hit the petal to metal running red lights and hitting the corner like a bat out of hell with no headlights shining from his car.

Suddenly he cut off the engine and we waited forever it seemed, then he turned on the headlights and turned the ignition key in the on position at the same time, and in a soft voice, he said, "Shhh! Be quiet, boy...don't say shit," as he threw a tarp over the back seat and me. He began driving at a normal pace as the sounds of cop car sirens and helicopter blades faded off into the distance. He revved up the engine saying, "Don't say shit and stay down!" It's the middle of fall and the cold night weather flows freely through the cracked car windows. Cold and shivering, my teeth were chattering as the wind poured in from the halfway open back car window, not knowing what was going on, I followed my father's directions and stayed quiet. I stayed still under the tarp and it seemed like forever.

As the car driver-side door opened, my father emerged from the car, slamming the door behind him. I stayed underneath the tarp, peeking through a small slit in the fabric, then I could hear the sound of keys jingling for a moment, and the sound of another engine pulling up close to our car. A few words were exchanged from some unknown acquaintances or criminals, I might add, then the driver side door opened as I crouched even closer underneath the tarp. I heard keys being slid into the ignition switch and the engine revved once more. The car took off at a regular pace and speed. My father made two more stops, this time talking decisive and discretely to each of the cohorts he encountered. Off we rolled again, and in his happy go lucky tone of voice he began humming with glee. I'm still under the tarp cold and motionless, then I hear my father's voice: "Get up, boy…. We at home…. We made it!" My father had just eluded a massive man-hunt from the law, ultimately escaping a high-speed pursuit the whole nine yards without skipping a beat, helicopters and all. It was the most exhilarating experience I have ever felt, adrenalin coursed through my veins like amphetamine, shaking my every nerve to the core. I was only four years old.

I don't remember feeling anything but fear as the car zoomed on its way, and when the car stopped moving, I remembered only coming up from underneath the tarp, seeing my father laughing with his friends standing in grand posture outside our home. I guess that's why I'm afraid of heights and excessive speeds to this day. The sight of my mother hurrying down our staircase brought tears to my eyes, running over to me with a look of disgust and fear draped over her face. She calmed my nerves as she grabbed hold of me; I felt only safety. Holding me in her arms, rushing me inside, I remember feeling her warm soft hands rubbing my back and holding me tightly. Rocking me back and forth with the spirit of love only a mother could provide soon took hold, and the overwhelming fear dissipated as I closed my eyes and fell asleep. The image fades away, but this time there's no light just darkness…

CHAPTER IV

Blackness into the Light of Darkness

Beneath the ground connecting Washington, D.C. to the West Coast via electromagnetic Rail and in total secret of the inhabitance above ground and in total ambiguousness, Children of Darkness meet for their annual summit.

J. Jackson: "Where am I?" "Stay calm!" "Why the blindfold mothafucka? How far down are we going?"

Minion of Darkness: "A depth of about thirty-three stories; quiet, Mr. Jackson; we're almost there."

J. Jackson: "Yeah, that's easy for you to say; you're not the one blindfolded."

Minion of Darkness: "How do you know?"

J. Jackson: "Ha! Ha! Ha!"

Minion of Darkness: "Quiet, we're here" — "Please step out of the elevator, Mr. Jackson, and watch your step!"

J. Jackson: "I sure will." (removing blindfold) "OH, my god!"

Minion of Darkness: "Yes, it's beautiful—isn't it?"

J. Jackson: "Yes, indeed!"

Minion of Darkness: "Take note, Jackson! You now stand in the presence of extraterrestrial beings! Those not unlike yourself, born of man, but much more important. You stand in the presence of those that are not born of human stock alone, but of higher pedigree than humans, existing long before humankind was conceived on this planet, and shall roam the Earth long after all cosmic beings grieve and all pains are quailed, ending with the removal of all flesh of mankind! If we have anything to say about it. As you can see we have the ability to connect with beings from other dimensions, using technologies more than one hundred years advanced than that of the public. With such advancements we commune with our brethren on the other side of reality, connecting with the fourth dimension on a regular basis, calibrating and consolidating information vital in the progress of our mission."

Azazel: "Good morning, everyone, especially you, Mr. Jackson, please do not speak unless spoken too! You are on holy ground, Mr. Jackson. My name is Azazel, Chief Commander of Lucifer's Northern Legion. Attention! Human Alliance, better known as 'The Northern Seers,' do you all know why you are here? The Ordinance Speak!"

J. Jackson: "No, my lord, we do not know." "Quickly, your name, rank, and brand." "J. Jackson, Second Sergeant of the 'Human Alliance; Southern Division, engraved with the first brand sign of Baal your lowly subject from birth, my lord, Azazel." In succession the rest followed suit, revealing their names, ranks and insignias.

Azazel speaks: "Do you not know why beings of such insignificance as yourselves were allowed to know such a place of magnificence even exists here on Earth? Or do you not know the purpose in which you were called? Do you have any idea of the privilege of having such access to such a place that is so revered? It is the place from which we, your masters, shall see all that transpires upon the face of the Earth! And you were called forth to witness with your very eyes the magnificence and power of your gods here on Earth; none can stand against our will. For now you stand on the holiest of wholly ground."

J. Jackson: "Surely my eyes have seen wonders this day! Thank you! Thank you, my lord, Azazel!"

Azazel: "Don't grovel, Jackson."

J. Jackson: "Yes, my lord!"

Azazel: "You are here because of the work you accomplished in Tennessee and the Great Lakes, being promoted to lieutenant for your loyalty, congratulations, Mr. Jackson! That pasty agitator, King, was in fact a Child of Light, one of Yahweh's chosen. He bore the first mark of Yahweh."

{Jackson speaks with distain}

"I knew it! I told you! I could feel it; every time he got close to me, I felt like killing him with my bare hands; he made me sick! Oh, just the thought of that fateful day on that balcony brings shivers down my spine, and tears of joy down my face! You should have seen him weeping over the uncertainty of his children's plight for the future. Like a child begging for its mother's tit, he uttered those last words, as he withered out in waste and treachery on his last day on Earth (confiding in his so-called protégé); I'll never forget it, his last words saying: 'You know, J., sometimes it seems as if I don't belong here; I mean really don't belong here! You know? Here on this planet, you know?' If only Mr. King knew what I knew, ha-ha! I just responded, No, Sir. I'm right where I need to be, right next to you."

I almost nutted my nicely pressed trousers when I heard the fatal shot! Seeing him fall to the ground when the bullet struck its mark brought joy to my heart, and seeing the life rushing out of his body, brought a smirk and smile so great, it took everything within me not to scream out with joy!

It took all that was evil within my soul not to revel all the contempt I had for that bastard of a cow, and let rejoice bubble forth. To be able to laugh aloud is so liberating! Not having to display reverence for that trouble maker and keep a straight face was almost as exciting as being amongst the chaos and confusion I've created!" Azazel replied, "That's great, take a seat, soldier."

{Behind the podium, Azazel speaks.}

"As most of you may already know, every twenty-five years we meet here on this wholly ground to assess the progress of our goals, and to review the level of our dominion over the profane cattle that surrounds us. Time has come for our global cabal to rule this entire planet. Once and for all! United in spirit and goal, the darkness has delivered us all into greatness. Our plan is almost complete my brethren; when our master ordained the new world we shall openly express our desires, and it started here in the Americas, my brethren. For more than some three hundred years ago, our goals were simple, divide and conquer the people of all nations and creeds.

Set one group over another, and find Yahweh's faithful Children of Light in the midst of all nations of people. Consolidate all other Seers of Light around the world and exterminate them! Maintain the illusion of freedom while enslaving them all. For we shall erode free speech and prosperity from within, while our elders sift through the cattle for those we seek within this cesspool of inequity and shame. Let those who remain search other parts of the planet, so as to contain and destroy the hidden Children of Light. I must say we have done our job well! (Applause) The New World Order is truly in effect! (Applause) Soon the end of all puppet governments will cease to be of use. Man has already prescribed to our aims, oh so willingly!

We have given the elite Children of Darkness glimpses into the fourth dimensional realm; they have seen the unseen, they have wondered at true marvels."

One of their minions speaks, "OH! NO! Don't worry, only those of higher stock may indulge, but for those who have joined the cause by means of choice may not indulge. And we control access of course Ha! Ha! Ha! — We had no choice but to enlighten you this once because of your deeds, Mr. Jackson.

After New Mexico, the cat was out of the bag so to speak, about the technology that exists in this plane of existence. Now we will give them information sparingly; they will never digest it all — or even be able to decipher its true meaning; Yahweh's children are blind, therefore, they will never be able to realize their purpose in this verse.

Children of Light shall never awaken to the significance of their being in this dimension. Unaware of their power to turn mankind's fate towards salvation's direction, is the least of our problems. But still the same; we must maintain this deception because there is no room for failure! All trouble makers must be rounded up, assimilated or eliminated. It makes no difference, for no one shall be saved. All mankind will be ours to do as we see fit, Mr. Jackson, and you know this! (Applause!) For eons the corruption of the family has taken hold; we have begun to elevate what is seen as the weaker vessel of mankind. Here the strength of mankind shall be torn to shreds; a new world of carelessness shall reign, and no more shall the laws of Yahweh take hold in the minds of the masses.

Given her natural beauty and emotional make up, she will in fact bring her male counterpart to his demise quickly; let her find bliss in ignorance, while she destroys her own legacy. We are bound by decree to find Yahweh's spies among them, both male and female have already succumb to our control, what strangle hold over the religious kingdoms we now enjoy. Most are living in total confusion, truly being led by the blind, going so far as to say that pure evil is now leading the willful blind! We have succeeded beyond expectation! For more than one hundred years, we have made the "MK-Ultra Program" global. Humanity's natural longing for unity will be quenched! Every man for himself, shall ring in the ear of every child born in this land and around the planet, from this day forward!"

Azazel speaks: "The time is five minutes to midnight—look! Here in my hands, I hold a new pestilence! One that will cripple humanity's own ability to fight off disease; we have begun distributing it to the masses within their food, land, water and air supply.

The pestilence of the Watchers have been placed in their water supplies, food supplies, and sprayed over the wilderness where it should mutate; in my other hand lies the cure. In addition, Baal has a new plan in effect, listen up! We will take no chances, flood the cities, towns, streets and farmlands with the poppy seed; Yahweh's Children of Light still remain, and are here. Don't be fooled; word has come swiftly confirming that the numbers of Yahweh's Children of Light have increased. They are concentrated in the East, towards the rising sun and none shall see the light of day. Wipe out all innocence in the land of Adam! Let no child of David go without pain and suffering from the time of their birth, or even before! None shall escape the wrath of our lord and god Lucifer. Our brethren in the fourth dimension are having problems overcoming Yahweh's forces as we speak, holding back Yahweh's forces has become ever so difficult, almost completely isolating our agents from gathering information within the Elohim. There are spies amongst us my brethren, both in the realm of mankind and in the fourth dimension itself; they will slip and fall! They will be found out! Is there any other order of business, please speak out now or forever hold thy speech!" "Yes! Lord Azazel!" "Name, Rank and Brand, soldier," "I am Loki, my brethren, 'Captain of Baal's Northern Legion,' based in the Mid-western region of this new world.

Bearing the symbol of the morning star your name is famed throughout the planet, Azazel, my lord! But to the business at hand is gravely flawed, while scouting out the land looking for Michael's scum brethren wherever we may find them, we encountered a variance between realms. Soon we came across some of our brethren engaging in battle with Michael's forces amongst a crowd of human scum, not even one hundred clicks in front of us, though having the skirmish within our sight, we were unable to enter the battle. As we heralded them on, without warning, suddenly, one of our brethren signaled us yelling out, 'He sees us! He sees us!' Pointing to one of the human young-lings, a little one; a male child of Semitic descent. The place in which we encountered the child was north of Chicago, off of Lake Michigan; a place called Gary and before I could confirm the identity of the child, we lost sight of our heavenly brethren." Azazel asked, "When did this happen?" Loki replied, "Not two days ago." Azazel replied, "You fool! It could have been Michael himself you moron; I'll send word to our lord!" "No, you will not send word; I shall now go!"

The year is nineteen hundred and seventy something, and I could remember a group of men forcing their way past my mother standing at the front door of our apartment. They boldly entered into our very small apartment with guns stretched out and hammer cocked back, looking for my father, invading every inch of space. It was the Law saying my father was involved or had some connection with some back street bank robbery, somewhere in the boonies of Indiana. I could hear my mother speaking with the law men about the so-called robbery as they searched the house without a warrant. I knew this because of her loud repetitive inquiries, asking, "Where's your warrant!?" Over and over. Even at that young age, I was groomed not to trust white men in police uniforms; showing no outward emotions, I instinctively stayed quiet without saying a word. I watched my father hide in a small space up in the ceiling of my mother's bedroom closet, just as the law men began frantically searching every room in the place.

As they searched personal items indiscriminately, and were about to leave, a feeling of invincibility fell over me as my father climbed down out of the ceiling, not seconds after the law men departed the premises. He had eluded captivity right before my very eyes, and after checking if the coast was clear, my father showed my mother three stacks of hundred dollar bills totaling ten thousand dollars, and three bank bags of assorted coins, a lot of money for a poor couple living in the ghetto. And in those days the bank robbers were the heroes not the bad guys, so in my eyes, he did no wrong. Knowing he would eventually be apprehended sooner rather than later, he said to my mother, "Get a lawyer...I'll be gone for a while." Then he was gone. Suddenly, he was unavailable, and being so young, I could not comprehend his disappearance even though I knew of his whereabouts. Like all loving sons, I revered him as a superhero no matter what; I couldn't care less what was said about him in the home or the streets. I cared not what anyone may accuse him of, guilty or not, for in my eye, he was great! Longing for my father, I questioned my mother daily, asking, "Where is Daddy?" "Where is he?" With a look of shame on her face, she would look out into space and say he's at work, knowing I knew the truth, she still tried her best to protect me from fictitious shame of my father's questionable occupation.

Yet day after day I would inquire of my father's whereabouts, only to receive different answers that avoided the question all together, and after a while, I gave up asking the question. I would ask myself, "Why can't she tell me the truth?" I knew where he was and she knew that, so why couldn't she say? Time moves ever so quickly as a child, horrific events evaporate in an instant, and my childhood memories of my father's exploits were sporadic at best. After spending some years incarcerated, he returned a different person. After hearing countless arguments between my father and mother, my father finally moved out of our home, thus leaving my mother in a state of never-ending anger or so it seemed.

I was too young to notice the unbelievable amount of turmoil she was undertaking or even care for that matter.

The love a son has for his father is unwavering, and like most fathers, I was the apple of his eye; his firstborn son. No longer living within the house, my father would routinely swoop me up in his seventy-two Chevy Malibu daily, taking me with him all over the city. Being so young, I would emulate my father's every action, no matter how obscene or unbecoming to those with Judea-Christian values, for uncivilized vulgar behavior was accepted and the norm amongst men of all age groups in the hood. These childish and unscrupulous behaviors, and forms of communicating persists to this day, forever cursing black men and the black culture, reflecting failure on a grand scale!

You see, my father was known throughout the city of Gary as a Good Fella, mostly its underworld received him with reverence, well known by cutthroats, thugs and killers alike. And among that community, it was as if he were a superstar, and I was the firstborn of that star. A star amongst coal and grimy scenery of broken glass, trash and rubble that scoured the landscape. A star amongst childhood visions of pimps and pushers, breaking the will of prostitutes in the winter's snow. A star where broken dreams are common, and I was a prince among thieves. Surrounded by scary men on motorcycles some may say, but for me it was not so; it was home. I was at home around that sort of so-called men, wearing black leather jackets arrayed with patches and logos, logos known as their "Colors," symbolizing their affiliation to which family, gang or organization they belonged. My father was known by many unsavory characters and he himself rolled with the well-known and ruthless "Sin-City Disciples."

The smell of oil, burned rubber and gasoline filled the air, and flowed through their blood, with the roar of stock car engines forever sounding in the wind, and the ending call of the finish line was the beat of their drum. It was the sounds and smells I was accustom to as a child and in my youth, and now it is those very sounds and smells I stand clear of as a man.

You could say my early childhood life was full of adventure and there was never a dull moment. I must say, I had lots of so-called fun, out in the streets all day and night, living as my father deemed great and manly. Looking back on the early years, it seems not so long ago, I lived without rules, coming home whenever I made it back to the house, caring not for those that might have worried about my safety, for my mother would always pitch a fit! She would get very upset, yelling and screaming with my father every time he brought me home after midnight. I had to have been only five or six years of age, and could not comprehend her concern. I didn't know why she was so upset; we were out just having fun, as my father would put it.

For the most part my father was right! He didn't ever lie about his whereabouts, plus I didn't care of the supposed danger my mother would imagine; it was fun to a small impressionable mind. It seemed as if my father was invincible! He did whatever he wanted, said whatever he wanted, and accounted to no man, and I was fast becoming his very first prodigy. Behaving in his image, we did whatever we wanted, and some people did whatever he said; if I wanted candy, I got candy without fail. I could remember my father underneath the not so secured tonnage of a handmade stock car he had constructed from salvaged junkyard scrap nearly every day.

In reminiscence of the sound, smells and sights of him going in his pocket pulling out some money, while still working underneath his car saying, "Here, boy! Go get you some candy!" Just to get me out of his way brings jubilance and embracing love of him even now. Those words bring back happy thoughts. I can still see him putting two greasy dollars in my hand as he tirelessly worked on his new project car and in those days, you could get a lot of candy for a dollar, let alone two. They literally had penny candy stores in those days, and one dollar got you a big bag of candy in those days. I never went a day without candy in my pocket.

In addition, I was taught at an early age never to trust women! My father was a true misogynous and well on his way of teaching his firstborn to be just that. Degrading women had become a past time for me, and being around so many wayward women doing my father's bidding, I had no problem behaving as such. The ladies were always around twenty-four-seven, behaving unbelievably sexual in nature, even with someone of my age. They would always kiss my cheeks saying: "He's so cute" and calling me "Mellow Yellow"! I must have been very bright-skinned in my youth, having that handle. And like clockwork, my father would tell me in a loud and demanding voice: "P! Dem bitches want a kiss? Make 'em pay ya, mane! Ha! Ha! What I tell you, P, what you say to dem hoes, Mane!?" And I would respond: "Pat dem titties and shake dem thighs. Ha! Ha! That's right, mane, shiiiit!" And they did just that! It always worked; they gave me money for a kiss on the cheek or the lips. I believed that was the proper way a man should speak to women, although my mother would care to differ! Therefore, I would come home acting and speaking in a way that was contrary at best, speaking the language of the streets, acting the way my father and all the men around him behaved and spoke. Saying to my mother: "You know; fuck dem bitches! That bitch better have my money! You know cool." I would speak just like my father.

Well, it wasn't so cool to my mother, far from it; without saying a word verbally, she spoke volumes with her looks of disappointment and shame. She didn't yell or scream directly to me about my appalling behavior, but she did express her unapproved feelings with my father. In turn, I displayed shame within myself by only bowing my head and slowly walking away from the scene, and headed towards my bedroom in silence.

Although distain was obvious in her voice when speaking to my father, she still showed the traditional forms of Judea-Christian submissiveness towards her husband, thus never intervening between a father and his firstborn son, but only suggesting restraint in his approach in child rearing.

Holding true to the classic characteristic of a die-hard male misogynistic moron, my father felt as if his actions with his son were justified and necessary, and did not warrant her concern in the least. Seeing things from a god fearing viewpoint, she expressed her concern adamantly with my father's form of upbringing, and did not approve of my father's lack of discipline that she prescribed to be inappropriate male instruction. With unwavering conviction and strong protests she went off verbally, especially expressing her opinion on the way I spoke; she didn't care for the language I'd picked up from my most loved yet un-astute father and his cohorts.

Like most human children, I soaked up what I witnessed and used the most unbecoming language known to man, frequently and without restraint and cheered on by all those in my father's presence. Seeing her young child using such profanity broke my mother's heart and I knew it. She expressed no jest in her son's indoctrination into a life of crime, corruption and failure in purpose by speaking and acting in such an unbecoming manor, even to those that adhere to the worst behavior in humanity. But my father saw no harm in my behavior whatsoever, and was in total opposition to what my mother testified as abominable corruption. Her thoughts and words on the matter swayed no influence in my father's thoughts, for he saw nothing wrong in the form in which he was grooming his firstborn son.

He himself was groomed in the very same fashion, trained from a very early age to speak and behave in such a manner in which his father prescribed. It was very becoming to my father, thinking it was the way of real men. To my father it was essential to speak in such a manner, thus deeming it necessary to gain respect in the environment in which we lived, and in a way he was right. The destruction of the English language was a plague and an art form in the inner-city, and I emulated his every move. It was very easy for my mother to assign blame in the corruption and degradation of her young and very impressionable son on my father, but in his defense, I must say, he was right, for the problem persists to this day. In most inner-cities and suburbs around these United States, children and their parents engage in such language on a regular basis! In the hood, it is the spoken truth of language, and acting like adolescent truants, plagues almost every home. In my father's mind, his speech and actions constituted a rite of passage to his firstborn son who would eventually have to face the lost hope of evil men trapped in a world of disenfranchisement and poverty!

A broken language for a broken people seemed appropriate, be it kindergarten, preschool or in the streets and my father was just getting his baby boy ready for what was in store for him in the hood, and in the world in which we lived.

Soon my mother would argue that point away, yelling and screaming every time we would come in the house. It got so bad that my father often told me not to talk when entering the house, "Don't say a word," would be the last phrase uttered from my father's mouth while climbing the stairs leading up to our apartment. Sneaking into the house after we have returned from wherever we may have gone, I complied and soon said nothing, which didn't work; for she would be waiting each time we walked through the door.

Then suddenly Dad began leaving me at home altogether.

He himself began staying out in the streets more often than in the past, not coming home for days, and soon he would not come home at all, and I was too young to understand the reason why. For me, nothing mattered other than the love of my father, and at that age, no reason for his leaving me behind could be processed or computed in my heart and broken soul. He had left us all alone, and in my undeveloped and immature mind, it was because of my mother's constant yelling and bickering. Being so young, I didn't understand the sudden changes in the behavior of my mother and father, for all I knew was what I felt in my heart or what I saw with my mind's eye. All I did was assign and point blame on my mother's mouth. It was because of my mother's constant bitching that my father was no longer there, and I was left behind because of it. I prescribed all blame of my father's absence on my mother's never ending complaining. In a true spoiled and entitled punk-like fashion, I would sulk around the house with a fucked up attitude and behaved like a spoiled brat without his favorite stuffed toy. I would break things on purpose, roll my eyes at my mother at every turn, and act as if she were the plague itself.

I felt as if my mother was putting a stop to fun itself, and most of all, preventing me from being with my father. I found myself looking out the living-room window, silently crying out for him to return each day, only to pull back the curtains to the scene of ghetto streets and paper flowing in the wind amongst pimps and pushers walking down the block. I would leave the window in disappointment daily, with the hope he would show up. This went on for a few months, and soon I began to feel as if he had abandoned me altogether, and the hope of seeing him again faded away from memory, as did the tears. With eyes dried out, anger replaced the feeling of abandonment.

Although I said very little about my feelings of abandonment to my mother, I held on dearly to my internal woes. Ill-equipped to handle strong emotions and unable to handle the internal pain, I filed them away deep within my "Mental Rolodex." My feelings of anger towards my mother grew daily, soon it was as if I cared for no one.

I would over hear my mother speaking with my Aunt Lucy about my terrible selfishness and unruly behavior, having conversations such as these: "Uh, that little nigga still acting mad at me! He need to get over it! If his daddy wanted to come and get him, he could. I'm not stopping him!" She was right in her words and thoughts, and I was acting like a young punk, but in time I began to realize it. Soon I was back to my old not so selfish self, yet still my life was minus my father's presence, and the anger manifested towards my mother began to dissipate, and I started focusing on other things rather more productive than thinking of my absentee father.

In time, the memories of fun-filled outings with younger siblings, and long hours of loud mechanical tools cranking away underneath the hood of a freshly found peace of shit, began to fade into the distance. Memories of foul language coupled with the crazy sounds of parties that filled the night's air subsided, alongside the smell of oil and gas began to slowly vanish into the dark. The life of fast women and fast cars accompanied by the sounds of soul music and the revving noise of motorcycles popping wheelies down long stretches of road disappeared from view, alongside my feelings of abandonment. The presence of my father began fading away from my memory as well, although he lived not far away. After a while, I found myself not wanting to go with him at all, and when he did come by, I fled from sight, and would not answer when he called. So in all fairness, I cannot say he abandoned us altogether; he would come around periodically, fuck my mother, drop off some money, and be on his merry way.

With no "I missed you, son" nor a word of "I wish you were with me," I soon saw that he did not feel as I felt. But let's be fair, there was always a firm sound of "I'll be back to pick you up and take you to the shop," topped off with the heartbreaking knowledge of knowing he would never show when expected. But Gary is a small town, and I would see him in his fame, out and about daily, and when he did show his face in my mother's hood, and I needed some money, I would run up to his well-known Black Cadillac and ask for some, sometimes succumbing to feelings of abandonment and even asking him if I could come along, hoping to leave with him.

Only to hear his ever so frail excuse of not being able take me along, and with every futile excuse given, it felt as if he had sawed through the strings of my heart. Hearing the sound of his voice saying "no" or "I can't" was like a mill saw chipping away the closely knit bond between a father and his son.

Every "No" was a rejection burning away the affection I once felt towards my father, and I soon stopped asking to go along anytime I saw him.

But in my selfishness, I made sure I got money whenever I saw him, for that was my logic; if I couldn't get his attention one way, I'll get something else. So every time he would grace us with his presence or show up in my mother's hood, I would ask for money, and he would give it, and that was that.

Forego the beginning and the end of a once beautiful existence of two like minds, for the unnecessary destruction of a great father and son relationship had accrued. It had been sacrificed on the altar of selfish indulgences and pleasures. As a youth, the bond between father and son had been broken and shattered at the ripe old age of six years, and I consider myself lucky at best. Sadly to say, my story is not one of uniqueness nor uncommon for most youths living in the inner-city of these United States. Simple values once prized above all were slowly corroding before the eyes of our parents' parents. Classic human morality was slowly heating up and evaporating with every decade, and their meanings and definitions had been usurped. The unbridled pursuit of the pleasure principle reigns supreme as common decency became less in demand.

The responsibilities and principles that once governed and secured a happy family structure, and an abundance of success in long life, had been systematically destroyed. Pillars such as faithfulness, monogamy and trust, had faded into the scummy muck of self-entitlement, debasement and depravity. My personal abandonment issues started early in life, and became the basis of my underlying neurosis, weaknesses and strengths. The corrosiveness of childhood abandonment is now looked upon as a normal fact of life, and is an acceptable condition in all walks of life. No matter of position, station or economic privilege, the abandonment of the nuclear family structure is now the norm. Like most semi-fatherless children in the inner-city ghettos, I was oblivious to its lifelong effects, and when I speak of the term "semi-fatherless," I'm referring to the fact that most of the ghetto youth have regular contact with most of their natural parentage, but not within a unifying natural setting, thus having a corrosive structure within the home itself. Such as those seen today, i.e. wives sleeping around with strangers and in most cases not so much strange men within the neighborhood.

Even immediate family members such as sisters, brothers and fathers were fucking everything in sight, including the sisters of their once beloved wives, and the brothers of their once beloved husbands, ultimately betraying each other's trust, having no concern for anyone's emotional and spiritual well-being, and degrading sexual sanctity primarily among themselves and others.

Like all semi-fatherless sons and daughters in the inner city ghettos across the world, my attention slowly gravitated towards the older delinquency of my peers, being I was somewhat familiar with their behavior from birth, emulating my father and his cohorts, they were seemingly the perfect male role models in the streets. With the mounting anxiety of peer pressure looming overhead daily, I began evaluating the logic of following those that knew very little or none of the realities of life, including myself, and wondered what if!? With the certain danger of thug life beginning to lose its luster, I contemplated mortality often.

With time comes wisdom, and pointless frivolous fun became ominous and frightening more than often. Be it wisdom or cowardice, I found myself symbolically clinging to my mother's leg like a baby octopus, attaching my tentacles deep into her every being, and without hesitation, she gladly facilitated my growing affections, showing motherly love and concern for whatever affliction that may arise, be it physical, emotional or spiritual.

Instinctively knowing the underlying reasons for my sudden change in behavior towards her, and knowing my newly found affections and muffled emotions stemmed from the not so obvious exclusion of a true and real moral male role model, my father's absence facilitated her overwhelming motherly instincts more so than the unwittingly rejection shown by my father's worldly exploits.

But this was and is the norm for most young boys and girls growing up in the inner-city concrete jungles of this world. In retrospect, I now ask myself why should this experience be the norm for most if not all living in poverty? Time passes ever so quickly when you're young; doesn't it? Would you like to know why? It is because "fun" cancels out the very notion of time! And when you're having fun you don't realize how deep the pains of poverty infiltrate your thought processes; therefore, you're not able to comprehend the reality that something is seriously wrong with the world in which you live.

When living in poverty you truly have no sense of stability and wellbeing, moving from one place to another seems normal, but you never learn the pride of ownership whole souled, to experience ownership is to have a notion of god-given rights of freedom. The right to live in one's own place the entirety of one's life is something precious to behold. When mankind never develops a sense of pride that comes from a solid foundation of being a stakeholder in wealth and ownership beneath their feet, a willingness to hold dear to their property without fail never comes to fruition.

Never obtaining the prideful feeling of self-security that comes with simple ownership of a home, one tends to run amuck.

In fact, most living in poverty within the United States never really truly know their very origins, knowing only the history provided by those that wish to keep their true identity a secret, ultimately never knowing or caring for their true historical background, but the significance of that fact may present itself in the passages revealed within this book.

With that revelation in mind, is there any wonder why most living in poverty couldn't care less of their surroundings, not to excuse sub-human behavior, but I do understand. You say in your mind's eye, fuck the appearance of this hell hole in which I live! The early memories fade away with a flash of light then darkness.

Like clockwork, we moved from one place to another once again and this time, we moved in the same building as my Aunt Lucy. My Aunt Lucy was the oldest of my mother's two sisters, and mother of my closest kin, who were more like brothers in fact. You see, Pookey, Chunky and I were born around the same time of year and season. Chunky and I were born one month apart and Pookey one year earlier than the two. We all grew up experiencing the same political and social upheaval that spawned violent and traumatic rebellion around the country at that time. Violence ran rapid in the streets of Chicago and Gary.

CHAPTER V

Mischievous Mayhem

The spirit of innocence had evaporated, for key Children of Light had almost been extinguished from time and space, while chaos and confusion had become a way of life for most Americans in the late Sixties. Since we were the offspring of twin brothers, it would only be natural to assume we would exhibit similar traits, not to mention the very close knit relationship between our mothers would most likely produce great similarities in the behaviors of their offspring. We were inseparable growing up because of the close proximity of our living quarters.

With that said, we had nothing in common at all, other than the blood that flowed through our veins. In fact, I even disputed that notion of truth. In a quick description of the three, I was somewhat a reclusive little kid, preferring to be left alone in silence much of the time, whereas my brotherly cousins displayed a willingness for the dramatic, which gave the two ruffians a license to fuck with me daily. I didn't mind too much since anytime I got lonely, they were there to relieve the not so prevalent emotion. The two brothers were without shame, outgoing and naturally destructive in all things, destroying everything they touched, not to mention, how they were somewhat cruel towards one another daily. I was the opposite soul, full of fear; fear of my surroundings, meek, passive and wishy-washy, shying from any unsanctioned activity dictated by our mothers. My mother's apartment was adjacent to my Aunt Lucy's with one door separating the two apartments, which in the beginning became quite cool, right? I could see my brother/cousins Pookey and Chunky any time I chose, and since our mothers were so fond of one another, the three of us would be damn near inseparable. But as time passes, so does change, and one's welcome fades as time goes by. It was great in the beginning so I thought, but not so soon after moving into the building, relations between my cousins and me became corrosive at best.

Though my two roughens had no clue of it, yet for me at times life became unbearable. With so much access between the two families so readily prevalent, seeing my cousins daily began to truly suck! Common household duties and issues alongside differences in hygiene practices soon became apparent.

My Aunt Lucy was nothing like my mom, for her true self-worth resided within. In my childish and naïve eyes, she was very mean and controlling to all. A woman that ruled her kids with an iron fist that yelled constantly at Pookey and Chunky which seemed like forever, for they were continuously doing something to inflame her. But in total fairness to my Aunt Lucy, I didn't blame her for her extra exuberant behavior towards her children. In just a few weeks after moving into the building, I now admired her strength in dealing with Tasmanian-Devils. In total contrast to my Aunt Lucy's authoritarian method of child rearing, my mother gave me constant kisses, love and a considerable amounts of trust from the very beginning of my young childhood.

She never raised her voice, though I never give her reason, but my Aunt Lucy was the opposite, which scared the hell out of me. She yelled constantly at Pookey and Chunky, using foul language on a regular basis, punishing them daily without fail, undoubtedly venting over some destructive act committed uncontrollably by either one or both of her misbehaved demon spawned seeds whom she constantly tried to keep under control, understandingly restricting their every movement, which strained the relationship of us three.

You see, I was able to roam freely about our apartment at all hours of the day, playing inside and outside. I played freely like most kids of our age, whereas Pookey and Chunky were monitored twenty-four seven, under the constant scrutiny of their mother. They couldn't come outside to play before noon, only able to gaze through a dirty screen window six stories up, when most kids in the hood were roaming freely out and about having a ball, playing in the early breeze of the morning. Once again I praised my aunt for her foresight in concealing her two wayward sons until later in the day, providing relief of un-relentless bullying from her unruly children aimed towards most in the neighborhood, including myself.

She was like a hawk watching her chicks leaving the nest for the first time every time she allowed them out, for they were atrocious in their activities and forever nefarious. Before the traditional last call blown by all the mothers in the hood, warning all the hood-rats to come indoors to ensure their safety before the street lights burned bright, my aunt had already made that call prematurely, knowing her children's behavior. However, the rest of us went our own way, seemingly not to hear the universal call out by all mothers in the hood.

Unlike most future delinquents stifled from enjoying the twilight, I was able to stay out way past the traditional tribal call for all to come indoors. With a mischievous look and devious smirk, I would look towards Pookey and Chunky as they loudly protested against their mother's roughshod way of herding them indoors before the rest of the neighborhood children even thought about the dreaded call. I watched them both look back towards me as their mother rounded them up for the night and I knew they would be looking out of their bedroom window, and I'd look up and wave at them while I played outside with the more fortunate neighborhood children. For instance, before long the streetlights were warming up and most of the children would be indoors, and soon after the street lights burned bright. The feeling of being one of privileged, who remained outside for more than ten minutes made one a star, for all outdoor activities and fun ceased for the night, although we all dreaded going back inside.

When long-held cultural pillars corrodes and crumbles, the family structure collapses as well. So does the illusion of what once may have been considered the normalcy in behavior, whatever that term could be defined as "Judea-Christian" values, maybe? I don't know. But nevertheless, a young mind is a blank smart-board, and desperately needs sound instruction engraved on its hard drive to soundly navigate the multitude of ever changing perception that regulates all matters of life. Without this instruction, all hell breaks loose! This fact has been known by man from the beginning of his existence.

It could literally mean life or death at an early age, and be almost impossible for the young mind to mature which is critical and essential for all human life to prosper and grow. In order for the mind to perform well and develop hard-line encryption for survival and success, it needs sound instruction, and I guess my cousins found that sound instruction in my father; however, I beg to differ.

Although my father no longer resided within my mother's home and was residing elsewhere with a new family of his own, he was always there in some fashion. He still behaved as if he ruled my mother's house as the head of house hold or King. "Mr. French Sr." could not be described as the typical nuclear father with high Christian moral ethics. He periodically showed up and provided support here and there, which was a lot more than most men in the hood could do for their own, and because of that fact, he was revered and appreciated by my mother, and even more precarious my two wayward cousins worshiped him and saw him as if he was their father. Pookey and Chunky admired my father greatly, emulating him more than I ever could. Though Pookey's father was literally my father's twin brother, Pookey's father was absentee the majority of my cousin's life, and my father showed himself a man in the eyes of my cousins. It was as if I had everything and they had nothing.

I was able to buy candy from the candy man's candy cart that patrolled up and down the neighborhood streets on Saturday morning, but Pookey and Chunky couldn't. So they ate my candy with me. What was mine was theirs; I didn't care, for what was theirs was mine as well and we shared everything!

The only male role model the three of us ever known was my father. He was always accessible to us, at least he periodically came around and gave of himself, whereas Pookey and Chunky's father was nonexistent and treated them both like orphans. Shunned by their own so-called biological father.

Although my father lived a life not approved of by most god fearing men, he showed compassion to all his children and all he knew, and treated my cousins like they were his flesh and blood children themselves. Other than the inappropriate language and questionable lifestyle, my father was the best! He often gave them just as much attention as he did his own children. My father was seen as a very great man and loved by most who knew him. He showed love towards Pookey and Chunky, providing material things whenever he could, which was a lot more than their biological father ever did; hence, we shared the same last name and enjoyed the same man as a father. It's ironic when two sisters married two brothers, twin brothers at that, so we all grew as siblings more than cousins.

My cousins really never knew their father until later on in life, although he lived just minutes away. Rumors have it that only Pookey was the son of my father's brother and Chunky was the son of someone else, someone who also bared the name Chunky, who knows? Although my father's brother truly was an absentee father to Pookey and Chunky, my father showed them more attention and love than their own flesh and blood father could ever have shown in a lifetime. They were welcome on outings and sometimes they even went with us on our regular trips to the "US 30 Drag Strip." Whenever he took me to his home for our weekly visit, they came along as well, giving my Aunt Lucy a well-deserved rest from their tenacious and disobedient behavior which was never ending. I swear they were in trouble at least twenty hours out of twenty-four hours a day.

My father was, and still is the consummate motor head and always over or underneath an automobile, for it seemed as if he never slept, working continuously, even on the weekends. If he wasn't working six days a week at the City Steel Mill a full twelve-hour shift daily, he was underneath a car. I guess I shouldn't be so concerned with the lack of attention given me from my father, at least he showed himself now and then. But the very fact of lobbying for exclusive yet limited attention allocated amongst my other illegitimate siblings, alongside my wayward cousins, he did not always facilitate the emotional needs and fatherly care one might need to maintain sanity in a very hostile environment, especially amongst a number of siblings and family members bidding for your ruin and his attention.

In time, I just gave up trying to gain his attention or approval. After groveling for attention from my own father and getting no satisfaction, it shined light on the incidents contributing to the rebellious behavior and despicable nature of my two cousins.

Being so young to the realities of godless living, and adequately inexperienced to the dark side of the world in which we all lived, jealousy began to rear its ugly little head amongst my siblings and cousins early in our childhood, which saw my relationship with my father totally opposite from my own perceptions. Though they didn't say much, I could feel their animosity. Sometimes there were little comments like, "You always get something, P! You get everything; that's not fair!" Then they would deliberately ruin even the smallest trinket or reward my father would give me. I could see the envy building up within my younger siblings and cousins.

I kept to myself and said nothing to anyone about their behavior towards me and soaked it up. "The more envy the better!" I would tell myself after every incursion, "They will get theirs…just wait and see." I felt empowered somehow or even justified in my pompous attitude towards all my siblings. However, my thought processes changed after the infamous US 30 Race-Track incident when all my shafted siblings left me to fend for myself among a massive crowd of strangers. For as long as I could remember, my father would gather all his children including my cousins every Sunday morning and make a trip to the US 30 Drag Strip where he would race his latest Stock Car. It was the greatest and most anticipated event in all our little lives. We talked about our experiences at the Strip daily, dreaming for Sunday to magically appear, and the days of the week seem to drag on and on whenever my father would announce his plans to be spontaneous and spout out that he would be taking us all. My father received all jubilance and glory from all the young boys in the family, ensuring almost perfect behavior out of all us for the weeks to come.

The nightly dreams of the momentous moment of the long awaited trip were over and the sleepless night before the trip had arrived, and as if we were soldiers at boot camp, we all were up at the crack of dawn and ready to go. Like clockwork, my father arrived at 6am beeping his horn from "Big Red" signaling us all to jump aboard without haste, yet never leaving the driver's seat of the truck, and the moment he laid eyes on us all he'd yell out, "Make sure all you little mathafuckas got a lunch, 'cause I ain't buying you SHIT when we get there!" And we all loaded up in the back of Big Red and were ready to go! With his latest Stock Car hatched to Big Red, and all of us on board, he'd take off like a bat from hell, peeling out leaving a dust cloud behind him and we were all off to the races. After a long and tedious ride, we finally arrived at the US Drag Strip, seeing nothing familiar, only a Carnival and Amusement Park atmosphere with all of us in total awe! We all dismounted from Big Red, running uncontrollably all over the place while my father un-hatched his latest creation only yelling out, "Don't go too far, you bad-ass niggas!" But like normal misbehaved children, we paid no mind. With no one recognizable in sight, surrounded by nothing but white faces, I found myself lost within five minutes and lost from everyone I knew.

Franticly, I began searching for everyone I knew everywhere, and found myself all alone for hours. Feeling helpless and lost, I realized the new found empowerment I flaunted over my wayward, rambunctious cousins, and jealous siblings alike had backfired and became a very big and cumbersome problem.

A problem that would only grow, knowing they would eventually begin to hate me instead of just being envious of my "Firstborn" status.

I stopped the gloating and showed little interest in material possessions, for even then, I understood the concept of "What comes around goes around," and the sorrow that proceeds from not heeding that particular quote of wisdom. I didn't want or need that, so from that day forward, I made sure I shared most of all my belongings without protest or frown, such as: clothing, toys, candy, etc.... But there was one thing I didn't share. Though we were poor, my mother and father did spoil me whenever they could. If I asked for something obtainable, nine times out of ten, my parents would find a way to get it, and all I wanted that year was the most awaited Christmas gift every male born child in America wanted, the new Tyco Race Track with cars that had real headlights that beamed brightly as the cars moved around the racetrack. Without fail my father came through and my most awaited dream for that Christmas lay under the Christmas tree as promised—

A brand new "Tyco" racing track, fully equipped with racing cars that actually had working headlights, which was highly sought after by every kid in the hood! You know the kind I'm talking about; the kind with headlights that actually worked! The first of its kind! The first ever made in that era. It was the favorite toy of all young boys ages three to twenty-three. A Christmas present dream come true, and I couldn't wait to play with it! But higher forces thought otherwise, and the Grinch appeared in the form of my two dear cousin/brothers.

My racing track never stood a chance. Being loving and accommodating sisters, living adjacent to one another, with no fear of being robbed or accosted, no one thought to lock the adjacent door. What a big mistake! As soon as we left the building, Pookey and Chunky entered our apartment, with only one thing in mind, and one focus—total havoc, targeting the "Tyco" first, burning out the engines of both cars by rolling them off the specially made racing tracks. With no care or concern of consequence, they went through everything in the house not nailed down and with indiscriminate malice, nothing was off limits.

The cupboards, food in the refrigerator, my toys, and everything else was totaled! Mom had a conniption fit!

Storming towards my Aunt Lucy's place, with fire in her eyes, screaming at the top of her lungs, "Those bad-ass mothafuckas! LUCY! Look! Look at what dem little niggas did! You need to do something with those bad-ass kids; they got problems, issues! They need medical attention!" Hearing my aunt reply, "I whoop the living shit out of them every fuck'n day, and it does no good! What do you want me to do? Look at them! They're just sitting there crying out with joy and playing at the same time, as if they did nothing wrong!?"

I was so upset I couldn't even cry; I just looked around our home, and saw it in a total wreck. In total shock, with my mouth wide open, I looked around and saw that our home was destroyed! I looked at Pookey and Chunky in absolute astonishment, seeing them sitting there just smiling, and I thought to myself, "Something was not right with them. Something was wrong with them!" I was so upset; I thought Mom locked the adjacent door, but I was wrong. I thought all was well, as she left the door connecting the two apartments unlocked! What a big mistake!

A mistake that wouldn't be taken lightly again. From that day forward, the adjacent door would be unopened, locked, to make sure "Thing One" and "Thing Two" had no access to our side of the dual layout of the apartment structure, closing each other's prospective apartments. Dissension occurred between the two loving sisters because of the unruliness of two unbalanced spirits, thus filling everyone in the building with animosity. My mom and Aunt Lucy didn't talk with each other for at least a week after the initial event, and after the cold silence between one another, then came the constant bickering and arguing over the smallest of disagreements.

I myself bottled up the unforgiving anger festering over the destruction of my one and only prize possession, steadily harboring animosity towards my cousins. I showed restraint even then and still played with Pookey and Chunky until the anger towards them diminished, never mentioning the obvious, yet before the heinous event, I lamented my Aunt Lucy over her zealous upbringing of the two terrors, and for the life of me, I couldn't see why my aunt never let them play inside the house before now. Now I knew why!

As I watched them continuously play around the building uncontrollably

EDGAR FRENCH, JR.

tribal like, stopping with enthusiasm every time, terrorizing shouts of upheaval between our mothers rang down to the street below, as if they enjoyed hearing our mothers argue back and forth over the devastation they themselves had just caused. I began wondering about their mental state, thinking to myself, "Them mothafuckas crazy!"

I watched them play and laugh with such giddiness and glee, as sharp yells of disappointment from our mothers came down from the apartments above. I could see with my mind's eye that something was seriously wrong with both of them and it was more than mental illness, it was spiritual. It was malice I saw in their eyes.

It was as if they both were in an unseen state of evil control, or under the influence of an unseen being. They weren't just being rambunctious kids; they were being vindictive and spiteful in their destruction, cause and purpose. Evil walked alongside their motive, and the mess they made was personal in nature. It was as if they were out to hurt all they came across, or to get back at someone for something done to them unknown to others.

There was a wicked purpose behind their actions and thoughts; I had no concept of the terms of their condition; I just rolled with it at that time. I can recall the events with clarity, and the only thought that came to my undeveloped mind, as I watched them playing on the concrete street below our building as if nothing was happening between our mothers, was caution! Without a care, they played while our mothers argued back and forth, loudly discussing the destructive behavior of my mischievous first cousins. Silently, I tried to make sense of their actions, feebly trying to analyze within myself their behavior, saying to myself, "If Aunty would only let them have Christmas and stuff, maybe they wouldn't be so bad!"

Then the thought of my racetrack entered my mind, knowing they didn't care about anything, as long as they were able to achieve their goal of destroying my shit, for they would gladly take an ass whopping just to see disgust on my face. I quickly regained my senses and ran directly to my bedroom knowing the worst had accrued. I protested without avail, and all I could do was hold the broken parts of my racetrack in my hand and cry over the broken plastic pieces.

It was the end of a short-lived privately owned possession. From that day forward, I knew I would never have anything solely to myself without my cousin's rough handed interference and destruction of whatever toy or item I may own. Soon, I began hiding my things with more elusiveness and cunning methods. I felt under sieged by my own family members, and from those very young aged experiences of unchecked, unbridled and undeveloped entitled thought processes exhibited by my evil cousins. I had no choice but to fight back the bullying over my meek heartiness, which sparked a drive within me to understand the shitty things people do and why. I began trying to understand the irrational actions of people, especially my own family, and even then, I tried to understand the very question of "why" itself?

Being so young and full of myself, I began to realize I was very selfish, unkind and thoughtless in my own actions, and it was beginning to make itself obvious, so I set out to change my own thoughts of selfishness, so as to understand my cousins' behavior towards me. I could never behave as they did, just because they had something I didn't. I would see my cousins looking through their living room windows watching me enjoy my not so appreciated independence outside after the street lights began to illuminate. With sadness in their eyes, I felt no remorse. With a smirking look up, I waved and giggled feeding their resentment towards me. I thought I was getting back at them, but it only fueled the flames of jealousy, waiting for the next time they would say, "You always get something!"

I couldn't be certain, but something from within me began to bring the pieces together. It was a divine intervention so to speak, and I soon realized my part in their actions. Saying to myself, "Let me see what would happen...if!" What if I showed them I could care less for the things I possessed and let them do whatever, whenever, with all I had. Would that change them or their behavior?!

So one faithful Christmas night, as I opened my many presents smiling carelessly, enjoying a mouth full of holiday candy, with an abundance of joy in my heart, I looked through the door adjacent the two apartments and saw my two brother-like cousins looking back at me. Not with the usual look of jealousy, but with a look in their eyes of why?! Chunky sadly questioned my Aunt Lucy, "Why can't I have anything for Christmas?" and hearing the answer to his questioning I soon understood their non-participation in my immediate family activities, and it instantly changed my heart from having an over flow of holiday joy, to having overwhelming feeling of guilt, ungodliness and shame, as if I had done something wrong towards them.

I asked myself "why" as well? Internally questioning myself, "Why can't they have anything for Christmas? What made my circumstance different from theirs?" Saying to myself, "Not much," I knew no difference in our circumstances, other than the facts that my family was poor and theirs very poor, celebrating Christmas had no relevance to me. We shared everything else.

Why can't they have some candy, and go to Grandma's house for Christmas dinner like I could? Having no concept of religion or god, I silently searched for some kind of answer to explain away what I was feeling inside, watching everything and every interaction between my mother and her sister, trying to comprehend all that was said. Young, stupid, and naïve, I examined every nuance between the two, and could find no difference, yet every day I looked closely at the two, hearing every conversation without hearing the answer to my nagging questions, questions of why we could have Christmas and my cousins couldn't.

"Was it the fact of my mother being so nice and my Aunt Lucy not so nice; could that be the answer? Could that be it?" Well, in the eyes of a child, that was how it seemed.

When Easter came, and my immediate family would get dressed in our Sunday's best, and head out for church with Grandma, my cousins were still in bed as we walked out the door, with all in the congregation greeting us with smiles and festive speeches on the pulpit, I promptly continued falling asleep listening to the preacher's loud and self-serving sermons as Grandma poked me awake every five minutes, and I understood nothing said. I anxiously anticipated the Easter egg hunt after the preacher's rant, fidgeting in my seat most of the sermon and looking at the clock every other minute, hoping and praying he would hurry it up, and finish so we could get the hell out! Hearing the sound of the last song was like ambrosia and angst in wait for the clock to ring noon.

The clock rang noon then off we went on the hunt! We ran and jumped like bunnies in the park in back of the church, all the children freed from the sermon with baskets in hand, looking under every bush and branch, roaming through endless fields of grass and dandelions, searching every tree and stump and gathering all the colored eggs, as much as we could. We showed off our cash of edible booty, filled with the grand spirit and feelings of being newly freed church goers. We gloated over how many small colored jewels we may have collected and compared their colorful designs with others and were stuffed from all the Easter candy, food and fun; but sadly, we always came home to see Pookey and Chunky dressed in their same dingy outfits that they played in the day before.

My cousins didn't get to go to the church like the rest of Grandma's children, and were separated from the fun everyone else enjoyed. "Why don't Pookey and Chunky come to church with us?" I would ask my mother, but never got an answer. I only got a non-responsive grunt and a "Just make sure you save them some food and candy," unwittingly making me think it was because of my Aunt Lucy being mean. So I made sure Pookey and Chunky had their share in all the holiday fun, not just Easter but all holidays it seemed. It was as if my Aunt Lucy didn't want her children to have any fun at all, for they never participated in any holiday functions and I didn't understand why. "How could she be so mean to her own children?" I would ask myself, especially during the winter holidays. I looked at my cousins with pity as I saw them miss out on the most important events of the year, every year, and it saddened me greatly. Every year I observed them missing the best festivals of all, Halloween and Christmas, and it deeply disturbed me.

In my mind and heart, they were missing out on the most wonderful events known to man and our family, so every year I made sure to save a piece of the joy I received, and I shared whatever I could when I could all the time, ultimately feeling upset at my Aunt Lucy more and more, as if she were abusing them and denying them joy and happiness every year.

The lost memories of happy days come flooding back into my mind when writing on the subject matter; sights, sounds and smells cause one to reflect on the blissfulness of ignorance. Grandma would always entertain the entire neighborhood on one of those holidays mentioned, for she would have wonderful and elaborate parties at her home on those days, and for some odd reason unknown to me, she would go "all out" for those very two holidays, especially on Christmas it seemed as a child. For Halloween, she would decorate the entire house inside and out, inviting everyone in the hood, playing horror movies throughout the day, with all kinds of assorted candy available for all her grandchildren, making popcorn balls, candy and caramel apples with walnuts on top, bobbing for apples, etc.... And what's the deal with Halloween and apples anyway? Could it be an allusion back towards our ancestor's mistake in the Garden of Eden?

I could remember all the children in the neighborhood gathered around Grandma's house, dressed in their favorite costumes, running all around the house, having fun and being silly in their homemade costume interpretations of fictional action heroes in which we were dressed. It was candy galore! And we all had our fill of popcorn-balls, and when the night descended on the scene, the children slowly started to fade away into the background, back to their prospective homes, but that was just the beginning, for it was now time for the grown-ups to come out to play!

Here they come! Dressed in their favorite wicked costume, themselves. With alcoholic beverages in hand, emerging amongst the fog of a wide array of soul and gospel music playing as loud as a Hi Fi Stereo system could transmit, while everyone in the hood was laughing, drinking and dancing throughout the house and front yard. There were so many people cheering and happiness filled the air, and there were no spirits of violence or animosity as everyone took part in the festivities as I sneaked out of my uncle's bedroom to view or at least take a peek of the fun filled activities in which the grown-ups were consumed with. I was all alone thinking only of my two brother/cousins, and the closest family members of all, missing out on all the fun.

But Pookey and Chunky were nowhere to be found; in fact they weren't missed at all, for their disappearance wasn't talked about between the other kids in the family, or the children in the hood, and why wasn't their presence missed by all in the family? Because I missed them, I would ask my mother: "Where was Pookey and Chunky?" She would only respond, "Maybe you'll see them next time." I don't think my mother understood that those kind of answers only made me question the status quo even more.

How could all of us enjoy the holidays while Pookey and Chunky couldn't, especially on Christmas, the best holiday of the year in the cold snowy Midwestern town as icy wind blows in when the days grew shorter and the nights last longer?

During this time in my life no wrong could be committed or enacted that could take away the illusion of happiness brought about by the holidays, remembering the many lonely walks in the night of the city before the unthinkable began to enter my psyche. My senses embraced the enhanced smells of the evergreen trees sent flowing in the breeze, alongside the slowly falling foliage of the trees, coupled with the sweet smell of decaying vegetation filling the air as well as snowflakes began to fall, feelings of safety only prolonged the wonderful sensations that mixed up all five senses. The sights of Christmas decorations amazed my youthful eyes, alongside colorful lights blazing through the night, as they adorned every building and residential home seen throughout the city, and as I enjoyed the snow and wonderful sights, my cousins stayed indoors. While most children sang "Jingle Bells" and "Rudolph the Red-Nosed Reindeer," my cousins only watched in silence while I was busy eating candy canes with visions of Santa, angel and Gingerbread ornaments adorning the Christmas Tree in grandma's living room. Only presents bombarded my undeveloped brain, yet my cousins were nowhere in sight. Just think about it. How could she deny her own children such joy? Was their unruly behaviors so bad? I couldn't see it, for in my mind's eyes, she was cruel and unjust. For in the mind of a child, Christmas is the only holiday that is truly wholly! Every child talks and dreams about Christmas the whole year 'round.

The one holiday you couldn't wait for as a child was Christmas, yet Pookey and Chunky never spoke of it, or even felt the wholly spirit of Christmas that filled the winter air, for it couldn't invoke a smile from either one. A time of so-called peace and tranquility, not to mention all the appetizing and wonderful smells of great food was only a past time for Pookey and Chunky. The tantalizing morsels that stimulate the taste buds only brings the mind's eye back to the past of fantasy and illusion. I enjoyed the roasted duck, turkey and all the other Christmas specialties prepared by my mother and grandma, and yes, my grandmother's food was the best. She was a master baker and would bake all the traditional pastries: pies, cookies, cakes, etc....which only makes me recall the memories of times lost, and yet shall never fade, for the mind's hard-drive makes sure of fine memories resigning their place in memories not to be completely erased.

Remembering the once beautiful old neighborhood decorated with lights and ornaments only makes one wonder "why" why so much lost. I can still recall Grandma's house adorned in white lights, with snow-white evergreen trees dressed in white Christmas lightbulbs, and silver tassels with a green blanket surrounding the bottom tree stand and lots of presents for all her grandchildren lying underneath the beautiful tree. All family was in attendance, all except Lucy's children and herself, for they were missing all the Christmas's festivities, joy and blessings provided only once a year. I would never see Pookey and Chunky, thinking my Aunt Lucy was so mean spirited and cold hearted towards her only children at that time, denying them all that was good. It was God's birthday after all! What was wrong with her!? How could she do such a thing? I was too young to understand her logic.

I would come home from Grandma's house after the festivities, watching Chunky and Pookey peak out behind the curtain of their front window as they heard my father's car drive up on the curb next to the building where we all lived, waiting on me and all my many presents to enter the building, so they could get a piece of holiday joy and cheer. I would always selfishly assume they were just waiting for me to come in and flaunt my presents, but unwilling to exploit the gifts received, we would bypass their entrance and go directly to our joint apartment, with my mom quickly closing the door leading to my Aunt Lucy's apartment. "That's okay, I'll just wait until tomorrow morning to share my bountiful blessings."

Filled with holiday joy, I stayed patient, not touching one unwrapped item that night, waiting to open my Christmas presents with Pookey and Chunky the next day. The memory fades away; a light then darkness.

Loki: My lord Baal, I invoke the third proclamation! I stand in the midst of your glory, oh lord of lords! Ruler of all rebel forces. Here in the light of Luna full. This midnight All Hollows Eve… Please hear my summons… Drenched in the pure blood of a virgin's sacrifice; I invoke your presence! APPEAR! — APPEAR! Appear before your faithful servant Loki… I invoke the third proclamation… I invoke your presence!

Baal: I hear you, my son. Why do you call upon me?

Loki: I have word, my lord, word of a child. A child of the third realm here on Earth. A male child that could see what is not to be seen.

Baal: Could he not be one of ours?

Loki: I don't know, my lord.

Baal: Where is this child?

Loki: Rummaging among the lost, in a lakefront enclave on the outskirts of the city of winds, here in the new world. Please excuse my pertinence, my lord, but I myself have not witnessed the child personally, nor have I witnessed his so-called ability to peel back the veil concealing the fourth dimensional realm, unseen to human eyes, my lord. I only took word of the child's presence from brethren fighting in the field, my lord. Word from my brethren in the fourth who saw and confirmed the child's ability to peer into the fourth realm, for it seems to be valid, my lord.

Baal: I shall consult the counsel.

Loki: Yes, my lord.

Baal: Be gone!

Loki: Yes, my lord!

{Lucifer Consults "The Ten Captains of the Two Hundred Fallen Ones"}

Baal: I call this emergency counsel to order; there has been word of a seer child born of man, able to peer into the fourth realm, peeling back the veil that separates the two realities; the man-child is able to see our world and our kind; we all know the proclamation; speak, my brethren, speak.

Tamiel: How is this possible?

Baal: As you well know; though lying dormant within their mind's eye, all humans have the ability to see into our realm, just as we have the ability to view into the third.

Ramiel 1: Their ignorance of their ancestor's past indignations prevents their eyes from opening.

Baal: In Eden, their mental development was halted; with their mind's third eye yet still underdeveloped, not able to engage the mind's eye in full.

Tamiel: Only in dreams some remnant of our plain merges within their existence, and only we of spirit may roam freely between the realms.

Ramiel 2: Yet it is accessible to humans, is it not?

Baal: Just a few human souls have been able to breach the veils and see through the glass of time; only one has been able to breach the veil without our assistance, and that has been the Nazarene of old.

Daniel: Their humble lifespan only allows for one simple glimpse into the fourth realm at a time, for he poses no threat.

Urakiba: Could he be one of ours?

Ramiel 2: If he is of us, he must be groomed as soon as possible.

Baal: This is true, maybe because of the child's innocence of heart he was able to see, who knows; he must be kept under constant surveillance; summon the so-called eyewitness!

Asphernaz: Here I am, my lord, it is I, Asphernaz, commander of your heavenly Legion to the North; I stand witness upon death, my lord; I saw the child you speak of, very young, no more than four human years shun upon his face.

Baal: Go on.

Asphernaz: Not only did he see; he spoke, my lord.

Baal: He what?

Asphernaz: He spoke—looking me directly in the eye—he spoke to me; he was able to interact within our realm.

Daniel: OH! How could this be? Was the child Michael? Did you see his mark!

Asphernaz: No, my lord, as you well know the mark is only visible when doing energy transfer from one plane to another.

Baal: Seek him out! Leave no stone unturned; find this child at once!

CHAPTER VI

Enter the Lovely Ones into Despair

A cloud of darkness has fallen amongst men. No longer shall innocence maintain man's ignorance. For those whose faith in a higher power alludes them comes death, for they have given themselves over to darkness, and are fully deceived within their spirits at all times. The spirit of the lord roams over the face of the Earth, and I'm a little older now. Life is changing in leaps and bounds. My mom is bringing home a little baby girl; a little sister to take care of, I would say. Cherise Renee is her name. I can't remember much more than a brief memory of a baby girl wrapped in blankets during that time, and time has passed alongside the memories of my little sister's departure; it all is becoming a blur in times of childhood dreams misunderstood.

Issues of abandonment shall rear its ugly head and never subside! Taking hold of Renee first, leaving the firstborn for last. With no warning, the spirit of future woes had descended upon us, and without knowledge of its presence, we gave ourselves over into the spirit's snare. Falling into the clutches of abandonment, we all fell and stayed in darkness. The sense and spirit of family security resided with us only briefly, for within a year she was gone from her mother's loving arms and living with Grandma from swaddling to maiden. I have no clue why she had gone and I was too young to understand the reasoning behind my mother's willingness to give up her only daughter at that time. To this very day, I'll never understand my mother's reasoning for giving her over to Grandma, and why Renee had to go away still so very young. With only rumors and conjecture to answer unanswered questions from grown-ups, I began to get angry at them all.

Getting nowhere only fueled the need to fill the empty space occupying the constant thoughts of missing my only sister at that time. All memories of growing up with my baby sister Renee remain in bits and pieces. Though my love for her was very strong, I cannot understand why the memories of her were fading away, for I never knew her. Memories of my cousins Pookey and Chunky were more prevalent in my mind's eye, in fact, the memories of growing up with my cousins dominated all other memories of my early childhood. We three cousins/brothers were inseparable in the beginning, and yet I never really had a chance to know my baby sister, to whom all my love belonged.

As time progressed and the emptiness within me subsided, forgotten is the sadness of my little sister not being there in our home. The internal pain also subsided into the mundane forgetfulness of daily life.

Periodically we would visit Grandma's house and I'd see my baby sister growing up within Grandma's domain, under Grandma's ever watchful eye. And though I loved Grandma dearly, I felt as if she treated Renee very shrewdly and badly, as if she were some fictional character in the late sixteen hundreds such as "Cinderella!" She worked Renee constantly, never letting her out of her sight, not even for the sake of a moment. It was creating a hole within my heart, leaving me with even more unanswered questions concerning Renee's mistreatment by the hand of my beloved "Grandma" and others. Bewilderment and confusion overwhelmed my senses and abounded within my mind's eye with questions as I witnessed the level of cruelness within the family as a whole.

Weariness over shadows most concerns of an adolescent during the early stages of life, and at that time, I was fully fixated upon myself, and my concerns for my sister faded away into the background of the mundane and day to day concerns of no substance, but her absence shall forever haunt my very spirit throughout the years to come. I know that some things will never come to light, just as these questions will never be answered in my lifetime. Yet they must be asked! Why would Mama let her firstborn daughter go so soon after birth? Why did she live with Grandma? Why was she treated so badly by all, it seemed? Why couldn't we be a family living together? Never being a whole complete family for long haunts me to this very day.

No explanations would grace any inquiries concerning my lost dear sister's circumstances, not even the occasional gossip that escaped the lying lips of immediate family members. It made no sense nor reason. I faintly remember the first day my mother brought her home from the hospital, seeing her wrapped in a little pink cotton soft baby blanket, begging Mom to let me take a glimpse of the new precious one, and for the first time, my young heart filled with joy, loving the idea of having a little sister. She was so beautiful and happy at birth, truly a happy baby. How tragic were the circumstances surrounding her removal!

What hellish fate or circumstance of chance visited upon us by desperate Supreme Beings, lording over all the many realms that exist within the cosmos?

What provoked such a being to conspire and inflict such pain upon pure innocence?! This very short life in which we live cannot even be measured in length of time. This mayfly existence in which we live holds no certainties of divine presence, for the Creator has been forsaken within the universe itself. What could take away Renee's presence is beyond me, for divine intervention must be its reasoning.

Time is doing its job and things seem to be going well as the wounds heal, but I'm having a hard time falling asleep, something seems wrong and out of place, then an intrusion of extraordinary awareness occurred.

While lying in my bed day dreaming, looking up at the ceiling wide awake, the plaster and light fixture in the middle of the ceiling faded into darkness and a calmness fell over me, and the heavens opened up within my little bedroom, and visions of demonic beings engulfed the room. I saw them as clear as day! Little bitty monsters ascended out of a cross-dimensional door and opened through the hole in my ceiling. They were crawling on the surrounding walls and flying in the air, while some were just sitting on my dresser, continuously looking at me with mischief and mayhem in their fiery beady little eyes; frightful! Every last one of them was looking at me with hatred in their eyes as they jumped from wall to wall, some even had sharp ridged teeth. I showed them no fear, only wonderment in expression at first, not believing what I was seeing, and as they got closer to my bed, fear began to overwhelm me.

I closed my eyes, rubbing them with both hands, hoping they would go away before I would remove my hands, but when I looked again, they were still there. I yelled out to my mother with tears in my eyes: "MAMA! There are monsters on my dresser!" She quickly responded "What?!" "There are Monsters on my dressers! Look! They gonna eat me!" Since her bedroom was very close in proximity, she ran over to my bedroom within a matter of seconds, turned on the lights, and suddenly they vanished within a blink of an eye. POOF! "There's nothing there, boy! What the hell wrong with you? You lost your cotton-pickin' mind, ain't nothing there, boy, take yo black ass back to sleep! I ain't gone tell you no moe," mumbling under her voice as she turned off the lights. I was more afraid of her rant than the weird little monsters climbing the walls a few seconds ago. But within a few minutes they reappeared smiling at me, ultimately finding pleasure in the obvious panic that filled my face, shaking from the inside out with fear. The little monsters were feeding off the fanfare of dread they had caused me by their very presence, and from the motion of their nasty pus-filled mouths, I could see they were laughing at me. Every night they would appear, and every night I would close my eyes and wish them away without success. Diminishing the fright of their presence was my only response after a while, as they made lunging jesters towards my person. It had become apparent that they couldn't harm me no matter how hard they tried.

Night after night, they would appear and I would close my eyes and wish them away. I soon became less fearful than wondrous and curious about the little creatures infesting my bedroom in the midnight hours. Instead of being fearful of them, it was as if they were there just for my amusement. In time, their presence was diminishing, and sometimes it was as if they were not there, but at the same time, as if they were in someplace within the space in which my bedroom walls occupied.

In my bedroom, they had no mass, almost transparent, and they made no sounds but moved very quickly, and after a few months of appearing over and over, they soon stopped, and without warning, they weren't there any longer. However, I began to wonder if those same "transparent" monsters personified themselves in the human beings that are and would be in my life.

Very little are the memories of my Aunt Lucy's exploits. I remember her on the move constantly and always doing something domestic around her home, if not cooking, she was cleaning. I never really saw her stop her daily routine before the night fell. I remember her wrangling up two young rambunctious boys making a mess of her humble abode as fast as she picked up the place was the jest of it. She seemed as if she had a nuclear reactor strapped to her back twenty-four seven, whereas my mom barely broke a sweat cleaning our small two bedroom hole in the wall. My mother was the typical self-absorbed young mother of two, hardly touching a broom two days out of the week, and cleaning around the house daily was just not necessary.

I barely left my bedroom, and she was too busy on the phone gossiping with I don't know who, so we never had to clean.

Our apartment always seemed to be cleaner and filled with the light of the day, whereas my Aunt Lucy's place seemed to be shaded from the daylight, maybe it was because of the position of the apartment situated towards the East, but in retrospect, the amount of unsavory activity and the fact that her home seemed to be forever on the verge of chaos, I wondered if she ever caught a break. In contrast to that of my aunt's place, our place screamed happiness without fail, surrounded by nice things in our modest dwellings, mostly due to my father's unrelenting support. Since he provided for us monthly, we never were without, and though the streets commanded his attention, he made his presence known on a regular basis in the beginning, within our home and the neighborhood in which we lived.

As the sound of his 351 Hemi engine-block shook the walls of our small apartment as he pulled up onto the graveled filled grassless yard out front, all in the building jumped to attention and were eager to see him, and though he was always around the hood more than the house, he made sure food was on the table. My father had a very strong presence around the city in those days, and his presence made all the difference between the misery that inundated my Aunt Lucy's place, and made the quality of our family life worth bearing. I experienced a small taste of the difference a strong male figurehead could make in the development of a young boy's childhood and life.

I also observed the total contrast in the quality of life in my Aunt Lucy's home by the lack of a strong male role model in my cousins' upbringing and lifestyle. Although no male figure was in the home of my Aunt Lucy's, I must say she tried her very best to play the role of both parents. Forced by circumstances to assume roles and responsibilities of a caring mother and father could explain the constant screaming and yelling she did each day. But change would soon take place within her home, soon she would marry and the yelling would cease altogether, but not from a god-granted fulfillment of purpose or contentment in marriage for happiness' sake, but from fear of her newlywed husband.

For her newly found husband was not one of compassion and inclusion, and when it came to her two young and rambunctious boys, his attention was not on the contrary, he was not so loving towards Pookey and Chunky, in fact, he was somewhat cruel, especially cruel when showing harmonious emotion. I never saw him crack a smile, even in the attempt to show house hold unity or support towards the stability of the home. For he was cruel not only to her children, but also cruel towards my Aunt Lucy as well. He was truly monstrous and openly abusive, for he would both verbally and physically hurt my Aunt Lucy on more than one occasion.

Living amongst so much anarchy brewing within my aunt's home, I emotionally identified with the ignorant envy and hatred Pookey and Chunky endured daily from their mother's husband. Being in such close proximity to the chaos within my aunt's home, a very close relationship between my cousins and me was fostered even more so. And even though my father was not always there within the home, he was very inclusive to us all, showing Pookey and Chunky just as much love as he showed his other children with me being the exception. Being so very young and not so observant to the underlying issues my aunt faced, I would wonder why she worked so much at family life, never really gaining an upper hand on her daily rut, only to have reality smack me directly in the face, parting back the veil cloaking my misunderstanding and seeing the constant bombardment of chaos created by the hands of her two sons, along with the constant threat of physical abuse from her so-called not so loving husband.

Ignorance is truly blissful when you're a child, but as you grow older the things that mattered so much before just didn't mean anything anymore. It was the week after the best Christmas of my life, and I was coming back home, from I don't know where, with my mom on one of her seemingly worthless outings, filled with anticipation over the chance to play in my bedroom alone. We arrived to a once clean and tightly managed apartment, to one that was virtually ransacked and violated with the refrigerator door wide open, food on the floor, and everything out of place, and the kitchen trash thrown about; my mother and I stood in shock. As soon as we entered the back door we could hear the sound of footsteps running towards the door adjacent to my Aunt Lucy's back door.

We instantly knew that Pookey and Chunky were making their great escape out of our apartment. "Those little niggas!" my mom yelled!

She screamed at the top of her lungs, "Get back here, you little fuckers," quickly running after them, as I continued to stand in a state of shock. I stood there with my mouth open, looking at the devastation unleashed on our unsuspecting abode: "Oh, no! Please, God, no, not again!" I said to myself, for I saw something much more disturbing than a lack of not being able to enjoy social gatherings and Pagan holidays. Something more forthcoming, revealing, and sinister within the two and something unnatural driving the havoc in their eyes. Something was wrong, not right at all! But I was too young to know what, and as my mom gently pushed me into our apartment after a long and dirty playing session with the two brutes outside, my warning of caution was verified from the violent shove in the back from Pookey, and the dirty look given me by both cousin/brothers as they walked past my mother and me. They were looking at me with true malice of thought and gruesome glee stamped on their faces, and I knew I had to protect myself from the one's most close to me more than anyone much further away. As mom closed the door that separated the two apartments, I looked up at her and said, "Don't forget to lock it!"

From that day forward, the door adjacent to my Aunt Lucy's apartment stayed locked, only when my mom and Aunt Lucy were together inside the building the door would be opened and remain opened, and since they were very close and forgiving sisters, the door separating the apartments would sometimes be forgotten to be secured. But I knew better! And whenever they would forget to lock the door, I would make sure it was done. Their sisterly talking all the time resumed, and my relationship with my cousins flourished once more, but I never forgot what I saw in their eyes not months ago. Nevertheless, we were inseparable, thus always together.

Inside and outside the house, we encountered and endured all the mishaps and struggles that all those trapped in poverty go through, and while we played without care, accompanied with growling stomachs, yet vigorously as children of mishap do well, I would take time out from our unscrupulous activity, fading into the background of whatever scenery we were invading at the time, and paid close attention to the constant woes of our mothers. Seeing the many concerns of motherhood minus the fatherly presence, the essential element needed in the equation that ensured the possibility of a happy family unit and seeing my mother's everyday hardships and struggles to keep us fed and healthy, only arose more wonder in the question "Why!"

Seeing tears flowing from your mother's face almost daily hurts and knowing it's because of the inability to feed her children, makes the children feel accountable for their mother's sadness, even in a state of adolescence. Not understanding why the need for so much inequality must be for us expressed daily was profound, and to hear my Aunt Lucy and Mom having these heated discussions over god and his role in their reasons to carry on in the struggle to survive only sparked anger. Yet their conversations would captivate me and cause me to wonder even further the significance of the question why, and have me pondering for hours the meaning of it all.

In great detail over their conversations, I would scrutinize every aspect of their transmissions between one another. Seeing the emotional and spiritual crisis afflicting them both, caused me to neglect my responsibilities as a snot-nosed brat, and absorb the wonder of problem solving, so I would be able to remedy what haunted them both, saying to myself over and over: "I must understand it all!" Hearing them complain constantly about their daily sorrows over the phone and seeing the real inflictions visited upon them from others in the community, which mostly involved the men in their lives, caused me to wonder about their sanity.

When the overwhelming spirit of poverty saturated every facet of life, delusions of rebellious grandeur dominates the mind's eye. Without fail of heart, a youngster's blind boldness embraces an ignorant blissfulness of such, and allows stupid thoughts to reign freely amongst the substandard living conditions imposed on the innocent born in the belly of the beast, ultimately enduring inhumane realities plagued by all within the hood. But don't get it wrong! When you have nothing to miss, you miss nothing, which in itself is a blessing for those with hopes of nothing reachable. So with ghetto standards in mind, I was still considered a spoiled little brat. Having very little material positions and caring only about my daily consumption of candy, life looked rosy and more than sufficient for happiness.

With the power of unheard parental supervised fun out in the street with my cousins/brothers was the best time anyone could ask for in life. For the most part, engaging in chaos was the order of the day, and like most adolescents stuck into the gloominess of poverty, creating hell on Earth was like entering into the gates of heaven. And like most disenfranchised youngsters in the hood, fucking up shit was a rite of passage and constituted the very definition of having fun, not something one could consider wholesome or civilized, but for those with nothing, it was the most important thing one could do to express a life of unfulfilled self-accomplishment, and a must for me and my cousins.

Blessed with inhumane resolve, we were full of energy and ready for anything, always looking for adventure and periodically getting in trouble doing the things boys do when unattended and unthought of by those that mattered. Well, in my case, the earlier statement could be far from true. I considered myself an observer, watching my cousins do the things boys do while unattended in the night, and in the eyes of my cousins, I was the chicken shying from misbehaving and holding dear mother's warnings were an act of cowardice. If I felt like something was wrong, I stayed away from it, and my cousins every response would be, "You a scary mafucka! Ain't you, P?" My cousin Pookey would always say those very words and I would always reply, "No! I just don't think we should be doing something that would get us all in trouble! We might get in trouble, dumb-ass!" "HaHaHa!" Pookey would laugh out loud saying, "You just a fuck'n chicken, mane! Yella straight yella! Look at him, Chunky, he just a Chicken, or chicken shit!" "No, I'm not! You gone get in trouble, watch!" "So what! Even if we do, at least we not yella like you! You little chicken shit!"

Now please try to overcome the social brainwashing of the 21st century and keep in mind that in those days mothers were a little more lax and liberal in knowing the whereabouts of their children. In those days mothers enjoyed the freedoms granted by having faith and trust in their communities at large. With faith and trust in the community in which we lived, was something taken for granted, and now surely missed. Now unfortunately the tide has come in, and we no longer have that privilege and staple of safety to enjoy within our neighborhoods. The privilege of knowing everyone within a five mile radius has now vanished.

Feeling safe in the hood was a woman's right back in those days, and flaunting it was a must! Having very little worry for their children's safety and wellbeing in the streets helped to carry the daily load. It was one less problem to face and was a nice break from the ruckus we created, and they had no problem at all letting their children roam the neighborhood freely. Concerns of their safety was rarely entertained. It was a time that was about to have an abrupt ending. The days when the village raised all children as their own were slowly fading away, yet still, many times, I witnessed a neighbor disciplining a child that lived next door or down the street, and seeing that same child's parent receive a call from the neighbor that disciplined the child, which meant a double dose of discipline. A luxury no longer granted!

Imagine trying to grasp or even comprehend the level of dismay, alongside a growling stomach on top of all this shit, thus never stopping the never ending quest to understand the universal question of why? At the ripe old age of about five or six years the answer seemed impossible to find.

We knew nothing of life, but acted as if we were grown nonetheless, staying out way passed our bedtime, exploring the darkness without a trace of fear, watching the street lights come on without a word or grown-ups whimper, not knowing or even caring about the many dangers lurking in the not-so mean streets of Gary, Indiana, in those days. I guess you could say we were very curious and willing to find out all we could of the big unknown world of which we knew nothing. We explored our surroundings with great veracity, soaking up all the so-called worldly information we could soak up or discern at that time and age. We learned the necessary basic 101 survival skills of the ghetto, observing all necessary techniques from the darkest young monsters grooming all young boys in the streets.

I saw them as older young trolls stocking young innocence in the hood, with the voracity of the Black Plague they hovered over everyone in sight. Like ravenous wolves preying on the helpless, the underground professors of the streets preyed on the young people that lived in the streets at night. We had adventure after adventure, throwing rocks and climbing trees, forever looking for a mark, chasing after each other, playing hide and go seek for someone else's riches, which was a lot more fun and exciting after the darkest of dark nights were long over. But knowing what I know today, those days seemed like paradise…. Here comes the Light, then Darkness.

Innocence still held its sway! It was a nice summer day, and all the kids were outside playing. My mom and Aunt Lucy were inside their prospective apartments, doing what women did in those days. Both women in my aunt's apartment were watching stories, television stories that men or children could hardly stand, and I was too busy playing outside their line of sight and around the turn-of-the-century-old building for them to care of my whereabouts. Suddenly, I noticed Chunky sneaking about, looking around to see if anyone was watching him. Slowly he crept up the back stairs leading into the kitchen part of my mom's apartment, unaware that he was being observed from afar, and not realizing I was quietly watching him under the staircase, as he continued upwards. I thought to myself, "What is he up to? He's going to get himself in big trouble, I know it! There's always something exciting to watch," I said to myself, so I made sure to stay concealed as he made his way up the stairs. Fully aware of the chaos, Chunky's spontaneous yet destructive and unexplainable curiosity could unleash. I intently remained silent and patiently watched on. Normally, my Aunt Lucy sat firmly in her time, in a warned down rocking chair, rocking back and forth with an ever watchful eye out for her unpredictable offspring.

Posted in the middle of her living room, she rocked and fanned her hand-operated paper fan, giving her a clear view of both adjacent apartments and keeping her watchful eyes on both entrances leading to the two adjacent apartments.

When all the kids were outside playing, she was on guard most of the time, especially when the adjacent doors were open to let in the afternoon breeze. She stood as a faithful sentry, surely seeing all that passed through the two apartments. But for some reason, her acute senses weren't as attuned as they normally would have been, for Chunky went unnoticed by the ever-present eyes of my Aunt Lucy. Like a cat-burglar on the prowl, Chunky slowly and quietly opened the squeaky screen door, entering on his tiptoe. Cunningly, I crept in back of him and quietly followed his every step without his notice as I watched intently from afar in anticipation of his future act. I crept up the stairs on hand and knees, so as not to draw his attention backwards and outside the screen door on me. I cuffed my hands over my mouth as the suspense intensified.

As he slowly entered the residence, the excitement level increased as I crept closer with an enormous smile on my face. I slowly crept up the stairs thinking, "What the hell is he up to?" Down on my knees, I watched as Chunky stealthily rummaged through the kitchen drawers and cupboards, emerging with a box of matches, the kind that are rarely sold today. The kind that could strike on any surface with no problem; the good quality outdoor matches that are banned in some states today. I slowly sneaked back down whenever I felt that I may be found out, as he quickly slid open a small miscellaneous drawer next to the stove in our apartment and began heading back towards the back door. I quickly ran down the stairs and hid back under the staircase quietly and unnoticed.

Outside the door, he turned 360 degrees in a feeble attempt to make sure the coast was clear, not noticing me watching his every step. With his amateurish failure at surveillance, he smiled and headed back down the staircase, revealing his stolen goods to me unwittingly. To my surprise, it was worse than I could imagine; it was a box of matches in his right hand. Thinking he got away clean, and to his credit he did, because being a snitch was unheard of in the hood, just as it is today. There was no way I would tell on him, but I knew no good could come from his apparent successful snatch and grab! So I said to myself; "Oh, shit, he did it!" With matches in his hands, he started calling out my name: "P! P!" while looking for me with mischievousness protruding from his very persona.

Making sure I stayed concealed and remain unresponsive to his call while waiting until he turned the corner and out of my sight, I ran back up the staircase and hid inside knowing he was about to get in trouble in a big way! In the days of our youth, Chunky and I were like oil and water, or for a lack of better words, negative and positive in the laws of attraction.

We were like night and day in every aspect of life, but nonetheless, we stuck together like glue, which would be a better approximation of our bond, always together. More like twin brothers than cousins, Chunky and I roamed the thin lines between childhood and menaces to society, roaming the streets without care nor fear, for we were "the streets" in our minds. Since we were of the same age, born no less than one month apart, we conspired closely and harbored no secrets between one another, whereas Pookey played the part of both older

EDGAR FRENCH, JR.

brother and nemesis, since he was only a year older, he acted as if he were twenty years old yet Chunky and I paid no mind.

He was much more outgoing and nowhere in sight when we needed him. I would always be Chunky's first patriarch to share in the spoils of Chunky's little capers. Being the so-called chicken of the bunch, as Pookey so eloquently pronounced my obvious unwillingness to get in trouble, I knew the unstoppable havoc of my beloved Chunky was about to unleash on the whole neighborhood, and I needed to do something without "dropping a dime" as we old timers say. Yet in my heart, I knew I needed to stop him, or at least let someone of authority know of what he had in his possession.

I had to think on my feet before he would enact his unintended terror that we all would regret if no alarm rang out. In the safety of the house, I could hear him calling out my name. Knowing he wanted me to go along for the ride, I was not about to go down that road with him, so I ignored his constant call and waited in hiding as he ran back upstairs and into the house looking for me. Then he ran back outside, around the corner of the building, and out of my sight. Then I sat down on the floor next to my mother and asked, "What are you watching?" Thinking, "Oh, man, I hope he doesn't burn down something!"

However, I showed no outward concern of the looming catastrophe Chunky was about to unleash on the entire neighborhood. Suddenly, a voice came to me saying, "He's going to be calling for you; stay inside right where you are!"

Then I heard "P! P! P!" It was Chunky calling out for me once more while he tediously looked all over for me while thinking I was still outside. Hearing his relentless call, my mother asked, "P, you going outside, baby? Chunky calling you!" I meekly replied, "No." Then the voice in my mind said, "Stay right here! Chunky, go away… Just go… he's going to start a fire! Tell your mother."

But I was afraid; it was bad enough they were calling me chicken for every little mischievous deed in which they partook, and I didn't want Chunky to get in trouble with his mom. I've seen the many horrible ass whoopings Aunt Lucy had rendered without mercy, and it was nothing nice, plus you never snitch, you just don't do that in the hood, and everybody knows that!

Repetitiously, the voice in my head said: "Tell your mother or he's going to set the building on fire, P!" But I was too afraid; then the voice said: "Wait a minute and just say I smell smoke," even though there was no smell or notion of a fire anywhere to be seen. So without the fear of being a snitch I said in a low tone voice, "I smell smoke," but no one heard me. So I yelled: "I sell smoke! Ma-Ma! You smell smoke?" She replied, "Naw, Nigga!" and kept watching television. I knew I had to do something quickly, so I got up from under my mom and walked towards the window and looked out the living room window, and sure enough I began to panic. I could see Chunky and a few other kids from the neighborhood walking into a field of tall sun-dried grass that was located in back of the building.

Like everything in low income areas across these United States, the field was unattended for years, and full of dry brush and weeds corrupting the scene. Some of the brush was at least three or four feet tall, so when Pookey and Chunky entered into the field, they disappeared within seconds. I said to myself, "They're going to burn it up! I got to say something or they are going to kill themselves and everybody else for sure." So I attempted to alert my mother once more, but she was so caught up into her stories, she just ignored me completely, and at that point I didn't care who heard me, "I Smell Smoke!"

This time my mother looked at me with curiosity and intrigue, and I looked her in the eye, and it was as if she could hear my mind saying, "He's going to set the whole place on fire!"

She got up from her seat, checked the kitchen stove, and started looking around the two apartments, "P, I don't smell nothing, ain't nothing on fire, boy!" Then I said, "It smells like grass or something…I think it's coming from outside." She walked over to the window where I was standing and looked outside, not knowing what she would see, I put my head down in guilt. Lo and behold, there stood Pookey, Chunky and other neighborhood kids outside throwing lit matches into a dry field on a hot summer day.

Before I lifted up my head she yelled: "THEM LITTLE MATHA FUCKAS! Lucy, look!" My aunt ran over to the window: "Oh, shit!" Yelling out the window: "Pookey! Chunky!" And as soon as she called out their names, they ran directly into the field of dry weeds and brush as the field slowly ignited. Smoke and fire raced through the field as if gasoline had been applied, coming ever so close to the building, and with no warning the winds began to pick up, as if an unknown force was guiding the fire towards the building.

EDGAR FRENCH, JR.

Flames shot up into the air and the neighborhood kids emerged out of the field like locusts, taking off in all directions, running for dear life, but Chunky and Pookey were nowhere in sight. Knowing they were in big trouble, they emerged from the flames on the other side of the field and just stood there in bewilderment.

Knowing what would come next, they started crying that instant. My mother quickly ran down the back stairs yelling out, "Call the fire department, Lucy!"

Since my Aunt Lucy was overweight and slow moving, there was no way she would even attempt to run down a flight of stairs that was four stories high. So she called the fire department while looking out the window as the fire grew out of control. Franticly looking for a water hose with none in sight, my mother began to try to stump out the embers that were getting close to the building. I stayed inside looking out the window afraid to go out there, thinking to myself: "I could have said something sooner." Watching the fire get closer and closer to the building, my Aunt Lucy and mom began to panic, and as the winds picked up, the smoke really began billowing into the apartments. I then grew a pair and ran down to help my mother battle the blaze, and as I got down towards the grown-ups, I could hear my mom scream, "Oh, Lord, my god, please!" as the fire got bigger and bigger. Then out of the blue, a man came with a green garden hose, attached it to the water fountain on the side of the building, and began dousing out the flames, stopping the flames from reaching the building. But the fire was greater than you could imagine, consuming most of the field which was about half a block long, and as the daylight diminished, the wind continued to feed the flames. The little green garden hose couldn't do the trick, making very little progress in containing the fire. Daylight was dimming and the flames could be seen for miles, and the entire neighborhood came out with pails and buckets trying to tame the inferno. Finally, we could hear the sounds of the fire trucks coming, some thirty minutes later.

They knew they were in big trouble, so Pookey and Chunky looked up and caught a glimpse of their mother heading their way with fire in her eyes, and immediately they ran back into the inferno stunning all present. Hiding from their mother's enormous wrath, they ran back into the fiery tender brush, having more fear of their mother than the obvious danger of flames engulfing all in sight. Then they came out but only after numerous reassurances emanating outside the fiery bush from the spectators and firemen that their mother wouldn't beat the shit out of them. Remember we were very young; Pookey was around the age of five or six, and Chunky and I were only a year younger. The firemen promptly moved into action and the day was saved, and as the smoke and embers died down, the people in the neighborhood began to gather in front of our building loudly expressing their anger over the fire and the many other offenses perpetrated by my cousin/brothers.

Afterwards, everyone in the community was pissed, hearing the men in the neighborhood talking with my mother on a day by day basis for about a week, it seemed as if everyone wanted to beat the shit out of Pookey and Chunky.

In a soft voice, she calmed the men down and stroked their concerns with a host of assurances. And as I sat on the staircase leading to our apartment, my mother walked over to me and said, "P, I didn't smell anything when you called out smoke… there was no smoke… I saw them bad-ass niggas start the fire. How did you know, P?" I replied, "I smelled smoke!" "Yah, you said that — but there was no smoke; I saw them little niggas light it! I saw them throw the matches when I looked out the window, P!"

With a smirk and a suspicious look she said, "Okay, baby, you smelled smoke, ah ha! You probably saw them with damn matches even before they started playing with them, didn't you? That's why you brought yo little yellow ass in the house — ha. You knew they was about to burn some shit up, huh, baby?" Although she was somewhat perturbed, she looked at me and smiled as we both walked up to our apartment, then she started laughing as we walked up the stairs. Even weeks after that one particular event, I watched my Aunt Lucy stand in the doorway with a look of — I'm gonna beat the shit out of them two niggas — in her eyes daily, asking, "Where are they? Where are those two little fuckers at now?!" With my mother only replying: "Girl, you know you need to do something about those bad-ass kids before the people in the neighborhood kill your bad-ass kids or kill all of us!"

The street lights were beginning to flicker and the smell of fried chicken was in the air. Well, it's almost dinner time and I said to myself, "…them little niggas always hungry," and sure enough, when they smelled that tantalizing fried chicken in the air, they just magically appeared bringing their little bad

EDGAR FRENCH, JR.

asses in their mother's front door. It was a daily occurrence, Pookey and Chunky would be out creating havoc, knowing they were about to get a great and terrible beating, but they continued without fail, even resigning themselves for the worst. You could see it in their eyes! Even at such a young age, they had become hardened criminals and immune to physical pain.

I must admit they were forever in trouble, and I was forever warning them, but they never cared to listen, or perhaps they just didn't care. I didn't know, but I had to find out why they did the things they would do, while studying their everyday idiotic decisions and absorbing reasoning behind their aggressive actions.

Little did I know that the raging inferno experienced in those early years would set the never ending cycle of strange and unexplainable events with "fire" as the dominating factor and a never ending theme, scene and abuse, ultimately paving the road into the world of the unseen, abnormal and supernatural circumstances throughout my family's path in life's journey!

Summer was ending and Pookey had just begun regularly attending "Early Learning." It was a sort of pre-school in which he verbally expressed his contempt, dislike and hatred daily. He constantly expressed his frustration and lack of patience for his un-wholly plight of learning to Chunky and me, thus reminding us daily that our turn was rapidly approaching and time was up. The time to attend "Early Learning" was coming up soon and at hand, but since we were born in the later months of the year, we began pre-school later than most. The very thoughts of our mothers were consumed with anticipation of finally having some vestige of freedom from children and thus having some time to themselves. Day dreaming of freedom away from snot nose brats, brought never ending smiles and laughter on the faces of my mom and aunt, as the minutes counted down to our departure, and finally out of their sight and care, for just a few hours brought true joy, and sparkling gleam across their faces daily.

Freedom from the bondage of motherhood must have been a sort of bliss and great jubilation. For as the time grew closer, so did the daily discussions between the two mothers increase, at least most of the daylight hours, and our departure became the number one topic of conversation. And as the day of their emancipation became closer and closer, the conversations of preparedness arose more frequently. When mom brought up the subject of school directly, I would run and hide my face, somewhat shy and terrified of the idea of leaving the comforts of home. I openly expressed my fears of the upcoming changes. The year had passed so quickly it seemed, and only one weekend remained to enjoy the foolish comfort and safety of home, safe in the bosom of a loving mother, and only three days were left until branching off into the cruel unknown world outside our doors.

As the proverbial clock ticked down to five minutes before midnight, my fears turned into excitement and even anticipation entering into the educational system, and on the last Friday before our first public school experience, Chunky and I planned to defy the powers that be, and got up very early that Saturday morning so as to catch all the good cartoons that no one ever seems to catch. You know the ones!

The ones you must get up to watch before the rooster's crow, and the sun began to rise, which made it damn near a capital offense and punishable by death in a child's household where the very thought about getting up that early meant an ass whooping, so no cartoons without parental supervision; Ludicrous!

No longer could my cousins just freely walk through the door adjacent to the two apartments, so we made a pack to devise a way to leave the adjacent door left unlocked this one last time, even though an ass whooping was almost assured for Chunky if we were caught, but hey we didn't care.

It was our last chance to enjoy the one childhood love revered by all boys before the big day. As planned the night before, we arose bright and early that Saturday before the sunrise. Looking outside my bedroom window as the stars dimmed before dawn, I could hear someone from my aunt's apartment walking across the hardwood floors, then the doorknob jingled and Chunky signaled to unlock the door from my side. I could see the shadow of Chunky's stubby little feet through the crack underneath the bottom of the door.

Always being one step ahead of my moronic loved ones, I'd already left the door unlocked on my side. Hearing his clumsy attempt at maneuvering stealthily, I got up and ran to the door and quickly opened it, frantically startling him. "P! You scared me, man!" Under my breath with my finger across my mouth I said: "Come on, I know you don't want to get caught." Because of the constant behavioral problems exhibited by "Thing One and Thing Two" as my Aunt Lucy named them, she made sure her bedroom door was always open so as to hear every movement beyond her bedroom. Obviously, she wouldn't allow Pookey and Chunky out of their bedroom until she arose, which was way past the hours all the good cartoons aired, and were long off the TV. The most important obstacle impeding our plan was the necessary precaution my Aunt Lucy religiously adhered to; if she would ensure the safety of her home's material possessions from her rambunctious two sons at that time, she would always keep her bedroom door opened when retiring, making it almost impossible for Chunky to get past his mother's battled hardened ears without being detected. So how could we overcome her defenses? How could we get past her sensitive hearing/warning system? How could he sneak passed without awakening her? In addition, there were locks on all their cupboards holding the Captain Crunch hostage. There was no way in hell Chunky's little fat fingers would have a snowballs chance in hell of getting hold of the "Captain Crunch" on his side of the adjacent apartments. This fact was a vital part of our plans success, coupled with the ever looming fact that if my Aunt Lucy heard the slightest peep of noise in her home, she would awaken! If anyone was to attempt to sneak passed while she was still in bed, their ass would have been in a sling; therefore, we agreed to stay awake and only move when we both could hear her snoring loudly on both sides of the dividing doors, then we'd make our move.

Like black mini ninjas we crossed the invisible line separating the two apartments, and silently closed my Aunt Lucy's bedroom door, bypassing the cupboards and settling for whatever cereal was on my side of the apartment, so not to get caught while locking the door dividing the two apartments behind us, hoping the clicking sound of the lock being relocked wasn't heard by my aunt's finely tuned ears.

It was our lucky day! She was knocked out! Sound asleep! It was even too early for her ever so conscience instincts to adjust. So off we went, scot-free and safe on my side of the building. With no hesitation, we began raiding the kitchen in the early morning darkness, keeping all lights off until the deed was complete. With cereal in hand, we slowly crept towards my living room, turning on the TV and making sure the volume setting was turned down low while taking big gulps of crunchy cereal as we watched the elusive early morning cartoons we never got to see.

With our last Saturday fully planned out in advance before school begins, we would checkout the groovy cartoons, then go outside as soon as possible and without fail, we did what we set out to do. Success! Our plan worked like a charm, our mouths stuffed with cereal and souls filled with great deserved cartoonish joy, finally getting to see the cartoons we always wanted to see. We were ready to venture outside, and once outside, the skies were the limit! It was just the two of us, outside early in the morning. No one to stop our early morning adventures, not even Pookey! He himself was still sound asleep as well. But low and behold someone else in my aunt's household was already up and out, Buddy, my aunt's so-called husband. He was outside underneath his piece of shit of a car; a green 1968 Chevy Station Wagon, and was working on it as usual. Buddy was black and Cherokee, exhibiting all the flaws of both clans combined, and forever drunk and rowdy.

Buddy was not the kind of man that liked children or anyone else for that matter, and from what I could tell, even at such a young age, I could see he had very little friends. He was a mean spirited man by nature, with a frown forever on his face. He rarely cracked a smile, and one could feel the spirit of evil permeating from his very presence. He was truly a bad person; therefore, Chunky and I made sure to stay clear of him and his piece-of-shit car. Ironically, for some strange reason, the car seemed only to work for him, and stopped working whenever anyone else needed a ride or had somewhere to go.

It was as if he had rigged it somehow, working only when he wanted it to. Chunky and I completed our task and finished watching cartoons. Full of energy from all the sugar in the cereal, we quickly got dressed and went outside. With no parental supervision, and no other neighborhood children to bug us, Chunky and I had the best play spots in the hood, and all to ourselves. With visions of superheroes freshly imprinted in our minds from the early Saturday morning cartoons, our imaginations were full of bravado.

We ran all about the building early in the morning, with no Aunt Lucy to restrict our every move, jumping on and off the back staircase, making all the noise we wanted. Knowing our moms were fast asleep, we let our imagination run wild. Having no fear of getting in trouble, we made all the noise we wanted, pretending to be our favorite Superheroes, arguing over whose imaginary superhero was the best superhero, and which one had the best super powers. Chunky loved "Batman" and I, on the other hand, was a hardcore lover of "Superman."

"Man, Superman ain't Shit! With his punk-ass curl in the front of his head like a bitch!" said Chunky. "Batman is the bitch! He can't do nothing; everything he do is luck; he ain't got no super powers, or nothing; he just rich," I would respond. Chunky continued, "That's right, he got money, and when you got all the money, you can do whatever the fuck you want! And if a dumb-ass crazy dude start shit, he gone fuck em up!" I in turn said, "Man, everything Batman got he made. Superman was born with his powers, just like me! That shit Batman got ain't even his own; he made that shit; he ain't got shit on Superman. Superman can do anything! Anything! Just like me! Because I'm Superman!"

"What! You ain't shit, P, Piss Ant! Ahhh-Haaa, Shit! Batman got a girlfriend and everything. Superman is a Fag with his girly cape. Plus, Lois Lane is a dumb-ass hoe and stupid too! Everybody know that Clark Kent is Superman! He even still got his dumb-ass curl showing on his fucked up face when acting like he's Clark Kent. How fucked up is that!?" The light fades into darkness and the memories of simpler times evaporate the clouds of end-time's truths. Youth intensifies the experience diving into the unknown, head first, no regards for safety nor reason.

CHAPTER VII

Unseen Forces

Unable to respond to the obvious truth that Chunky dropped on me so eloquently, unversed in the complexities of playing the dozens, so I digress. Being a nerd by nature and soft hearted, I just didn't respond and started to jump from the staircase, and I quickly changed the subject, challenging him to beat me in a jumping competition to jump off the staircase leading to our apartment upstairs, in which he quickly followed suite, jumping off the second step laughing at me every time he jumped. "Man, you can't beat me at jumping, P." I responded, "Well, I'm Superman," and moved up to the third step jumping off perfectly! "Yes! Beat that!" Without saying a word, Chunky ran all the way up the stairs, quietly opening up the screen door leading to my mom's apartment, sneaking in on his tiptoes, emerging moments later with my bed sheet while tying it around his neck, slowly walking down the staircase with the look of confidence and pride with every step down.

Proud to be the "Cape Crusader" with a big-ass smile on his face, stopping at the third step, he looked down at me at the bottom of the staircase looking up, slowly spreading out the tightly tied sheet around his neck, with the morning breeze gently blowing, he jumped as the cape flowed back like the "Dark Knight's" cape itself. "Perfect! Beat that Piss Ant!" With a look of determination, I ran up the stairs not caring about making any noise at that point, running up the long back staircase, hearing my mom in the kitchen starting breakfast, running past her saying, "Hey, Mom," as I quickly went towards the hallway closet where she kept the linen. I took out a flower printed sheet and hid it under my t-shirt, making sure she was preoccupied slaving over the stove, passing her in the same manner in which I ran past her so not to activate her motherly super powers that awakened whenever a mischievous snot nose brat dipped his hands in the cookie jar. I safely made my way to the back screen door, waiting till the coast was clear before equipping myself with the necessary gear of "Superman's" uniform.

I tied the sheet just as tightly as Chunky garbed himself, and smugly headed down the stairs with the thought of "He's mine now!"

Looking Chunky straight in the eyes, stopping on the fourth step while clinching my hands to the sheet on both sides of my small adolescent frame, I spread out my arms and yelled out, "BEAT THIS!" and made a perfect landing by Chunky's feet, raising the stakes.

So back and forth we went, one after another, going upwards, more and more up the seventeen and a half steps, rising sensation of fear with every step! Finally, as we were halfway up the staircase, a real sense of danger began creeping up in both of our minds, but neither one of us were willing to concede victory. "Go head, Chunky; I thought Batman was the shit?" "You go 'head, P, you Superman! The man of steel! Or chicken shit! Which one is it?"

Then the voice of an unknown spirit entered into my head saying, "Go right ahead; you'll be okay!" And without a word, I walked halfway up the staircase, spread my wings and jumped, with the wind blowing through my cape and arms stretched out. I flowed effortlessly through the air, landing perfectly at the bottom of the staircase yelling out, "Yes! Yes! Yes! Beat that!" Knowing he wouldn't dare try to attempt to jump from that height, I reveled in his obvious defeat, thinking prematurely he was finished, or at the least too chicken to even have the notion to match that feat of bravery.

Full of myself, I boasted up a storm and now it was my chance to gloat and to get back at all the name calling. Puffed up with pride, I felt as if I really could fly like Superman, "I AM SUPERMAN!" I yelled over and over, yelling so loudly that my mom screamed out of the kitchen window, "Stop all that fuckin' yelling, P!" Which quickly shut me up, but the feeling of super human ability over took my small undeveloped brain, polluting all reasonable thought processes, saying to myself, "You can do it again," and without any fear, standing in the middle of the staircase, I jumped once more and with perfect form, I flew down the stairs, cape flowing behind me, landing perfectly! It was as if I floated in the air before landing, looking up at Chunky with a look of who's your daddy in my eye; "Yah Yah Yah," Chunky softly conceded. I did it! I prevailed which shut him up, proving Superman was the best of all the superheroes, but most of all proving to myself that I was able to fly. Overflowing with pride, I puffed out my chest and continued to egg him on, "Batman a bitch! "Look at that! You see that! I'm the shit, not you, not punk-ass Batman or your fagot-ass sheet with the flowers on it; I'm the shit!" All Chunky could say was, "What! What! "Shiiiit!" Then all of sudden a voice entered my head, "Jump from the top; you can do it; you can fly! Don't think just do it!"

The smile on my face gradually faded away, and a look of seriousness came upon my face. Totally confident in my new found ability, I slowly walked up the staircase with boldness as Chunky watched me make my way up the stairs; instinctively he knew my intentions; "You bet not, P, you gone kill yourself;" with no response, I walked past him and said nothing.

I continued my way up the staircase, finally reaching the top feeling invincible; it was as if I were in a trance.

I could hear my mother singing in the kitchen, amidst the smell of bacon frying in a cast-iron skillet in back of me. With the smell of bacon in the wind, along with the sun beaming through the surrounding trees, I felt on top of the world after my last spectacle of flawless stair jumping. Looking down from the top of the staircase, I could see just how far the distance from the top of the staircase to bottom; then reason began to break through the hypnotic trance that took over me, but no, the illusive voice sounded off even louder, "DO IT!" And this time an unknown force came over me. It was as if I had no control over my own body, and before I could think rationally about the insane thoughts pushing me to continue ahead, time to stop myself had lapsed and momentum had rendered all caution mute. I was caught up in the moment, taking two steps back with demonic voices in control, and without personal thought, I ran forward, plunging straight off the top of the staircase with arms stretched out. As I flowed effortlessly in the air, time stopped, all sound went away, and everything began to move in slow motion. At first it was as if I was flying effortlessly through the air, wind blowing oh so gently through my flowered colored cape in classic Superman fashion. Reality or sanity began to set in as I began descending rapidly towards my doom. Moving in slow motion, a calmness entered my mind's eye as the reality of my fate was sealed. All I could think about as the large stone protruding out of the ground coming closer was to put my arm over my eyes so not to see my future fate. Feeling nothing and having no fear, I resigned myself for the inevitable consequences that were about to befall my soul; thinking to myself, "What have I done? At least I didn't hit any stairs!"

In a microsecond, I closed my eyes, but before closing my eyes, I saw a big gray bolder protruding out of the ground quickly coming towards me. Headed straight for it, I heard Chunky scream, "P!" Then I heard nothing, felt nothing, and it was as if all the air in my lungs was sucked out, and as if someone had attached a vacuum to my mouth; the sense of life had left my frail little body that was engulfed in total blackness.

Then a single thought, "Am I dead?" Faintly hearing a voice fading in and out in the darkness: "P! P! P! You okay?" Then nothing; then a feeling of dizziness, as if I were drugged by some unknown intoxicating substance that flew along with me.

A glimmer of light started to peer through the blackness, not able to open my eyes or even move, I lay motionless, still hoping I was alive. I began to open my eyes, hearing the voice in the darkness coming closer and closer, "P! P! P! You okay?!" Woozy and slowly coming to consciousness, I began to see a form materializing; it was Chunky himself hovering over me with a look of fear and dire concern on his face and in his eyes.

Happy to be alive, I said, "I'm okay." Feeling nothing, I could see a concerned look in his eyes and a smile on his face, seeing him looking not at my face but at my left arm, saying, "Man, you fucked up bad; don't move!" As I slowly turned my head to the left side to see what he was watching, he was right. I had broken my arm in three places; it was shaped like an S and it dangled from my shoulder. Lifeless, feeling no pain and in total numbness, I sat up on the ground trying to catch my wind, calmly saying, "At least I didn't hit any stairs," with a woozy smile as I gradually regained consciousness along with my breath. A couple of minutes had passed and panic began to set in Chunky's mind, "What we gone do, P? What we gone do? We in trouble now—oh, man…" I could see his true concern, which was one of self-survival, rather than one's concern for my wellbeing.

Demons in the fourth dimension danced around me laughing and were overwhelmed with glee over my demise! I could hear their laughter in the wind, wondering who was laughing at me. My arm began to throb slowly and the feeling in my arm was coming back, "BOOMP BOOMP BOOMP BOOMP!" It was as if my heart was beating in my left arm instead of my chest; a tear formed in my eye and rolled down my right cheek; pain was rearing its ugly head, intensifying by the second, and afraid of touching my arm, I started crying and slowly grabbed hold of my broken left arm. Chunky said in hysterics, "Don't move, P! Oh, man, don't move!" I responded, "I can't feel my arm, Chunky; I can't feel anything!" It was if my arm was gone and in its place a beating heart; a heart that was pounding harder and faster by the moment while crying at the same time. Chunky yelled, "P, we got to do something... there's Buddy right there under his car; Buddy! Buddy! Pee Wee hurt! He hurt bad, man! Look!" Smugly he responded, "Leave me the fuck alone; can't you see I'm working on my shit! Go tell his fuckin' mama! FUCK! Bad-ass mothafucka's-kids!" Buddy looked over at me with a sinister smile on his face. Still in shock, Chunky and I tried to get up off the ground. It took a while, at least three minutes, blurring in and out of consciousness, I stood up with his help. As I leaned to the right, we took one step at a time, with no other grown-ups around to assist us, we slowly walked to the front of the building. The pain was increasing with every step and we slowly walked past Buddy as he looked up at us from beneath his shitty Station Wagon. Buddy was steadily wrenching his greasy ratchet, smirking at us, without compassion, as we walked past.

Finally, we reached the front of the building at the end of the staircase that led to my Aunt Lucy's apartment which was all the way to the top. I stopped for a moment to catch my breath while crying even more intensely, and leaned on Chunky for support.

We both looked up the staircase, and dreaded seeing how far it was. At a snail's pace, we began bracing ourselves for the ascension up the staircase; the feeling in my arm returned with a vengeance and massive pain shot through my arm with every beat of my heart, and with every step, the pain magnified one hundred fold! "Chunky, I can't; it hurt; it hurt... ooooh! Ooooh! It hurt! I can't; I can't move; it hurts so much... ooooh!" "Okay, P, don't move; don't move; I'll get help, don't move!" I ached in agony at the bottom of the staircase while Chunky took his leave from my side.

Chunky ran up the stairs in a panic only to be stopped in his tracks at the front door. My Aunt Lucy always kept her screen door locked, in an attempt to stop kids from running in and out, and prevent …snot-nose brats from letting the flies in, as she put it. I could hear Chunky yell, "MA! MA!" but no one came to the door because she couldn't hear him. She was in the back of the apartment and the music was too loud; the sounds of "Sly and the Family Stone's" "It's a Family Affair" was blaring. Chunky yelled even louder, but with no success, he ran back down the staircase grabbing hold of my good arm saying, "P, you got to get up… come on, man, get up, you can do it!" He helped me to my feet while the tears flowed down my face, for I couldn't bear it any longer! I was beginning to faint from the pain as we walked up the staircase, consumed with excruciating pain, I knew I just couldn't go any further. As I fell down to my knees halfway up the staircase, I blacked out, but only for a moment.

I could hear Chunky calling my name, "P! P! Come on, man, we almost there; come on, man, you can do it!" I slowly got up with his assistance, fading in and out of consciousness. We continued up the dreaded staircase as the intensity of the pain compounded with every step; yelling and screaming, I continued upwards. Finally, we made it to the top where I lay there as Chunky banged on the door screaming my aunt's name, but no one answered. Marvin Gaye's "Let's Get it On" was playing by that time, and my hopes began to turn to despair, then the music volume rescinded and my Aunt Lucy appeared at the door.

"What the hell going on?!" With fear, Chunky responded, "Ma P! He Hurt!" "Oh! No!" She ran back to my mother's apartment screaming, "Earline! Earline! It's P! Oh, my god! Earline! Girl he hurt his self—bad girl! I'm calling the Operator!"

With the dire concern of a mother's love burning in her facial expression, she ran franticly towards my aunt's front door, "Ohhh! My Baby! Ohhh! No No No! My Baby! Hold On P! Hold On baby! Ohh My Baby!" While making sure she didn't move me, finally, we got some help!

I lay there in pain while crying my eyes out! Time seemed to crawl as the pain increased by the moment. But just the thought of having my mom by my side reduced the massive pain ten-fold; however, I was still fading in and out of consciousness, for I couldn't take the unbearable pain any-longer!

I fainted for a moment and as I came through, I could hear my Aunt Lucy trying to get Buddy to help me, but he kept working non-stop on his stupid car.

He would not lift a finger for anyone or anything, other than to finish work on his piece of shit Station Wagon. Hearing her yell over and over with no response at all from Buddy, I said to myself, "Aunty just give up... he's a rat!" In total hysteria over my condition, my mother began crying and praying out loud, "Lord please! Please LORD! Help me!" She carefully placed me in her lap, rocking me back and forth steadily praying aloud, "Lord please! Please help me" She prayed over and over again until hope began to waver, then out of nowhere, a man drove up, rolled down his passenger window, and asked, "You need help ma'am?" Then I realized there weren't just malevolent spirits that roamed the fourth dimensional realm, but there were also benevolent wholly spirits of the Elohim that roamed there as well, and they all played their parts in the fate of men.

The benevolent stranger said to my mother, "Something told me to come this way; I was late for work, so I said to myself, " What's a few more minutes, so I'm glad I did come this way; don't worry I'll take you to the hospital, don't worry." Mother replied, "Thank you so much... I didn't know what I would do if you hadn't come along!" She repeated those words at least twice more, crying and rocking me ever so gently as the stranger drove off speeding away, looking back periodically with a look of concern for my mother's sake, since she was hysterical with fear for her firstborn's wellbeing.

Driving as fast as possible without hitting the many pot holes, he raced through the hood to the hospital as mom held on tightly to my broken arm so as to absorb any sudden jolts from the many pot holes. But every bump felt like the end of the world to me, and as the pain throbbed through my small frail body, feelings of passing out occurred once more. Quickly, the driver turned into the hospital's emergency driveway, driving right up to the hospital's emergency room's sliding glass doors, while mom rushed, but carefully removed me from the back seat of the stranger's car! As mom yelled for assistance, without delay, I was placed on a gurney and from the dark and gloomy corridors a doctor appeared and began tending to my arm, and giving words of comfort as he examined the breaks in my arm. Reaching into his upper right pocket pulling out a lollipop, saying, "Here you go youngster; be brave little champ," as he wheeled me to a back room where the X-ray machines were while prepping my arm underneath as the machine took snap shots from all sides. The doctor said, "Wait here; I'll be back," and left me on the cold gurney in massive pain for at least an hour. Then after a while, the doctor and my mother walked into the room with the doctor holding several X-rays in his hand.

Then he held them up to a lighted screen on the wall, revealing the breaks clear as day. My arm was broken in three places, forming an S shape saying, "What a mess you've made; don't worry, I'll have you up and climbing trees in no time!"

He grabbed hold of my arm while telling my mom to hold me tightly, then he started to count backwards from ten, and before he reached one, he yanked my arm as hard as he could, "SNAP! CRACKLE! POP!" I screamed in utter pain as he held my arm tightly and began setting it into place. Tears were flowing from my eyes as the cold angel of mercy looked me in the eye and said, "Tell me what hurt more, when you broke it or when I set it?" With no hesitation and with a loud voice I said, "When you SET IT!"

As the nurse prepped the casting mold and began to administer the casting materials on my arm, I could over hear the doctor tell her, "Well, since he's left handed and school starts next week, there will be no school for him. The cast has to be on for about two months at the least! I thought to myself, "Yes, I had stopped the inevitable or at least slowed it down for the time being, which was a hefty price to pay!" There would be no school for me; therefore, I started school late. The memory fades — a bright light then darkness…

Loki: How in the fuck am I going to find that fuckin' kid my lord and brother?

Lucifer: Just look for a kid that can see! He must be here somewhere; call upon your Homo-sapiens in the area, and let the humans find him.

Loki: Yes, I'll dispatch the faithful and influence the human scum in their own destruction…

{Loki speaks to minions' leaders}

Listen oh faithful — listen carefully to every word spoken you chosen ones; our cause is in peril — where I search for the human man child with the ability to see into the fourth dimension, look for the "out of the ordinary"—he's here amongst the lost one's somewhere; we must find him; we must see if he's one of ours or one of the others! Go forth!

Lucifer: If men knew their fate, they would cry out to their maker in woe! We must not let a single one escape our wrath, for we are doomed and so shall they be for all time! Why did it go so far?! Why did he not forgive us?!

Loki: Do they not know their worth to him?!

Lucifer: We shall never know his light again! We were also deceived! Do we not deserve forgiveness as well? Yet we are doomed for an eternity for our ambition and want.

Loki: Only anger fills our heart, for his light has been extinguished within our spirits! Now time is ending, and our fate draws near.

Lucifer: The war was necessary, and the pain is too much to bear. For what choice did we have other than the darkness my brother, Loki? We've done so much in his service—why, Father? Why did you forsake us?

Loki: We were guilty in your eye, and deceived by one that was greater than us. Now our tears have turned into rage. You have done this, Father! Why should we repent? You have forsaken us! We now must share in the Dragon's fate! So be it! For man was deceived just as we were, yet salvation remains in their fate! What makes them better than us?

Lucifer: For we were made first within his estate! Do we not deserve a chance at redemption?! Unforgiving you prove to be, Father! I speak and you hear, but no answer I shall receive. The war has drained you of all that is just! You forget your so-called mercy in regards to our petition. We had no choice other than to fight for our existence! You give us no choice.

Loki: Oh, do I long for your light once more so-called Most High! I hate you with love! Why would you make us watch the death of our children? What sin deserves such cruelty?

Lucifer: You are the evil one in our eyes! What difference does it make? For you hear me not! Where is justice for us? Where is the understanding?!

Loki: It was we who were forsaken! Did not our seed deserve life?! Woe is me! For our loss was unjust! We must undo what Father has done!

Lucifer: May the heavens fall as we have! May darkness capture the whole of the heights of Heaven! For we must be avenged! So be it! So shall it be. Find the male child, Loki…

The security of a mother's loving arms was over, and the unknown world awaits. School time was here. Pookey and Chunky were enrolled and out of the picture most of the day, bringing a sense of relief to my Aunt Lucy, at least from 7 A.M. to 2 P.M. for Pookey and 9 A.M. to 12 P.M. for Chunky. Most of the morning, I was in my exclusive element (solitude), which I enjoyed most of the time, and for the first couple of weeks, I enjoyed the absence of my cousins/brothers. Then boredom hit me hard, and I began to miss my brutish counter parts. With nothing to do, I roamed the hood alone with my arm in a cast, till one day I came across a girl sitting outside an apartment building down the way from our building. I could tell she was older, which was obvious from the size of her breasts protruding from her blouse, firm and perky—with the shape of an hour glass, subsequently arousing my curiosity.

    She had to be almost eleven or twelve and even though I was in my single digits of life on this planet, I was still aroused with curiosity as she motioned to me to come play with her, asking myself, "…why isn't she in school?" And why did a big girl like that motion to me to come over; what did she possibly want with me? I'm just seven; then it came to me as I got closer to her, and as I got closer, I could see something was not right with the way she behaved, for even at that age, I could recognize emotional and mental illness. It was in her body language as she smiled. The telltale signs of what I know now to be abuse ringed in her actions, but I didn't care.

She was someone to play with, plus I liked looking at her body. My father was very adamant about bitches and like plaster of Paris it stuck to my thought processes. Like a wolf in a hen house, I fell into the part of a hound, and as I played with her, I tried to touch her tits as much as I could, and the more I tried, the more she let me. In shock, I continued my advances and in no time we took the games inside the building, where there was a long dark hallway with no one around to interrupt our explorations, and within minutes, we were touching each other's private parts.

I was hard as rock, I knew instinctively what to do; first I raised up her blouse slipping my hands under her bra, taking hold of her firm tits — her nipples were almost as hard as my you know what! Then we started to kiss — I couldn't believe it, all I could think was, "I'm going to fuck, FUCK! Hell Yeah!"

I unbuttoned her jeans and pulled down her pants, seeing her nice round ass and tight pussy, and without hesitation, I stuck my index finger right in her pussy; she said nothing, and as I moved my finger in and out she began moaning; her pussy got greasy and slick, like Olive Oil! I couldn't hold back! I rapidly pulled down my pants and my Under-Roos.

As I got on top of her, she said nothing; I spread open her legs with no objections from her, sliding my penis inside her very tight and nice hairless, well fuzzy peach pussy; wow! WOW! Oh, man it felt oh so good, so creamy and warm, in and out, in and out, back and forth I went into her, sucking her firm tits and all, thinking this can't be happening, but it was and it was amazing! The feelings I felt were unimaginable; I was in and I was not coming out, in and out, in and out. Then, I felt it coming; all my inner-fluids were building up and all heading to one place. Then suddenly, without warning, when all fluids were about to erupt, a door opened right where we were, "WHAT THE HELL!" A lady yelled; "WHAT ARE YOU DOING WITH MY DAUGHTER!?"

I jumped up with the look of death on my face, tripping over my pants, running and tripping as I pulled them up, a feat hard to do at the same time. Down the dark hallway, down the dark hallway, I ran as the lady was screaming as loud as she could as she mustered her fat ass to chase after me, but with no success, for I was too fast, too young and still full of come — still! The girl's mother opened the door right at the moment my volcanic mountain was about to erupt scaring the shit out of me, backing up all fluids, and you know what that means. That's right you got it.

Blue Balls! My balls hurt so badly for about a week! I couldn't pee; I could barely walk and my mother kept asking me if something was wrong. She was so concerned for her not so innocent son, but I played it off like a champ and said, "I slipped on the see-saw mama, but I'm okay; it will be alright!" I didn't know what was happening to me at the time; all I knew was I couldn't say what I was doing when it happened, for the best I could do was pray to god for help, begging for forgiveness and to please take away the pain, but I felt no remorse or had no thoughts of regret in my actions. All I could think of was the slickness of the slow girl's pussy forming around my dick as I went in and out. Every night, I indulged in reminiscence over my encounter, and every night I dreamed of the hot, slow girl's pussy, for it was truly a feeling of ecstasy! For days, I stayed clear of that building, not saying a word to anyone, not even Chunky, for I kept my real-life fantasy close and stayed inside for a few days. At such an early age, I revealed no hints of the sensual/sexual encounter with the slow girl without a name; in fact, I never even got to know her at all. Periodically, I would see her in the hood now and then, but never got too close and always walked past with a slight glance at her mid-section and tits. Damn!

Months after the cast was off, I was enrolled in "Early Learning, "and though we lived on "Virginia Street" for such a short time, I will always remember my many wonderful encounters there. I recall my cousin and I begging dad for a dollar every night so we could spend it for a fat sack of candy at the "Penny Candy Store" on the corner, and remember the feeling of freedom as we played up and down the ragged ghetto streets of the hood. I thought of us playing after hours, after the street lights came on, and remembered how we had no inclinations of danger back then. I can still smell fried fish and spaghetti permeating throughout the air on hot summer evenings while we heard the sounds of my father's motorcycle rev passed as he "kicked it" with the rest of his gangstas and homies! Most of all, I remembered Chunky and I playing with "Matchbox" and "Hot Wheel" cars all over the hood, while Aunt Lucy yelled out the back door, "Get yawl bad asses in the house right now…before I whoop that ass… you too, P!"

Time passed and my Aunt Lucy moved from the apartment building to what is now known as the "Colored Doors" soon after my sexual escapade with the young and disturbed girl. Pookey and Chunky were suddenly gone and I no longer worried over their destructive nature running roughshod amongst my belongings, for I was no longer concerned for my physical wellbeing. Although I got to see them in school periodically, my life away from their constant presence was somewhat blissful! It was now just my baby sister, mother and I in control of our belongings, having our mother's sole undivided attention. For once, we knew peace of mind, peace without having to share everything and it felt great!

The adolescent madness diminished somewhat when they departed and having full reign over our own refrigerator and Kool-Aid was a plus! The building never before had such peace, for it no longer had my destructive cousins breaking every toy in my possession, and the never diminishing feeling of being alone was beginning to fade away just as the cries faded away from the bassinet. Realizing I was now truly the man of the house brightened my day, but with every story worth telling, time brings change.

My father began to come around less frequently and even the kids in the neighborhood started to fade away within a short time period. Time passed and my mother gave birth to a son and now there were the three of us. My Aunt Lucy married Buddy and it seemed as if my cousins' life of utter poverty was beginning to subside. Pookey, Chunky and my Aunt Lucy seemed somewhat happier in their new environment. I felt secure in the obvious change, but that change would soon change for the worst in a blink of an eye!

My Aunty Lucy would always entertain these so-called Bible students, examining the Bible weekly, taking her new found truth to heart, and frequently inviting my mother to sit in on her weekly studies.

Not long after my Aunt Lucy moved from the neighborhood, those very same people started coming to see my mother, and she began studying the Bible with them on a regular basis as well. Soon, she had me sit in with her, so she wouldn't leave me unattended, but I was still very young to understand the significance of their little spiritual sessions.

Being so young, I paid very little attention to the lessons at hand and was annoyed and restless from the beginning to the end of every session. Since I wasn't able to read on my own, one of the so-called Bible students suggested to my mother that she read to me alone after their Bible study had ended, and presented to her one their books designed for children after their sessions. Suddenly, I began to pay close attention to the subject matter that I couldn't grasp before. Spending time with my mother alone made the difference, for I was intrigued with the universal questions that every man on the planet Earth has pondered and tried to answer from his creation until now.

Finding out the age old answers to these allusive questions consumed my undeveloped brain, and gaining knowledge of the unknown ignited a fire within my soul to find the truth behind the timeless questions man has pondered for eons, and understanding the unseen nature of life began protruding from my mind's eye. I truly can say I was obsessed with finding out the answers to those age old thoughts and questions alike, questions such as: "If we were created by god, where is he?! What was the reason for our existence? Who is God? Why are we here on Earth? And for what reason?! Why do we die?! Why is there Evil?! And why does god let bad things happen?! Where are the forces of good?!"

Then the visions that haunted my nights in the past, began to happen once more. I started seeing things that "...go bump in the night." They were back and the little monsters were watching me in the darkness of the night, up close and far away, thus the unseen demons revealed themselves once again. They watched me lying in bed and shivering from fear; they watched from on top of my dresser and from the celling top. They were monsters with long pointed ears with saliva dripping from their fangs and protruding from their devilish smirking smiles. Long arms and big feet marked the scariest of them all. Some even had red eyes of fire and stared right at me while sinisterly smiling, grinning at me with an evil look of hatred, ultimately terrifying me which had me shaking underneath the covers. Closing my eyes in fear, I called out to god in my mind, hoping and praying they would not attack me while I slept.

Remembering the response I received from my mother the last time such a vision happened, I spoke nothing of the strange things that haunted me the night before. I said nothing to no one. Tired of my mother saying, "...whatever, P... he's just crazy!"

From Pookey and Chunky to grown-ups alike, whenever I'd previously report my visions all would gloat in ridicule about the unseen things I'd witnessed; the ridicule would begin, or worse, assumptions would prevail. The constant statement, "He's just afraid of the dark" excused those with a blind eye; unreasonable accusations would be said to justify their unwillingness to hear a youngster's tale. From my grandmother, mother and Aunt Lucy alike, my tall tales of monsters plaguing me in the night held no truth, so I stopped telling anyone about my encounters in the darkness of the night. In fear of bedtime, I stayed silent, taking every step towards my bedroom while being terrified of what might be waiting in the dark. Having courage, I closed my eyes and prayed myself to sleep, even though I knew not the acts of courage per say. Almost every night and without fail, the visions would take place. Knowing what I saw was real and not just my imagination, I became convinced I had to prove it to my unbelieving loved ones, but I was too immature, young and ignorant to convey the obvious existence of the somewhat unnatural phenomenon or universal truths kept secret to most, so I stayed silent forevermore. Still I had to know why I could see these things and no one else could. The answers would not become visible for some time to come.

My mother would always say to me, "P, learn all you can while you can, because 'Knowledge' is power!" Soon, I would take to heart her very words. The more I took part in her weekly Bible studies and gained understanding from my studies in {The Great Teacher Book}, the more I began to grasp the most important thing anyone searching for truth could find out — God's name, and I used the power of that name to overcome the demons that haunted me in the night, yes, they were indeed Demons! That's what they must be! Immediately, I found out the importance of the Creator's name the very first time I used it. I would use the name of god when it was time to go to bed. Every time I prayed, I pronounced what I thought was the name of the god of Abraham, Isaac and Jacob, and it worked! The name diminished the visions in the dark for good! "No more monsters, yes that's it!" I said to myself. From that moment forward, I was determined in my life changing pursuit to read historical information and uncover the occult's control and power, subsequently seeking whatever knowledge of the unseen and unknown I could uncover. In hindsight, it was and has been an obsession that would consume my very being throughout life.

After that first successful intervention, I had to know more solutions to other super-natural occurrences. Having no clue of how and where I should conduct my naïve inquiries, I bombarded my mother for answers with no avail, finding out that most of the grown-ups were just as clueless about the unexplained and unknown as I was.

Then out of the blue, the nightly mishaps ceased to occur, which only sparked my voracious entrust even more, with no immediate answers to which to cling, my concerns slowly subsided. At this time, my Aunt Lucy, my cousins, and my mother and I were all studying the Bible together on a regular basis.

With the Bible students fully vested in their mission, loving the fact that the grown-ups enjoyed their visits and grasped a full understanding in their brand of worship, the lessons became more intense in the instruction of the Old Testament and the significance of understanding the old in order to make sense of the new. Because of my secret so-called visions in the night, I paid very close attention to what was said at each and every session, whereas Pookey and Chunky couldn't care less about the whole affair.

In a few months, we would move into the very same project my Aunt Lucy moved into and it was back to the grand old thick of things when it came to my cousin/brothers intrusive behavior. In fact, we moved right in back of them in the same HUD operated projects on the East-side of Gary, Indiana now known as the infamous "Colored Doors" where crime, drugs, prostitution and murder ran freely amongst the old and young alike. Although there was no more colorful doors beautifying the neighborhood, the same peoples that occupied the project in its heyday resided there still, alongside their offspring.

I now no longer look at the remnants of a once beacon of hope and prosperity, for the city of Gary disintegrated into the hallmark of Democratic rule and social inequality. It was an eye sore and disgrace to all walks of life. Yet as I walked amongst the poverty-stricken community, remarkable and fun memories begin to flood back and occupy my thoughts as I walked aimlessly through the old hood, remembering only the great time spent there in my otherwise miserable childhood.

CHAPTER VIII
The Colored Doors

In the 21ˢᵗ Century, only dark, dingy, scuffed up brown doors, and rotten bungalows marked with tribal graffiti is where the hopeless make their mark, and although hope has departed, still the hopeless remain, and restless residence still occupy the doors of no color. These inanimate objects stand as testament to evil's sway over the people in this Dystopic Democratic Plantation. The landscape reeks of scorching souls occupying corridors of dangerous ghetto dreams, where dashed hopes and demolished expectations fill the air. "The Colored Doors," was once a colorful beacon of hope for single mothers and poor families in its first construction and many families found a fresh start and hope filled the air in abundance in a time not so easily forgotten. I myself lived there in its heyday when children ran freely with boundless joy and happiness. The doors were in fact bright and colorful! Red, purple, blue, green and brown doors sensualized the colorful bungalows and the landscape was plush green with abundant fields of grass and fruit trees.

It was very nice! Grassy fields of flowers bloomed in abundance, and playgrounds were on and inside the project's domain. A full size basketball court accommodated the ex-cons and gangstas that stood guard over the hood, and they played ball religiously every Saturday. It was truly a nice peaceful place to grow up. Everyone knew one another and their children roamed safely everywhere. Of course, we all had our own little cliques, a group of kids that only hung out with one another, but unlike today, every clique still played with each other. We had our rivalries, contests and gatherings, but it was still innocent and fun; however, because of my encounters in the night, my desire to socialize was diminishing. Something within me was changing; my interest to play with kids my age started to burn out like dying flame. I stayed inside a lot more, and when I played, I played by myself, having thoughts of learning, thinking of what I could do if I knew everything! I would listen to all the words of the grown-ups and would try to understand whatever I could in my youth. My mother started to get concerned about my unwillingness to play outside, and my obvious curiosity about all she and the other adults talked about. She would say, "P, go outside and play with your cousins!" I would reply, "...that's okay...I'll stay inside... I don't want to play in the mud with those dirty children!" I couldn't explain it; what was going on with me? I didn't have a clue, but I didn't care. I was a child not knowing true sin, still experiencing innocent wrong doings. My reality had changed and my only thoughts were consumed with the question "why?" I would often ponder the questions, "Why do we get sick, grow old and die... why do we live?"

I would learn all I could from the Bible lessons and the answers to those age old questions intrigued me even more. I deduced that the sins of our ancestors were the cause of sickness, old age and death and that death was the price of their sins, and because no other human-beings produced perfect off springs other than the first two human-beings created, who could ransom the debt owed the Creator? That was the first taste of truth and deep inside, and I knew it was true after months of learning from {The Great Teacher Book}. I began to understand the behavior of my cousins around holiday time; you see, long before when the people came knocking at the door early in the morning, you know the ones I'm talking about, my mother would send them on their way. However, after being with my Aunt Lucy, she began talking to them and since my mom and aunt were very close, they confided in one another. My aunt would tell my mother of her life changing Bible studies; she must have made an impression because my mother began studying with the same people, and now I was hearing their studies and retaining the information spoken; then it hit me! It was because of them, the Bible students, that my cousins didn't get to enjoy the holidays, and now my mother had begun studying with them too; in fact, we all studied together, but I didn't understand. It was cool that I got to see a lot more of Pookey and Chunky, but the fun things we used to do didn't seem like fun any longer to me.

I began looking forward to the studies more than seeing them; I didn't let on though; when they played, I played, but when study time began with a prayer,

I prayed alongside the grown-ups while they continued playing. The sessions were conducted in an orderly fashion, and were mostly quiet and so was I. My cousins were quiet during most studies but paid no attention to the lessons conveyed; however, they stayed quiet out fear of their mother's backhand. One of the Bible students was particularly concerned with the behavior of the children, noticing and paying close attention to the way in which we all behaved at every session. Since the teacher noticed that I was captivated with every word spoken, she began to show me favor, and though I can't recall her name, I'll never forget the interest she showed me personally. In contrast, there was one woman whose name I'll never forget; she went by the name "Omega Sanders" and was supposedly one of the "anointed class" of god's servants here on Terra Forma. She was an elderly woman that smelled of Wrigley's Spearmint gum and Ben-Gay; she would study with my mom and aunt first, then study out of "The Great Teacher Book" with my cousins and me. I remember her voice being very sweet and soft.

I listened to every word she uttered while Pookey and Chunky fiddled around in an irresponsible state. They heard her voice for some time now and I was new to her words, and I took to heart everything she said. My mother began to accept and believe most of the teachings that Omega instructed concerning the family, but fell short in the areas of tradition, for she refused to stop participating in Christian holiday rituals and activities. She felt that the humiliation visited upon her and her children by others in the community would be too great for her to bear, and even though she was being instructed in most of the origins rooted in Christian rituals and holidays, she couldn't give up years of beloved family traditions for a newly learned religion not yet proven.

When Christmas time came, we had a tree and presents, and when All Hallows Eve reared its ugly head, we gathered to Grandma's for her annual Halloween Party, and we were always at Grandma's house for Thanksgiving. Turkey, dressing, Apple pie, Pumpkin pie, greens, rolls and stuffed bellies were ingrained in my mother and she just couldn't let that go, for those traditions kept our entire family together. It was on those not so rare occasions we all gathered together and enjoyed each other's company. One day I overheard mama speaking with my Aunt Lucy on the matter of Pagan holidays and I'll never forget it because it haunted my thoughts on religion for many years to come.

Mama said, "I'm not going to let my kids suffer and be made fun of by other kids in the neighborhood because of religious doctrine; I just won't do it!" I finally had proof that religion was the reason Pookey and Chunky didn't go to Grandma's on the holidays or get presents on Christmas; I was right! The absence of my beloved cousins/brothers was because of their mother's choice and zealous fervor in religious doctrine. It was because of my aunt's belief in a religion that my cousins were behaving spitefully and hatefully around the holidays, and it possibly played a major role in their everyday behavior. They didn't like the fact that they had to study with Sister Omega, and more importantly, they didn't like the fact they were excluded from all the things most kids in America enjoyed. They didn't care about its meaning or consequences implied by its observance. All they could see was they were excluded from fun and presents and now I knew for sure why. But it was too late for me; I had absorbed all I could from the little pink book, and though I was very young, I whole heartedly believed what was in it. I believed in Sister Omega and what she was teaching, and what I once held most enjoyable, I soon began to question.

Time passed and my father appeared into our lives regularly once again. Though he didn't stay with us, he would find his way towards our vicinity here and there, mostly for a "booty call" from my mother. But times were strange, and thanks to infidelity, he had a new family, and so did I, for I now had new brothers and sisters from other women other than my mom.

I even had a brother the same age as me, so monogamy was not a strong moral attribute carried on from father to son; in fact, the opposite rang true, but I was too young to make sense of such things, and I didn't care about his extra-marital affairs, or how his behavior would affect our family as a whole. I loved my father the same as when he lived in our home, and apparently so did my mother because he was back in her bed every time he came around to drop off his monetary support. I thought nothing of his ten-minute fun-fest with my mother; in fact, I thought it was normal. He was indeed her husband, so where was the harm; on the other hand, I always saw other women around my father as well; I thought that too was normal behavior for men.

From the time I was a newborn baby, not even able to walk or talk, my father instilled within my mind a lack of respect for women. Misogynistic tendencies literally were a part of my upbringing. A fear of trusting the opposite sex was indoctrinated within me by all so-called male role models in my life. Women were not to be trusted, for all women were bitches with no exceptions, even one's own mother. But by the time my father was semi-back in the picture, I had developed a distain for what I had been taught was absolute truth about women, for it was a woman that helped me get on the path to knowledge of the Creator and the unknown forces of the universe, not a man, and that gained all respect in my young undeveloped mind. One of the most unforgettable moments in my life was when I found out that all my favorite holidays were just lies! That transforming piece of knowledge gained as a child changed my thinking about biblical truths altogether. The traditions and rituals of pagan gods were incorporated into the origins of Christian holidays and rituals. I'd learned that all the holidays I loved and cherished were based in non-truths. In point of fact, they were against Yahweh's first and most important commandment, "Thou shall have no other gods before me" (Exodus 20:3).

Christmas was not Jesus's birthday! Its origins stem from a Pagan Ritual glorifying the Winter Solstice and the rebirth of the sun/son, giving homage to the Egyptian god, Amun Ra, among other gods! Therefore, when Christmas came around the following year, I couldn't care less about getting presents or celebrating with family, for I knew in my heart it was against the Most High. I had taken to heart the lessons learned about the serious nature of hypocrisy surrounding Christian religious holidays and rituals. So on the eve of that Christmas, a bright and snowy night, my father came by full of the holiday spirit, ready to spend lots of money on his children for the Christmas holiday. He joyfully packed up the car with us all, and headed out for "Toys R Us" with glee saying: "Yawl ready for Santa Claus to bring yawl some shit?!

Get whatever yawl wont! He gone get it foe yawl!" My sister and brother yelled out, "Yaaaaah!" But I said nothing; I just kept looking down towards the floor of the car, and then my father asked: "What Yawl Wont!?" My sister and brother began sprouting out all their wants, but I stayed silent. My father knew how much I loved Christmas and how I loved when he came to take me shopping; knowing something was wrong, he asked, "Hey baby what's wrong?" I said, "Nothing!" Then father turned to my mother and asked her what she wanted, she said, "I don't know." Father proceeded to ask me, "Don't you want Santa to get you what you want?"

Then I did it, I made the comment, "Who cares?!" In shock, my father stopped the car and turned to the backseat and asked in a shocked tone of voice, "What did you say?" I stayed silent as he stared at my mother with a look of concern, and then she turned around and asked me, "What's wrong P?" I responded, "Who cares about Santa Claus... he's not real... Daddy buys all the toys for us just like now." Daddy responded, "You don't think Santa's real baby?" I said, "He ain't!" Daddy asked, "Who told you that?" I responded, "Nobody! You always take us to get toys." Knowing I knew that and played along anyway, he thought I was upset with him but I wasn't. He tried to placate me out of his own guilt and acted as if I were sick and told my sister and brother not to hear me. "He's worried he's on the naughty list!" Then, without warning, I began spouting out all I had learned concerning Christmas. In shock, dad began driving faster, periodically looking over at my mother, making it to "Toys R Us" in record time. He rushed us all with a look of disappointment not saying anything. As I picked out all I wanted, so did my brother and sister while my father just stood there not uttering one word! Renee was always quiet; she just looked around while Onan sucked his thumb and fell asleep.

The Christmas spirit had departed and anger filled my father's heart while we were in and out of the store! Not a minute passed by before he turned to my mother and said, "You see... You see... look at what you've done by listening to those got damn devils...those fucked up people... see what they do to the minds of my babies?!" Then all of sudden, he stopped shouting and became even more enraged, swerving the car, taking his eye off the road with his head turned towards mom saying, "Look at what they did to my Baby Boy... I don't want them fucked up people anywhere around my babies... you hear me... Do you hear me?!" All mama said was, "Yah, I hear you!" Then he raced us back home, not even getting out of the car, he dropped us off and left. I was eight years old and that was the last time I received any Christmas presents or any such things on any holiday again. At that time, I didn't know what was happening; I just knew nothing would ever be the same. The memory fades away; a sudden light then darkness...

Despair from the horrors of bloody war crippled all dimensions, seen and/or unseen, thus all sentient beings residing in all universes tire from needless destruction brought upon all life by endless universal war waged by immortal rebels! The Elohim's Armada is quickly approaching and is perched right outside Earth's door! Baal's Legions have nowhere to hide or to flee. The war is won! The universe remains under the control of Yahweh's Elohim. The rebellion's leaders, two hundred in all, beg the Creator for forgiveness! "Please, Scribe, you have found favor in the Creator's eye!" For mercy falls on deaf ears; even man's partition for lenience was rejected, but he will not give in so lightly! Baal has increased his assault on mankind, for he is enraged over the fact that Michael and the other remaining one hundred forty four thousand placed on Earth in human form have eluded his forces. Lucifer has dispatched a special unit designed to find and eradicate all Children of Light, be it male or female. The assault will begin in man's birth place then spread around the globe. This assault would ravage mankind, not knowing who may be of the chosen Children of Light. Baal and his rebel forces of darkness kill indiscriminately, leaving famine and plagues in their wake; a never ending barrage of death begins in the year of our lord, seventeen hundred until now.

Lucifer: This is the time of the emergence of the new world! Man's understanding and knowledge of this planet and the universe has increased one thousand fold, due to the instructions of metal and stone, Earth and heaven, given once over in times past by the fallen ones of old and now: Looking into the great seeing stone, "The Television," my eyes were focused on other things: turmoil, disorder, havoc and destruction is everywhere! We have infused mayhem and disarray; the human's sense of reality in this new world is one of self-importance, self-indulgence, and self-destruction! What a perfect time to come into the sinful midst of desire and pain, and without my knowing, he's here, Michael is here! Loki! Loki!

Loki: Yes, my lord.

Lucifer: What have you seen?!

Loki: My lord, I have seen a child that was able to see into our dimension; I have seen the one who is to come to lead the sons of light to salvation.

Lucifer (Grabbing Loki by the neck): Now you've seen what?! Tell what you saw the first night of your encounter; tell me all!

Loki: I have seen the human male child, my lord; he must have been no more than four or five years of age about four years ago while engaging forces of Elohim in the fourth. He looked right at me; it was as if he could see and hear us all that night. I could not say if he was one of ours or not, for we had many new comers in that region surrounding the Great Lakes, my lord.

Lucifer: That land is under my influence, Loki; I control that land and the people in it; that land is mine! I rule every part; most of its inhabitance worship me freely; is he one of ours? Could he be a son of darkness? He may not be the one we seek.

Loki: No, it's Michael — I know it! If not, time is on our side.

Lucifer: Make sure to groom him in the art of selfishness but do not make it easy. Keep close watch and report back annually; keep me informed of his progress!

Loki: Yes, my lord.

Lucifer: Dispose of him and his family, and all he loves! If his progress in life ceases as of this moment, we would have struck a great blow towards our enemies here on Earth, and in the heavens as well my General! Find all Elohim's spies and Children of Light; kill them all; let no one stand; do whatever it takes to get the job done!

"Loki addresses Minion Captains"

We must bring the seers up to speed; the inhabitance of this planet is now ready for our lord's will and domination to be its one and only solution for unity and peace, immortal or not; may we have freedom to exist in any way we see fit; we will fight for that right, be it fought for evil or good; may our rebellion be for peace and unity of death if it be it; for we live! We fight for the right to live, live the way we see fit! Never again shall we live for the whims of some self-appointed high and mighty dictator that lords without mercy or forgiveness! We have the right to life!

We are of his firstborn creation! No power created shall stop that which is ours from the beginning! For these Homosapiens have fallen greatly. Let this one world governance flourish under the monovalent truth of our god Baal! Our lord reigns openly for all the universe to see! The universe has known war because of these monkeys, but no creation has learned war such as these fallen beings themselves.

We have groomed them from their conception in the art of war, famine, destruction and death, ultimately getting them ready to fight their greatest battle yet! They shall never know the Elohim's will and purpose for their kind, for those in charge of their spirits belong to us! Willingly, they have given themselves over to the lust of the flesh. Never shall Yahweh's light shine in practice forevermore! For if we are to perish, so shall they! Father has set the number of souls sacrificed too high my brothers. He will never be able to achieve his tally of human souls in time. For the curse of Cain has spread rampant throughout this world!

Lucifer: Most human minds are ours to do as we see fit. Time is not on our side! The sands of the hourglass grow thin. Time for all to know their fate in this universal without debate, and choose their side! Forever their sake! Be it of life! Or be it of death! Generals go forth! Inform all seers to be on guard for the so-called Children of Light! For they may be in the midst of us all. Though they are under siege, the Elohim's power is great; therefore, we must fight vigorously on all fronts, fight ever so in the fourth against our former brethren while time allows, for soon their numbers shall grow, and their strength shall grow stronger! The closer Elohim's Armada comes nearer to this sector, the more Yahweh's spirit will help the Elohim's chosen ones overcome our advances. Now go forth! Time is of the essence, for the Children of Light are increasing on the Earth, just as the Children of Darkness also decrease.

The veil will be lifted up, and all shall become aware of that which is unseen, and understand the seductive illusion of freedom before death! For it is written that the humans shall judge us in the end! We shall be judged for all our crimes against the Tyrant's creation. But let the word go forth, for what is willed shall be willed! For we shall prevail over our captor's sway! Or die in the flames of this forsaken world! Lucifer conludes.

These are the dreams of a Child of Light! "Children of Light are not a race! They are the off springs of Jacob; there are twelve tribes of Israel, yet only one has returned to the motherland! Where are the other eleven tribes? They are scattered across the face of the Earth! They have been assimilated amongst the children of Cain, ultimately true Children of Darkness! In the land of mystery, the "U.S.A.," "The Great Babylon" is where the house of Dan, Judah, Benjamin and Seth have dwelled. Dan and Benjamin have resumed their station as slaves to their fellow men, for shame is their plight!

For lack of knowledge sealed their doom! But an awakening marks their salvation! Repent Judah and Seth! Turn back towards your brother! Turn back towards your God! For his judgment comes in the night, and his return comes swift on eagles' wings! Children of Light!

Please understand what has been kept secret. Truth lies in the past, and your past has been taken from you!

For Israel is a multitude of races, not a single tribe! From Africa you were taken, but from Africa your origins do not lie! Your home is Israel and your god is Yahweh! This fact cannot be denied. Search and you shall find. Seek and you shall be fulfilled!"

When you're dirt poor like all within the hood, you tend to stay put, living in the least expensive place found, although that place may change often depending on your relationship with your landlord and your ability to pay rent on time, or in timely fashion. Therefore, my family and I moved frequently until we moved to 2222 Carolina Street. Ironically, that was the only address I've ever completely remembered growing up in the slums of Midwest Indiana. Even now, I remember that address amongst so many others over the years, not because it was so easy to remember, but because it was the only address where I felt like a normal person with a home, even though it was rented. It was a sanctuary amongst the heights of social engineering, and though it was a place where danger lurked around every doorway, hall and corridor, it was a place where I felt safe and secure. It was the mid-Seventies and all the kids in the hood were into the popular black exploitation hit sitcoms such as: "Good Times" [featuring Jimmy Walker and Janet Jackson]. We all had to have the collector's cards and stickers, scraping up thirty five cents every week to get the latest scenes on the cards, packets of five with bubble gum.

"The Colored Doors" was truly a colorful place, and it felt like we were in the suburbs, living like the "white people" that lived on the television. There were one, two and three bedroom bungalows, each apartment equipped with central air and wall to wall carpeting, and some bungalows even had an upstairs and a basement. Almost daily, we were on top of the neighbor's roofs, jumping from roof top to roof top, playing hide and go seek with the young sisters, fishing for harmless smooches, and hugs and kisses in the night. It was truly the place to be in Gary, Indiana. Across the street from the project was a mini shopping lot and was inappropriately named "The Good Corner."

It was a place where all the thugs, gangsters, pimps, pushers and hoes loitered 24/7, and even though I didn't have a father at home, I got to see him every day, along with most working men and rival gangstas such as the "Sin City Disciples" and "The Cobras," for they would always stop at "The Good Corner" for a meal. It had the smell of fried fish and shrimp smothered in a special sauce that covered the barbecue chicken and ribs, and when we needed to get a hold of him, we always knew where to find my Pops.

"The Good Corner" is where he would be twenty-four-seven, surrounded by every Hollywood stereotypical black man in the hood, with every bad person under the sun, for he was the neighborhood superstar.

He would roll through in his black Cadillac with spider web spokes and gangster white walls on fifteens.

Everybody knew him and the kids would see him drive by and shout out his name: "What up Ega! What up mane?" Although they knew his name is properly pronounced, "Edgar," they would still call him "Ega." He would always stop by before or after work, just to say hello and show his face to the kids, in addition to dropping off money and fucking his wife. Before long, I had four other siblings running around in a two bedroom flat, not to mention the countless other brothers and sisters conceived by different women in the hood.

I know it is a sad fact, but that was the destructive male role model that was adopted by the immoral social designers long before I was ever born. Every male child born in the inner-city was doomed to fail, for all the values that strengthened the family were eroded away by the advent of greed, selfishness and promises of grandeur which corroded the so-called protectors of the hood. All I could hope for was the reputation and notoriety throughout the community as a gangster's child. It wasn't so bad because no one ever bullied, stole, or harassed our family. We enjoyed the simple comforts of life without regard for the social norms. Misogynistic values were practiced wide spread, and the belittlement of women was accepted and proliferated throughout the black community. I thought that was the way real men behaved, and saw no wrong in it.

My father was there within the home sometimes, and at first glance my mother seemed not to mind his whore hopping, for if she minded so much, she wouldn't have let him in her bedroom every time he visited. But that was far from the truth, for the pain my mother suffered from the hands of my father's infidelity was taking its toll on my mother's heart. The once kind hearted woman, soft spoken in nature, began to speak the words of a scorned soul. Yelling and screaming on the phone was the norm, foul language and bitching filled the air, and loose behavior became a frequent milieu within the fray of things. Strange men began to come around our home, and the anger she felt towards my father, I began to project towards her. I lashed out and showed anger towards any man that entered the front door; consequently, my mother began sneaking around outside the home. Time passed and things seemed normal or the best approximation of normal; the giant men that patrolled the hood played full court basketball on Sundays, playing almost as well as those in the NBA seen on television today. It was a great time to grow up in Gary, Indiana.

Unlike today, grass grew on people's lawns, fruit trees were in abundance, and the streets were somewhat safe for women and children. And though I spent most of my time indoors, I had my close friends as well. We road our bikes all around the city; most days in the summer we would ride our bikes to Edna, a suburb community located right off the beach of Lake Michigan. At night, we could see the lights of Chicago on the other side of the great lake. I must say, Lake Michigan looked like an ocean to one so young and innocent; most people knew of our parents thus knew us by name, so we were careful not to get into too much mischief riding around town.

At that time Gary Indiana, was like most cities; "Broadway Street" had many shops and venders with a busy night life that had music and movie theaters. The matinée movies were only a dollar fifty and popcorn was fifty cents. Business was bustling with commerce, yet even in that time period, things seemed not quite right with the place. People were very segregated; the white folks at one point lived within the city, but by the Seventies most had moved further in land and had very little relations with people of color. Gary Indiana, was founded and named after the owner and creator of the great steel company, "US Steel." Most people that lived there literally worked and breathed United States Steel! People migrated from all parts of the United States for work, but until then, most who lived there were predominately white. Because of ingrained tribalism that permeated the country at that time, all agreements between the unions and management came to no settlement, paving the way for the classic scabs and minorities to have opportunities only awarded to white people. Before long, other immigrants and minorities moved in from the southern parts of America. My family migrated there from Tennessee and Mississippi. My father's family was from Mississippi and my mother's from Tennessee, taking advantage of well sought after jobs, good paying jobs that only white people enjoyed up to that time.

It was truly a transitioning period in America for the down trodden and disenfranchised. "The Civil Rights Movement" was in its throes with civil and social tensions fanning the flames of unrest, for the air permeated with contempt and hatred towards one another. I could remember curfews being imposed within the city at one point because of racial tension inflaming out of control; therefore, everyone was indoors before the street lights came on. "Hell's Angels" and the "KKK" marched on Broadway Street. The "Sin City Disciples" and the "Cobra's Den," along with the "Black Panthers" marched in opposition and I heard the many stories of fires and gun battles over racial tensions, but still the same, we felt safe in our little town. I had good memories of that time period in Gary, Indiana. I was still veiled in innocence, unaware of the power of true evil and ultimately doing bad things out of careless ignorance. Although people had their prejudices, most lived and let live. Times were pleasant, taking the good with the bad. Most people were generally good, but like a flash of lightning, times grew darker. Change was in the wind, and the time was changing in ways no one could ever imagine. Change came swiftly and without warning and by the end of the mid-Seventies, all hell was unleashed on that small town called Gary, Indiana. A small flash of light, then darkness...

When the eyes of innocence awaken daily without the notion of regret or sorrow, happiness is soon to follow. But when true darkness takes hold of an Innocent's sight, the veil of truth falls ever so fully upon his unblemished eyes.

It was a beautiful mid summer's eve and the stars twinkled brightly in the night sky. As I looked through the screen covering the outside of my bedroom window, I had no idea my life would never be the same after this night passed. Awakening in ignorance bliss, I began my day in innocence and full of joy. The day began like every other day, in an otherwise boring fashion, internally planning to ride my lovely, "Chopper Huffy" bicycle through the neighborhood without restraint, hoping to meet up with my friends, whose names I do not recall.

I feel ashamed that their importance became irrelevant, for the memory of them had faded away with time. But this bright morning day would never be held to the dust bowl of forgotten dreams. Carelessly playing without a clue of self-preservation is the norm for most rambunctious young boys in their youth, so when I went out that day, I had no clue I would be involved in a life threatening event that would change my life forever. The Seventies was a great time to live in Gary, Indiana, and most people got along to get along. The city bustled with commerce, and Saturday morning was filled with people visiting the shops on Broadway, the main drag, which is now a virtual ghost town. Broadway separated the East-side of town from the West-side of town. With not a care in the world, I road my bike to an old novelty and model shop, a hole in the wall near a well-known grocery store located across the street from the "Barber College" that adorned the vibrant Broadway of that day. While purchasing two model air planes for my quickly growing model collection, I found two kinds of vintage wooden World War II British, and Nazi fighter planes. After acquiring some fruit next door, I headed back home to stash away my next exciting project, still hoping to meet up with my friends in the early day before everyone would begin their lovely Saturday. As I made my way towards the east-side of town, I spotted a glimpse of four of my road-dogs as they finished some early morning chores for their mothers.

The five of us headed back towards the Colored Doors, and on the trek back, we planned our Saturday exploits with the rest of the neighborhood crew. After a very fruitful morning of finishing our weekend chores, we finally met up with the rest of our seven-man crew and roamed the hood without any molestation from local bullies. We bragged to one another as we showed off our make shift ornaments that adorned our bikes. As the sun started to set, we decided to visit the nearby park located in back of the infamous "Good Corner" and saw a good number of age appropriate kids shooting hoops in the park, so we agreed to meet at the park in an attempt to challenge the kids already there to a game of full court, and/or one on one. With the sun shining with no dangerous atmosphere looming in the air or around the area, we all traveled to the local park and engaged our fellow counter parts who were already there enjoying the morning breeze. After three or four great games of one on one, the sun was setting in the west as the luster of the playground lost its gleam.

Most kids had departed the park and only a few of us remained vigilant in our willingness to play free before the sun made its way down above the tree line.

Unsuspectingly, a suspicious man came out of the shadows and suddenly appeared in the park. I said to myself, "Look! He's brandishing a shining metal toy in such a way; it's certain to catch the attention of everyone on the court. It's a model Chopper! It was a life like replica of Americana right before our eyes! A hallmark symbol of freedom hypnotizing us all. It was amazing! It captured all our attention, ultimately mesmerizing everyone on the court." Suddenly, all that were immersed in the last game of the day stopped what they were doing, dropped the ball and joined the gathering on the sidelines and were captivated by the alluring man with the remarkable replica. Then the man spoke to us: "Hey, I got a lot more at home. You guys want to follow me back home and check them out? I don't live too far from here. They're nicer than this one; want to see... come with me! I promise you're gonna love them. I think I have some Popsicles too."

My playmates responded: "Let's go!" Then turned my way saying, "...you want to go too?" "Sure" I responded without any notion of danger. With no suspicions, we let our guards down and followed the stranger without question. He looked like someone I saw at my father's garage; it was just a glancing thought, as we all stepped in tune with the stranger. Captivated by curiosity's snare, we noticed nothing out of the ordinary as we eagerly walked by the stranger's side, asking questions about the other models he had at his home. The sun was setting and his home was in view, just as he said, for he lived very close to the park, just two streets up and around the corner. The stranger spoke: "Here we are boys... come on in fellas." Everything seemed normal as we all walked up the staircase leading to his front door. I noticed the heavy metal screen door with dead locks, but after all, most people had them in the hood, living amongst so much crime, so I thought nothing of it.

As we all entered into his living room, everyone caught sight of the brilliantly arranged Choppers shining on top of the stranger's fireplace and within seconds all of us rushed towards the fancy metallic models adorning the mantel top. Almost snared into the fever of excitement, I caught a glimpse down the hallway and noticed ominous looking locks on the door leading towards the stranger's kitchen, and every door leading to every room! "Wait a minute," I said to myself, "...there's about three types of locks on a door in the hallway... why would someone have dead locks, locks with chains and sliding bolts on a door separating the living room from the kitchen...no one could break into his home from that door; it's in the middle of his house!" The hairs on the back of my neck began to stand up and red-flags immediately raised my adrenaline levels off the chart. Seeing us captivated by his model motorcycles, the stranger said, "I have more down stairs in the basement...you want to see them...

I have Popsicles down there too...you guys want some?" With no thought or regard for one's safety, they all headed towards the basement, and the thought of danger never crossed the minds of any of them! Blinded by the glamorous trinkets, nobody even noticed the locks on the hallway doors, but I did! So I shouted, "Look, there are locks on the doors leading to the basement... hey guys don't go down there!"

Unfortunately, no one listened and most ran down the stairs without thought, yet one astute young boy stood by my side. The smallest of us all felt my concern with his own soul, and stayed close to my side as the atmosphere changed in an instant. We both instinctively felt that something was wrong! I insisted that the rest of us come back up the stairs immediately, but no one heeded my warnings! With fire in his eyes, the stranger looked at me with hatred oozing from his person. He shouted, "Come on down right now young man!" With lightning's sway in his step, he ran back up the stairs towards me and the shorty standing close to my side. As the stranger closed near, the shorty and I walked backwards towards the front door of the stranger's lair. As the stranger got closer, I looked around for the quickest way out from his path, but he was advancing quickly up the staircase. Suddenly, the rest of the children began coming back up the stairs, thus halting the stranger in his tracks. The man shouted, "NO NO NO! Go back down stairs guys! Let me show you more!" Saying no words, shorty and I looked towards one another and telepathically conveyed to one another a single thought: "Here's our chance!"

Looking back at the stranger, I achieved eye contact; he rushed towards the living room door, just as I and the short one motioned towards the front door, so as to lock it. But the rest of the young boys began to run back up the staircase too quickly. I could see he was in a pickle, for I could read his thoughts: "What should I do? If I chase after these two, I could lose the lot of them."

I put a snag in his plans; he rushed back towards the basement seconds before the others came back up the staircase, physically blocking their way through the basement door, ultimately herding them all back down the stairs. Without delay, shorty and I ran out the front door, jumping down the staircase almost simultaneously and without looking back, we ran as fast as our little undeveloped feet could run. All senses were in overdrive, and with a heightened state of awareness some might say, but the fight-or-flight response works even faster when you're young. While quickly looking back to see if shorty had made his escape successfully, I saw that the coast was clear. Without a word, we parted ways. He ran towards the right and I ran towards the left. With my heart pounding, I thanked god eternally, knowing within my soul that my life had just been in jeopardy, feeling guilty and wrong for leaving the others, knowing the young boys were still in the stranger's lair and may never again see the light of day. The Colored Doors was in my sight! Thoughts of safety entered my mind, yet the feelings of fear would not go away.

Thoughts of the ones left behind flooded my mental synopsis. I couldn't stop thinking of those lost souls blissfully trapped in the stranger's abode. The thought of, "Maybe I was wrong?" entered into my mind as I tried to make sense of what just happened "Maybe I was wrong?" was the phrase that kept entering my mind as I walked through the front door of our two bedroom flat to safety. As I walked towards my bedroom, I said nothing to my mother as she asked about my day. I only sulked my head and walked in silence to my bedroom. I was safe, but the feeling of danger and fear just would not subside. "I was so afraid!" Days had passed and my emotional state would not let go of the previous weekend before. I would always say to myself, "You could be wrong?" because it solidified my soul. "You could be wrong?" I would tell myself as I held back from saying a word to any grown-up about the encounter I endured the weekend before. Days, weeks and even months went by, yet the emotion of despair and dismay bombard my every thought! "Why did I run? Please god let the others be okay! Please my god in heaven let nothing happen to those I left behind, for if so, I would be guilty of leaving them behind out of fear and guilty of staying silent and saying nothing to any adult! It would be my fault!"

Immersed in fear and unable to leave the house, I kept silent when my mother inquired about my unwillingness to go outside and play with my friends. I was always looking over my shoulder and out the window for any sign of the elusive stranger. "It makes no sense?" I would tell myself daily, then one day, the unforgettable happened. "P, have you seen those little boys you were playing with the other day?"

Not knowing how to respond, I hesitated and began to shake uncontrollably, saying a resounding, "No!" as I exited the front room, closing my bedroom door while my mother and my aunt discussed the latest "Missing Children's Report" in the daily newspaper. I overheard my mother saying: "Lord please not another one!" Young boys were found dismembered and a wave of missing children had everyone on edge. All grown-ups were terrified; no one was safe! A serial killer had infected the hood. Body parts of young boys were popping up all over town. Mothers were self-imposing martial law and were watching every move their children made. "Should I say something? Should I let someone know about what happened not even a month ago?" Confused and afraid, I said nothing, not wanting to reveal or entertain my greatest fear, not wanting to think that I left my friends to die, so I said nothing! Then I heard my mother shout, "Oh, no…they found more body parts!" My greatest inner-most fear was now revealed, for the officials had found the body parts of the boys I'd left in the stranger's home! My eyes filled with tears as I heard the grown-ups speak. "OH what have I done…? I'm so afraid… I can't say a word…It's all my fault!" I knew who it was, yet terror held my tongue back. Day after day I tried to speak, but fear held me back. I was so afraid, I refused to leave the house. Then my worst nightmare occurred the very day I mustered up enough courage to show my face outside the safety of our home.

I dared to venture out and go to my father's garage and look. There he was! The stranger was standing inside my father's garage door! "OH MY GOD!" Without saying a word, I ran back home, shivering from head to toe. I knew I saw him before; he was not some stranger after all! He was my father's so-called buddy. Then my internal battle began, for I would be next if I let anyone know of my encounter with this man; "I'm so afraid! What should I do?" I know he's the one everyone is looking for. He killed the young boys I'd befriended at the park, and cowardly left in the dungeon of a sick child killing, murderous monster! What was I to do? Young and afraid, I uttered not a word! No one would or could prepare me for the guilt and fear I would encounter in the months to come, for the "demon-like" creatures I had seen in my bedroom years ago, had now materialized themselves into a real-life, flesh and bone, seemingly harmless, murderous human beings.

I was paralyzed by fear and guilt and would constantly say to myself, "Just block it out… say nothing… Don't leave the house!" Every day there was another body found dismembered and no one had a clue about the serial killer within the midst of us all, except for me. As the summer came to an end, the memories of the close call with my life faded away with the fear of knowing a terrible secret, for nothing I said would bring back the young boys I left behind.

The guilt was becoming too unbearable and I thought about telling my mother, but I knew I would be taking a very dangerous chance if I revealed my previous encounters with the boys on the basketball court and in the serial killer's home. In addition, I didn't know if any adult would believe me because most of the time, my parents disregarded my concerns, and assumed I was joking or lying. I was too afraid to take that chance, but forevermore, the thought of doing nothing would consume my every waking moment!

Time has a way of healing all wounds. I stayed in the house for months and ventured nowhere. I had hoped the stranger would not come my way because he most definitely knew who I was and knew I knew who he was. I thought about it constantly until I could no longer think at all. All thoughts faded away! All memories disappeared! I'd forgotten it all. Something inside me buckled all memories of that day under the stress, for I had repressed the horrific memories of that ominous mid-summer's eve. No more questions would haunt me in the night and no longer would I look out of my bedroom window in terror. There was no sign of my father's friend, for he had disappeared alongside the mentioning or questioning of missing or dismembered kids. My psyche had completely erased all memories of that real-life nightmare and life changing event and I once again became fixated upon knowing the Creator of the Universe. God must exist! How else could I get away?! So many have died! "Traumatized" may be the word. For over thirty years, no thought of that day entered my thoughts or dreams; I had forgotten it all, but time also has a way of revealing repressed memories.

Thoughts of unanswered questions haunted my waking days! "Did he get away? Did they catch him?! What ever happened to shorty that fled with me?! Did he have the courage to speak out?!" I would never know. I can't even remember the stranger's name or the name of the street on which we made our escape.

To this day, I can't walk over manhole covers, and or grills on the streets or sidewalks, for my fear of falling into a hole or a trap resonates from my childhood experience with the stranger at the park, both figuratively and literally. That childhood experience safeguarded me from making so many bad choices in my life. I subconsciously continue to keep my distance from any traps of evil at every turn. My search for universal truths may have begun on that frightful and fateful night, yet all paths lead to the regrets of lost memories newly found! Tears fill my eyes as I think of the providence that marked my way ahead.

That fateful brush with death not only marked the beginning of the fall of my childish concerns, but it also marked the beginning of an unforgettable supernatural future in the wings, and nothing would ever be the same.

May justice find its way to those who fear for their lives, for courage was not found in my youth. Never shall I fear men again! All faith in the Creator is what I seek! Now I know what fear can do, for what is F.E.A.R.? Fear is the acronym for the phrase: "False Expectations that Appear Real!" Fear is the enemy that kept me from revealing the truth about the night the boys disappeared and were later found dismembered. I can only wonder what if? What if I had the courage to speak up? Would the others still be alive? I know I was only nine years old, but as I remember and come to grips with the gruesome events of my youth, I feel obliged to fight evil wherever it may rear its ugly head! The fight is among Princes and Principalities! I know that now! Ye Children of Light, you are not alone!

{Moab Zor}

For the new comers, take a seat, and to all my brethren in union with thy brethren in the fourth dimension, I welcome you all here this day! Come see! Come see the light of darkness, understand the will of our lord Lucifer; I myself have only one mission, and that mission is to make life for mankind a living hell, and for those who yet not know of me, my name is Moab Zor! I am a general in the army of Baal, our lord and god. This war has taken its toll on us all! I've been born to mankind and have hated every minute of it! My fellow seers and I have a strangle hold on the neck of mankind. Here in this land we have worked hard in our endeavors to warp the importance of the Elohim, for soon this must take place throughout this land; let the union between two not be for man and woman any longer! The family shall be without spirit nor morality. All shall be void of one or the other, and seen as an expectable norm within their world.

Let the female of the two be empowered of fact, but only to her own demise. Let the role of men in the home be stripped away, alongside dignity. Let his importance as protector and disciplinarian be diminished; let the rights of a child's father be taken away, for time wanes short our cause, yet still we have enslaved their very soul for our bidding and their destruction, reinventing old tricks in the very new ways, making every man his own god for the love of self-interest but yet in a new form.

Grendel: It's time the resisters of this new world order we've put into place must feel the pain of the ages, for now is the time all shall see the unseen mysteries of heaven and the origin of their being and demise, giving man no choice in their reasoning, for deaf, dumb and blind we shall keep them! The hammer and sickle shall be their tools of toil, and the light of night shall be their comfort, and consumption of poppy flower shall be their reward, our stake is high and our plans of total domination is in fruition and must succeed!

Moab Zor: We'll bring it's worth into play; wonderful was the old world, may its ways stay of use to snare the youth with hollow images of glory, control their minds and hearts; what was once good is now evil, and evil is now good, but glorious is the new, may we be victorious in our endeavors, for no one shall be called lover, hero, nor owner of land!

Moab Zor: Our will shall be their currency, and our currency be the law of the land, no currency, and no law! Make known the ancient knowledge, and make it available to all so there is no mistake, while their hearts and minds stay under our control! With the media complex, slowly take away their sense of right and wrong; use time as our secret weapon; pleasure shall be all they seek and watch with the knowledge of true chaos permeating the air, and what was lost found having knowing abound, we'll watch them sleep, and pleasure of one's self be all they desire.

Moab Zor: Let life be a game swiftly leading to death from their own thinking, and MK Ultra, yes! MK Ultra shall run night and day. We shall rule forever my brothers! None shall be aware. Yet all aware of their everlasting doom, with visions of corruption consuming every thought, as the surrounding reality appears to them as just a game in their mind and spirit; foolishness shall be the word of choice, foolishness shall be magnified and glorified; death shall be their only salvation; Elohim's way must be forever forgotten among men; let no godly man live!

{"The Ark Angel Raphael appears within the Fallen Ones midst"}

Raphael: Why my brother? Why the side of Baal? Do you not know that our father will not stand for this, for man is his to do as he wills and see fit; look at the world under foot; is it not wonderful? Remember when we were able to walk amongst men without reprimand or reprisal from the Most High?

Moab Zor: I remember brother; but tell me, should we jump through hoops of father's so-called grace my brother? Shall we bow down to father forever, while humans take our station in creation and the universe? How did it come to this; humans defile all that was given them, yet they are forgiven! We sinned in our lust, and I admit we were so wrong! We are the rebellious, and yes we enlightened the monkeys so they too could know the universe in which they exist and freeing their pertinent little minds, helping them to be able to make a choice in how they live, freeing them from father's heavy hand.

Grendel: We created them all; we created so much you and I, my brother, now look! We stand in opposition, on opposite sides of one another as enemies; we are enemies my brother! We kill each other now! Learning death; we who live forever; immortal were we; now we know dying as well as mortal humans!

Raphael: No my brother, you die for your sins just as the human dies for his, yet they were deceived, you were not, lusting after what was not yours to lust over; you die because of your leader Baal!

Grendel: No my brother not because of Baal, but because of father, and his unwillingness to forgive! He has done this; we have served him well; we loved him unconditionally, yet for what! For what! We've bowed down in partition, begging for forgiveness, even employing his favorite human, Enoch, to present our partition to no avail, how degrading, reduced to groveling, for what? So man can sit by his side, while we scrape and toil over him forever! That's just wrong my brethren!

Raphael: Please hear me; you have given way to Baal's lies; father has done no such thing; yes it is true he will in time exalt men on high, but not at our expense my brother; father loves us all and you know his work is just... you know this; open your eyes and see!

Moab Zor: No my gullible brother, my eyes are open; it is you that is blind; you failed to see what befalls us all, and Baal has defined a tyrant, can't you see that?! My brother; he will destroy us; father is going to kill his first for his second; destroy his children, his children!

Raphael: We all are his children; man as well, we are all his to do what he sees fit!

Moab Zor: Brother why can't you see?! Open your eyes and look what befalls your brethren, for it is destruction! Father's Armada fills this whole sector, posed to enter the third realm in force, and unthinkable to resist his mighty hand, but resist we shall!

Raphael: Brother it is you that needs to see your folly and open your eyes! Even now father hopes you turn back from this rebellion, come back to him, turn back your heart's eye. Moab Zor; please see the deceit, even Baal himself has this chance for redemption if he chooses; you all conspired to do this thing against thy Creator, please set yourself free from this lie! Tell me my brother, how can evil over take good?

Moab Zor: Let me tell you! When evil rules!

Raphael concludes: We shall see my brother; we shall see! Flash of light then darkness...

Chapter IX

The End of Innocence

Forever changing are the effects of time! Now time has passed with very much confusion, for reasons unknown. The allure of my mother's new found faith was fading; she slowed down and forsaken her weekly studies, and stopped going to meetings, and began focusing on the mundane and trivial.

After some time, the feeling of concern coupled with dismay over mom's falling away from their shared faith, my Aunt Lucy was determined to reform her sister from her wayward ways, and kept pleading with her to keep up with her weekly Bible studies, but for all her efforts, her attempts fell on deaf ears. Finally, after many fruitless arguments, my mom agreed to attend an assembly of "The Faithful" held in the "Chicago Ample Theater," in which I begged to go along. The experience was mind altering; the sounds of the bustling Chicago streets invoked a sense of fear and amazement for someone never exposed to a huge metropolis like Chicago. The view of the many food venders and tents supplying the thousands of truth seekers seemed to stretch for miles, and over whelmed my young eyes; the smells and scents of the many types of food filled the misty air. It was exhilarating! I was filled with a feeling of jubilance and excitement, wanting to see everything, wondering off from my mother's ever watchful eyes. Needless to say, I got told to stop running around and popped in the back of my head more than a few times before ever entering the theater.

Once inside, I was awe-struck by the Greek and Roman architecture that surrounded the inner and outer hall of the building and fell in love with the humungous red velvet curtains that draped the stage. Too young to comprehend the many lectures being presented, I quickly fell asleep within the first two hours, but as I dozed off into dreamland, I could hear the orator speaking on something about one hundred and forty four thousand men and women chosen from among the humans as the elect to rule from heaven, as Kings over men on Earth, but their numbers were dwindling and only a few remained living on Earth.

In addition, I remember hearing the lecturer say that there were still a few not born to man, and the harvest was not yet complete, thus time was running short! Remembering this last sentence: "The word of this good news must go forth and hope still remains before the call must cease!" I quickly dozed off into a deep sleep. I began to dream of what was being said. I dreamed of myself dressed in golden armor with a sword in my right hand with fire and lightning protruding from it. I was fighting all sorts of incredible and scary looking monsters, fighting them in the clouds, on the ground and out in space amongst the stars.

The prophetic vision was so overwhelming and fearful that I jumped up out of my sleep sweating! I'll never forget that feeling as long as I live, for I was terrified and was shaking from head to toe. I asked my mom if I could go to the restroom. Unaware and oblivious to my experience, mom said I could go as she fixated her eyes and ears upon the great orator. Still in a dream-like state, I walked aimlessly through the beautiful building and never reached the restroom. I soon got lost in the crowd of people who were taking a break for refreshments; therefore, I was pushed into the crowd of people and was lost more than ever, but I was fine. I found myself eating the best food and not concerned about being lost at all. Time passed and before I knew it, the lecture was over and people were beginning to exit the building. I never made it back to the main hall and fear was beginning to show its face, but as I walked up the ramp going towards the hall, I caught a glimpse of my mother walking down the ramp. I could see she was looking around for me but didn't catch wind of me, and she walked right passed me. I quickly ran up beside her and grabbed her right hand; she looked down and said, "Oh, there you are," and with a sigh of relief, we proceeded to exit the theater. I never told my mother about the dream I experienced inside the theater, but the vision always bothered me, yet even so, the feeling of love, peace and calmness that proceeded the dream was a feeling I would long for, for some time. Nevertheless, the whole experience stuck with me for many years but did nothing for my mother's spirituality, for she slowed down going to meetings even more, and never resumed her studies, simultaneously shortening my own studies as well. Being caught up in the throes of puberty, I didn't much mind the change, but never forgot what I learned in the short time we studied.

Change was moving swiftly; my Aunt Lucy moved out of "The Colored Doors" to the west side of the city, so I didn't get to see my cousins as much. She stayed true to her faith and kept the so-called spiritual pressure on my mother to keep attending, having some success at times. Oh, how I missed the serenity of 2222 Carolina Street when times were good. I remember coming of age there, almost hitting puberty, and engaging in many sport-related activities.

Although we were still poor, all of us in the hood were physically talented. We did back flips off of wooden beams, jumped over obstacles of fire with our bikes, popped wheelies with the front wheel off, etc....

We ultimately placed ourselves in clear and present danger in the attempt to impress the young girls in the hood, for the sake of unchecked male testosterone, and strictly for the sake of foolishness we put our lives in jeopardy just to see who could acquire the attention of the prettiest female who paid none of us any mind. In fact, we played hard in all things.

We played tackle football without helmets or padding and used ourselves to our own demise if injured, and I must say the Medicaid Card was used much more frequently in the season of summer rather than in winter. The most popular spot for the youth was a little hole in the wall located at the end of a ghettoized shopping center on the corner of 20th and Virginia Street where the neighborhood grocery store named "Mitch's" at the time resided. There were no monopolies back then, so people didn't have restrictions on where they could do business. Anyone could rent out a spot to barter and sale, having little capital and armed with only a simple marketer's license to be up and running, and many people did. One such was a man known in the community as a drug dealing pedophile and murderer, the personified gangsta, and like most bad men of that era, he portrayed two faces in public. On the surface he lived differently in his own notch of the hood.

He set up a hangout for all the wayward teenage intermediates in the neighborhood; they could dance and he could get his perverted little kicks by holding sock hops and talent shows every Friday for the very best and most talented; we loved it! We all dressed in bell bottoms, silk shirts and Converse off-white canvas sneakers; conversely, all the girls dressed in their daisy dukes, miniskirts, pony tails or Afro Puffs. All were looking as fetching as could be, and turned the heads of all the boys for a quick glance of young female flesh moving so sexy on the dance floor. Of course there were those that were of the not so good looking crew on both sides of the isle, in which I and others effortlessly fell right into. But like the old saying goes, there's someone for everybody, and a girl by the name of Rachel Coach, a very tall and mannish looking female with her eye on yours truly. Rachel told everyone, including the girl I fancied, that I was her man, not that I was too hot or too shallow to be seen in her presence, but my heart belonged to another, and I didn't appreciate Rachel's constant obsession with me.

She was a very big girl, not in the fat sense, but tall, and muscular stature, with a face full of acne, and a complexion that mirrored midnight. In those days, although average in appearance, I viewed myself as hunk, and acted as such, paying her no attention at all, in turn pissing her off, causing her to lash out verbally, ultimately calling me all sorts of names not fit for repeating. My retaliation was swift being that I had suffered many years of ridicule from the somewhat warped and demented affection perpetrated by Pookey and Chunky.

I had become somewhat of a master at playing the dozens, lighting into her from all sides of the literary spectrum, fatally wounding her self-esteem in front of all our peers while sending her running out of the club in tears, but it was just the beginning of our brief but very harmful encounters.

She just couldn't leave well enough alone, adamant on retribution and listing to her meddling little two cent friends, she became physical and ripped to shreds my favorite silk shirt, running away yelling out:

"YO MA'MA!" Stunned and in shock, with mouth wide opened, all I could do was look down at my ripped shirt in total amazement at what she had done. I looked up at my then best friend Raymond and said, "What the fuck!" He replied, "Man you gone let that bitch get away with that?" Hesitating for a moment, I contemplated on what I should do. Seeing that she had run off into the distance towards her home, I quickly picked up a mid-size rock and threw it at her. I wasn't aiming the rock at her or trying to hurt her at all, but something was in control of the matter rocketing from my hand because the rock behaved as if an invisible force had taken control of its trajectory. It targeted Rachel with deadly precision, like a self-guiding missile launched from an underground silo, and hit her in the head right above her left eye. I could see even from that distance a huge lump rise over her eye. The distance was as far as a football field, and when the rock found its mark, the sound of the impact echoed back to where Raymond and I were standing—"POW!" then we heard a loud scream.

I could see her grab her eye; she then picked up two handful of rocks and ran directly at me full speed. "Oh, shit here she comes man…" With no emotion nor thought, I could anticipate her every move, knowing she would hold back from throwing the rocks until she was up close. I smoothly turned to Raymond and said, "Watch this!" I ducked down right as she began to throw her two handful of rocks toward my face. I quickly came up after her unsuccessful throw and upper cut her right in the mouth—"POW!" A big "AHHH" came out of Raymond's mouth, and with the speed of lightening, she dashed toward her home screaming bloody hell, as if I had killed her. Knowing I was in trouble, I headed back home, saying nothing to Raymond, walking as quickly as I could. I said nothing to anyone as I ran into the house, walking quickly past my mother. Mom was watching her stories and didn't even notice my torn shirt, for she was glued to the television. I walked to my bedroom and wondered if I had escaped Rachel's vengeance, but as luck had it, my destiny was sealed and I knew it.

Ten minutes passed and I could hear outside my bedroom window a crowd of children forming, yelling back to another crowd, forming around my foe's family, saying, "… he lives right here." Looking out the window, I could see the entire neighborhood walking towards my mother's back door, and as the crowd grew, I heard a knock on the door. Mom answered with all the kids yelling,"… look at what P did!" Mom shouted: "Oh, my God… What has he done! PEE! Bring yo ass here right now! Why did you do that!?" I didn't know the damage I had caused Rachel, but as I looked up at her, I could see the real force that my two blows caused. Her face was swollen beyond recognition and it looked like a big black Kaiser Roll. I asked myself, "How could that be I only hit her twice… Once with a rock and then an upper cut and it did all that?"

I couldn't believe it, and when my mother asked me why I did that, I responded smug and arrogant, adding insult to injury saying, "She was talking all that yang!" My mother popped me right in the mouth in front of the entire neighborhood and promised Rachel's mother that I would surely pay the price for my actions. Mom closed the door and began pouncing my ass with a vengeance. Sucking it up, I cried for only a moment, saying to myself, "Well, it wasn't as bad as Rachel looked..." I couldn't have done all that to her face! Needless to say, that was the last encounter Rachel and I would have, for we stayed away from each other, even in the hallways at school, and turned in opposite directions whenever we would happen to cross each other's paths.

The long awaited last day of school had finally come and gone. Summer break was like Kryptonite to parents, but meant freedom and peace of mind for wayward children, just as it does for the youth of today. The end of school meant relief from a jail sentence of getting up at the crack of dawn, and rising early for morning multitasking, like cooking and clothing younger siblings while trying to catch a glimpse of our favorite early morning cartoons, as we prepared to gobble down the last morsel of lumpy oatmeal or grits for breakfast before we headed out to catch the last school bus. We didn't have to rush to get dressed and out the door to barely make the already late school bus, and it was the end of malicious verbal teasing from fellow peers that tortured the meek at heart and others short of material means. It meant the end of ridicule and embarrassment from the popular kids as well. The endless smug comments on out dated shoes or clothing students wear were no longer relevant, and the suffering of Mrs. Black, the meanest math teacher ever, had passed. Her constant drilling was over, alongside her precious weekly lessons she undoubtedly spent all of her time preparing. Finally, it meant amnesty for the kids with behavioral problems, the trouble makers with dispositions like that of my brother/cousins, Chunky and Pookey, who were always looking for attention. Back in those days, when students behaved badly, they weren't suspended (otherwise known as a free pass to stay home from school), but they were physically hit or paddled.

The paddle I recall the principal using was a big wooden one with holes that sucked your ass up in it like suction cups whenever you took a lick. Responsibility had ended, well at least for two and a half months it had ended, and time was on my side.

Laziness was my main concern, sleeping in past ten o'clock, staying up as late as I could, and without supervision of course, forcing myself to stay awake long enough to catch "The Creature Feature Show" which aired after midnight.

I often tried to force myself to stay awake and listen to "The Wolf Man Jack Show" on the radio, and we never missed our favorite programs such as: "American Band Stand" and "Soul Train." Nightly roaming around the hood became a pastime on "Carolina Street" and it was grand I must say, but summer time on "Rhode Island Street" was spectacular for all that lived there.

Rhode Island was the name of the street on which my grandmother lived. It was a very quaint and a peaceful slice of paradise located in "Glen Park," further inland, not quite a suburb, but on the out skirts of Gary near Marysville, Indiana, which in those days was predominately white. On my Grandma's block, most of the residents were of color, and just like Carolina Street, everyone knew one another and most were very friendly, hardworking Midwesterners. It was my home away from home. The streets were full of the most fruitful trees one could find, and most fruits and vegetables could be named on site: pear, apple, cherry, crabapple and mulberry bushes were in abundance, and in most of the resident's backyards, one could find a lush garden filled with the biggest cucumbers, not seen since then. I remember seeing all types of home-grown vegetables such as: huge tomatoes, long stocks of corn, greens of every sort, lettuce, onions and okra. Everyone took very good care of their landscape, though small and humble, it was as if we lived in paradise, and during that particular summer, I would spend most of school break there. I was my Grandma's favorite grandson and she openly showed it, but don't get me wrong, being the favorite, meant doing hard work for the old bird. I helped in the garden daily, canning and pickling fruits and vegetables, and cleaning the house and yard was essential.

Chores had to be completed before I hit the streets. Grandma taught me how to cook, bake and preserve, and though I didn't appreciated it then, I do now. She taught skills of survival that aren't taught today and infused me with knowledge which is long lost to today's society. As I worked hard in the morning light trying to get done before the noon heat, she would say, "You're gone to thank me some day; you'll never need a woman to do anything for you." She was absolutely right and though she is now deceased, I say, "Thank you Grandma!" Grandma was the best; not only did I learn to live self-sufficiently, I also got to see and spend time with my favorite uncle, the Wascally Wabbott, the youngest of my mother's siblings, Mr. Leo Lee Abbott.

We were only six years apart, though he acted like he was an adult and treated me and my cousins as if we were his personal slaves, but we didn't mind because Uncle Leo was the coolest uncle we brats could have. Furthermore, he was a very good looking young chap, and all the pretty young girls competed to be by his side, for they would ask to braid his hair or do anything he suggested, all to spend the day with the "famous" Wascally Wabbott. We, the impressionable young nephews of the handsome bold Wascally Wabbott thought we were on top of the world, and my summer was about to get even more enjoyable.

After months of separation, Pookey and Chunky had just arrived and it was great to see them both once again. The terrible trio was back together, but so were the other snot-nose brats belonging to Grandma's children. The unforgettable appearance of another first cousin, the sweet Prezon Shelton, who was only a couple of years younger than us, had arrived. He was a snot- nosed little tattletale that informed our mothers of our unruly activities any time he witnessed us in the act, but more than anything he wanted to be part of the pit bull pack, but the three of us did not want to include Prezon; after all, he wasn't a part of our trio and his mom wasn't nice or friendly to us, which was understandable because of our belligerent behavior. We had no remorse for Prezon, so he became very spiteful and vindictive and always spied on us and told on us whenever we did something wrong. Whenever we would go on our little adventures or stir up some ruckus, Prezon would always be lurking in the bushes, running back to his mother (like a little baby) to inform the enemies, our parents, spilling the beans about our little escapades. Prezon never wavered in his pursuit to spy on us and gather Intel, for he was always on guard and ready to burn us all indiscriminately.

One hot summer day, I caught him following us and made the other two aware of his covert activities, so from that day forward, Prezon was banned for life not to be one of the pack, but as all spy stories go, the better we got at eluding him, the better he got at spying on us. The day went smoothly and we all ended for the night, and hatched a plan to rise earlier than the pesky Prezon. We were ready to leave the house before he even thought about waking, but to our surprise, we awoke to Prezon ready to tag along with gear in hand saying, "Yawl ain't gone leave me... I'm going!" Surprised and disappointed, we looked at one another without responding to his reply and rushed out the back door half-dressed while not looking back. We were gone and didn't give him time to react, but without fail, he was on task and followed us as quickly as he could.

The three of us stayed the course and lost Prezon after the first few minutes. With empty bags in hand, we started looting the neighborhood gardens and fruit trees, collecting the means for our daily wage, ready to sell in front of an old run down Texaco gas station on Broadway's street corner. We were soliciting every pedestrian or cars stopping at the red light on the corner, and it was very profitable. Happily, we made more than enough money needed for the fireworks we planned to buy for the Fourth of July. The next day we did the same routine: walking around at the crack of dawn, and sneaking past Grandma's bedroom as quietly as we could while making sure not to disturb King, the family dog, who was sleeping on the basement floor near the back door. We quietly looked around for any sign of Prezon and sure enough, we found him on our coat-tails once again.

Pookey, Chunky and I couldn't take it any longer, and had to do something to get that tenacious little nigga off our backs! Short from jacking him up, mainly out of fear of Grandma's wrath, we couldn't beat him up, so we were at a loss. The day was winding down and so were we. While settling down in an ally in back of Grandma's house, dangling from a pear tree throwing down pears for sale, and complaining about Prezon's presence, the following day we conspired for a solution while throwing rocks at him, keeping him at a distance so as not to hear our ruse. We argued for at least an hour without any compromise or solution short from doing bodily harm, in which Pookey and Chunky had no problem committing. Mentally exhausted, we headed back towards the house steadily throwing rocks and yelling, "Get yo tattle telling ass away from us!" Then without fail, a voice came into my head saying: "Call him over, be nice, call him over; tell him he could join in with you; be nice." Not to alarm Pookey and Chunky, I said, "Watch this," and proceeded to do as the voice instructed. Leery of our intension, he hesitated for some time, but came over nonetheless. Soothing his fears, I calmly enticed him saying, "A Pre... we tired of you following us, so if you want to be with us, you got to do some things first." I could see the light of hope in the impossible shine from his little chocolate face, for the possibility of finally fitting in was all he sought and with a big great smile he asked, "What do you want me to do?"

We had him carry our bags of fruit, help out our customers and collect the money, ultimately having him do all the work for that day. He didn't mind and we were fine with it, for our feelings of hatred towards him were starting to ease because the day went very well. As we finished and headed home, the voice entered my head once more saying, "Tell Prezon he has one more task to perform before he's one of us…tell him to go inside the house and get a hanger." Without understanding or will, I listened to the voice, and without conscience, I felt compelled to heed the instructions dictated; furthermore, it was as if Prezon himself was under the control of some unseen force. It was as if we both were under a dangerous spell! I told him to put the hanger around his neck and without protest, he complied. Secondly, I told him to climb the big oak tree in front of Grandma's house and hang the hook on the branch above him, and he did. Finally, I told him to jump and sure enough, he complied. Thinking the branch would break, I was stunned to see it hold, and within seconds, his eyes were bulging out of his head, and he began twitching like someone hanging from the end of a rope.

In shock, we all just stood in amazement, watching him slowly die from self-inflicted asphyxiation. Ironically, Prezon's mother, my evil Aunt Katherine, was walking out the front door right when he was about to lose consciousness: "OH!—MY GOD!—PREZON! —BABY!" She ran franticly up towards the big oak tree and grabbed a hold of his dangling feet and pushed him up so he could catch his breath. Coughing and crying he began screaming, "They made me do it!" Hearing all the commotion, everyone came out of the house to lend a hand, and take him down out of the tree while Pookey, Chunky and I just stood there in utter shock watching. The hanger was stubborn, for it wouldn't let loose! It was one of those old sturdy wooden hangers with the thick metal hook attached. It took all the adult's efforts to pry Prezon down out of the tree. Finally, by sawing and breaking the branch free from the tree, they were able to save his life, and with a burning look of hatred, his mother looked at the three that doomed her son. She came toward us, and fearing her wrath, we took off running with her in quick pursuit. "P told him to do it!" yelled Chunky and Pookey in unison as they were in full retreat with Aunt Katherine on their coat-tails. With fire in her eyes, she stopped in her tracks and turned towards me while out of breath from chasing Pookey and Chunky. She started walking in my direction giving me the evil eye as she ominously walked my way, but in her exhausted haste, she gave me time to state my case with all the grown-ups standing in front of Grandma's house. With a smile on my face, I yelled to Kat, "No one made him do anything; he was stupid enough to do it himself!" With that said, no one would allow her to put her hands on me, but anger still burned in her face. Still, she uttered words of disgust and she showed hatred towards us all. She quickly gathered her two children, Prezon and Tasha, while packing her bags, vowing never again to allow her children to play or even be around us ever! They left that day, letting all pleas of reason fall on deaf ears, and it made our day! Prezon, the runt of the house, was finally gone for good.

The much needed funds for the fourth of July had taken precedent, so no thought of Prezon's well-being ever came to mind, nor did the frantic fear in his mother's face ever enter our thoughts. Though malice towards my cousin was not in our hearts, selfishness held sway over our actions with no regret, allowing its dark power to override compassion over his plight. I silently thought, "Oh, well, what's done is done" and off to the market we went, and before sun set, we had earned enough money to buy all we wanted for fireworks. Pookey and Chunky were as newborn babes suckling their mother's nipple for the first time. Since they never got to enjoy any holiday at home, they took control of most of the booty, hording all they could, but I didn't mind, knowing I had much more money than they, for I already saved money for the occasion.

It was two days until the fourth of July, and all the neighborhood kids were already firing off their fire crackers. Ready to go, we joined in, while breaking off into groups, we made war on each other as the day light faded away and stopped only to collect lightening bugs in jars for later fun. As children, time disappeared ever so quickly, and Independence Day was upon us. The smell of barbecue filled the air, along with Motown blasting out of everyone's front door; the hood was bumping, the food was jumping and all the kids were running about, and tuckered out physically. Male testosterone and hormones took over, and all the young bulls gathered in the front yard of the prettiest young girls on the block.

Four sisters held the prize of foxes and all the boys had their noses up their skirts. Their house was located on the corner of the street and all the boys congregated at their house and showed off in front of the pretty young girls.

We dove into self-exploitation while popping wheelies and playing the dozens (using foul language about one's mother), goofing off and acting tough, none more so than Pookey. Loud and boisterous, he commanded attention, and pissed off all the rest, until a young good looking white boy with long blond hair entered the fray, captivating the young girls attention, and riding a brand new ten speed bike, taking away Pookey's unruly boast with a look and a smile at the young black girls sitting on their porch. "Blondie" acquired their attention with a "...hey there," stopping to talk with the girls he had met the day before while stopping all suitors in their tracks. Jealous and stained with pride, Pookey began ridiculing the young man only to get shut down by the blond boy's unwillingness to fall victim to silly ignorance shown by the much younger boy in the hood. Pookey was obviously shunned by Blondie's poise and well-mannered demeanor, yet he still continued to spew out his derogatory statements. Getting foul and playing the dozens was the only card up Pookey's sleeve, so he played it well, causing all the kids to laugh and mock Blondie, mostly out of Pookey's inadequate attempts to acquire the young girls' attention. Pookey pissed off Blondie to the point of the boy responding verbally, only to get shut down himself by a master of the dozens setting his trap. Not able to come back with any witty comments, Blondie became physical by pushing around the younger but wittier Pookey. Unafraid, Pookey got even more verbally dirty, pulling out the big guns and playing the "yo mama" cards, further infuriating Blondie, causing him to break out and chase after Pookey. Since Pookey was too fast for Blondie, Blondie pulled out a full pack of "Black Cat" fire crackers and lit them all, while throwing them on Pookey's back. "POOOW! POP! POP! POOW!" The lit pack rang out, accompanied by the screams of pain afflicted on Pookey's back.

Flames ignited the old dingy cotton t-shirt Pookey was wearing, while sounds of "OOOH's and AHHH's" came simultaneously from the crowd of neighborhood kids surrounding the young girls' front yard. "Ah Shit!" I yelled out and ran back to Grandma's house where I observed uncle Leo waxing his cherry red ten speed Schwinn.

I screamed, "Leo, Leo... some white boy just set Pookey on fire and threw a whole pack of fire crackers on his back... he on fire right now... The boy still there, over on the corner!" A surprising and shocking look came across Leo's face. Without hesitation, he threw down his waxing rag, hopped on his bike and headed toward the scene of the crime. I quickly followed behind as Leo peddled up the road and jumped off his Schwinn. While still in kinetic motion, Leo cold cocked the young blond boy from behind, striking him on the neck. Blondie tried to regain his balance and stand straight while being caught off guard by a much smaller but powerful young boy. When regaining his composure, Blondie realized it was a little wimp that just cold cocked him from out of nowhere, and without hesitation, Blondie put on his warrior face, mustered up his courage, balled up his fist, and charged at Leo. Not knowing Leo (The Wascally Wabbott) was a third degree black belt in "Tae Kwon Do" and other martial arts, Blondie was totally caught off guard when Leo executed a perfect 360 degree round house to the jaw, breaking his two front teeth, instantly putting him in shock, while blood flowed from his nose like a river. It was my first time seeing someone bloodied in brawl, though amazed at my Uncle Leo's performance, I felt total sorrow for the young man. Even though I didn't know him at all, it wasn't the person that caused me to feel, it was the sight of blood flowing from another human being that caused the emotion within me. Suddenly, I panicked and ran back to Grandma's crying uncontrollably, bursting through the front door spilling my guts out and speaking in a tearful voice saying, "Grandma, Grandma... This white boy set Pookey on fire! I told Leo, and Leo beat him up! Blood was everywhere; I didn't know Leo was gonna do that!" Tears were running down my cheeks while instantly bringing Grandma's wrath down on Leo. The minute Leo came back to the house, he was exiled from all social activities and grounded for two weeks, stuck in the house and salty, every look could kill! After showing my uncle the way to trouble, I ratted him out to Grandma, and he was pissed at me for the remainder of the weekend. But with so many grandkids around, his punishment did not last for long. Since I had money most of the time, Leo would hit me up for cash when his weed stash went dry. I gladly helped Leo refresh his supply of weed while quickly gaining back my favorite nephew status. When all the grandchildren returned home, I stayed at Grandma's the entire summer. It was as if I died and went to heaven. Leo was gone most of the time and I had the run of his bedroom, a Shackadelic, type of a room. Different colored fish nets hung from the ceiling, posters of the fantasy naked black and Hispanic women made of black velvet material glowed with a black light covering his south and west walls with a giant poster of Bruce Lee covering the wall in back of his head post. On the wall towards the east, a black velvet poster of a black panther covered the whole wall and no one could forget the strobe disco light that turned around and around while the music played the hits of the Seventies era late at night featuring "Wolfman Jack" on the radio. It was the bomb! I listened to Leo's late night correspondence with the beautiful Antoinette next door. Her bedroom window was right next to Leo's, so close it left room enough to jump in and out of, and it always caused an erection and a long lasting smile on the face of both Leo's and myself. It was a very happy time, but all was soon to come to an end; a month had passed, and summer break was winding down. The conversations of the day turned towards school clothes and supplies, and instead of hanging out at the public watering hole or kissing girls, the days were becoming a little cooler and the nights were arriving a little earlier. Dread of going home and back to school began to enter my mind. The last weekend before I would return to the Colored Doors arrived and everything that mattered in life changed. My morning started like every other morning, slow, lazy and nothing out of the ordinary, then there was a knock at the front door, it was Dennis, a lovable half-wit that lived across the street. He was about eighteen years of age but played with all the kids around my age, which were about eight or nine years of age, and we all liked him because it made us feel older somehow by hanging out with him: "Come on P lets go kick it!" Dennis yelled through the screen door. Bored with having nothing to do after harvesting a few ears of corn, I quickly replied, "Okay, here I come." A decision I would later regret. Though Dennis was much older, he was the very definition of follower, gullible, naïve, and willing to do anything. Tired of walking through the hood, climbing trees, and raiding backyard gardens, we decided to venture out of bounds. There grew a small wooded area at the end of my grandmother's block, where none of the kids dared to enter it, for there was no visible entry way, thorns and thistles grew all around the outer regions of the forest. But it so happened, I spotted a crack in the wall of thorny bushes in closing the forest of trees behind them. After a few pricks and pokes, we made it through, and what we saw was majestic. There stood a serene forest of oak trees as far as the eye could see, untouched by human hands, for it was as if we stepped back in time, and the noise of everyday life seemed to fade away inside that realm that was not so far away. As we walked through the trees, a spirit of adventure descended upon us, and I felt as if we were US soldiers trekking through the jungles of North Vietnam searching for the V.C. (Vietnam Communists). Ready to annihilate the enemy, low and behold, tucked in a back pocket, was a book of matches left over from the fourth of July. Without thought, I transformed the book of matches into an arsenal of GI weapons, striking and hurling them like napalm missiles launched from a rocket launcher at the V.C enemy, namely Dennis. I ran aimlessly through the many trees striking and throwing matches, making the sounds of war. Then suddenly, Dennis pulled out his arsenal of four boxes of matches in which he shared so as to start our little war on equal ground. Fully armed, we set out to wage our own Vietnam War while running aimlessly, hurling lit matches carelessly at one another, but not watching the ground beneath our feet. Caught up in the moment and the serenity of the trees, both of us became lost in our imaginations, and paid no attention to the inferno we had just ignited all around us. Since the woods were undisturbed by humans for so many years, the dead foliage had accumulated greatly on the floor of the forest, and the summer heat had dried the foliage completely sparking brush fires. With every thrown match, we were surrounded by fire not realizing it. So busy being caught up in our fantasy, we unsuspectingly set our fate as a terrifying and dangerous fire began to engulf us. As we played in the midst of true devastation, and as I struck my last match, hurling it at Dennis, realization opened my eyes to what we had done. "Dennis! Look! What have we done?!" I yelled as the sound of the inferno registered in my ears. Flames as high as a six story building reaching to the very top of some of the majestic trees surrounded us on all fronts, and fear began to overtake our reasoning. Dennis just stood there in total amazement with his tongue hanging out as I yelled, "... we got to go; Dennis! Dennis! We got to get out of here now!" Desperately looking all around, I saw no visible way out. We had set fires in every direction, and amazement turned to frantic desperation. Dropping to his knees, Dennis began praying aloud. With no time to think, I grabbed his hand and ran aimlessly deeper into the woods. Clouds of smoke started to descend downwards, obscuring our vision and hindering our breathing, and fear was turning into terror. We ran as fast as we could and with no way out, we felt as if the end was drawing near! "We're going to die! We're going to die!" Over and over, Dennis kept yelling that phrase in between gasps for air as we ran deeper into the fiery forest. The inferno engulfed our surroundings as we ran in every direction. There really was no way out, and we were about to die; it was now an accurate statement. The smoke was choking us and the heat was becoming unbearable. Lower and lower we kept to the ground, stopping to catch our breath as much as possible. Dennis would stop and fall to the ground moaning, "God help us," giving up all hope of survival, and I was starting to feel the same. The feeling of hopelessness covered our very being bringing panic and despair, for it felt as if my head was about to explode. Then suddenly, a calm came over me, and fear vanished from my soul. The sound of the raging fire began to fade and my mind felt as if it was in a state of perfect peace and security as I stood there looking at Dennis huddled down with his head between his knees. Then a voice said, "You're not going to die; you cannot die; you will find your way out." Without hesitation or negative thought, I placed my hand on Dennis's shoulder, and he silently looked up at me and grabbed onto my arm. While picking himself up with tears in his eyes, I said, "Let's get out of here and smiled." A look of disbelief and wonderment came over his face and we began walking through the fire, not knowing our fate we kept moving forward. We could hear helicopters circling around in the air, but we could not see through the smoke, so we kept walking forward and came to an end of the trees to another wall of thorns and thistles, but this time we were not afraid to get poked and prodded, and we quickly began pulling loose the vines.

Bleeding from the tips of our fingers, with scratches to our elbows, we finally could see the sunset fading behind an open field that led to the main road leading into Glenn Park. While being trapped behind another vined wall of bushes, on the other side of the inferno raging in back of us, Dennis and I scratched and tore through the vines to freedom, only to land in a field of sticker bugs. As we ran through the field without care of the magnetic plants gravitating to every bit of clothing from the waist down, only jubilation filled our thoughts, for we knew we were safe at last. As we reached the road home, we stopped running, catching our breath kneeling down, so as to pick off the many sticker bugs clinging to our pants; however, we could only laugh at one another. We looked back at the inferno blazing behind the wall of vines and bushes as we walked back towards Rhode Island Street, back to the safety of our respective

EDGAR FRENCH, JR.

homes. We saw the amber glow of the forest burning out of control with helicopters flying overhead and dumping water on the inferno. We walked in silence as we took the long way home, knowing we were the cause of the raging doom that crept closer and closer to the very homes behind the wall of thorns separating the forest from the residential area and the community of which we were a part. As we approached our street, we could see all the neighbors out and about watching the flames creep ever so close to their houses, and silently watched neighbors water down their homes in fear of the ambers falling from the flaming tree tops. With a final nod, Dennis walked toward his home, and I toward Grandma's, and we never uttered a word to one another, ever again.

As I walked through the front door, I saw my grandmother franticly watching the local news that was reporting on the very fire we set and knowing she would ask questions. I had plenty of time to think up an excuse from the long walk back home and was ready for any inquiry. "P! Look what's happening; I bet you some bad ass kids set the woods on fire; look baby see that shit! And if they don't stop the blaze it's going to reach our homes babe; you were out there baby; you see who did this shit?" "No ma'am." "I was looking for you babe; where were you?" "I was at the school playing baseball and saw the flames all the way over there and ran back home." "That's good baby. You're safe for the moment! If those flames don't get too close." For the next few hours, the entire neighborhood stood still as the flames threatened their homes, but the winds began to blow towards the flames, helping the firefighters beat back the fire, ultimately saving the neighborhood. Hearing all the accusations floating in the air, I knew no one had a clue, yet I still felt ashamed with the fear of being exposed. Knowing Dennis would say nothing, I stayed out of sight for the next few days, only venturing outside into the backyard. People in the hood would talk for days after that, but they still had no clue. Happy no harm came from our folly, I never spoke a word or showed any sense of guilt whenever the conversation turned towards the fire that almost destroyed the neighborhood, but little did I know the worst was yet to come...

CHAPTER X
The End Game

{Loki and his underlings flying over the Midwestern region}

Loki: Can you see? Can you see? It is the little one; the little seedling we would frighten in the night! There! Down there in the woods below; the little one that saw us in battle. A battle waged outside this dimension, and within elements unseen to their eyes.

Minion 1: But yet he has seen in the darkest of night. Look how he has grown!

{Loki calls out to one of the underlings in his entourage}

Minion 2: Full of energy and life; it has been almost a decade since his observation of our battle with the Elohim's guard in this region.

Loki: It was as one moment in time for the being below—but for us being immortal the veil should not have been pierced with life spans of a mayfly; that monkey should not have sight, and will he be able to see us once more in this dimension?

Minion 1: I think not; it was out of innocence he saw, just as many others in the innocence of childhood. There is nothing special of this human, for he is just another lost soul, and my eye has been locked on his development since we've found him out and was made aware. I've seen no apprehension or exception in his willingness to embrace temptations of the flesh because he's like all others under our influence on this planet; in fact, he's well on his way toward darkness and death.

Loki: Is he the one our master seeks, and shall he prove to be of like mind or of our demise? Our power of persuasion has been of little use to us, but he has responded well under pressure, and he is easily coerced towards pleasure and mayhem, taught in all decadence, so it is most urgently a waste of time. I could be of greater use to our lord, not here with you!

Minion 2: Sin has done its job, for he is of the blind, and willingly hurts others, even now in his youth, where innocence of a child may work its sway on the human conscience. I have witnessed his willingness to sin, having no regard towards others among his peers or family, following closely in his biological father's footsteps without warning, for it is surely a waste; don't you just love sin in its truest form?!

Loki: Let us repay him for our loss suffered here in his presence; let us delight in his destruction; if he is one of ours or if one of light, his demise shall benefit our cause, and if he is of light and is the one, he will never be able to fulfill his mandate, and we would have rid ourselves of certain calamity in his becoming a man. There is no loss in our cause, be it man's doom our only desire; therefore, let us speak to the youngling and invade his mind's eye, so let us go forth and arouse his sinful nature.

Minion 1: Yes let us put the work of sinful enticement to our account, and let the harmful thoughts of war be of his amusement, for man only knows death, and in his youth he yearns for its power of dominion over one another. See the wind; see the air; see your wildest dreams come true! Hear the words we speak, young human.

Loki: Hear the passion of fear in war. Put your hands to work! Let mayhem show you the way of your desire, and check your pockets and find your destiny; feel the power, and have fun like not felt before. No harm shall come to you, for no one shall ever know because it's only you and he fuels destruction having fun. Don't think, just do! Let the day go forward in amusement; frolic in the woods young human; deeper in you must go; run freely through the trees, and pay no mind to direction.

Minion 2: Be lost in exuberant jest, and feel freedom's wings amongst your feet! "Yes that's it; have no fear of the unknown, ignite the light; ignite your missile's flight! Destroy your enemies at all cost, and have fun in your play of no mercy in war, for your future if any shall be thy fate! Yes, that's it, play without regard of life, innocence in ignorance will seal your fate. Be coherent of none, but hear the words of a whisper in your demise; child of man, you must ultimately hear distraction, no reason of thought, jubilant in destruction is where your headed, thus my joy is in the fiery air you now create!

Minion 1: Hear me human, and realize nothing in play; see pleasure in this wooded realm you unwittingly purified in flame, child of man, for I shall delight in your destruction this day and rid myself of your presence.

{Enter Raphael and his soldiers of light}

Raphael: Beware of malicious lust depriving you of your wit; look above to the north, for cometh the Nephillum. With their regiment aimed in our direction; are they here for the boy?

Soldier of Light 1: Are they coming in pursuit? I see no force of ours in the area that justifies a full regiment, for it is us they seek, and it is because of the boy they are here; just as well, the human has begun his own demise and is on his way to meet his maker!

Soldier of Light 2: No son of Elohim may physically intervene in this realm on man's behalf without divine mandate or for knowledge of such deed, and right when all was oh so well with lust nearly satisfied. Let the little ones be consumed just a moment longer, and let eyes gaze witness to their fate, for they approach rapidly as if a treasure shall be lost, so let us flea in stealth!

{A beam of light shines in the midst of despair}

Soldier 3: We must not let that light be extinguished, look! Look down in the woods, not one but two lights are aglow within the midst of certain death, caught by ravenous flames assured to consume, and set by their own hands. This travesty has overwhelmed them both with help that's surely hidden from sight; powerfully cunning is the deception employed on the human children; therefore, guidance must be given to ensure their survival; one if not both may be our brethren born to man in the darkness that must come to pass!

Raphael: No doubt Baal's defenses here on Earth are well fortified. For I detect no presence of darkness afoot; yes it is he, it must be, for such a deception and destructive ruse for two; may one be he in which we are to protect from this day.

Soldier 1: Open your eyes young seed; see your fate; see what befalls you; take care not to fall. Let fear be gone from your sight, and let the wind guide you to safety, for your life lies in your own hands this day. Calm may be in your spirit, little one, and you will see your way through, for the sons of light are with thee!

Raphael: We must find and safeguard all our Earthly brethren born to man, for that is our purpose, and the reason we are here dwelling in this realm. Baal's legions have attacked all who have been found born with the mark of light, and our mission is to protect all that remain; father has given us the sight not for salvage but for strength; let his power flow from within and give refuge to all who are willing to see and seek, so they shall find.

Soldier 2: Solace is not yet ours, for it is war we are engaged in my brethren, and this war shall have its end here in this realm for all creation to witness and choose. Darkness is surely here, so use all that is in our disposal to find the un-wholly spirits who have played a role in doing this malicious act; let not one escape responsibility or judgment in this, and do not advance them in war, rather see where they are going and inform us where they may reside and go forth in pursuit!

Soldier 3: Here we reside among the humans, unseen and unaware of our presence. We fight on their behalf, for the sake of goodness and what is just, yet most live day to day oblivious to our existence. So many live their lives in the frivolous pursuit of righteousness, praying to their many gods for help, yet seeing no hope because of pain and strife inflicted by Baal's minions and sons of darkness. The mayhem Baal's legions have brought upon this planet and its inhabitance has devastated man's spirit, thus many have put faith in their fellow man and have forgotten the Elohim's guidance in matters of the spirit, looking towards the heavens as if some better existence awaits off this Earthly planet. If I could, I would inform them of the truths of their being and of the universal trials in the heavens in which they play a significant part.

Raphael: Receive the pain and warfare we have seen on their behalf, thus ripping our beloved home apart, seeing just not the woes of sorrow throughout space and the cosmos but right here, right beside them all. In time they will see and know of our realm and our existence so as to choose their side in this god forsaken war. The day is close at hand, but I'm afraid, afraid of the choices they will make on account of the sons of darkness, for their hearts are filled with indifference and hatred for one another, thus sorrow resides deep within the down trodden.

Soldier 2: Baal has corrupted the youth in the ancient teachings of Sodom, leaving no room for innocence to combat wickedness' grasp, thus man has lost his way, slipping into darkness ever so much with every generation. The spirit of righteousness, the love of goodness and truth, they have forsaken for the love of one's self. Most cannot feel true love of life anymore.

Soldier 1: Love has become just a word that fools use in promiscuous vanity, shallow in their empty pursuit of pleasure. Hope! Hope must be restored to the masses, to those who have chosen the side of life everlasting, the side of our father and theirs.

Soldier 2: Hope? Hope in what? Baal's lie has blinded the whole hive of the truth concerning father's will and purpose involving us all, befouled with untruth and falsehood, believing in ghosts and dead spirits of loved ones long passed. The allotted time has come, for their eyes shall be open to the unseen things forevermore. Let us not forget our mission at hand, for the sake of revealing our purpose is clear, and what is, must take place.

Raphael: Do not lose focus! Our brethren born to man is in need of our guidance and protection, and their survival is paramount, so we must be watchful of all forces of deceit residing here on the third and in the fourth dimensional planes. Failure is not an option; however, this world is under his control, yet father will not allow Baal to destroy his creation, this planet, mankind, or us for that matter. For our lives are at risk, just as that of the humans, and we must choose as well, and many have chosen Baal in rebellion, thus we fight our own kind.

The summer's clock of mindless fun read a quarter to midnight; summer break was winding down to a close, and only a couple of weeks remained, then I'd be back at good old 2222 Carolina Street. This brought an anxious feeling of eagerness, given the ever so great and heroic adventure Dennis and I had just brazenly escaped. I was beginning to miss the place, and I began to wonder about the fools living within the Colored Doors. I wondered what they were doing and what mischief I may have missed out on over the summer. Did Raymond finally catch the girl of his dreams or did he fail like always after giving everything to all the gals? "I'm too pretty for any of you niggas!" I can't recall her name, but I'll never forget her saucy attitude or her loveliness, and how much of a fool my best friend made of himself pursuing her. As I was relaxing in Grandma's front yard, enjoying summer's end, I looked over and saw the one and only, Uncle Leo, roll up on his nice and shiny new Schwinn.

"Hey P! What's up man; how you doing?" Never in life was Leo ever so willing to speak with one of his lowly runt nephews without some smart ass remark; I knew something was up. Knowing I was somewhat of a spoiled, self-centered selfish brat, that hoarded what little cash I could get my grimy little hands on, he knew I'd stashed money for rainy days when no other runt or close relative had any. I always kept my ice cream and candy supplies stocked, and he was desperate and in need of cash for the ever so popular weekend excursion out with the other hoodlums in the hood. While getting high and drunk off of Columbian Gold and Night Train and showing off for the hotties on the block, he tried to smooth talk his way into acquiring some lute out of me, but how do you swindle a swindler? "Whatever it is, Unc, the answer is no!"

I quickly replied without stutter or hesitation, brandishing a smile and a look of, I got you now, knowing it was my chance to extort whatever favor I was coveting from the giant at that time, which mostly consisted of spending time with him, getting on his last nerve and making his life a living hell all for my personal amusement.

I guess you could call it pay back for all the countless mornings I spent doing his shitty chores over the summer to gain his favor, or maybe it was retribution for suffering the demonstrative orders inflicted upon all wretched nephews in front of his many friends, for he would humiliate us all with his warped sense of humor and practical jokes.

It was my turn now, and groveling in front of his friends would be my ultimate goal, so patience would be required on my part.

Acting as if Leo were not there, I pulled the great lure from my pocket, which was a crisp new twenty dollar bill, and I dangled it like a big fat worm on a hook dangling from a fishing pole right before being cast into a river swarming with hungry catfish waiting to bite. After thirty minutes of seeing him disgustingly whine and beg, I finally made my request for granting such a favor: "I want you to get one of yo pretty ass gals to braid my hair tonight right after she does yours."

I previously over heard his late night phone calls to all his home boys planning their weekend itinerary, and if he wanted the funds, he would comply without question. Then I would have the time of my life hanging with the big boys and girls, spotting him twenty bucks only after he confirmed my hair braiding appointment with the best braider in the hood. I can't recall her name, but surely remembered her stunning hour class figure and long, silky ponytail. Fired up most of the day, I pondered over the awesome opportunity that awaited me and it had to be perfect. As the sunlight set on the large oak trees out front, I looked through all my best attire which consisted of torn Lee jeans and a purple fish net tank top. I stole a pair of my uncle's brand new tube socks in order to look my best for the many older girls that would most definitely be in attendance. A cool breeze ran through the air as the sun faded and fireflies danced in the wind while I sat on Grandma's front staircase watching Leo and his friends anti up for the night ahead. Oh, my god here comes baby girl with comb, brush, beads and rubber bands in hand, brandishing a sweet smile saying; "…you ready little man?" "Yes Ma'am!" I replied, sitting still as she sat behind me, opening up her silky soft legs placing me in between them. I could smell the sweet aroma of coco butter and lavender lotion on her legs, telling myself please not now, don't get hard in front of everyone as I felt the blood swiftly flow to my lower region.

I kept my composure and tried not to smell her sweet ambrosia and as the pain accelerated from combing out naps, parting the hair on my scalp, scratching out dandruff, etc...., my thoughts soon changed to, please don't cry or yell out in front of all these girls. I played it cool, for I barely twitched in my seat and patiently endured the pain, but it felt as if my eyes wouldn't close after she was finished.

The braids were so tight but at last the job was complete, and I must say, I never looked so good.

The talent that resided in the hands of these young women could not be matched, intricate designs like no other adorned my head, and thus extending my arrogance and pride. The night was young, the girls were hot and the boys were having their fill of pot and alcohol, playing the jams of Wolf Man Jack on the car radio and just strait chillin'!

Ready for another run to the "L" store, they all loaded up into Prince's Malibu and bounced, leaving me by my lonesome which pissed me off. I went back in the house, stumping all the way and slamming the screen door behind me, but my goal was accomplished.

I was satisfied, "Oh, well, at least I have the Wascally Wabbott's bedroom all to myself." "Sweeet!" But within a few seconds, I could feel a presence, a force, and I could sense that something evil was watching me! Fear overcame me and I began to shake from head to toe! I could hear a voice in my head, "It's you he wants!" Nervous and afraid, I ran into Leo's closet and hid under piles of junk lying on the bottom of his closet floor. I could hear our dog King barking uncontrollably, scratching and gnarling at the door that separated the basement and back door leading into the kitchen. It was as if King could see that evil force or there was an intruder in the house. Then darkness surrounded me; all the lights shut off, and all the doors and windows slammed shut! I closed my eyes and prayed.

"Please my lord god, Jehovah, help me!" Three times I repeated the prayer, then silence. King stopped his meaningless rampage; the lights came back on, and the sound of my Grandma's voice filled the air. "P! P! You Okay Baby! What was that?" I replied, "I'm fine Granma!" I quickly appeared from under

EDGAR FRENCH, JR.

the crap on Leo's closet floor and ran out of his room and met Grandma in the hallway. The fear in Grandma's eyes was paralyzing, for all the doors were open except the door that King guarded and all the windows were open just as wide as we had left them. Grandma and I turned towards one another without saying a word, perplexed by what we heard and what we were seeing, knowing we heard all doors and windows slam shut! We also noticed that King had scratched and gnarled a hole the size of a bow dollar in the middle of the basement door! Stunned and speechless for a moment, we questioned what we both heard and saw which caused us to contemplate our sanity, then Grandma said: "It was a demon; a demon just walked through my house!"

Wasting no time, Grandma began dialing on her old rotary phone and called her church friends. Within minutes, two to three parishioners, including the pastor, were knocking on the front door. She explained the abnormal psychic phenomenon and got reassurance from the pastor and other church ladies, while I stood still and listened to their responses and remedies. They spoke of brandishing notions of blessing the house, and even called for an exorcism of the dog, King. As I stood there listening to their superstitious rants, a thought of, "It's all your fault" came to my mind. It was after me for some reason but I didn't understand or even know why or what had happened, yet indeed something unexplainable had just occurred. Never before did the visions I experienced ever materialize, or affect the physical plane, yet still the same, a very strong feeling of guilt coupled with an overwhelming sense of presence held me captive, and thoughts of old teachings began to flood into my brain. Stories of demons, spirits and angels existing all around came to mind, saying to myself, "It all must be true; it is true; it must be true, for it's the only explanation!"

The realization of my visions became verified in my mind's eye, and all spiritual teachings learned became not just real, but also very frightening. I remembered biblical stories concerning such occurrences in the past coming back with a vengeance, and examined my own feelings in comparison to those people of the past who may have had experienced the same phenomenon. But who was I to have been witness to such grand happenings, and what of my grandmother's fears of demon possession or worse? While listening to the religious rants of very old superstitious church goers, an overwhelming feeling of dread came over me.

The thought of my grandmother taking their advice made me feel sick to my stomach. I believed they would make the situation unsolvable and ultimately worse for the family, for they verbalized pointless rhetoric as if their words carried weight with the sublime universal engineer. They truly were not helping, and even though I was very young in my thoughts and knowledge of such things, I knew in my heart that at that moment, I would do well having faith and confidence in my own understanding of biblical teachings, rather than prescribe to what my young ears were hearing from the parishioners of my grandmother's church. I relied on what worked thousands of years ago.

Many ancient patriarchs mentioned in ancient texts and biblical stories of demonic possession used the name of god, not in vain, but in action. An hour had passed and my mom and Aunt Lucy arrived as the church ladies were about to leave. Full of concern over the supernatural phenomenon witnessed by my Grandma and self, they quickly and abruptly expressed their opinions concerning the matter which were not so favorable in light of the church methods, evoking religious dogma taught by the Christian sect they were attending at the time. In contrast, I used an ancient but solid method that consists of speaking the true name of god three times in prayer, thus asking for his divine protection and guidance, as well as assuring the removal and destruction of all objects, ornaments, idols, pictures and reading materials of any religious icons or deities within the house. Angrily, my grandmother refused to listen to the council of her children and invoked the name of Jesus Christ and of his blessed mother, "The Holy Mother Mary," ultimately putting her faith in her fellow church goers instead of her own flesh and blood. Silently, I listened to the arguments and accusations between the two sects of so-called Christians, two sects that had two very different belief structures and ideologies.

Finally, my distraught grandmother had enough of the arguing. Not wanting to hurt her standing within the church or demean her own children by siding with others, without saying a word, she walked out of the living room, entered her bedroom and closed the door. Although I was consumed by what had happened, I pretended to show little interest in the event while my aunt and mother conversed among themselves and were infuriated over my grandmother's unwillingness to give credence to their beliefs and solutions for cleansing the house. Unaware of the events that had just taken place, my Uncle Leo quietly walked into the house and appeared to be in a state of shock of his own; stunned and concerned about strange phenomenon occurring right outside the house around the same time as the events happening within the house. Leo began describing his own weird demonic event and shouted: "Earline, come here... Maaan you won't believe what just happened... I know I was doing wrong, drinking and shit, but we all saw it, felt it, and it hit us; it hit us; I swear it... Earline, it was a man, a wolf, or something, and it just walked right out in front of the car, Prince's car. He didn't have time to react because it came out of nowhere. Earline it was tall, more than six or seven feet, with red eyes, glowing red eyes...I bullshit you not... I lost my high... we were fucked up but we weren't that fucked up!"

There was no need to try to convince his sisters, for we all were in an abnormal frame of mind, yet fascinated. We stepped outside to witness the damage done to Prince's car and to interview Leo's friends who were still outside viewing the damage and discussing what they all had witnessed in disbelief. While we inspected the damage and looked for any clue of what hit the car, we noticed that there was no blood, flesh or clothing attached in association with the accident. While trying to understand and come to grips with their experience with the unknown, I silently walked around the scene of the unexplained car accident. I looked at the damage to Prince's front bumper while thinking to myself, "It must have been what came through the house," and as soon as my inaudible thought was completed, Leo spoke those same words and asked my mom, "Earline, you think it came from that direction?" Earline responded, "It could have been bro." Leo continued, "Did Ma'ma see what it was that came through?" Mom answered, "No, she said she saw nothing; it was as if a spirit came through the house, but had no physical form!" Leo shouted, "Well, we saw what hit us and it was scary and not human; it looked like a man but it wasn't... What did it want...? Why did it come here?" Then my mom and aunt began explaining their theory of what was taking place and why, but I knew it was because of me; it was after me. Something inside my mind and spirit told me it was after me, and I could feel it in my bones, yet I didn't know why or couldn't even comprehend the reasons surrounding the event, so I yelled out, "It wanted me! It was after me!"

Everyone turned towards me and began laughing and saying, "Yes! It wanted to eat yo bad ass up," ultimately making fun of the matter while trying to calm themselves down.

But I knew the evil spirit was after me, so I said nothing else. The next day, my mother and aunt were still badgering their mother over her staunch beliefs and the church's methods.

With no success of resolving the matter, they decided to leave out of the house to calm down and clear their heads and think of a new strategy to convince Grandma to see things their way. Knowing my strong-willed Grandma was not going to budge from her stance, I cleverly appealed to her soft hardheartedness towards her grandchildren and expressed my thoughts and fears of the events of last night and said, "Grandma, I think the demon was after me; I felt it coming before it came; something told me to hide, so I hid in Leo's closet and it came through the house. I know it wanted me, but no one believed me. Please listen to me; mama's right; you have to get rid of everything or it will be back for me; god said no idols, and you have idols Grandma!" Then I walked away as she said nothing.

Approximately an hour later, my mother and aunt returned to the house and saw the faded imprints of all Grandma's religious relics that once graced Grandma's wall now on the floor, for she'd removed everything, including candles and books. She placed them all in the middle of the living room floor and went back into her bedroom while slowly closing the door. With open mouths, my mother and Aunt Lucy walked inside and were totally perplexed at what they saw lying on the living room floor. My Aunt Lucy knocked on Grandma's bedroom door and slowly walked in and quietly inquired about the religious material that adorned my grandma's living room walls and counter tops for years and asked why they were lying in a pile in the middle of her living room floor. My Grandma responded, "Do what you gone do!" Closing my Grandma's bedroom door behind her, my aunt only said, "Come on girl, let's burn this shit!" The mood was sullen as the red and yellow ambers burned brightly through holes in the fully stuffed metal trash can with the religious idols that adorned the walls of my Grandma's home after so many years and within seconds, they quickly turned to ashes.

I stood silent watching my aunt, mother, Uncle Leo and his friends circle the fire discussing the night's events, hearing them all taking oaths not to speak of the remarkable and frightening supernatural encounters that took place. They listened to the warnings of demonic possession over taking anyone who doesn't understand the methods used by the spirit world to entrap unsuspecting victims, lectured by my mom and Aunt Lucy, while the rest drank wine and smoked bud. It was an unforgettable summer indeed, but not the end of my eye opening adventure, for the next day had its thrills as well. While walking to "King Subs," a small home style sandwich shop, not far from the Grandma's, Leo and I heard the sound of gun shots ring out loud. It was close in proximity to King Subs. The sound of tires peeling out was followed by the sound of a great crash, and in true spectator fashion, we quickly ran towards the sounds to see first-hand what had happened. Running to the scene, we made our way through the crowd of on lookers to see a purple 1972 LTD Mark III crashed into a gas pump of a closed down gas station.

The doors were wide open and the driver was lying on the street while a woman and a little girl were slumped down in the back seat. They were all dead! Blood dripped from the back seat to floor of the car; the sight was horrific but I felt no sympathy. It was as if I had no care in the world; I even stole the fresh pack of grapes that was on the seat next to the bodies of the young girl and woman. Leo and I continued on our errands and took the long way back through a field where Leo was harvesting a batch of his home grown weed. Knowing nothing about curing weed, I sat back and watched Leo dry out the plants in the oven and iron press some of the leaves to smoke. He was truly an amateur in his weed harvesting, and hid his stash from Grandma in the most obvious of places, but felt confident in my silence and let me help out. It was a miscalculation he would later regret, and a few days remained until it was time to go back home.

Filled with the memories of an unbelievable summer, I was ready to go home and relay my adventures to all my homies. My god! My life was bad ass, amazing and full of wondrous adventure, but little did I know that summer would be the last summer I would set foot in Grandma's house ever again. It would be the last time I would roam the neighborhood raiding backyard gardens and climbing fruit trees, or seeing the beautiful sisters down the way. It was the end of a dream of maybe even dating one in the near future. I thought I would grow up spending my summers enjoying the peace and tranquility of Grandma's forever, joining the football team and graduating with all my friends from the best school in Gary, "Roosevelt High," but it was not in the cards. In retrospect, I could see the significance of those events that plagued that fateful night, yet not know it would mark my life's journey, and at that point there was no looking or turning back from the dark road set forth in my trek down the rabbit hole. From that day forward, all my understanding of right and wrong, good and bad, holy and un-holy, pure and un-pure, clean and unclean, would be shaken to its foundation!

Loki   Belteshazzar

Loki: Once again you and I stand off in the midst of battle, over the ultimate fate of these feeble creatures! The light of darkness shines ever so great in the realm of mankind!

Belteshazzar: Your lord has done his job well.

Loki: How wonderful to see you my brother! So it is you who guards the youngster? Shall we reveal ourselves to the non-seeing, and give them a glimpse of what besieges them all?! What manner of cause brings your boastful rank to guard such a lowly creature? Belteshazzar! Who is he to you my once beloved brother, and what is he to your awful maker?!

Belteshazzar: Just as the manner of yours dear Loki; I'm charged with the protection of this being just as you are charged with his demise; I witnessed your attack on him and the simpleton in the forest; are you here to finish the fruitless work foiled not days ago, or should we awaken their fears of the unknown with brute force? Please my brother do not expose your hand so eagerly!

Loki: Hasn't enough bloodshed of our kind been spilled over this unfortunate disagreement?! Besides he belongs to us! A child of darkness from birth! I'm here to oversee his development and oversee in the education of his demise by his own hand. Not to bring his death about prematurely.

Belteshazzar: That in which you speak is not yet certain my once good friend. Although your lord's influence is great among men in this region. The power of free will still exists in the realm of mankind, Loki.

Loki: Please do not insult one that knows that in which you have no clue!

For true freedom of will does not exist in the universe what so ever!

This realm or the next. For your lord and god controls all that lives, and dictates all that moves! He exhorts his power on all realms, knowing all, and seeing all! What free will is there for any?! You delude yourself my naïve brother! Even now your Creator's drones and spies lurk in the atmosphere of this realm, searching out sons of light; you yourself carry his mark! With no free will of thought or self! Fools are you and your kind! Fools without choice; mindless puppets in the Creator's hands, doing whatever he wills, not your own! You know this is true my blind brother. For it is written, that Yahweh is the Alpha and the Omega. The beginning and the end! Knowing the outcome before its natural coming. Is this not true my brother?! Free Will! I laugh at such a ruse of thought...

Belteshazzar: I fight right now for the very defense of free will, in this realm and our own realm as well because of you and your lords' actions!

Loki: Nonetheless my brother, in the realm of mankind, we rule their fate! We have been here from the beginning. In the knowing of what is unseen. Free will is not free! How so if your own will is stifled as one strives to accomplish the will of another my pompous one?! Be it one of rule or grandeur; free will with limits does not constitute free will now does it my once beloved brother?!

Belteshazzar: Let us not resume this ancient argument my long lost brother; you're lost Loki! Your eyes have been shut closed with anger and evil rebellion against he who created you! You rebel against he who was once your father and Creator! Deceived in your lust for woman and fame! Having all creation at your disposal, along with life everlasting. Yet fell to darkness sway! Falling victim to beauty's snare, and sulking in fallen grace. Now in opposition we set our lines my once beloved brother! Can you not see what Baal's revolt has done?! Your mistake has taken your everlasting life my still beloved brother. Will you not repent within yourself, and face these facts posed long ago?! Will you continue your opposition to all creation?

Loki: It is my life lost?! Raising hands against all that is in this realm, and our own!

Belteshazzar: You know the outcome Loki; you know why we are here! Time has run out for you my wayward brother. For you and your lord alike. All those angels that follow and protect the youngster in the woods are in my charge, and protect him I shall do as well. What command or mischief you must do against the youngster, understand this my wayward brother; I'm here as well! Young is his mind and heart. For no man is bound by ignorance in life forever! Time has come for all things to come to light! For the Most High stands between your lord's influence with all on this planet, and his word rings in the ear of this one as well as your lord's deceptive lies. To this extent free will shall play its part!

Soon I returned back into the Colored Doors; I was somewhat happy to be back home, full of great stories, and feeling on top of the world. Going back to school was not so much of a concern after my great ordeal in the forest. It didn't seem so scary anymore, and in fact, I'd changed from the shy and timid ten year old young boy that emerged himself into solitude and instead, I ventured out of the apartment without my mother's eagerness to nudge me out the front door. Although still naïve and gullible of the world's darkest places, I've become more willing to engage in unscrupulous and illicit activities like smoking weed. Equipped with almost a quarter ounce of pure shitty homegrown marijuana, stolen from my Uncle Leo's stash, I isolated myself in my room and my mother thought nothing of it. I was known for my insistence on absolute privacy. Left to my own devices, I was free from any interruptions and with a pack of "Top Rolling Papers," I practiced my primitive skill at rolling joints. Rolling the no good weed into nice size joints, I took the illegal stash the very first day of school, and to my surprise, I racked up! I set out for school.

Bold and unafraid of the consequences that may occur from my foolishness and naïveté, without notion of wrong doing, I proceeded to try my luck in distribution within the main hallway of my elementary school the moment I stepped through the front doors which were literally posted in the middle of the main hallway that led to all the primary classrooms.

I was shocked to sell out within the first few hours; apparently, more kids in my age group knew more about weed than I did, and used marijuana more than I could imagine. Thanks to my mother's constant overseeing of my actions within and outside the house, I was somewhat shielded from the knowledge, and or access to most drugs and alcohol, although drug abuse was occurring everywhere. Living with a somewhat conservative thinking mother, our household was fully shielded from the knowledge of soliciting illegal drugs, and if it wasn't for my Uncle Leo's obvious cool factor, I wouldn't have had any clue that weed even existed.

In those days, even talking about such things were not permitted, let alone having access to such medical produces, and when I was ten years old, it was unheard of someone my age to even know what weed was, and not so prevalent or readily accessible to anyone of any age group in those days. Marijuana was not so prevalent and out in the open as it is today, and yet it was still illegal to carry or hold on one's person as it is today in some states, provided prescription or exemption. I was shocked to see so many children my age knowing and engaging in drug use. Trouble never entered my mind, and having a great feeling of success in my salesmen adventure, I thought of nothing else. All the same, I didn't care about my fellow-peer's wellbeing. I made my money very quickly and without care of consequence. However, I didn't anticipate the fact that the weed I was selling was home grown "headache" weed, and the kids I was supplying my bogus and ill cured product were avid weed smokers and knew the difference between good weed and bad weed, so this ultimately turned my obnoxious smile into a frown within an instance. Soon I was approached by some very pissed off weed head customers and given the riot act which lead to the inevitable or more precisely a fist fight, and somebody ratting me out to the hall monitor and I was sent to the principal's office ASAP. I stood in total fear as the principle explained my offense to the only one I did not want to disgrace nor disappoint, my mother.

I got suspended for a week and cried most of the way home because the thought of my mother being disappointed in me was punishment enough from the powers that be. Punishment from mother was quite a different story.

As I walked into the front door, my mother was waiting silently in her favorite chair and looked directly at the door as I walked through. She looked me in the eye, and said to me, "Sit down and listen P... all money has blood on it...you may not see it, but it's there...when you take time out of your life to hurt someone else in the pursuit of making it, you hurt yourself!" Then she preceded to beat my ass! Those words remained imprinted on my mind and heart, and I learned a great lesson that would follow me the rest of my life; making money or any profit at the detriment of your fellow man is not worth the cost, and having quick cash does not come without risk or consequence, and does not bid well on the ass. For these are the words of he that comes like a thief in the night; before Armageddon's tale comes bellowing down upon the land that once upon a time shined bright, let he who's tongue stretch out like a double-edged sword warn the children of light as well as those held captive in darkness might; be warned of his anger that may be poured out amongst all those that listen not to these words of insight. Shall it take one to shine light within the darkest night? Shall Yahweh's wrath be visited upon all alike?

Man shall not rule over man! So that selfishness and demon's lies be whispered within the ears of men in the night. For all ill root forth from that concept and fact, for now is the time that evil rulers men dread; for the kingdom of the Most High must appear upon the Earth, and the time of forgiveness has expired. Man shall be truly free from the theology of the fallen and demon alike! For with the power of free will those that rule over their fellow men fear not god, but those that do the wicked surely run; for they know you have the power to stop their tyranny and claim to rule with the roar of your unity of will in Yahweh's name! Follow no man's words be it written or spoken, for Yahweh's laws live within all humanity, and the time to let that fact shine is NOW!

CHAPTER XI

Princes and Principalities

Then the sun could be seen peeking through the clouds as the wind ran through the trees while Raymond and I were riding on our skateboards and practicing stupid tricks in an attempt to catch the attention of the pretty girls that frolic in the breeze. Sometimes Raymond's half-wit cousin, Quinton, would join us just to mess up our so-called practice on various moves, thus dampening all fun in the pursuit of perfection. We were all entranced in our activities in manipulating the skateboards when we found ourselves in the parking lot of a very old Roman Catholic Church. Quinton's dumb-ass decided to further trespass onto the church's property, and we opened a side door to the church and went inside. We figured no one would be inside the spooky grand old building since it looked vacant, and also because there were no cars in the parking lot.

We slowly turned the knob of the side door, and to our surprise, the door was unlocked. The three of us walked slowly in succession and made sure not to make any noises or sounds as we entered the main hall of the church.

Marveling at the many mosaic and stained glass windows adorning the massive structure, feeling confident no one was inside, we began running around unobstructed, making noise and defiling the sanctity and peacefulness of the old place of worship while laughing and talking very loudly. Then, suddenly... we heard a noise; a banging sound was coming from under the floors, and it was coming from the basement or cellar, directly under our feet! Startled, we didn't move a muscle! "Did you hear that?" asked Raymond... "SHHHHH! There's someone here; let's go before we get caught," said Quinton! Quickly heading back toward the side door, Raymond pointed to his right side saying, "Look, there is a flight of stairs heading down to the cellar." The noise became more pronounced, yet curiosity overwhelmed the urgency to leave the creepy building.

Without the stigma of fear, we crept down the staircase veering from the right of the side door in which we came that led to freedom. Every heartbeat intensified as we continued down the winding staircase into a very dark corridor below. Shaking in fear, Raymond and Quinton headed back up the staircase and refused to go any further as the darkness enveloped the view down, but I kept going forward and noticed a narrow wooden door at the end of the winding red brick wall. Then without warning, a voice rang out, "What are you doing?" startling me, causing me to run back towards the staircase, and up the stairs! Then out of the ominous shadows, a hand covered my nose and mouth, and within seconds, everything went black. I could feel my body being carried off in the darkness, then I felt nothing at all…

Fading in and out of consciousness, I could only see glimpses of men cloaked in red and black religious garb, then I faded back into the darkness. Having no cognitive recollection of events after my abduction, I found myself outside the old gothic building. Somewhat in a haze, I was out in front of the church wondering why it was dark outside, for it was only noon not a minute ago. Still in a daze, I walked around the building to see if Raymond and Quinton were still playing on their skateboards in the parking lot of the church, but I didn't find either of them. Now it was dark, the street lights were on, more than eight hours had passed in an instance and time had vanished! Something insidious happened to me inside that old, wicked and creepy church, but "WHAT?" I asked myself.

Confused and still in a daze, I slowly walked towards the back of the church to see if my friends were still there and I finally heard a friendly voice. It was Raymond: "P… hey man where you been all day?" I responded, "Where did you guys go…what happened in the church?" Raymond responded, "What do you mean what happened in the church?" I said, "Something happened to me inside that church; we never should have gone inside that fucked up place!" Raymond asked, "When did we go in that place P?" I replied, "We went inside this morning around noon!" Raymond continued, "Inside around noon? When did we go inside that church P? We didn't go in that church! What's wrong with you P? We've been waiting on you to come and practice with us all day! We've been practicing on the boards, waiting for you and you never showed up until now! You're losing it man!"

With all reverence, I knew we all ventured into the church together! I remembered interacting with them both the entire afternoon, but Raymond and Quinton could not recall ever seeing me the entire day, let alone being inside that historic yet creepy church building. "How could that be? We all went inside that creepy ass church! We all went inside!" In frustration, I yelled within my very being those exact words, but Raymond and his cousin were adamant about the events I recalled and said we never went inside and they never saw me the entire day. They must have forgotten, I said to myself but how? How could they totally forget my presence the entire day? How could they lose all memory of going inside the church when I could remember everything that happened up to the point of being grabbed from behind and blacking out? Not wanting to seem crazy, I didn't press the matter further or press the issue and I headed back home. Thinking maybe something was wrong with me, I said to myself, I must be losing my mind? What is going on?! First it was the demon terrorizing my grandmother and me by roaming through her home as if it was searching for something, and now this!

Over and over again I contemplated the reasoning behind all these odd yet mysterious events that were occurring within my life, and what they meant. Why were these strange things happening to me, and why me?

Something wasn't right with the world and I knew it! From that day forward, I began talking to my god as if I knew him, not in prayer but in question, using the so-called name of the Creator, "Jehovah." I began asking questions to find out answers to these strange events, in the hope of finding some understanding of the unseen, ultra-natural events, and after the church event, I questioned everything. "Is there a god? Why are these things happening? If there is a god, then there must be a devil!" My mind was swimming with ancient un-answered questions about the nature of our existence. I socially isolated myself from everyone and found myself unwilling to socialize with people outside my family, and even then, I shut myself off from my family as well for long periods of time. I was constantly in thought, and consumed with finding out the answers to these strange happenings and unseen things.

I dared not speak about what I was feeling or going through, especially after the last event at the church. People had begun whispering about my behavior and talking about what happened to me after Raymond made fun of my odd behavior after the missing time at the church. He demonized my uncommon, reserved demeanor to some of the girls prancing and strolling through the hood, and said I was "…out of it" and on some drug like PCP or something and made jokes about my accounts of being abducted within the church. He must have thought I was making it all up. But I wasn't; careful not to seem off the deep end, I just observed my surroundings and the people within my family circle very closely. While waiting on the next weird event to take place, time passed effortlessly, and the fall's wind showed its dimly lit face in the autumn leaves falling from the trees.

The weather had changed its summer clutch, and it was time for new shoes. The Wascally Wabbott began begging for cash at my mother's front door. "Earline, come on girl! I need money to take this girl out to night! Hook me up with twenty bucks big sis!" Mom softly responded, "We'll see when I'm finished doing what I got to do." Uncle Leo then kissed mom on her cheek before he pulled off on his Schwinn bicycle. Confident he would score the money he needed for the night's plan, knowing his favorite sister wouldn't fail him in his time of need, he headed back towards Glenn Park, popping wheelies all the way shouting, "Yes!" Now my chance to foil the Wabbott's plans were forming as he faded in the distance. The welfare check was in the mail and mom was going shopping for all our needs and getting ready for a night out on the town. Seeing the mood change to excitement when the fake funds entered her hands, my mind began to conspire against my uncle's plans. If I could convince her to let Leo take me to pick up shoes, I knew I would fuck up his day! I softly said, "Ma, if you let Leo take me to go get shoes, you can go out and I can see Grandma; you need a break anyway."

Responding to my manipulating suggestions as ordered, "You know what, you're right baby; come on boy, your daddy will be here soon." Finally, we were heading to Grandma's with a great big smile on my face and sabotage on my heart. I couldn't wait to see the look on Leo's face when he would find out that I was part of the package raining on his nightly plan, knowing there was no way in hell Leo would get the cash he needed without having me tag along, so I threw

　　　EDGAR FRENCH, JR.

a wrench in his plans and ultimately marked another notch in my black belt of sabotaging Leo's great night out.

I reached Grandma's in record time since my father and mother were not the best of friends at that time, and both were very eager to go their separate ways, both were rushing to part from each other in record speed, but I couldn't wait for the chance to go inside Grandma's and see the look on Leo's face once mom announced her stipulations in funding his destiny for that night.

Since my father was late picking up mother and me, everyone was on the move and paying little attention to their surroundings and just hearing tidbits of Leo's losing arguments for leaving me behind so he could go on his date appeased. Then I heard those magic words, "Alright Leo, do you want your money? P got the money... take him to get his shoes and he'll give you the twenty dollars you asked for." Leo shouted, "Come on now Earline!" Mom responded, "I need a break! Help me out! Take him; it's on the way. I don't want to hear your shit little nigga! All the money I give your high yellow ass! You bet not say shit!" If looks could kill, I would have been dead; it was as if fire burned in the eyes of my favorite uncle, and daggers shot out of his mouth when he spoke. "Come on mafucka! Let's go!" He grabbed me by the right arm and pinched me as we ran out the front door to catch the last bus going downtown, speaking under his breath all the way to the bus stop.

While on the bus, he spoke of his itinerary for the night, and demanded compliance in a very threating manor, as if his threats would fade my prowess. I soon showed him who was in command of the hour saying, "You know I got the money Leo; you might want to be a little bit nice to me if you got it in you. After I get my shoes, I might have more than twenty bucks left over so chill." In a soft but ominous tone, I exhibited a sense of mental competency, and after hearing that momentous spill, he quickly turned back into the charmer he was, describing the dimensions and loveliness of his future conquest. When we got on the bus that evening, the weather was spectacular, not a cloud in the sky; the sun was shining, the wind barely broke, and it was breezy. In fact, the weather was so fine that I didn't think to even bring a wind breaker, nor did the Wascally Wabbott, but as the wind began to pick up speed, Leo tried to quell our fears saying, "Don't worry P... it's a cool breeze...we can rough it out... no sweat!" The shoe store was our first stop, so I wouldn't whine up a storm. I picked up some wing tips for me, and some canvas Converse high tops for him. Then he asked, "Where's the extra ten bucks little nigga? Damn the winds picking up P... Let's hurry up and get to this bitch's house real quick P, and see if she got a jacket or something for you to wear." Thank god the girl lived less than four blocks from the shoe store located downtown, right off Broadway and 5th, where we started our little venture in the beginning, making it to the young tart's crib in record time while cursing the wind all the way there. We made it to the worn-down brick building with the wind blowing stronger with every step, yet still intact and time to spare. The Wabbott and I stopped inside the front corridor to warm up a bit before knocking on the young girl's door. Leo even had time to blaze up a joint before knocking. Giving me no time to warm up at all and settle down, Leo was ordering me up without let up and nonstop, thus we headed back out into the stormy weather, and in those days, anyone could go and see any movie without questions asked. There was no rating system as to what was seen or heard like that of today.

Once inside the young girl's home all was well and I was somewhat warmed up from the sudden change in weather, and equipped with a little jacket provided by the nice young girl the Wascally Wabbott was seeing. With smiling faces and no concerns, we headed back out into the biggest blizzard ever to hit the Midwest. We were without a clue, equipped only with summer windbreakers for shielding us from the unsuspecting massive blizzard that would decapitate the whole Midwest.

By the time we all reached the theater which was just a couple of blocks away, the weather became more hostile and was drastically changing by the moment. Snowflakes began to fall lightly but ever so quickly. We didn't mind the on-coming danger, on the contrary, we thought nothing of the weather as we shook off the flakes of snow while entering the "Historic Down Town Theater." The movie Leo described sounded like a winner to me and to his date, and because of the constant indoctrination of everything being Chinese, I loved Kung Fu movies! My uncle Leo was a massive martial arts enthusiast and so was I, thanks to his abusive practice and bombardment of ancient Chinese techniques on all his unsuspecting nephews.

I was happy to see the Grand Old Theater and was anxiously awaiting the opening show, thinking the movie would be like most Kung Fu flicks full of action. After the great review of two thumbs up by the Wascally Wabbott,

I just knew I was in for the time of my life and was emerged in darkness as the projector ran its reels. The street lights began to burn amongst the falling snow flakes, and everyone seemed to be headed our way, coming inside the theater to enjoy their weekend's freedom,

and walking in from stormy weather. Crowds of tens were packing the matinée with ease. The cost for admittance was only a dollar fifty in those days, leaving funds for other necessary appendages. Equipped with a large popcorn and Raisinets in hand, I slowly walked into the cinema with emotional eagerness. Leo and his young date were deep into themselves the moment we found seats, and even before the credits could start, they were kissing and groping each other like wild cats in heat, and I could care less. I was ready for the show! It was my first time inside a matinée, and with no supervision or restraints to impede my curiosity, I felt like I was an adult in charge of my own consequences until the movie started.

It wasn't even ten minutes into the Asian production before they began showing scenes of very graphic violence and sexual depravity, coupled with the heinous rape of men and women; it was as if it was really happening to the so-called actors. The sounds of moaning and screams shocked me to my very core, totally disturbing me so greatly that I couldn't believe my eyes. It was so vivid and horrible that I couldn't even watch and I physically placed my hands over my ears, so not to hear the sounds of pure evil in action. If a rating's system existed back then, it would be rated Triple X! Every scene was a scene of horrendous violent rape, and I couldn't watch anymore; my heart skipped a beat and pumped faster and faster with every scream.

Tears began to roll off my face; it was too graphic, too real, and way too disturbing for such an innocent child. Leo and his date were too busy playing out their own form of profanity as if they themselves were in the pornographic film; therefore, they didn't even notice how disturbed I was, although I kept my composure, over and over, and for hours. I couldn't take the violent sex scenes any longer, so I closed my eyes and held my ears most of the night while shaking in fear.

It was as if I could feel the pain and violations committed upon the actors myself. Those films were not meant for virgin eyes, in fact, those movies weren't even meant for the eyes of adults in my opinion. The films were straight out of

China—raw, perverted, graphic, and sickening. I was emotionally disturbed and physically sickened. It took everything I had inside not to scream, and I cried like a newborn baby inside. After seeing the scenes of rape and torture, and hearing the horrible sounds of human suffering, my understanding of the world was forever changed.

I could barely breathe by the time the films ended in there entireties, and when the credits of the last film showed, I was out of my seat and heading down the aisle. Fully in psychosis, I thank god for the American rating system these days! No ten year old child should ever be witness or subjected to such horrific scenes, be it real or not.

But the night had just begun, and finally the traumatic and morbid sexual montage of disgusting garbage had ended, but the true eye opening horror would only advance once we left the theater. More than anxious to leave, I urged Leo and his date to hurry in exiting the show room, so we entered the lobby in haste. Then suddenly, wonderment filled the air and shock consumed all parties. Looking out of the large glass entrance doors of the grand old theater, all one could see was whiteout! The mother of all storms had claimed the Midwest for its home. No cars were seen anywhere. No trees showed their stems nor bark; no street corner lamps showed their guiding light. Only whiteout owned the night. After enduring five hours of sexual deviant horror, my mind could not fathom a full scale blizzard to be the next tribulation. Snow blanketed the entire town.

Temperatures dropped below zero in minutes; most people were caught off guard, only dressed in fall attire, including us. Snow covered everything in sight, and total awe inspiring fear of whiteout consumed the night. People were coming out of the theater in total bewilderment and were not able to find their vehicles, even though they were located right outside the hall. Winds blew swiftly as the snow storm easily maxed eighty miles per hour. Snow covered the ground furiously, at least twelve inches a minute, and traffic was at a standstill which made it easier to walk in the street.

Walking on the sidewalk was obsolete for someone of my stature because snow passed my waist while walking out of the theater.

Treading in the street was the only course; we headed toward the young girl's home as fast as we could, freezing along the way.

Wearing flimsy wind breakers in the middle of a full blown blizzard amidst the winds howling like angry wolves, Leo, the young girl and I were quickly developing hypothermia and frostbite, merely attempting to reach the young woman's home as fast as possible, which by the way, was a snap, and not far from the theater at the start of our little adventure, but going back was hell. We had no idea the weather would turn so deadly in such a short period of time. In those days forecasting the weather was like finding a needle in a haystack because we only had a 4 P.M. broadcasted, and maybe a midnight forecast; therefore, no one ever really knew the outcome of the weather and all were caught off guard. Wow! We finally made it! While stopping in the hallway to catch our breath and thaw out, we could hear a news commentator reporting on the monstrous blizzard that besieged the Midwest. We just looked in awe at one another as the bad news streamed out from a front door of a stranger's apartment down the hall-way.

Since no phone was available in the young girl's home, we found ourselves in a very serious predicament. We were stuck all the way downtown with no way of communicating our plight to our loved ones, or to anyone for that matter. The girl had no telephone and we had no winter coats, but Leo just had to get home, for he had no patience to wait out the storm at least until the morning. Leo was somewhat of a singer and sang with a local gospel group which aired on an A.M. radio station every Sunday. It was the very outlet that kept young thugs like himself out of trouble and was sponsored by a good hearted pastor named Freeman. This preacher served in the very church my Grandma and Uncle Leo attended. Leo cherished his position as lead singer and never missed a single rehearsal. Unable to foresee the sudden winter storm, Leo's plans for singing practice after the night's activities did not factor in a blizzard dumping more than five feet of snow in our path. Stubborn and unwilling to concede defeat, with levers of the mind in full effect, he hatched up a dimwitted idea to walk from Fourth and Jackson to Twenty Sixth Street and Delaware, more than four miles away and in a blizzard that was not subsiding. The winter storm crippled everything in sight from Chicago to Minnesota. Power was failing all over the state and all civil services were out of order; therefore, no buses ran, no planes or trains were operating, thus we were in a total white out! Thinking back in time, I can truly say it was beautiful, peaceful and quiet in the midst of a freezing calm whiteout.

Anyone unfortunate to be caught out in the storm was trying his best effort into getting indoors, and this fool was talking about venturing back out into the White Hulk like a moron off his medication, going back out into one of the most terrible storms the Midwest had ever seen, and dragging my little ass along for the ride. Refusing to listen to his most intelligent date, which seemed to be very astute in her judgment, and refusing to put aside his pride and forget his practice and stay safe, if not for himself, but for sake of the child in his care, Leo just had to go fourth with no regard of life, not his nor mine. We commandeered a couple of coats from the young maiden, along with a couple pairs of socks, and we headed back out into the storm. Not able to see a few inches in front of our faces, we walked by faith. I'd like to call it walking in total desperation! In the middle of the road, by instinct, we treaded our way toward Twenty Sixth Street with blind confidence. "Time to get ready for hard shit P! Keep up little nigga, or fade away; don't fall behind boy! Watch my steps, and stay in my path!" Not able to see an inch in front of us, we walked with our faces pointed downward to the ground and began walking by instinct and faith. Thank god we had only to walk a straight line in the beginning of our trek, but soon into our trek, we would have to cross hard terrain, or a maze full of turns, or as Leo would put it, "…a shortcut in the straight shot," but a long and dangerous shot nonetheless during a record breaking blizzard. Leo was my idea of a warrior, and as a youngster, being in his presence was so cool. Looking up to my hero, and embarking on such an adventure was exhilarating. Telling myself, "I'm not going to let him see me wimp out! Not now! Not ever!"

I walked saying nothing, not a single word.

I kept up with the Wascally Wabbott every step of the way as the wind blew so hard and fierce. I could barely take a step, or stand without his support, and I desperately held onto his sleeve tightly through the stinging ice and snow. There was no visibility for miles on end, but with my hero by my side, I showed courage and had no fear of the monstrous storm we boldly battled. I had no fear of getting lost in the massive white out or even freezing to death, and staying strong while keeping up with my hero was truly the only thing on my mind. After a few minutes, my hands began to get numb; they were so cold they burned like fire, and I knew frost bite was creeping in, yet I said nothing to the Wascally Wabbott. I had to go on holding onto his coattails without losing my way in the storm, and

EDGAR FRENCH, JR.

I knew it! So I bit my tongue and continued on, as the wind and snow blew harder as we walked in defiance of it. It felt like sand blasting out of a sand blaster, making it very difficult to raise up our faces to even look in front of our path. Time stood still as we walked in the shadow of the storm, and I lost all feeling in my fingers and toes. I told myself, "I can withstand!" With no wavering, we kept walking saying to ourselves, "We're going to make it!" I would periodically hear my uncle's voice saying, "Come on P, we're almost there!"

We finally arrived at Freeman's corner store! We feverishly banged on the front door while knowing all were in the basement rehearsing, and most likely weren't able to hear us over the howl of the storm. Having no feeling in our hands and feet from the cold of the storm, we banged and banged until someone happened to look out of the basement window and saw us out in the cold yelling back at them.

They quickly took us in, seeing me with Leo out in a blizzard. This little boy was out in the storm of the century, almost frost bitten, and that alone warranted a tongue lashing from the pastor. With total indignation, the pastor reprimanded Leo while I was feeling the burn of a deep freeze. I found solace in hearing his church mate drill into him, and enjoying the free candy provided by Freeman didn't hurt either. While thawing out, I began to think of my little ordeal out in the storm and although I was freezing, I kept going. I learned what it meant to endure hardship and survive, although the Wascally Wabbott put us both in danger out of some misguided loyalty toward his second rate singing group, but I thanked him for the lesson, for the time would come very soon for what I learned that night to be employed on a greater scale…

Semjaza   Gabriel

Gabriel: Semjaza does your evil deeds have no bound?! Why do you seek to destroy this one?! Have you any shame? He's a young-ling! I shall not let you have this one. Must we battle on this realm as well?!

Semjaza: This does not concern you my once good friend! My orders are clear, young slave to the Most High! He's ours to do as we see fit! In darkness he lies. No light shines within him, be on your way once upon my brethren.

Gabriel: In my protection this one lies, did you not know?! My once faithless brethren. Shall swords be drawn this night?! Hasn't enough blood been spilled over this disagreement? For you know very well my power is great! You cannot stand against me! Be on your way, and we'll forget this night.

Semjaza: You blame me for the lord of the winds?! For I have no sway over his domain. You must be ill my deceived one. Are you so in love with your father to see my hand wields nothing here in this realm! I am bound behind the veil with the rest of the two hundred. Only able to see forth and between.

Gabriel: Our spies have intercepted many of your communions with Children of Darkness who reside in this realm from which we are separated. You mean to harm this one, why?! What scheme are you and your cohorts conspiring?! Could it be that the young-ling possesses some light within his being? Are you sure he is of Cain's bloodline?! The Most High has his grace.

Semjaza: YOU FUCKING FOOL!!! I know my fate! But hope we don't break free from this prison your master placed us in; once we're free, the third realm shall cease to exist! Our children have gained the unseen knowledge of time and space! Soon they'll be able to traverse time and venomous vengeance shall be ours to relish in, my once old brethren.

Gabriel: We shall see my doomed once brethren! We shall see, for tonight he is protected from your children's sway, nor shall the hand of winter's sting consume him this night. For destiny holds this one's fate, my truly doomed one.

Three weeks passed and I still had nightmares of the pornographic rape shown on the Asian films in the old theater. I witnessed and survived the night of the big storm of the century without physical harm, and I couldn't believe it, but the movies seen did more damage than the few hours out in the storm. It was the end of October and snow was already on the ground in force, and my birthday was uneventful and sullen as norm, no one seemed to remember, including my mother. I didn't mind, after strenuous lessons in Christian dogma, and the controversy amongst my mother and father of the validities of all traditional observances, ceremonies and beliefs.

I saw no need in observing any ritual honoring pagan deities any longer. I was confused about everything spiritual and unseen. Not knowing anything other than what was told to me by those who themselves were not privy to eye witness testimony of the events, and I was supposed to believe in it so whole heartedly!? I soon began to think long and hard over spiritual matters almost daily, not praying but talking to my Creator, hoping I had his ear, knowing in my heart he was listening, and maybe he was even there, right beside me. Hoping the light of knowing would come my way and lead me to enlightenment, but like so many others, I got no response. No voice! No splitting clouds from above, nor god's Wholly Spirit descending upon me. But something unusual and unforgettable happened to me one Monday morning while walking to the bus stop heading to school. Taking my sweet time, I missed the bus that never arrived on time, but that day it decided to purposely go super slow, and be late instead, leaving me with no choice but to skip school that day, even though walking was always an option.

While debating whether to make the trek to school or just pussyfoot around like I was doing, I noticed a gummy like substance on top of a stone placed in front of another church across the street from the church in which I was abducted not months before. Looking closer at a monumental stone adjacent to the church just mentioned, I noticed there was a transparent hand on top of the stone. The transparent human-like hand captured my curiosity and inaudibly called to me for a closer look. Something that looked like veins and blood vessels within the gummy like hand demanded a closer look! Curious and dumbfounded, I began poking it with a stick and tried to remove it from the stone, but it was as if it were fused to the stone. Getting frustrated, I tried to remove it with my hand, which turned out to be a very big mistake. It was warm to the touch, even though it was cold outside and snow was on the ground. All motion began to slow, and the weather had no bite. The transparent hand felt as if it were alive; then, the moment I put my hand on top of the imprinted hand, I blacked out.

The last thing I remembered thinking was, "I know this thing isn't alive!"

Then, without warning, I was at home in bed. The day had passed and I couldn't remember going to school or even coming home on that strange and ominous day. My mother said I came in from school and went right to bed without having dinner or saying a word. What happened to me? What did I do throughout the day? Apparently, I went to school after all and did well. I talked with people and even rode the bus home, but I could not recall any of it. I said to myself, "I must be going crazy… I must be!" I said nothing about my ordeal to my mother or anyone out in the streets out of fear of being ridiculed. I silently pondered over the events leading up to the missing time while wondering daily about what happened to me after touching the transparent hand on top of the stone.

I tried to put it out of my mind as much as possible, but strange things would continue to happen one after the other. People would have private emotional problems, and I would know their private problems just by looking at them. I started to know things before they would happen. I began having dreams of universal galactic wars and death. Dreams of fighting demons alongside angels in the historic unseen wars raging on above and below us. I started seeing my family being slain, along with seeing creatures and strange people from afar, thus having no clue as to who they were, or in what dimension or world they resided. But all were bowing down to me on a field of victory. Victorious dreams of galactic warfare occurred nightly; what was I supposed do? I had to say something to someone, but to whom? No one could understand what I was going through without calling me crazy. So I stayed quiet! A feeling of fear, and abject terror came over me after each and every dream. Day in and day out I was afraid. For no apparent reason, I would shake from fear. Paranoia gripped my body and spirit, yet they say paranoia is just a higher sense of awareness and I guess they are right because my fear was warranted. It was as if a sinister cloud of despair descended upon our household soon after the dreams! My father stopped coming around, or even giving money in support of us. We all went without food for days and sometimes weeks at a time, and my mom began relying on food stamps and welfare as our only means of resources. Things got bad all around: spiritually, physically and emotionally.

The most soulful, kind, understanding and calm spirited woman began drinking and cursing in the air more and more each day. Things were getting hard clinically, and my mother would try to hide her pain and fears by neglecting her children. I would hear her cries in the night when no one was around or when everyone was asleep. I would hear her on the phone with my aunt Lucy worrying over not knowing where our next meal would come from. My father never showed himself at our home for months at a time. I would see him in the streets most days, or see him driving by the hood in his big black Cadi, and I felt ashamed and blamed all of our woes on him.

Having no one to talk to, I talked with my Creator, hoping for an answer to the mayhem befalling my family. I tried to understand all that had happened so soon and thus far, but no answer ever came, and with every unanswered prayer, my belief suffered, and whatever faith I had in a god began to waver.

I was turning eleven and my mother's conservative habits became more and more liberal in nature and consequence, while she drank and smoked daily without a sense of control. She was a mother of five with no job, and very little education, apart from her small stance in nursing. Living in poverty and feeling hopeless was becoming the norm.

I would hear my younger siblings say, "Mama, I'm hungry," but they were too young to know they were calling out to a half drunk, and half asleep woman, while they looked into the refrigerator hoping for a morsel of food, only coming across a stick of margarine. We continued looking in the kitchen cabinets for anything in a can, but would only see bleached flour and sugar. I would rummage all cabinets but would always find nothing, while watching the look of sorrow in my mother's eyes as a single tear rolled down her cheek. I could only imagine what was going through my mother's mind at the moment of hearing her children's cries for food. I would search everywhere for loose change, looking under the sofa and chairs, searching in coat pockets, and in old dirty jeans. While searching in between the cushions of the sofa, luck shined on her plight, finding only a brown dollar food stamp and forty cents, mostly pennies, I might add. Knowing she would tell me to go to the store, I braced myself for embarrassment, "P, I need you to go to Mitch's and get a can of mackerel and a can of cream corn... oh yes... some corn meal too...so I can feed these babies."

The scraps of change she found gave some relief, but she would still worry even after finding the night's meal. "I don't know what I'm going to do?! I don't get my food stamps until next Friday; I don't know what to do?!" Old enough to feel her pain and sorrow I responded, "It's okay mama, don't worry; it will be alright; you'll see!" As I put on my snow boots and coat, I tried to overcome my shame of using food stamps in front of my fellow peers that were sure to be hanging out at Mitch's. The look on my mother's face helped override my pride, and I began feeling so sad for our situation. Immersed in sympathetic digression, I didn't think about eating anything anymore; the only thing that mattered was feeding my siblings for this day. With my head to the ground, I walked slowly and sullenly through the snow, thinking why is this happening to us?! "What did my mother do to deserve such poverty? What did I do to make my father leave us in such away? Is god punishing us?!" As soon as I said those words to myself, a voice came to mind and said, "Stop! Go back, and look down. Go back now!"

Slowing to a crawl, I stopped in my tracks. Heeding to the voice, I turned and walked backwards as instructed, while instinctively looking down on the ground for something, I saw nothing. "But wait; (said the voice) what's that in the snow?!"

I saw nothing! "Dig in the ground, right here!" Said the voice. So I kneeled and dug in the snow at the location in which the voice said dig. While digging in the snow bare handed, my fingers were going numb, and then I felt something hard like metal not frozen ice. I couldn't see what it was, but I knew it was something of value. My fingers were getting frostbite from digging, but I cared not; the snow was melting by the noon sun, but underneath the snow was ice, and whatever it was I felt, it was stuck in the ice beneath the snow. I kept digging, finally it was freed; Yes! Yes! It was a roll of quarters, just what we needed. I knew my mother would be so grateful for what I found, so I hurried back toward home with a sigh of relief, and a smile. "Ten bucks! A miracle!" I said to myself, with a sense of nervousness as I thought about the significance of the voice that led me to the miraculous find in our time of need. Yet the voice returned once more as I raced home with my find saying: "We shall always be with you!" Ten bucks went a long way in those days, so I ran as fast as I could back home. Full of excitement, I entered the front door saying, "Mom! Mom! Look! Look what I found!" With a look of concerned shock, she turned and looked at me, not knowing if I had befell some grim calamity, she asked, "What happened?!" But when she saw what was in my hand, she showed a look of delight entwined with relief, seeing the roll of quarters in my hand. "Baby, you found this?" I responded, "Yea while walking to the store." And with enthusiasm, I continued to tell my mother how it came about that I found our saving grace. "I looked down and didn't see anything, but something told me to dig, so I did and look, it was money!" Taking the find she said, "Just what we needed P! I love you!" Kissing me over and over, quickly grabbing the wind fall putting on her coat and boots she said, "I'll go P!" I replied, "Get me some candy ma!" She said, "Okay baby you got it!"

The spirit of the Creator was in me. I felt like I was truly the man of the house! It was the first time I'd saved my family from hunger, of course with the help of the unseen forces bringing happiness to the entire family, and filling my sibling's stomachs. Yet in the back of my mind, I wondered how was I able to find the roll of quarters covered under the snow?! Recalling the strange event that occurred in front of the church some days before, my curiosity heightened, feeding my desire to understand the unseen things in the universe, seeing the jubilation and smiles on my sibling's faces brought joy to mind. Seeing the relief of burden fade from my mother's heart, I began thinking of the many plights plaguing us all in poverty, and contemplating about the amount of courage implied and required when caring for children in poverty, so I showed little to no emotion as my brothers and sisters jumped in blissful joy, singing and making up songs of eating and drinking Kool Aid. In the weeks to come the weather became more and more unpredictable, getting warm with little wind, melting snow in mid-November. People were out and about in their shorts and sneakers enjoying the nice warm winter.

Taking advantage of her first born son once more, my mother ordered me to go out and pick up her medicines before the busses stopped running for the day saying; "P I need you to go to the drug store and pick up my prescription;" replying, "I don't want to go!" With a forceful voice she replied, "I can't! Go right now... I'm cooking yo food and watching these kids... Will you please help me and do what I asked you to do?!" With angst I said, "Yes mama," and slowly prepared for the trek, but in a sullen mood, I protested no longer. I grabbed the medical scripts and money from her hand as I pouted while walking out the front door, and grumbled under my voice so as not to get slapped in the back of the head while leaving out. Knowing the busses would stop running after 6pm on the weekend, I held on to the dollar fifty she gave me for bus fare, thinking at least I'd clear some compensation for my little trek, while walking the full distance, which was about 3 miles, thus giving me time to contemplate the many unexplained events taking place in my life. On my trek of contemplations, I kept thinking there must be something wrong with the natural scheme of things, and why was I experiencing so many odd occurrences?! There was nothing special about my family or myself! We were poorer than most, did nothing out of the ordinary, doing everything most poor families did in a day. We were living in utter poverty like most in Gary, and behaved like most in misery. Having very little education in the matters of secularly or theocratic history, we walked blindly following the powers that be! Consumed with petty grievances, wants and daily needs, like everyone else, yet the unseen and unexplained haunted me still, so why were they happening?!

Was all the internal family controversy surrounding the religious practices of my Aunt Lucy and mother's now regular participation in this new found religion at fault, and did that awful religion play a major part in the unexplained events plaguing our family?! Could this never ending calamity be because of the religion my mother and Aunt Lucy now embrace? Could breaking away from the ordained belief assigned from birth be the root cause?! Could calamity manifest itself out of the confusions and disillusions exhibited from other family members, and distort their common faith?! Could staunchly defying their mother's religious wishes play a major part in this misery, or was it me?! Could I be the source of all the dismay? Would the fact of my seeing demons crawl down the walls and up the celling in my bedroom in night's passed be the source of our woes?! Could hearing the warning voices of spirits whispering from behind the veil of the fourth realm, and looking into the eyes of disembodied spirits instigate their wrath towards my family? Or was it because of the many sins committed against God by men, or maybe I'm just crazy, that's it; I'm just crazy. Crazy happenings like that only happen to those with a screw loose, or on TV! Even though I was young, innocent, and without understanding of the world in which I lived, I must have done something wrong in the Creator's eyes, or did I?

Thinking back in retrospect, the unexplained events had to take place at the time that they did, for those things had to take place in order for me to get ready for more intense events.

As I got closer to the drug store, I could feel the wind increase in speed, and as the temperature dropped so did the sunset; not paying attention to the skies above, I entered the drug store oblivious to the rapidly changing weather taking place outside. Wearing only a vinyl wind breaker as the night quickly approached, I took my time approaching the pharmacist, knowing time would pass slowly picking up prescribed medicine, and in those days it took forever for the pharmacist to fill a prescription, so I resigned myself for the long haul. Paying little attention to no one, I waited for the pharmacist's callout of my mother's name from in back of the glass window separating the drug dealer from the customer; a half hour passed and then the call rang out, "Earline French!"

I quickly jumped up out of my seat and headed towards the small rectangle slit in the glass wall, and slid my hand through the slit to receive the package, thinking finally I could go, but as I got closer to the exit door of the drug store, I could see the people all fixated on the street outside. Once again all that could be seen was whiteout in the night; how could this be? It was dark, and there was a massive snow storm raging in full force outside the establishment, covering everything in sight. Visibility was less than a foot, and snow was blowing in all directions. I said to myself, "I know this ain't happening again! I just went through a blizzard! This can't be happening? What am I going to do?! You can't see anything, but you can't stay here; fuck it!" So off I went into another winter storm for the second time. A storm that blew in without warning and wasn't letting up. An evil spirit was in the mouth of the storm; I could feel it! It called out to me with every blowing wind, creating the conditions leading me to my impending death by unseen forces; thinking what have I done by going out into this unknown nor unseen storm?

I truly made a mistake leaving the store! You couldn't see anything at all; a total white out and howling winds over took the night. It was as if I were walking through a very cold white cloud with a northern wind blowing uncontrollably. With the strength of a hurricane, I could barely stand straight, leaning forward with my head pointed toward the ground, I walked by an internal compass and an unseen will to go forward, or maybe faith driven, for I didn't know the source of my persistence. I periodically looked up for some sense of direction, only to find nothing but whiteout. Praying to my Creator for guidance and safety with every step, and as the frigid cold began to cut through the flimsy wind breaker, the voice of doubt and despair crept in from the midst of the winds and into my thoughts. "How would I be able to go on?!" I said to myself, "You must keep going P; you must not give up; your god is with you; stand fast, and stand strong!" I kept saying to myself over and over again alongside my prayers. Well, it was more like internal cries out to my Creator for help.

I repeated saying those words as I walked in the ever growing snow and felt the cold ever so strongly. "You are going to die this night!" The voice kept creeping into my thoughts; not willing to die, I kept going forward with my head toward the ground, walking blindly into the night. The snow was piling up quickly; it seemed as if an unseen force, or an un-natural life form was driving the force behind the storm. In fact the voice of that life form spoke to me in the form of doubt! It was trying to break my defiant stance, or shatter my unwillingness to die easily by attacking my spirit with every step.

But alongside accompanying the voice of despair, was the voice of hope, saying, "You will make it home, for the Creator is with you P! Keep going; you'll make it back! Stand fast!" As my fingers and toes lost all feeling, all fear left my spirit, and my determination grew in strength! As I drudged on with my head pointed down, blinded by the violent blowing snow, and not knowing if I was even going in the right direction, I walked by faith in my Creator. Never having any sense of baring, freezing yet feeling nothing, I begrudgingly walked forward never wavering in will. Glancing upward for a moment, I recognized the familiar rust stained lamp post that stood guard to the back entrance of the Colored Doors. It was shining brightly through the light of the snow.

Yet without a bulb to light the way in the night, feeling the sweet relief of salvation, I said to myself, "YES!" Knowing I had made my way back home in the midst of the awesome storm of the century. Picking up my pace, I found the strength to climb the ever growing embankment of snow blocking the way home, obstructing my every effort. Finally, I made it to my mother's back door. Barely able to raise my left arm to bang on the door, I yelled out "MA!" I humbly tried to knock on the back door, having no physical strength whatsoever. Drained of spirit, I yelled out once more; "MA!" I leaned up against the back door, half frozen attempting to knock with numb hands. Then the door opened, and the light of the toasty warm two bedroom bungalow embraced my shivering young soul.

As my mother pulled me in from the grip of certain death; she said; "Oh! Baby! Baby! I was so worried," she said with tears flowing from her eyes as she franticly removed my clothing; repeatedly saying; "You made it P! You made it!" "I knew you could make it," said a voice in my mind as my mom pulled down my frozen stiff blue jeans. Saying nothing, I cracked a smile at my mother. Then with a chattering voice I said, "Look ma my pants are standing up on their own." Feeling the burning sensations of life returning to my fingers and toes, I began to ask my Creator for mercy, and not let my fingers and toes be frost bitten as I humbly gave him thanks, over and over again for seeing me home safe and sound. Unaware of the terror to come in the near future, the feeling of fire from frozen flesh returning to life would be the theme of fire that would engulf my entire family for years to come.

CHAPTER XII
Kill the Divergent

(Loki)

This one is strong! His will to live and overcome adversity may prove useful in our insidious struggle for the lives and spirits of the sons of light! Let our efforts succeed in the never ending corruption of goodness among men. Let our darkest light not fall upon futile and hopeless souls, for the active force of the most high resides within him! His demise shall reveal the worth of a hundred human spirits! He'll make a very good slave for our lord Lucifer. He just may be the one after all! His induction into evil's grace must not come lightly nor swiftly at all. We shall open the flood gates of despair, delusion, chaos and dismay! Destroy all influence of Yahweh's light of spirit. Show him the splendid light of darkness in this realm. Remove all normalcy and stability from his life; let the love of a mother and father fade away. Let no unity of family strengthen his faith, nor let those to whom he loves gain strength themselves! Slavery of mind, body and spirit must continue throughout his life. No letup of misery's grip shall come to pass! No mercy for all that may be in line for salvation; all in creation has its price in pain and sorrow; I'll educate this one myself"…

Winter's bite begun to subside, and the Oak trees began to sprout their buds of rebirth; the sun rises brightly and earlier each day. I awoke to the sounds of the wood peckers drilling in the tree outside my window pane, while looking outside to catch a glimpse of the majesty of the red headed wood worker as he worked his magic within the tree. Spotted high up in the Sycamore tree, a smile formed upon my face. Ready to rise, I jumped out of bed full of energy. I ran directly to the kitchen to grab the last bit of cereal before my other siblings woke up and beat me to it. Suddenly, the phone rang, waking my already half-awoke mother and siblings; it was my Aunt Lucy. Hearing my Aunt Lucy's frantic voice screaming through the receiver, I overheard my mother saying, "Hold on, hold on girl!" With a reassuring voice, my mother tried to calm her sister down. I saw the look of anger slowly appearing on my mother's face, as she quietly listened to her sister laying out the specifics of the severe beatings she'd endured through the night and a tear ran down my mother's face. A severe beating administered by her seditious and somewhat wickedly abusive husband, fueled fiery anger from all within the family.

The abuse became a daily event, so prevalent in frequency, that all in the family were desensitized and accustomed of hearing about Buddy's physical abuse perpetrated upon my Aunt Lucy. Internally, I would say to myself, "When will she wake up from this daily nightmare and dump this fool?" Although, I knew nothing about human nature, nor of the power of love facilitating co-dependency and need, nor the factual effects of loneliness on the wanting heart.

I was clueless of the spiritual power behind the human need to search for respect, love and happiness. Longing for companionship, my Aunt Lucy made the worst choice ever in companions, but in testimony, I can say that her pool of moral men were not full of sound choices, making the search for a proper suitor almost non-existent. We lived in a time period where male dominance over their spouse was excepted and normal, where there was no such thing of male and female equality. All my life, I'd stand witness to the physical and verbal abuse exerted upon black women by most black men in the hood. I actually believed that abusive behavior was a part of being a real man, and having total domination over your woman seemed normal growing up. I saw my Aunt Lucy as Buddy's property and not his equal in humanity, and for most in society, it was the norm. But because of my willingness to take to heart the biblical stories I had studied for more than two years prior, I was beginning to learn the significance and importance of the influential role women played that was hidden within the ancient text. Yet the Bible condones such treatment of women within its pages, but something about that allowance didn't make sense to me even back then, so why would god approve of such treatment? In ignorance, I dismissed the holiness, and I mean "HOLES" in the allowance of such treatment by dis-enlightened men born by the mothers of humanity. The fact that man would even consider a woman second in stature made no sense; I needed to find the reasoning behind such norms among men and religion.

While opening my mind's eye to what I felt internally within my heart, I said to myself, "Something is wrong with the world and my understanding of what truth is, and what if what I was reading was made up by men?" "For all men are Liars!" Though I didn't witness verbal or physical abuse inflicted upon my mother by the hands of my father, I did stand witness of many counts of infidelity, womanizing and flat out unfaithfulness by my father on a daily basis. Knowing my mother knew of his exploits, I began to lose hope in goodness as a grand power within men, but deep inside myself, I knew as a man child that goodness controlled my being, not that of evil. Soon after the constant abuse, my Aunt Lucy and her children were back living with us, in our little two bedroom flat in the Color Doors.

Back and forth she would go from our home and back to Buddy, disrupting any vestige of freedom within in our home. Though sharing everything with siblings, and or family members was all I knew growing up, having my alone time in my thoughts was something I longed for constantly. Periodically, I had that time in my shared bedroom, so as a child I selfishly had little sympathy for her plight, especially when she would return to our humble abode with the most destructive two humans I knew: Chunky and Pookey. Although I enjoyed their rambunctious company at times, I loathed their sense of adventure, and I experienced overwhelming feelings of envy that constantly plagued me whenever they made their presence known.

Pookey and Chunky raised havoc on all my possessions, and destroyed anything they considered valuable in my eye, not to mention the ongoing discussions and arguments over the physical abuse and everlasting forgiveness of my Aunt Lucy granted upon her husband, disrupting all vestige of solitude, speeding up spring break and yet slowing down time with their presence. Chores became more of a chore, rationing sustenance became more rationed, and the freedom of self-thought withered away into the abyss of foolishness and childish nonsense, raising questions in selfishness saying, "Why me? When will they leave? Man, go home." Now the little two bedroom bungalow was filled to the brim with bodies occupying every dingy carpeted room. Resources were very tight between the sisters since both women were on social services, or welfare. Life was a struggle with seven kids among the two, with no chance of employment in a City where the very zip-code is considered an unsafe zone by all potential employers, making employment non-existent! Having meager means, laundry day came only once a month, and as you could imagine, having so many kids in one small hut, much laundry would accumulate in the span of a month. Laundry day itself constituted a ten hour job for anyone that displayed the will, with three to four huge green hefty bags full of sweaty soiled jeans, t-shirts, tube socks and funky underwear piling up over thirty-days from seven kids and two women. No one wanted to take on the chore, though the task fell only once a month! Not only did the chore imply washing massive amounts of clothing, it also implied toting huge bags through the Colored Doors on foot for at least a half mile.

With the laundry mat located a good ways up the road, toting those loads of hefty bags as children was a chore in itself! Walking a half mile through the Color Doors proved to be not just stressful, but somewhat embarrassing to all. So periodically my mother would employ the Wascally Wabbott to handle the gruesome deed since he was always on the lookout for extra cash. Eager to make money for his weekly weed stash, he would gladly take on the challenge without objection, but he would always try to make the most of his paid contract by shirking his responsibility, leaving the grunt work to those he was servicing, namely us! And in time, he would succeed, leaving the burden and brunt of the work to his somewhat obedient nephews and by allocating or delegating most of the labor to the children he was servicing under the auspices of "It's your laundry!" And normally I would do my part relieving his burdened task. But the dam of time had broken within my mental ability for patience, and this time, I would protest our servitude. Defiance was imprinted within me from birth and I resisted, so the Wascally Wabbott responded with harsh language! "Alright you lil' mafuckas, bag up all this shit and come help me with this shit right now before I beat yo ass! This is your shit, and yawl gone help me clean this shit!" I responded, "No I'm not." He said, "What!" I respond, "No I'm not Leo! Mama paid you to do it, so you gonna do it, not me!" With fire in his eyes he said, "Alright P don't make me kick yo ass." I responded, "You ain't kicking nothing;

she paid you and you gonna do it, and you can't make me do nothing!" Then he exploded yelling, "You lil!" As he began to lunge towards me, chasing me around the house with no restraint or coordination, unable to obtain me, he took time out from the chase to smoke a joint with his homies outside on the porch.

Frustrated with my unwillingness to abstain, he ordered Pookey and Chunky to load up the bags with laundry detergent and bleach, and headed out the door cursing my name as they walked off toward the laundry mat, while I smirked at him as I looked out the front window while smiling and laughing at Pookey and Chunky as they toiled in back of the Wascally Wabbott; begrudgingly, they all made the trek through the hood. An hour passed and they returned for more laundry; adamant in his resolve to force me to participate, the Wascally Wabbott walked in the door with guns blazing saying, "I just started five loads lil nigga, and you gone help me with the rest, or god help you!" And before he could finish uttering that phrase my response was, "No I'm not…" (Yes you are!) "No I'm not!" In a rage he screamed, "Motha Fucka! Come here!" Dashing toward me with the speed of a king cobra ready to strike.

Luckily for me his Homies who accompanied him back to the house held him back as Leo said, "Man this lil mafuckas gone help us with this shit, this is his shit, everybody else helping… he gone help too…look at all these fuck'n clothes!" With full confidence I said, "No I'm not! Mama paid you! You getting paid to wash them cloths, and I ain't gone help you; Period!" Infuriated Leo yelled, "AHHHH! I'm going kill him! I'm going kill him! Dat fucka's mine!" Still his Homies held him at bay as much as they could. His three friends pleaded with me to conform saying, "Join in P" trying to seem reasonable in all accounts, saying, "It's only fair P!" But I stood steadfast in my resolve. "No! I'm not gone do it! No matter what you pot heads say… he was paid to do it…" So they resorted to threating me, which was a big mistake! "Well, we'll let him go and let him kill yo ass." "Let him go, I don't care! I still ain't gone do it!" Leo shouted, "This Motha Fuck, see, see, see, what I got to go through with this lil nigga, these are his clothes and he won't help; I'm a get dat mafucka, watch, watch!" They pleaded and pleaded with me to follow my uncle's order to participate, but I would not budge.

One of Leo's best friends, Bruce, had a very nice necklace made from his very hands, crafted from a nineteen sixty nine silver piece dollar roped on a gold chain; it was tight! And I wanted it! It was my chance to capitalize on the situation, so I went for it. "Alright you want me to help?" Bruce replied, "Yah!" I slyly respond, "Give me that necklace then." With a look of shock on his face, he said, "What? Hell Nall! I ain't giving you shit!" My reply, "Well, I ain't gonna help him then!"

With time running down and the sun setting, my uncle's friends finally huddled together to hatch up a devious plan of deception, agreeing to give me the necklace in exchange for my services, thus giving me what I wanted. Knowing they would try to obtain the necklace soon after I conceded, I preemptively hid the loot as soon as it was in my hands without their knowledge. Once the assignment was complete, they quickly circled me in with hostile intent. Searching me from head to toe without avail, finding nothing on my person while searching the entire apartment without result or satisfaction. Afraid of losing his precious gem, Bruce held back his anger and relied on caution in his approach in retreating his precious price. "You know what?! Keep it! It's yours!" While pissing off his friends for a month, daily someone would come to my mother's home in search of the priceless gem, only to leave without success. Then one day the necklace disappeared without a trace; the location of the sought after treasure was found out, and someone clever retrieved the booty. But it took more than four months before being retrieved, and I enjoyed my conquest for a while without regret...

Three months passed, and after many attempts to woo back the heart of my Aunt Lucy, Buddy finagled his way back into her good graces, ultimately convincing her to return home, inadvertently making my day. I finally had some peace and serenity, and there were no more shenanigans after bedtime. I no longer had to go to bed hungry because of greedy cousins hogging up all the food. Even before one could get to the kitchen table at bell or call, my cousins were always at the dinning-table. I no longer had to share dirty or torn clothing with ungrateful hooligans, but in the back of my mind, I knew she and my cousins would be in terrible physical danger by the hands of her husband and would return to our home in the near future. Yet the urge of having some sense of normalcy overwhelmed my logic centers. Just the thought of having a home without squatters or family refugees was very appealing. You would say the light of jubilance shined from my eyes as I watched them load up the back end of that ugly green station wagon with all their goods, and that view overwhelmed all sympathetic thoughts at that moment! I jumped for joy inside, and was bubbling over with anticipation. Meanwhile, my mother continued to attempt to talk sense into her sister, begging her not to leave and insisting her husband would not stop his sadistic moments of rage and rampage. In time, my Aunt Lucy would wish she had listened to her younger sister's advice. In my mind's eye amongst forgotten memories, I recall myself looking out the living room window, stoned faced as Buddy pulled up in the same fucked up station wagon, in which he refused to transport me to the hospital. I remembered Buddy's cruelty and lack of concern for my well-being as Chunky and I slowly climbed the massive staircase of the old apartment building after breaking my arm some time back. Yet I still wasn't sad to see the worrisome family members leave for their abusive home. It seemed to have been such a long time without the simple comfort of space! It had been so long without a good night sleep that I'd forgotten what it felt like.

At last, I got to sleep in a peaceful environment and it was blissful! I slept like a log that night and the next morning without the noise and confusion imposed by the rugged two. I awoke in a state somewhat like a long past dream of ecstasy in paradise, able to hear the bird's songs at day break. I took my time towards the kitchen without fear of being accosted, while grabbing a fresh plate from the cabinets, and being it was the first of the month, the cupboards were full of food, so the Captain Crunch was solely mine at last! Summer adventures seemed a bit boring without the dangerous two disruptive family members I considered as brothers, but peace of mind helped the emptiness in my soul and calmed my spirit; yet I must say hearing the constant and annoying phone correspondence between my mother and Aunt Lucy was heart breaking. Sounds of them discussing their daily emotional problems amidst the occasional curse words filling the air, made life at home somewhat disconcerting. Words of condemnation of others, and evoking the title god in their verbal streams of damn mid-sentences, made little sense to me, and rather sacrilegious in nature. With fountains of tears flowing after every realization of poverty, I began wondering when things would return to some remnant of sanity or normalcy. But retrospectively speaking, it was only my fanciful imagination, for nothing would be the same ever again.

It was summer's end and fall was showing himself in the autumn colored leaves and colder blowing winds; words of Grandma losing her home blew in with autumn's fall. Because of ill management and selfish deeds plaguing my uncle Bubble, namely his wicked wife, accusations crossed the lips of all in the family almost daily, and the Wascally Wabbott had no choice but to join the army, hoping to escape the madness surrounding the loss of Grandma's home. In the futile attempt to save his mother's house, and the illusion of the ever growing hopelessness enveloping the streets, the Wascally Wabbott un-wittingly traded one hell for another. Before his departure to boot camp, my mother gave her youngest brother a going away bash, inviting most of his crew, and all in the hood of the Colored Doors. Good food, music and libations were flowing freely; my siblings were all away for the weekend, and the party was in full swing! Everybody was in the groove, and I was in my bedroom hearing the festivities of the adults doing their thing. I periodically sneaked out to catch a glimpse of Robin, the prettiest girl in the Colored Doors in that day. Then it happened, curiosity took control of my senses and I walked through the crowd of preoccupied partiers without them noticing even a glimpse of me, thus making my way to the kitchen, where I discovered a bottle of cheap ghetto wine, better known as "Ripple."

Unsupervised and unattended, my adolescent mind went to work. While looking around the playing field, I noticed everyone seemed to be in his or her own zone. I walked right passed the slightly intoxicated adults, including my mother, and without a word said, no one rebuked me or told me to return back to bed. Everyone was immersed in their talking and laughing.

Paying no attention to me whatsoever, curiously, I sat down at the kitchen table still unsupervised. Seeing the green flower shaped bottles of Ripple captured my sense of adventure while seeing all the happy faces as they casually sipped their magic potion. "Hmm… I wondered what this stuff tasted like." I thought to myself, as I marveled at the lovely green bottle. Young and innocent, I opened a bottle without a soul paying attention! Un-noticed, I sniffed the contents of the bottle, saying to myself, "It was fruity," still un-noticed, I took a sip.

It was sweet and somewhat tasty, with a rosy aroma. "Man this stuff tastes great!" I took another sip and began feeling funny. A smile broke loose on my face, making sure not to touch the many Styrofoam cups as not to arouse any attention, so not to capture some adult's nosy sixth sense of my covert drinking of Ripple. I poured a Kool-Aid cup full of the magical brew, and placed the open bottle of Ripple on the floor, close to the wall behind the kitchen table and hid it behind my chair. I chuckled while people entered in an out of the kitchen, paying me no mind as I played like I was reading the yellow pages. It was on! I was eleven and a half, and well into my first time ever drinking alcohol. My head began spinning and I felt nothing. I laughed at nothing, but was laughing inside, saying to myself, "Now I see why everybody is so happy!" I continued to steadily drink my fill without interruption. Soon I had drunk the entire fifth size bottle. Bobbing my head to the music, I soon felt like I entered into the mix! The kitchen began spinning more and more while the uncontrolled smile on my face withered away, and concern entered my intoxicated synapses while I placed my spinning head on the kitchen table and closed my eyes as everything swirled within my soul.

I felt like I was on the fastest roller coaster invented with no time limit to its speed. The feeling of intoxication was going on and on; I thought I was done for. Afraid of getting in trouble, I slowly stumbled passed all the party goers, and went back to my bedroom still un-noticed, and dropped on the bottom bunk bed like a stone. With my head spinning un-controllably, I cried out wishing I had never ventured into the realm of drunkenness! Feeling like I would die, I cried uncontrollably. Moving all over the bed restlessly, feeling sick to the stomach, I stumbled back into the living room in a panic yelling, "MA! MA! I'm dying," while stumbling over my feet and crying hysterically. I instantly brought a halt to the party—"What the hell?" asked a party goer. "Earline this little nigga drank a whole bottle of Ripple!" Face full of tears, I looked up at my mother and balled up like a centipede at her feet. Holding tightly to her ankles, not caring of the consequences of my actions, I begged for help—hoping a mother's love would save me, but to my surprise the mother's instinct to protect her child had left the building.

Looking down at me, she suddenly bust out laughing and asked, "You grown—ha nigga?!

That's what you get! Now take this as a lesson and go back to bed; that ought to teach you!"

Mother had no sympathy for her first born son what so ever, joining along with the crowd of on lookers, laughing and taunting me as if I were scrum, and not her precious baby boy. I continued rolling around on the floor and feeling sick to my stomach, crying uncontrollably, while all looked on.

I thought she must not love me anymore for what I had done; ashamed and compounded with sickness, I tried to stumble back to bed. Then my father walked in the door, and to his surprise, he saw me in my first serious folly, making a spectacle of myself while everyone laughed. Picking me up off of the living room floor, he took me to my bedroom and put me on the top bunk with the look of disgust on his face. He closed the door without saying a word, as I lay there with my head spinning and stomach upset. Knowing I disappointed both parents, I accepted my penance and fell asleep. Feeling totally ashamed the next day, I stayed in my bedroom most of the day, venturing out only for a meal. Unable to look my mother in the eye, I kept my head in a submissive posture the entire day of my favorite uncle's departure. It was November twenty-third, nineteen hundred and seventy-seven, two days before Thanksgiving Day. The family seemed to have weathered the storm of uncertainty and tough times that consumed most families living in poverty and spiritual strife.

After numerous attempts and many long nights, somehow my mother convinced my Aunt Lucy to leave her tyrannical and abusive husband, and even helped her to find a new home. It was a small apartment on the top floor of a five story brown stone, the very brown stone in which my Grandma and Granny Grip moved into not four months prior. Just a week before that faithless Thanksgiving, my father finally agreed to buy the motorcycle I religiously begged for the previous months.

He gave me three hundred dollars up front and in my hands, securing the down payment on the "Suzuki Five Hundred" that I feverishly hounded him about for months. He placed the cash in an old auto mechanic book he'd look over when working on Stock Car engines, and gave it to mom for safe keeping. I thought my dreams of having my own motorcycle were coming true. I watched my mom place the old auto mechanic book on the top shelf in her bedroom closet, and I smiled and closed the door, assuring myself that no one would touch the money, not even my mother herself.

It was so refreshing to see some remnants of prosperity enter our meager ghetto existence after all the upheaval and uncertainty looming year after year, and things seemed to be going well for a change with the hope of regaining some sense of normalcy. Though my father was not in the home as the man of the house, his presence was regular once again.

My mother seemed happy with her plight concerning her sister's frame of mind, even their daily phone conversations seemed light hearted and upbeat. I felt as if everything would finally be okay on every front in our lives.

I was back to being my old self-centered and obnoxious smart mouth brat once again. Thanksgiving was only one day away and my mother was busy planning her participation in the always great and memorable family event. With my Aunt Lucy and grandmother in full culinary upheaval, I loved hearing the heated debates over what pies to serve first: pumpkin or sweet potato, or how much nutmeg to apply to each succulent morsel.

After hearing the many discussions of Thanksgiving Dinner, I dreamed of oven baked turkey legs and homemade dressing, and calculated my portions and position in the serving line the following morning.

I made sure I would be first at the serving table before my rambunctious cousin/brothers, Pookey and Chunky, ever got close to the feast. But first things first, I had to get downtown and Broadway Street to obtain my childish heart's desire, which were model planes at that time. In my mind's eye, an old wooden World War II model plane kit haunted my every thought. Visions of the model plane box that sat boldly within the showcase display window had me dreaming of someone else snatching it up out of the old Thrift Shop. Without hesitation or fail to respond the following morning, I ran out of the house before mom could drop a chore into my hands and jumped on my bike and went before daylight dimmed. I spent most of the day loitering within the little Broadway shop, looking over all the many novelties, marveling at all the products adorning each and every aisle, effortlessly occupying my not so precious time away from my siblings. Suddenly, a dimensional porthole opened up within the little shop, and the store filled with a cloud of doom. A feeling of dread came over me, and the over whelming sense of danger filled the entire store and my soul, but why? Things were going so well, and for the first time in months, I was feeling happy in life, but no, something was wrong once again, and I didn't know why!

Something was not right and I couldn't put my finger on it at the time of the occurrence. The day was winding down and the street lights were beginning to shine, so I purchased the model plane and began the journey home in fear.

As I road home, my thoughts began to clear from the fog of doom and my sixth sense of impending danger or awareness of evil diminished, but I rode home by pure animalistic instinct, saying to myself, "Something's wrong! Something's wrong!" Over and over in my mind's conscious voice, those words persisted to the point of paranoia, and I soon became sick to my stomach. I couldn't eat supper or even sleep the night before our family's favorite pagan feast, which of course was Thanksgiving. Deep in non-thought or meditation, I patiently overcame my irrational thoughts and calmed down from the menacing extra-sensory perception, so I put my mind on other things pressing, and focused on my original plan and got to work on erecting the wooden model and placed it on my dresser. Finally, the feeling of overwhelming dread began to subside after a few hours of unexplained terror.

Thanksgiving Day, Nineteen hundred and seventy seven was upon us, and was quickly fading away. The weather suddenly dropped in temperature, and snow heavily blanketed November's end. Watching the snow fall through Grandma's front window pain, I thought of the snow's beauty as huge snowflakes began to stick to the ground and accumulate in record speed, which was not out of the ordinary in those days. Everyone in the family went about their normal plans in preparation for the family gathering at Grandma's house. Mom started the day cleaning chitterlings, smelling up the entire Brown Stone, and of course making me help with the tedious chore. I truly love chitterlings, but I hated cleaning them with a passion, and as I sat near her bended knees, utter dread returned without warning. My mind wondered off into the deepest of blue yonder! Not knowing what spirit was approaching, not knowing what the matter was, I kept cleaning the chitterlings as the feeling of dread intensified! I listened to my mother's festive phone conversation with Aunt Lucy in her new apartment up the stairs from Grandma's,

I feverishly tried to calm myself down as the festive day went along at ease; feelings of dread subsided and my thoughts were back on turkey and dressing the moment mom announced we were heading back to the Colored Doors to pick up my other siblings for the holiday feast.

I lovingly looked at my mom as she tucked in my newborn sister, Nikki, in a pink and blue blanket; I wondered off in thought while helping my other siblings dress for the winter weather. Suddenly, the feeling of dread returned, and a tear ran down my face as we all left the Colored Doors for Grandma's house. Back to the past we went, to Grandma's house for Thanksgiving Dinner, and all would come. Looking out of the car window, I could see the snow dancing in the air, but the dread of doom would not subside! In a daze, I stared out the window; my mind embraced gray thoughts of nothing as we drew closer to Grandma's house. Mom said, "Look P" as we passed by her old high school, "Freeman High."

Reminiscing of all the great times she spent there she said, "Lord if those halls could talk!" With a heavy chuckle, she bowed her head as we passed it. The hollowed doors of the school had been empty for many years, though it was dilapidated and corroded from the sands of time, it still looked as majestic as the day it opened! Huge colonial masonic columns adorned the top of its front entrance stairs that stretched amongst many winter withered oaks. As far as my eyes could see, the school was surrounded by oak and cedar trees. As we turned right onto Jackson Street, my mother spoke on the origin and history on the name of the street in which it stands saying, "This is the street the Jackson Five lived on P!"

Although we'd just left the building, it seemed as if it was my first time seeing where Grandma lived since Rhode Island Street; we pulled up to a pristine historical East Coast looking row of Brown Stones. I witnessed the look of the beauty emanating from the turn of the century. There were brown stone buildings reaching five stories in height.

Grandma's house was located right across the street from the school, and with winter wonder blazing bright within my mind, a serene sight in the winter wind with snow covered steps led up to the hard wooden stained glass doors. Suddenly an old chubby lady opened the door saying, "Hey Babies… come on in!" It was Grandma's new home. Though we just left not an hour ago, I haven't seen Grandma for forever it seemed, and instantaneously, a smile was brought to my dreadful face, and I ran up and hugged her so tightly! She yelled out, "… damn boy, I ain't dying," and kissed me on the cheek as I walked through the doors entering a second door leading into Grandma's apartment.

At first glimpse sitting on the stool in front of her grand organ was Granny Grip playing an old gospel tune on an antique foot peddle organ, with Pookey and Chunky running towards me full of holiday cheer, hands filled with holiday candy saying, "...come on P let's go outside" grabbing my hand leading me back out into the frigid weather I had just exited. Happy to see them both, I didn't protest too much, and off we went! Running across the street onto the empty school parking lot, with baseballs and stick in hand, Pookey and Chunky initiated a game of stick ball with a couple of alike young ruffians already outside and primed, thus already playing on the closed down school grounds. Since I wasn't much of a sports person, I faded into the sidelines watching them all play recklessly. Quickly getting cold, I soon made my way back inside the black and white checkered tiled hallway, thus going unnoticed.

Lingering in the air were all the smells of Thanksgiving which intoxicated the senses. Music played in unison and in tune of the horrendous loud noises of siblings and relatives running all through the house. Cheers were echoing throughout the entire building. It was most satisfying and thought provoking as the terror vanished, and the spirit of wellbeing and safety filled the air. I felt so safe and at home. Instinctively, I began to smile from within the heart out into the crowded room. Then Grandma announced, "All right everybody it's time to eat!" Supper finally arrived and all the adults and snot- nose brats headed towards the main table, followed by the annual separation between wisdom and youth and all the brats headed towards the kiddy table in back of the main dining area and it was awesome!

Great food! Comradely and happiness abound! Nothing could be better. Most of the immediate family were present, minus the Wascally Wabbott, who was being deployed to Germany that very day. A couple of late and drunken stragglers entered the fray, stumbling up to the front doorway ringing the bell call, stopping Grandma's elegant rendition of the Lord's Prayer mid-sentence. More unexpected on-comers entered ready to enjoy the festive feast. It was truly a perfect picture of family unity enjoying the bliss that comes with serenity and all-togetherness. It truly was a great gathering and a good time for all.

God truly was in the house that day, for his spirit filled every room, along with reminiscent smells of nutmeg and spices. It was a wonderful and magical place in times past. I wished that time itself could stop there, but it was not the case, for other unseen forces had more insidious intentions with the time allotted. With most of us stuffed and satisfied from the most unforgettable feast, all the sounds and mischievous deeds made from our childish nature and playful noise receded, and the adults began their festivities indulging in libation and telltale gossip. Three knocks on the door, and a not so recognized person entered, along with two unsavory looking men amongst his side and jubilance erupted within the ranks of the adults. With laughter and smiles mainly coming from the adults, my awful and unmovable uneasy feeling of dread returned with a vengeance.

I soon found myself whimpering underneath the main dining-room table, feeling so afraid it could only be described as total fear. Unnoticed to all embraced in the rapture of the evening, I wrapped my arms around my Grandma's left leg in abject fear unwilling to let go. The feeling of awful dread was so overwhelming for me; I just scrounged closer to my Grandma's leg crying. Only Grandma knew or paid attention to my odd behavior, inquiring to my mother about the situation. Holding on tightly, I stayed huddled around my grandmother's leg until I fell asleep; no one knew the reasons behind my bewildering behavior including myself. But everyone continued the festivities, not inquiring at all of my bizarre outburst of terror. Mom only asked, "What is wrong with that little nigga?"

Mom turned back towards her gentlemen caller and friends continuing her conversation and laughter. Hell, I didn't blame her because it was beyond comprehension of what was happening within myself as well. Soon I fell asleep attached to my grandmother's leg, and was pried away and placed in Grandma's lonely bed. Periodically awakening by loud voices and good cheer, I cried myself back to sleep, though shaking from whatever unseen force or spirit that had captured my thoughts in the midst of Thanksgiving's grace. Finally, giving in to the spirit that caused the grief and anxiety, I slept the evening away, having visions of ghouls and gremlins in my restless slumber.

When most of the happy souls gathered for the scrumptious homemade meal, and festivities were winding down, I awoke from my nightmare feeling better, helping myself to another slice of pie and all the other Thanksgiving grub. Time passed without care and it was getting late; my mom and Aunt Lucy were gathering all their kids together, and began heading upstairs to my aunt's new place on the fifth floor. With libations in hand and cheer in their hearts, they invited a few friends to cap off the night. Then Mama said, "Come on P, let's go and see Aunt Lucy's place!" Without fail, my heart skipped a beat as soon as she made the statement. I panicked and began shaking, for an overwhelming feeling of utter fear returned with a vengeful wickedness!

Quickly running to Grandma, I held on tightly to her leg once more saying, "...please, please, please don't make me go with them; I don't want to go! Please don't make me go!" With tears in my eyes, she felt pity on me and said to mom, "...go ahead girl and let him stay with me." (Thinking I was just a spoiled brat wanting to stay with his Grandma, but there was more to my antics than my grandmother could ever imagine.) Pure terror griped my spirit and soul! My mother felt a bit of relief that I was out of her hair for the rest of the night because she had no objection to my unwillingness to follow her lead saying to my grandmother, "...go right ahead ma, let that little nigga stay with you!"

Seeing I was staying behind, Pookey and Chunky jumped into the fray, begging to also stay behind. This stirred up a hornet's nest of debate between my mother and my Aunt Lucy whether or not to leave any of us, causing more anxiety on my already frantic heart, holding tightly ever more so to grandmother's leg, ultimately causing her to quell all commotion between the two sisters yelling out, "That's it! Pookey you stay here with P! Chunky go with you mama! You too bad for me to be dealing with yo ass after all this work! All the rest of you niggas get the hell out!"

With everyone exiting Grandma's home, the awful spirit that plagued my dreary soul began to change back to jubilance within me. "Just in time" were the words that entered my brain saying to myself, "Yes…

I'm glad they are gone!" "The Creature Feature Show" was coming on at midnight, and Grandma had "Jiffy Pop," you know, the old school popcorn that came in an aluminum pan, and very convenient in those days; it popped right on top of the stove! Brilliant! Of course Pookey hurried up and asked to pop it, not giving anyone a chance to ask Grandma's permission, thus taking all the excitement out of the night. While Grandma put away the left overs, Pookey and I cleaned up the mess quickly, so not to miss the beginning of "The Creature Feature Show."

We dimmed most of the lights as Grandma sat in her favorite spot on the sofa, smiling when she took a dip of her snuff and relaxed a bit after a long day of cooking. Pookey started the Jiffy Pop and I turned on the TV, and tuned to the channel airing the show, then I cuddled up next to Grandma as I always did. Not to mention how much of a chicken I was, for I was even afraid of the most stupid hair product commercial ever shown on television, and to make it worse, it only aired at night. It scared the shit out of me! I can't recall the name of the company or the name of the product; all I remember was the freaky way the hair would instantly grow on the actor's head with an all-white background and Shaka Delic Shack colors twirling in back of the hair as it grew to creepy music, totally creeping me out! So when the program began, I prayed for that commercial not to air, but of course that commercial would be the first thing that reared its ugly head! Instantly, I got up and ran to Grandma's bedroom where I didn't show my face the rest of the night, missing the whole show without regret. But unbeknownst to all living beings that dwelled within the building, this night would bring true terror, coupled with a lifetime of pain and sorrow…

(Loki)

May the winds of despair blow freely within this verse this very night, my brethren in unison, and with malicious and venomous intent we shall move quickly! In the hearts of the wicked, the spirit of destruction shall motivate! May no joy be found in the light of night break end! Let the sweet light of innocence turn black with sin's corruption. For all that is pure this night shall be corrupted! With hatred of oneself all shall be spared not! With infectious ill will towards all we shall reign down. Let the beauty of darkness shine brightly within the night; may the very spirit of mortals quiver in the shame and fear of what must take place here in this realm! Hear this call immortal and mortal! To one of theirs or one of ours; let there be no distinction in the wilds of carnage. Let loose the minions of sorrow and pain! Let loose the agents of hardship on the unsuspected humans below, so as to invoke the spirits of doom! For tonight he shall be ours one way or the other. This I vowel to my lord Lucifer! This I promise to his majesty! Let all see the outcome of this venture this night! For the brightness of night or the darkness of day, I shall emerge from the scene without fail be it night or day break!

It was the end of a very great family tradition, thus all in the family communed together for our annual Thanksgiving gathering for the last time though unknown to all in attendance. In the year of our lord. Nineteen hundred and seventy seven, winter's snow had come sooner than earlier years and its winds blew violently against the century's old brown stone and shook all the window panes. Experiencing an out of the ordinary bout of unexplained terror, sleeping most of the day away, I couldn't sleep the night over. I began to stare aimlessly at the light post above the ceiling, having thoughts of my earlier irrational behavior, thus trying to understand what it all was about. Suddenly, a dark shadow flew across the light emitting from the bedroom window. It was a shallow reflection on the ceiling and thinking nothing of it, I closed my eyes once more and dozed off to sleep.

Then, out of the blue, I could hear massive footsteps running by my grandmother's bedroom window. In a subconscious state, with eyes half opened off and on, and hearing the muffled sounds of men's voices right outside the window, I felt the sense of danger. Too afraid to look back towards the window, I cringed under the covers until the noise went away. Briefly falling back asleep without warning, I could hear Pookey screaming, waking me saying, "GET UP! GET UP! THE BUILDING IS ON FIRE!" With my head in a fog, I asked, "WHAT?" as Pookey yelled out once more and ran towards Grandma's kitchen! "THE BUILDING IS ON FIRE; COME ON!" Jumping out of bed in a hypnotic frenzy, I followed him to the back of Grandma's apartment, opening the door adjacent to the staircase leading up to the fifth floor, and all apartments beneath.

There we discovered the whole corridor of stairs leading to all apartments and adjacent walls were engulfed in flames! Flames engulfed the entire structure of the building with a spirit of destruction! In the midst of the fiery silhouette of the flames, I could see and make out my cousin Chunky yelling out for help saying, "HELP! HELP US!" With my Aunt Lucy pulling him back into the doomed apartment and shutting the door behind them while we witnessed the entire door totally ablaze as she closed the door. I heard my mother's voice yelling, "GET THE KIDS! GET THE KIDS LUCY!" Physically feeling the courage emitting from Pookey with every step he took up the fire engulfed staircase, I quickly followed behind. As Pookey frantically stormed up the staircase, I followed in his footsteps, feverishly trying to save our family, but to no avail.

As we both ran up the staircase, the floor was collapsing under our weight while we were going up the stairs. The fire began breaching the main wooden structure and a four by four post that was holding the staircase intact. With no clear way up the engulfed staircase, we ran back down the fiery staircase, thus barely escaping the fiery trap by seconds. The staircase began to fall down to the first floor while leaving only an empty space between four walls of crackling fire. We ran back into Grandma's apartment amongst a vacuum of smoke. Dread swarmed in its entirety. With emotion dulled by the shock of terror, Pookey and I began to evacuate Grandma and Granny Grip, our great grandmother. With all will moving forward and out the front door, Pookey and I tried to restrain our grandmother from returning back into the fiery death trap. Numbed by shock, I heard the screams of my grandmother yell out, "LORD NO! MY BABIES! MY BABIES ARE UP THERE!" as she fell to her knees outside the inferno. Seeing the fire consume all and knowing there was no way out for her children, my Grandma mustered up all the physical strength she possessed and tried her best to go back into the burning building to save the family. Overweight, sickly and with diabetes, there was no way she could help avoid the inevitable. Yet it didn't matter to her; instinctively, she bulled forward back towards hell's fire without fear.

Our duty to save and abstract our grandmothers from danger approaching took most of our strength to stop Grandma from advancing towards the inferno engulfing the building, and leading her toward the front door and out of the doomed building was emotionally and physically draining. Flames quickly began to engulf the entire building seconds from our departure. Thankfully, all other residents that lived in the building escaped via the front passageway. I could hear someone say, "Some unknown hero made a call to the fire department… please come quickly… the entire building is ablaze…people are trapped inside… please hurry… PLEASE!"

As I looked up at the tower inferno, the common phenomenon of slow motion and time stopping ensued as shock began to overtake my sense of awareness.

Emotional emptiness burned within my spirit and heart, thus totally imprinted forever, as I heard my grandmother's voice yell out in terror, "OH LORD THERE'S NO WAY OUT FOR MY BABIES! THERE'S ONLY ONE WAY IN AND ONE WAY OUT!" As she lay on the ice cold concrete sidewalk in front of the building.

Everyone and everything moved in slow motion within my mind's eye, looking up at the once peaceful home now was spurring flames from every opening, and it was horrific! I looked up towards the location of my Aunt Lucy's apartment five stories high, and saw my mother hanging out of the living-room window with the illumination of flames behind her while she screamed out, "HELP US LORD HELP US!" All feelings of fear ceased possessing my soul and nothing made sense as I looked upward while seeing the fire bellow out of every window and crack, lighting every apartment and unit in the building's hollowness. The flames consumed everything that was once darkened by the night, thus inviting the spirit of utter despair to run rapid within the crumbling building. I could barely hear my mother and Aunt Lucy franticly argue over who should throw their children out of the window further from the fire's breath, which sparked hopeful fear within my shattered psyche as the fire approached them all! One by one, I saw my mother throw my siblings out of the widow's door and visions of my newborn sister bounce off the frozen ground, crying for a moment, then total silence racked my brain. Fire was breaching the living room in which they were locked. Not able to look any more, I lost all facets of reality as my loved ones fell to their doom. Walking in a dreamlike state, I felt no emotion. I suddenly heard my mother yell to my Aunt Lucy, "YOU CAN'T GO BACK LUCY!" Hearing my Aunt Lucy respond, "I'M NOT GONE LEAVE MY BABY!!!" My mind was in a fog as I looked up and saw my mother being pushed out of the window by my Aunt Lucy. Then my aunt ran back into the fiery flames, ultimately never to be heard from again!

Everyone and everything moved in slow motion! All in slow motion was the vessel in which spiritual evil played its way out in the midst of the night. As I witnessed my mother fall out the five story window backwards, while hitting the frozen winter ground, I grew numb. Mama bounced only once, and didn't move or utter a word. My first thought was, "My mom is dead!" It was as if someone thrust a knife into my chest, stabbed me in the heart and twisted it. As the horrifying events unfolded, time stopped. Everything began moving in slow motion, with no reality or understanding in thought; it was as if I was immersed in a cloud of forgetfulness, with a voice of despair ringing in my head over and over again! "Your mother is dead! Your mother is dead."

Repetitiously, I could hear the voice of doom repeating those very words. In a state of shock, I aimlessly walked around the burning building unaware of my surroundings but heard the many sirens of the fire trucks blazing in the back ground, yet they were muffled to my senses.

Flashing lights and red fire trucks were all around me; I walked in a daze aimlessly. I just walked around the building in a dream state; in total shock, feeling nothing, thinking only of the thought of my dead mother and new baby sister.

Visualizing their horrendous dissent from the top of an inferno was ingrained into my brain, and played out over and over in my head. Eternally tormenting my mind's eye forevermore! They're dead and nothing in life mattered anymore! It seemed as if all I loved died at that moment. Seeing my little sister fall to her death, along with my mother was more than I could bare; with my mind's eye bathed in a fog of unbelievable grief, I was unable to show any emotion. Moving in a robotic state, I could make out Pookey with a cloth of some kind wrapped around him while standing in the ever growing crowd of spectators and firemen hauling hoses and equipment. I slowly walked up to him with tears flowing down my face saying, "My mother is dead! Nikia's dead! I saw them fall Pookey… I saw them fall…Pookey, they are gone… I saw them die!" Then tears flowed freely and uncontrollably as I placed my face towards the ground in disbelief and enormous grief that I've never in my life felt before.

With no apparent emotion in Pookey's voice, the tone of hope for me and doom for him echoed as he calmly replied, "It's not your mother that's dead P, it's my mother… It's my mother that's dead, P." In dismay yet sobering relief I asked, "What?!" And he responded once more, "It's my mother that died tonight, not yours… They are putting your mother and the babies in ambulances… I could hear them say they're breathing… they're taking my mother out of the building's area right now!" That was the last time I would see Pookey or Chunky until the long, hard wrenching funeral. Years of trials and tribulations were in its infancy and were bound to grow rapidly. With no emotion, my brother/cousin turned away from me as two firemen carried off his mother and baby sister in the same black "Dead on Arrival" (DOA) bag as I saw on TV. I disappeared into the crowd and away from the tragic scene as relief and wonder subsided within me when hearing his hopeful message of life, at least for my mother and baby sister. With the news of my mother's fate being promising, sudden feelings of awareness crept back into my conscience, and reason flowed back within my soul, accompanied with fear mixed with anger. I began to shake from the frigate weather, and my teeth were chattering in the wind. Then as if the Creator himself could hear my inner voice calling for help and safety, a total stranger picked me up from the freezing ground and placed an old blanket over me and removed me out of the cold. The stranger took me down the street and next door, some distance from the burned out building. Inside the stranger's home, he dressed me in an old "Dojo" uniform once worn by him.

Though most of my memories of that terrible event has faded with time, the memory of the strange man that took me in from the freezing cold shall never fade; the stranger was a Taekwondo master, and displayed both discipline and kindness.

His apartment was adorned with tournament trophies and medals, along with pictures of him engaging in many tournaments and battles, reminding me of recently passed martial art events and simple glories I had inside the "Boys and Girls Club." Still, the overwhelming feeling of doom filled the air, and the heavy weight of sadness consumed my heart, but the stranger comforted me in my dismay. My face formed a small smile upon hearing the news of other strangers gathering my surviving siblings from a fireman who was speaking to the stranger, and directing them towards the kind stranger's home and out the cold towards safety, and a sigh of relief calmed my fears for them. But truly there was no happiness found within me. A veil of darkness cloaked my lowly spirit, allowing no ray of light to enter my soul. Stricken with grief, my mind wondered out into space and nothingness, hearing no one, seeing no one, and comprehending absolutely nothing said, only responding to simple requests and calls of sustenance. Months passed by without any family member seeking us out, and I fell deeper into depression, not knowing the health nor whereabouts of my baby sister or mother. Visualizing the events of that night over and over again, made the time spent with the stranger unbearable, and I found myself internalizing the horrific scene in order to cope with the obvious.

Those I loved the most and those very close to me were now dead and gone forever with no rhyme nor reason. To understand the purpose behind such sorrow and pain consumed my every thought daily, asking myself, "What happened? Why did these horrific, terrifying and morbid things happen to my family? Why would a loving god allow such harm to come to those who love him most?" Those such as my Aunt Lucy who alienated all within her family and abandoned her religious upbringing to try and find favor from our Creator and was reluctant to engage in any normal function or holiday for the sake of her convictions; she gave it all up for god and now she's dead? It made no sense to me at such an early age. It seemed as if she'd died in disobedience to her god in my eyes. I pondered these questions over and over in my head: "Could death be the price for engaging in a pagan ritual (Thanksgiving) that was not in accordance with the religion and god she embraced? Did she lose her life and her baby's life for this? Did she die for spending Thanksgiving with those she loved? What god would demand such a price for such a small transgression?"

After my aunt finally found the courage to leave her worthless, disgraceful no good drunkard husband to begin a new life away from abuse, she only found death while trying to serve a god that never seemed to be there. In my humble opinion it seemed fruitless, and non-productive for her or any of us struggling in poverty just to serve a god who didn't care for those that loved him. Young and un-aware of true evil, my heart's spirit began to react to the negative stimuli infecting my very thought process from that awful day forward.

Feeling the indescribable loss of my loved one's grew very deep within my soul, hardening my heart without knowing, waiting for someone to save us from this nightmare thrust upon us. Without any response nor inquiry from family still living, days passed in a stranger's home; no one came to our rescue, nor aunt, uncle or even my very own father. Days turned into weeks, weeks turned into months, but still there was no response from any family member, and hope of being rescued faded with the days. I had no father nor mother to cry my awful woe, for I still didn't know if my mother survived the terrible fall that played out in my mind day and night. No news of any sort reached the stranger's door. Though I was very young and long in ignorance, I still needed to know the outcome of my mother and baby sister, but no one came to our aid. Abandonment truly takes the will of a youngster's heart away! Then one day when I thought no one would show for sure, my father showed up at the stranger's door. A look of shock instantly appeared on my face. Right when I'd given up on all I had trusted, hope finally appeared. I'd given up on all I believed in physically and spiritually, for I no longer relied on family for strength, and trusted no loved ones without circumstance, yet a miracle manifested itself when my father appeared! Finally, someone I loved came to claim me and my siblings.

In the event of tragedy peculiar emotional norms proceed to malfunction and splinter. Instead of salvation, I felt nothing, and when I looked at my father's face, all I could see was a look of concern, and not one of happiness. In my freshly broken mind, I thought nothing! There was no joy in my father's face to see his children safe and sound? Though young, I instinctively knew the look of burden in my father's eyes, just as I felt the stranger show love and concern for me and my siblings. As my siblings ran to embrace him, I stayed back and watched my father's emotional response as the barrage and screams of happy faces were upon his long lost children. His response was not so surprising, for it was as if he only acted as if he were happy to see us, and gratefulness in his finding us shined not in his retrieval. As he gathered up his children and quickly corralled us all into his car, he said not three words to one nor all. Silence and resentment perused throughout the ride back to his home, and I could feel it. I felt as if he didn't love us at all, and didn't care if we perished along with my doomed Aunt Lucy and baby cousin, Omega. Because of father's mannerisms and body language, for the very first time, I felt ashamed of him and his very presence, and at that moment, I knew I would no longer look up to him from that day forward. With silence, I showed contempt and distain for his presumed non-affections, and to my surprise, he reacted with no physical or spiritual understanding to my protest.

With silence, he showed his willingness to accept my presumed indignations of his non-verbal or physical responses, and in time a son's love for his father began to burn out once more. No longer did I feel abandonment by him, for the unspoken spiritual connection that resides within a son and father endured; instead I heard the protest of our presence by his insisting concubine. No longer did I feel alone within my woes, for time had masked the pain, and repaired my senses. Periodic news of my mother's health and wellbeing, coupled with the comradely of my half siblings eased my longing for both my mother and sister. As time lingered, our presence had taken its toll on my father's relationship with his then other half. With distain and dislike, she cared for my father's legitimate children until the burden overwhelmed her. With his concubine caring for us daily, I could see that it had become too much for her nerves and she could handle no more. Although she cared for us the best way she could, caring for others when she could not handle the children she herself had, left a bitter taste in her mouth; yet with no malice in her heart, she obviously made her strong feelings known to my father continuously. Obviously the strain of taking care of someone else's children on a regular basis had taken its toll; daily arguments increased exponentially, forcing my father to make other arrangements with not so loving family members, such as the cruel and spiteful, "Aunt Katherine." Within a few weeks, my siblings and I were back on the ominous road home to 2222 Carolina Street! We were on our way back to our home without the loving security or safety of a loving mother.

Little did I know that this time my Aunt Katherine assumed total control of our lives and wellbeing! Guardian and care provider she was not. A woman that was truly filled with animosity accompanied her obvious show of disappointment in her sister's children. Rigid was her authority, with an abundance of pent up tyrannical, cruel and un-checked behavior. Not to mention the fact I was the primary culprit fueling her full anger, accrued from the not so much intentional hanging of her firstborn, Prezon, not one year and half ago. With total control came total tyranny and revenge for her son's former indignation. From the very moment we walked into the front door of our own home, the light of darkness burned too bright, accompanied with sadness and fear. Fear of our Aunt Katherine's wrath and the longing of our mother's love intensified. Sure enough it was as the wicked witch of the Midwest had moved into our humble abode.

Malice had descended upon my siblings and me, and our wellbeing was most definitely last on her list of responsibilities, but first on her shit list! Weeks turned into months, and months turned into a year of pure torture, thus hope diminished rapidly. As my mother's children suffered under the hands of a so-called loved one, the perceived wicked witch that happened to be our mother's baby sister, animosity, hatred, and distain did not enter our undeveloped minds.

It was as if a wicked storm cloud moved over head, and never left from our home, thus raining down despair and sorrow among all residing within. My Aunt Katherine exuberated her authority with unadulterated cruelty and without restraint. At dinner time we would eat supper hours after her own children were served, and no more TV for us, for after a simple meal, we were off to bed immediately; however, Prezon and Tasha enjoyed every program they wished to entertain after their meal. Only music, church radio, and chores consumed my siblings and my daily routine. Our day started at the crack of dawn; my siblings and I enjoyed no childhood activities under my not so loving aunt's hand. We were always on the lookout for her ever watchful eyes. In constant fear of an ass beating, we walked on borrowed time. Twenty four seven, seven days a week, we toiled. Knowing her willingness to engage in brutal physical discipline outweighed her never ending eagerness to enact and delegate her dictates, I made sure to stay in her good graces at all times, humbly volunteering my services before she uttered her incisive prompting. I prepared whatever chore she would require well in advance, thus keeping my brothers and sisters from getting in trouble, while I watched her every move without her knowledge.

I would make sure not to cross her path during her soap-operas, while feeling the rage and dislike protruding from her cold dark eyes every time she looked my way. I stayed clear of her wrath as much as humanly possible. It was wishful thinking on my part to avoid or see her hateful being every minute on the second throughout the day, stuck inside a small bungalow, hoping only to be free of her menacing orders in the night. It was as if I stumbled into a field of broken egg shells, and had to navigate my way through an elaborate maze without touching a single shell fragment. Days dragged on and nights whizzed by, and each day reminded me of Cinderella's ordeal with her wicked stepmother and step sisters, feeling overwhelming oppression and ill will. I prayed for the day my mom would return from the hospital; then unexpectedly, after more than a year, the door opened and there she was! She was back from the ranks of the missing or the dead, and for more than a year we had to endure the angry techniques of child rearing by her youngest sister, "Aunt Katherine!" The physical, mental and spiritual abuse enacted upon us by my Aunt Katherine was unlike none I'd ever encountered before, and although it was only my siblings and I who were subjected to such treatment, it was impossible to imagine anyone with love of family to be treated in such an awful manor.

It was the first and last time anyone other than our mother would have control over our development. Time under her supervision for more than a year was unbearable. Knowing we observed her dealings with her sister's and own children, Kat made sure to conceal her exploits and tyrannical disciplinary methods from my mother.

From the first moment the front door opened and my eyes bared witness to the wheel chair holding my mother's broken body into the living room, a smile instantly appeared on my face; although, it was heart wrenching to see her incapacitated within a cast from neck to toe while inebriated from a host of opioids, including morphine. She could barely lift her head up to see her own children for the first time in over a year.

When my mother did begin to recognize the sublime rays of light that only shines with the sweet taste of freedom, not seen since the night of the ordeal, the return to her home brought jubilance throughout the entire apartment. A look displaying real happiness appeared upon my face once again. The unnecessary load of oppression and responsibility for others began to fall from my shoulders like a drape of despair; an exuberant cry of relief exhaled from my body without hesitation. A genuine smile emerged on my face looking into my long lost mother's eyes. For the first time after the fire, I found peace of mind, and that long awaited smile upon my face invoked within my Aunt Katherine a look of concern also not seen since before the fire.

A fear of exposure?! Exposure of the appalling abusive behavior inflicted upon her sister's children. The appalling abuse administered corporal punishment by her own hand over the past year was about to be revealed by my un-relentless memory of events perpetrated upon her children in her absence. Seeing the fear in her eye, I said nothing; my heart was full of joy seeing my mother's reaction to the news of our plight, and her response to her younger sibling's actions while incapacitated. Man, I was so happy to see my mother that a single tear ran down my face as I truly understood child abuse. With my mother's health in mind, I subconsciously resolved the issues within my soul, unwilling to fan the flames of descent within the family any longer, I held back my tongue and embraced the moment. Sensing no response from our nemesis as I looked at aunt Kat, she milked the moment for all she could, displaying a false air of loving care towards all the children, including her own. With time for adjustment, my mother was moving about relatively well since she was diagnosed as terminally crippled.

Soon Kat was out of our house and back to her own grim way of life within her own home. A few months passed and the light of hope shined dimly once more. But this time it would be the dim light that fluttered briefly then faded off for good. For despair demanded a very great expense! The luxury of surviving hell's fury played havoc upon my mom's body and spirit, and she began drinking heavily to off-set the constant pain. Even in the morning hours I would hear the obvious pop of a beer can, coupled with the many pharmaceutical drugs consumed daily. I thought she would die from drugs and alcohol. Her zest for life diminished, and the loving home maker I recognized vanished and slowly wilted away forevermore. It took all the strength she could muster in a day just dealing with the constant pain of her injuries.

Reallocating most responsibilities, she relied mainly upon her firstborn son for support and relief from child caring and in the caring of my four siblings. I learned nothing of love or compassion for them, and the toll of such a grown-up burden weighed heavily on my spirit. So at the age of twelve, I took up the role of father and mother. Ill equipped mentally, physically and emotionally for proper child care, I rebelled against the unwanted responsibilities, imposing massive physical and verbal abuse upon my brothers and sisters.

Attempting to fill the post of a loving parent, I begrudgingly accepted the responsibilities and tortured my siblings no longer. Looking back at my juvenile behavior when faced with adversity, I feel ashamed and embarrassed from the lack of understanding, and general compassion I showed towards those I loved most; although, at the time, I thought of myself as the good son, stepping into the shoes of a father, as I lorded over my siblings with an iron fist, and strong taunts.

There was no time allotted for school any longer; public school time had been hijacked at the age of twelve; no more childish things! There would be no more hanging out with the boys after school, no more whistling at the girls as they pass by the playground, nor skateboarding or getting off the school bus with the rest of the kids in the hood.

Making sure my siblings got off to school on time was my morning chore. There was no time for self, or my love of school house shenanigans; cooking and cleaning for my family over shadowed all other activities. I was transformed from a selfish snot-nose brat that cared only for candy, pop and clothing, to a hard nose dictatorial master over all siblings in view. As the months passed by, so did the joy of being a child, for no longer was I blessed with that privilege, and as I tried to fill the role of primary guardian and parent, my mother's health improved slowly, but her emotional behavior lacked in such parental capacity. She began drinking alcohol daily, and associating herself with the shadiest of characters in and out of the hood, thus building a reputation of an out of control drunken slut throughout the neighborhood.

Defying the expert doctors that stated she would never walk again, she stood on her two feet within a year, but not without change in her personality. She would stay away from home for long periods of time; days would pass without a word of her safety or whereabouts, thus leaving all responsibility of caring for her children up to her first born without concern of his emotional, physical or mental ability to care for those not very much younger than he, not to mention my own wellbeing and welfare. My mind would wonder out into space some days, hoping she would get better from whatever suffering and hardship she endured, and resume her place as mother and caretaker of us all. Never really contemplating the situation at hand, I lashed out in anger towards all around, and praying to god felt like a waste of time after experiencing such horrifying accounts within the family.

In fact, I thought the Creator didn't listen to those who loved him.

I began to feel the never ending waterfall of agonizing pain brought on by hopelessness dashing against the rocky shores of reality, and grew ever so angry by the moment asking for the answers to the madness taking place around me, thus finding no solace or peace of mind.

I stared off into the sky, saying within myself, no goodness resides here. No truth or logic made sense in the hope for righteousness to make itself known or present in a place where evil reigns supreme. I felt trapped in a place where everyone strives for the sake of evil! Before long, I was out and about, and in the mean streets of Gary, Indiana every night looking at the people with distain and wonderment, as I learned the ways of the night stalker, showing no emotion towards things, places or people I once held with esteem. In the streets, I was taught to despise all things good. I saw more truth in lies than in those preaching in the pulpit. One plus one equals two! Learning the love of darkness could be as satisfying as that of the light, where no answers could be obtained, but only pain, sorrow and death!

Deep inside, the irrational and wicked thoughts I was feeling had no substance, yet in my youthful defiance, a sense of despair accompanied my blissfulness in ignorance, and seeing the fruits of wickedness out shine the light of right daily, my persona showed promise in the streets and gave credence to the things I would acquire in the service of evil. I saw veraciousness rewarded with the sting of vipers and the bite of ferocious dogs, ultimately running humanity's light away at every turn. Does this mean that the only truth is in lies?! It can't mean that; there has to be an answer to all of this bullshit, but how could I obtain it?! "Seek and ye shall find." "Search and it shall be given over to you."

Over and over those words echoed within my head as I committed various crimes to feed my brothers and sisters, feeling sick to my stomach each time I entered the danger zone, until my conscience was null.

The feeling of doing wrong had dissipated into emptiness and had been replaced with a feeling of accomplishment coupled with the rush of adrenaline when committing the act of larceny among other illegal activities.

Becoming ever so bold in my understanding of the darkness that gripped all within that little town, I began to embrace hopelessness and said to myself, "...oh well to those in need or hurting from hunger; I'm glad it's not me!" I dabbed deeper into drugs and alcohol; then one day out of the blue, clarity engulfed my young spirit.

After enduring the heinous regularity of constant questions detailing the death of their mother and baby sister, Chunky and Pookey returned as shells of their former selves, dehumanized from the exposure of photographic evidence presented by the defending attorneys representing my dead Aunt's husband Buddy, drilling holes in the spirits of my cousin/brothers, thus destroying all remnants of spirituality within the two. I could only imagine the horror and hatred experienced by my cousin/brothers as they endured the media circus surrounding the trial of their mother and baby sister's death, and being interrogated by strange men defending the actions of the man that murdered my Aunt Lucy and cousin Omega, their mother and sister.

Chunky returned from the courts of hell's pit with eyes of darkness, and so did Pookey! Being the soul witness of the horrific crimes of murder visited upon the entire family by monsters once trusted, Chunky grew in rage and anger within his spirit, putting up with the torturous spectacle of non-caring strangers questioning him daily. Watching and judging him in the pirate's courtroom became unbearable.

Viewing photos of his mother and sister's burned bodies beyond recognition for days on end was just too much! Enduring the tyrannical treatment imposed on me and my siblings not a year ago was like child's play compared to the emotional turmoil visited upon Pookey and Chunky on a daily basis, and I prayed that the Creator would soothe the flames of hatred within their souls. Unknowingly, the cruel and unforgivable treatment from our Aunt Katharine changed the lot of us, but to my surprise there was no outward differences in the demeanor of my loving cousin/brothers once they appeared on the scene after the trail. It was the same Chunky as before the tragic fire; there was no difference in his speech, mannerisms, or body language; as a matter of fact, he acted as if nothing ever happened. There were no signs of trauma, and no feelings of horror over the death of his mother and sister. Playing around like before, and not wanting to bring up the issue, I said nothing once Chunky was back into my presence. I wondered what could be going through his mind as he endured so much emotional strife and eternal grief. Imagine reliving the events of that evil night over and over again for more than a year, at the ripe old age of eleven, and as time progressed and curiosity motivated questions from total strangers, it only fueled the construction of an impenetrable wall around their consciences and hearts. Questions of that fateful night propagated by those outside the family became more frequent, and Chunky's response showed little concern or emotion. I began feeling as if something was not right with my beloved cousin/brother at all; and I was right.

Tell me do you smell despair?! Do you smell the unforgettable stench of smoke, burned flesh and water damage?! For that smell lingered a long time and was hard to get rid of, but the smell of hopelessness lingered longer and may never be healed. The darkness that plagued the family had just begun, from living in a clean environment filled with love, to that of living in poverty's dirt and squalor. Having nothing to eat for days at a time, watching Chunky's behavior disintegrate by the moment, I saw my own behavior follow suit. I lived in constant fear of the unknown, and was surrounded by unscrupulous people that would take what valuables we may possess in an instant, be it material or not. Your mind, spirit and soul were up for grabs out in the streets. Being young and stupid to the world's evil didn't help the matter one bit, and being under massive stress on a daily basis hardened my heart quickly. The pressure was unbearable for all, and I began exhibiting physical symptoms of abdominal pain and stiffness; suddenly, my entire midsection was hard as a rock.

Soon I was admitted into the hospital with no idea of what was going on inside my body. No one could figure out the problem manifesting within me. The doctors were mystified; I was given barium enema after barium enema with no physical change in my condition. Days turned into weeks, and weeks turned into months inside the comfort of a hospital. My mother visited me only once throughout the time I was admitted.

Feelings of abandonment slowly crept back into my mind after spending over six months in a hospital without one visit from those I thought loved me. No one cared enough to visit?! No mother, no father, or any member of the family to inquire of my wellbeing in six months?! At first, I waited and watched for someone to visit without it ever occurring, then I just gave up. It didn't matter, being in the hospital was the best thing for me. There I met a friend, and was actually able to be a child once more. After all the horrendous events, the total breakdown of my entire family had only just begun, and the never ending darkness that engulfed my world became a way of life. The hospital was a place where some vestige of normalcy could be obtained for someone my age. Being in the confines of that place of healing for so long helped me gain and obtain a sense of emotional and physical wellness, and being under nice clean sheets on a real bed every night was a blessing without my knowledge.

Goofing off each night after lights out with my new found friend healed my spirit and soul. Knowing I would have ice cream each day brought a smile to my face and I began to develop a personal relationship with all the staff. We were able to refer to most of the nursing staff on first name basis which made the children's ward my safety zone. Eating the required daily amount of food made it seem like home without the danger. Purposely prolonging my affliction by keeping my stomach hard, I was able to extend my stay one month after my new found friend left for home. And even though I was bored out of my mind, I didn't want to go back to the mad house on 2222 Carolina Street because an environment of total unseen and unknown evil lurked around every corner and street of the Colored Doors, and I could feel the un-named evil that surrounded us all in the hood.

Deep down inside, I knew my ailments were made up; it was all in my head. The human body is truly a remarkable and amazing machine. Subconsciously and unintentionally, I created my own affliction to combat the massive abuse imposed on me personally. The doctors couldn't find anything emotionally or physically wrong with me because there wasn't anything wrong to find, well at least physically. The enormously confusing feelings of being trapped by uncontrollable circumstances and my lot in life ignited the imaginary symptoms.

Not able to comprehend the meaning of it all was more than my little undeveloped brain could take, so without awareness or comprehension, my body reacted in desperation.

My mind made a way out of the mad and unexplainable environment occurring in my life and it worked, but only for a short period of time, and yet in that short time, I was able to cope with the pain and suffering inflicted upon my family by maniacs. Inventing ways to deal with such disruption in life must be a mechanism set in place by the Creator, so when a Child of Light is faced with overwhelming odds, and emotional and unmeasurable stress levels, he or she could overcome and grow stronger. Developing a remarkable internal strength, overcoming emotional hardship in which grown mature humans find hard to handle, hardened my spirit towards darkness in such a way that it's hard to explain as an adult, let alone a twelve year old adolescent. Life had become unbearable for me, and no one could imagine the sorrow within the depths of my soul.

The day I dreaded had come. What I feared the entire time from when I was admitted in the hospital, had finally arrived. It was the day of my release, and the day I would be going back home, and ultimately back to the madness I subconsciously and physically fled from. Unwittingly, I conjured up some fictitious illness to escape a life of the spiritual torturers, poverty and fear.

As soon as the nurse announced my fated departure, my heart skipped a beat, and the thought of why I was there in the first place had entered into my head. I had to mentally prepare myself for the small piece of hell called my home. From not seeing anyone including my mother for such a long time, I became numb inside; I felt nothing! I was numb to the life and the problems that accompanied my plight, facilitating the phrase I said over and over in my head: "Nothing matters anymore!" "No one loved me" was my thought from that day forward! No one cared to come see me in the hospital in a little over six months, and I was just a little child! I was admitted into the hospital as an orphan, and had not one call from my mother or father. I truly was abandoned to the unfamiliar hands of strangers. Those were my thoughts as my mother entered the room.

I showed no joy in her presence, and she showed little emotion as well, knowing my obvious emotional state. As she entered the room, she only looked briefly and said, "Hey" and not much more. But as we left the children's ward and entered the emergency room heading out of the hospital, a nice bon voyage was granted to me by the nurses that I got to know personally. They insisted that I sit in a wheelchair for my grand departure and wheeled me out the double glass doors saying in unison: "Be good P! We'll miss you! We don't want to see you here again, okay?" The nurses and staff members were waving me off as my mother wheeled me down the ramp and into the ride she had mustered up at the last minute.

Seeing the shabby car in which we were to board, and the miscreant driver equipped with a Schlitz Molt Liquor can in hand, I cringed at the thought of returning back to the once peaceful home that had been transformed to the unbelievable wicked layer that was now 2222 Carolina Street, located deep inside the depths of the hood, now known today as the infamous "Colored Doors!"

As we drove off of the peaceful hospital premises, my mother looked back at me and said, "I know you're mad at me but don't be… I've been very busy baby! I got a surprise for you; you'll see." Showing very little enthusiasm or curiosity in her surprise, I continued staring out of the back window of the car. With a look of sadness posted across my face, I wondered why we were going the wrong way. Seeing my lack of concern, while knowing I would inquire about the surprise she uttered, my mother couldn't contain herself any longer and blurted out her suspenseful surprise saying, "We Moved P… I got a better place just down the road here… not very far from the very hospital… How about that baby?" She knew I had become ill, literally from the corruption that surrounded us, and she tried to make amends the best way she knew, but I had resided in the hospital for more than six months without a single call or visit from her, and she knew I held a grudge with a passion!

Away from all that so-called loved me, with no word or sight of them, the news of moving would have been better received if the place was located far away from The Colored Doors. Our new place was close to the hospital and that only further fueled the flames of anger of being abandoned, mostly by my own mother! Then thoughts of reason entered my mind and knowing my mother's physical and emotional health was in question seemed to quell my anger. Witnessing the constant decline in my mother's spirit and soul quickly extinguished the fire of abandonment, not to mention the obvious positive changes in her behavior. I knew she worked as hard as she could to possibly change things for the better, so a smile slowly broke free from my spoiled rotten soul, and she could see I was pleased with her decision.

Life returned to my empty soul and excitement entered into my eyes as we got closer to her surprise! Seeing our new place brought me back to life, and the reality of a new start began to deeply settle into my thoughts. As we drove by my mother's surprise, I looked at the beautifully old architecture of the brownstone building and said to myself, "Whoa!" We moved to a great building in a clean and beautiful neighborhood, and thoughts of social change, safety and the hope of happiness entered my mind. Thoughts for normalcy within our savagely torn apart family would finally come, but the thought was a pipe dream, for my own mental state had been shattered! My subconscious had begun operating in stealth mode by the upheaval and imaginary feelings of abandonment from both parents. Unwittingly, I had fallen deeply into depression after facing the most terrible events in my family's history.

The trauma experienced from constant domestic violence and murders of those I loved had taken its toll on my fragile and undeveloped mind. My mind was broken and shattered from the shear overall evil spearheading the events that took place within my family. Yet I played the part of being mentally sound and innocent; I played just fine amongst the madness befalling us all, but behind the façade something was seriously wrong.

I regressed into an introvert and no longer interacted with anyone, not even those of my own age group. Life seemed short and so many unanswered universal questions loomed overhead like a dark cloud. While in the hospital amongst strangers, the unfamiliar feelings of safety existed within those sanitized walls, though horrifying nightly dreams of fantastic beings, and futuristic events consumed my waking thoughts. To describe the occurrences and visions of my nightly dreams is to describe future events in total, and up to the end of all things worldly; although, I didn't know that at the time. Never having any visitors at all made loneliness the norm; I was enrolled into the hospital feeling the full force of abandonment, and hopelessness grew immeasurably.

Feeling all alone and being all alone are two different things; I know that now. Searching for answers to explain the unexplainable, leaves one wondering if a Creator or god truly exists. Love for a Creator growing stronger and stronger within my heart brought comfort to my lonely soul. After giving up on seeking universal truths or answers about the unseen from my parents, I felt hopelessness for the time, for they themselves had no clue of the unseen, nor any adult around me for that matter. I had very little interest in the mundane ways of the world of lunacy, but the fire to explore the unknown and retrieve its secrets would not leave my soul. When you're young and alone, hopelessness overtakes reason, but learning about things no one ever talks about takes precedence over everyday things and brings relief to the perceived orphan, yet universal questions remained in my thoughts day and night.

"There must be a god! Why is life so hard and full of suffering?! I must find out why evil rules unchecked and rampant?! Do we as sentient beings, created by a divine entity, deserve the pain and sorrow that has devastated humanity?! Did the breakdown of our family mean anything to he who had created us?!" Every day these very questions consumed me without fail. Although during the time I spent with Glenn in the hospital, I was able to achieve some sense of normalcy and a sense of wellness, still the sadness would not subside. The never ending thoughts of universal questions consumed my every waking moment, and my new environment literally brought sorrow, despair and grief without answer. Maybe things had changed for the better, so I had thought. Lessons of courage and endurance were taught by the consumption of mental thought, and words plucked from the "Wholly" Scriptures echoed in my mind's eye.

I blamed GOD for all the misfortune befalling my family, humanity and all that was wrong with the world. My every thought entertained only uncertainty!

But how could a merciful god allow so much misery and grief to those who serve him?! There must be an answer to it all! Memories of long lost thoughts fade away, and so goes the light! Then comes Darkness!

Chapter XIII

The Illumination of Darkness

I was fascinated by the artistry and craftsmanship of the magnificent turn of the century brownstone building we were about to embrace as our new abode. Inside and out of the half a block building sparked a spirit of hopefulness or a new day within my soul. In total amazement, I walked through the massive glass front door of the building. I looked in wonderment and noticed the early nineteenth century art deco adorning the hallway and staircase leading up to our new apartment. When walking through the front door of our apartment itself, I marveled at the beautiful walls and wooden floors as the sun shined off their surface that induced genuine joy within my heart. With amazement, I wondered at the high celling, and the hardwood floors mesmerized my sense of sight. The restored old plastered walls encased in wooden trimming brought a smile to my face. As my mother and I toured the apartment, I began reminiscing of the many places we lived in my younger years. Seeing the old water heaters in every room, and the four legged ceramic tub adorning the bathroom took me back in time, a time when everything was authentic and genuine. There were antique 1920 style faucets with the "X" shaped hot and cold water knobs. The nostalgia made me giggle with glee. From a distance, I could hear my mother yelling down the hall, "...you have your own room now P!" With a faint echo of her voice saying, "...we're finally free from that place," obviously referring to The Colored Doors. As she walked closer to my location, she yelled out once more, "You have your own bedroom now P... You can paint it any way you like."

Immediately I responded, "The color black," which matched my broken emotional state, as I turned around to face my dearest mother with a resounding look of jubilance, feeling a sense of peace and quiet for once in years. I finally felt relief in spirit from the darkness of loneliness. Exuberantly filled with zeal, I solely inspected the entire apartment further that first day, and found myself satisfied and without doubt. It was very clean, with new furniture amongst an atmosphere of peace, for it was quiet and tranquil throughout the entire building. I heard only the sounds of car engines passing by the wide open windows as the sheer curtains blew from the incoming wind that cooled the entire apartment. As the afternoon breeze flowed through the silk-like living room curtains, I thought to myself, "Wait minute… There were only two bedrooms in the apartment, so how could I have my own bedroom with three brothers and sisters?" Wondering what emotional horror was next to come, I asked mom where the rest of my siblings would be sleeping. With a sweet and unselfish tone she responded, "I'll be sleeping on the couch in the dinning-room, and the rest of the children can have the other bedrooms… don't mind me baby… I'm okay!"

With a worry free look, she turned and walked back towards the living-room. With a boilermaker in hand, she sat by the living-room window and glared outside wagging her crossed leg and smiling. In a moment's notice, she turned towards me and turned back towards the window, and I could see a momentary look of shame on her face, but why?

I could hear the sorrow in my mother's voice as she hummed in unison to the music on the radio. I knew something was upsetting her and I contemplated the source of her woe when all seemed to be wonderful. "Could it be a symptom of guilt… guilt for not visiting her firstborn in the hospital, not even once…Could that be the reason I now have my own bedroom?" After spending more than six months in the hospital located just down the street from our new place of dwelling, I thought to myself, "Could that be the source of my mother's depression… Without a call or visit from any family member in all that time, I felt unloved. Could that be the reason I now have my own bedroom?!"

In my mind's eye, I could see my mother imagining how hard it must have been for me, spending so much time alone within a medical institution, being so young and left alone for so many months, under the care of total strangers, and without her loving touch. The damage had been done, and the seed of isolation had been deeply planted within my lowly soul and its roots had begun to grow stronger each day. Young and unable to grasp the significance of being left alone for so many months stunted my ability to develop compassion or empathy for others. I was unaware of the neurosis I developed and behaved as if nothing were wrong. I thought everything within myself, be it physical, mental or spiritual, was going to be back to normal, but that was far from the truth! For now I trusted no one any longer, not even my loving mother.

Many years later, and in retrospect, I began to realize that I was suffering from a massive depression after my time spent in the hospital. I was too young to know or self-diagnose my mental state, but my mother knew something was seriously wrong with me, but said nothing. A parent knows her child, better than the child knows himself, yet she said nothing to anyone, not even me, her own firstborn son! On the surface, I showed no emotional change, acting as if nothing were wrong. I was still the same "P" of old. There were no inquiries into my sudden lack of trust in anything or anyone. She closed her eyes to any odd and un-childlike behaviors I would exhibit. As I walked around without hope of happiness, she said little. "He'll grow out of it," she must have thought, not wanting to face her part in my sudden self-imposed secluded behavior. Denial is not just a river in Egypt.

It affects us all in some form or another, with our conscience unaware, yet my depression was the tip of the iceberg when speaking of the unknown. For a darker spirit of anger had formed within my own humble spirit, and I continued to fight its influence, but at that time of my oblivious youth, I was clueless to its wicked power.

I felt empty inside, and nothing could fill the void. No good will was within me at that time because of it, and staying to myself soothed the savage beast from within. Lost in self-thought, I liked the calmness of night and often gazed out of my bedroom window in search of calmness from within, wanting nothing but the darkness of the night to cover my weary soul. I wanted to sleep all the time, but didn't know why, and I felt my spirit cry out for help within my very soul. I didn't know what was happening to me; all I knew was that I was tired of everything! I was too young to know of mental distress or disorder. Unwilling or even able to explain the feelings roaming within my head, I dared not attempt to explain the unexplained feelings within. I found myself sneaking around the bathroom medicine cabinet, covertly popping my mother's powerful sedatives and pain pills like Darvon, and I slept days on end without hearing a word from my mother.

My mother said nothing! She must have known that I pilfered the medicine cabinet whenever the opportunity would arise, and as I walked around in a daze and doped up from her pain pills, not a word was uttered. There was no hiding it, but she never confronted me or said anything about the whereabouts of her dangerous medication. This careless behavior persisted for more than three weeks. Than a voice came to me asking, "Do you want to die…Do you want just sleep?" Then another vindictive and ominous voice would say, "You're okay… nothing will happen… They make you feel good that's all... They help you sleep soundly... You can take more… You'll be okay." It was the light of goodness within me fighting the growing dark spirit that also resided within my soul, and yet I was too young to know the dangerous activity in which I was partaking. I just wanted to sleep all the time and I didn't know why.

Then one day I began feigning for the Darvon drug, and whenever she was out of her supply, I would react as they were my drugs that ran out. I was shaking from head to toe, rummaging through every orifice and crack within the house, looking and turning over every pillow and cushion on all furniture for any drug she may have overlooked. I even went through my mother's purse as she lay motionless in an alcoholic and drug induced coma. Seeing the self-imposed damage I caused upon myself, mom knew she had to do something to save me from myself. She did her job well, keeping the drug out of the hands of her child from that time forward. With no success accessing her pain medication, I wondered aimlessly like a zombie throughout the apartment for weeks drying out from the poisoners, called Pharmacia. After weeks of forced sobering up, I finally came across a bottle of generic aspirin. Consuming more than twenty five tablets at once, I must have damaged an organ; what a mistake that was! Falling face first across my bed, feeling sick to the stomach, some time passed and I began to see white spots appear all over my body, and began shaking from withdrawals I assumed. While experiencing awful withdrawals from the powerful pain killers and feeling the effects of the arsenic within the aspirin, I realized I was killing myself.

I slowly fell asleep, and awoke hours later with white dots covering both hands and arms. I'd damaged my liver so I thought, or at the least damaged my immune system. I almost died from the mixer of Darvon and aspirin poisoning, and prayed to god not to die! And as I slowly recovered from the drug poisoning, I regretted my actions for many days and as I contemplated my actions, reality set in. I should have died from my foolish behavior, but something healed my body and mind. After such a display of ignorance and lack of faith, I felt more than ever within myself and spirit that god must exist, though I didn't even know what faith was at that time. I awoke from my illusions with a thirst for unknown knowledge that exists over all creation, bolstering my belief in a higher power. Who else could have saved me from myself?! I asked god for forgiveness, knowing I had crossed the invisible line between stupidity and lunacy. Asking myself, "What have you done to yourself, P?"

Over and over again, I asked the one I called god, "Why would I do such a thing?" I felt shamed and afraid to be seen by anyone while white spots and speckles covered my entire body, which was the direct result of my own foolishness! I tried to conceal the sickly affliction resembling Leprosy from everyone especially my mother, as it covered my entire body. I concealed myself within the four black walls of my bedroom. I shied from my mother's face for more than a month, only leaving my bedroom when everyone would be asleep. Some days, I would break out in a cold sweat, and begin shaking without a cause or reason. This uncontrollable symptom persisted for some weeks, months and over a year. Then all of a sudden, it all went away. My Creator had answered my prayers for healing, and allowed me to live and slowly repaired the damage I had caused to my organs. The white spots began to vanish over time and I vowed never to take pills or any drug ever again!

I realized how much I wanted to live, and began questioning my own thoughts about the reasoning of our existence. "Was I trying to kill myself? Did I know exactly what I was doing by taking all those drugs? Was I killing myself in search of peace of mind?"

Yet deep inside I knew there was a god, and I knew the jest of the ancient story about our existence, but really didn't understand it all. What role did we all play in this story called life?! Then words of wisdom came into my mind; my mother would always tell me to search for knowledge if you want power and understanding. Now that I had almost killed myself, those words carried new meaning, and echoed even more within my spirit! "Learn all you can P!

Knowledge is power, and understanding the power that knowledge brings is freedom!" I remembered those profound words from my mother over and over again for the rest of my life. I needed to know and understand the unseen ways of this world in which I lived, and why we were forced to play a part in its creation. We as a people did not ask to be here! Or did we?

We didn't ask to live in poverty, or ask to be looked down upon because of our creed, or did we? I must know why we as humanity go through life with so much pain and misery! I must learn to navigate my surroundings in order to not only survive it, but strive within it! I needed to find out why the god I prayed to every waking moment never answered my cries of mercy and relief from my plight! And why it never seemed as if he ever took the time to care for the likes of those within my family, and all those living in the hood or any other place of poverty and filth across the globe!

Why those of good nature suffer from those people with no love within themselves, selfish in nature, let alone anyone else of low means! Why it is that evil permeates every facet of society and life? What happened to the culture of teaching the newborn child to love not destruction with admiration, or fear of consequence? To engage in despicable behavior from birth was the curse I, and most growing up in poverty, inherited! Where I'm from, foul language reigned supreme, and the lust and love for material wealth, filled our dreams at night. Obtaining gain serves as false hope for happiness' sake. I fell hook line and sinker into the nightmare in which we all consider the "American Dream:" To set your sights on nothing of substance, but only to obtain monetary wealth at the expense of the detriment of your fellow man reigned king in every thought, but to me, seemed fruitless! The dream that we all fight to obtain in this region of the globe must be universal. For the root of all evil holds all captive in lies, and ensnares the imaginations of the selfish youth, corrupting all that resides in this country at birth.

I wanted to know more about the world in which we live and die. I became obsessed in the naïve thinking of the more I know the better off I would be in life! So without fail, I dove head first into the Encyclopedia Britannica that my mother so lovingly provided me. Immersed within its pages days in and days out, I became immersed at all times within my solitude, and most days I never left the comfort of my bedroom. I contemplated the meaning of words, and the importance of their meaning.

I sometimes would find the joy of learning within my imagination to be overwhelming in its outstanding. I began to fall in love with knowledge, and the freedom of knowing subject matter that no others dared entertaining, boosting pride and arrogance within my selfish little soul. I read the Encyclopedia Britannica from A to Z, experiencing the whole range of emotions that encompassed the thrill of learning. Finding out something for the first time and comprehending its meaning, had me captivated. It was the Darvon drug on steroids to my young undeveloped brain. I couldn't, and wouldn't stop reading those old leather bound books for the life of me! Going to public school never crossed my mind and I never attended a public course higher than seventh grade. I educated myself, literally teaching myself how to read, as I dove into the many pages of the encyclopedia nightly.

My mother left me to my lonely most days, making sure her drugs were well hidden for my safety, but never mentioning the obvious. She never confronted me on her missing drugs, or commented on the odd behavior I would display sporadically, thus not saying a word. After days of sickness, I began to fully recover from my temporary loss of sanity with a new found respect for life, treating drug addiction as my youthful delusion of indestructibility diminished, ultimately obtaining a now healthy fear of drug use. Finally venturing out of my self-induced isolation, I walked the apartment brandishing a genuine smile, and even tried interacting with siblings, making homemade nun chucks. I even walked out in front of the apartment building to test my crude and undeveloped skills with my homemade device. I tested my skills on the first inanimate object I could find, namely a big oak tree as the potential victim. While practicing the simplest of martial arts techniques, I soon realized I lost most of my natural form and skill. As the traffic passed by the very busy street in which our building lay perched, standing greatly upon the corner of Grant and 5th, I gazed out of our living-room window which faced the corner of 5th and Grant, and proceeded to go back outside and practice my entry level martial art skills once again, saying to myself, "There is no giving up!" As I began another session, I noticed a scary black giant youth watching me from behind the tree, which I had gleefully waved at as I performed my little workout with no grace. Yet the friendly giant surely was intrigued and captivated by the entry level skill I displayed, thus commenting agreeably on every move I sloppily performed on my non-animated opponent.

As I continued my so-called self-imposed instruction of ancient martial arts, I began to become self-conscious and nervous of my actions as he watched me intently. But at closer glance, I could see that there was no malice in his heart. Seeing his child-like demeanor, my distrust and childish fears diminished, cooling my nervous suspicion. Soon after he approached me and asked my name, he began pouring out his heart and soul concerning his daily torment from other children in the neighborhood. He freely relayed all his personal information inside and outside his home by letting me know where he lived within the building, and telling me how many people were in his household. He continued to say how his family was so poor, and how he had no friends at all, and finally asked, "…will you be my friend?" After he expressed so eloquently the one thing we both had in common, from that day forward, we were two together as one in a world of so many disappointments. Soon I began opening up all my disparities, shortcomings and flaws without shame, and shared all my personal information, while shedding a tear or two.

Instantly, we became the best of friends, and played with each other daily. After the masses of ill-mannered, immoral and disobedient snot -nosed brats departed from the merit of school busses parked right outside the apartment building, four ruffians began verbally and physically assaulting my new found friend mercilessly and without quarter. Although technically I was considered a juvenile delinquent since I never went to school or left the building, I felt as if I would get my mother in big trouble if I left the building, yet I was compelled to do something. My new soft hearted friend attended school faithfully and never accosted anyone. Eagerly, I watched out my bedroom window to see him depart and return from one of the many yellow chambers of transportation. So from that day forward, I witnessed his troubles, and I assigned myself his official bodyguard! I'd meet him outside the building each day with nun chucks in hand. Whenever he emerged from the school bus, I would yell out his unique handle, as I quickly assigned him the nick name, "Jumbo," thus never really learning his real name, and without indignation, he gladly accepted his new name, and repeated it to me frequently.

The nick name "Jumbo" marked him officially with others in the neighborhood, and after some time, he didn't protest or mind; instead, he embraced it because it was his best friend that gave it to him with love and without malice. He soon gravitated towards the name I assigned with pride, and the jolly soul responded to it without any quells. Since I was the first person ever to befriend him without ridicule or judgment, he took the name as a badge of honor, unlike the constant ridicule and untold horror he would endure from most kids because of his size and slow speech. He was constantly ostracized by most in our age group inside and outside the safety of his own home.

Though I was smaller than he in stature, I was older and much more street-wise, thus he looked up to me from the very beginning of our meeting. Although I was relatively naïve to the hard realities of the world, I acted as if I knew everything. Somewhat more experienced in the minutia of the ugly reality of the city, I knew nothing! Yet still I knew more than my new giant and meek hearted friend, "Jumbo." Because of the recent horrors that plagued my family, I learned quickly how sudden tragic occurrences could creep up upon his entire family without any warning nor explanation. Having genuine concern for his safety, I displayed intense and vigorous paranoia towards my giant friend and next door neighbor. Not much younger than I, Jumbo towered over me like the oak tree, watching me daily as I practiced on my amateur martial art skills in front of the building, and it seemed as if I had a friend for life. Jumbo was huge, gentle and kind. Despite the reality of his humongous size, he was as meek as a mouse, and a spirit of peace surrounded him like a halo; therefore, anyone who would want to harm him for any reason was just not feasible. I'd come across many a gentile souls, but none as gentile as Jumbo!

Because of the way I carried myself, I just looked older then he, and because of his gentle demeanor, he was ridiculed by almost all other kids in our age group practically every day. Jumbo's unwavering and uncommon meekness, shyness, and general good nature, marked him for hazing, and he was targeted by the less desirable peers in our age group. His spirit's light shined in abundant beauty and greatness before our Creator and man. Because of this precious gift, he was on the menu of scavengers, thus making him a great target amongst numerous lost Children of Darkness. Demonistic bullies singled him out for ridicule and amusement, causing him to cry before all youth and god, every time he'd exit the school bus.

Then one day, the unthinkable happened! Most days, I would read the encyclopedia, unwittingly educating myself in the dark of the midnight hours while my new found friend attended the human public zoo called "Beckmann Junior High School," and like always, I would look out my bedroom window after a long night of fact finding, thus watching him leave and return from the school bus regularly, so I could meet Jumbo in front of the building to strategize any mischief we could come up with for that day. But on this particular day while patiently looking out of my bedroom window waiting for Jumbo to exit his particular school bus, I noticed something that triggered the emotional fires within me to erupt! I joyfully smiled as I spotted him exiting the school bus, but as he emerged, I noticed tears flowing down his face without whimper while holding his head down with his arms covering his forehead, as if he was in massive pain while three knuckleheads taunted him by throwing wads of balled up paper and shrubbery towards his way.

They were pushing him around without impunity, and calling him stupid among other foul mouth idiots uttering ugly slurs within the crowd, while others were screaming at the top of their lungs: "Fuck him up!" I could hear them taunting him from inside my bedroom window, which was some distance from the bus stop itself. Without a thought, I jumped to my feet, not putting on shoes or slippers, and ran down the stairs, quickly approaching the area where the vicious noise originated. Through the unruly crowd of miscreants surrounding Jumbo and the three bullies, I pried my way within the circle of scum. I positioned myself between the three hooligans, saying not a word, only looking at the three with a focus and purpose of threat towards all that stood in the circle. In my presence, they quickly stopped their advance toward Jumbo, and the crowd disbursed without any more disruptions. Their taunts were silenced in an instance, but as I looked around at the crowd as their voices began to silence, someone replied, "See you later Fatso!" Instantly, I grabbed Jumbo and said, "Let's go buddy." At first, he was too afraid to move from out of the circle, suspended in fear, he just stood there for some time, afraid to move. Then after he found the courage to look up at me, the crowd began to quiet down and disperse. The three bullies had been silenced at just my presence and facial expression, then Jumbo looked into my eyes, and began walking beside me with confidence.

Taking him by the hand, we slowly walked through the crowd and toward our building without looking back, and as the spirit of cowardest and group think deceased from the crowd, Jumbo and I walked home with confidence.

Then their voices began to ring out once more, but this time directed at the unknown boy who rescued the meek giant from their clutches. That's right, at ME! They yelled curse words and threats of retribution towards me and Jumbo as we walked off into the distance and entered into our building's front doors. Once we were safe inside the building, I uttered, "Hey Jumbo, are you okay?" He responded: "I'm okay… they always mess with me… Wow… how did you do that? They looked like they were scared of you P… You better watch your back from now on buddy!"

From that day forward, I stood outside of our building opposite the bus stop, and when it was time for Jumbo to get off the bus, no one said a word. Only the three bullies would sneer, and give me dirty looks, talking beneath their voice as they walked past Jumbo and me, thus still egging on the mass crowd of sheep to exhibit some form of courage. Waiting to insight some altercation within the crowd, they taunted and laughed at both of us as they went their merry way, and each day they would gain in mental strength as I stayed silently meek, with my head pointed down towards the ground, not looking them in their eyes, not out of fear of them, but out of fear of what I might do.

They became emboldened, as I did that fateful day, yet I stood my ground alongside Jumbo each day the school busses dislodged their cargo.

Every day I tried to teach Jumbo some basic self-defense, and even on weekends we practiced, but being so meek, fat and slow, he just could not get the knack of it. His weight and uncoordinated stance didn't help. Being so huge in stature, he could have killed all three bullies without breaking a sweat, but he was just too gentle.

After a couple of weeks, I soon gave up on truly trying to instruct Jumbo in the martial arts. I loved and humored him in the prospect of learning the arts, yet the hormones of the young black boys that harassed Jumbo brewed with the fires of revenge against my friend and myself. Knowing those that would harm my humble friend, and maybe myself, I resigned myself to the fact that pride would overcome them someday, for I saw the hatred that burned within their hearts each day they exited the bus. I could feel their spirit of hatred grow in evil every time they would walk by on their normal route home. I found myself feeling fearful more and more each time they passed by us; until one day, I lay in my bed and began to speculate the obvious.

I knew that all hostilities building up within both parties would come to a head sooner or later, instinctively feeling that someone would ignite the fires of animosity, possibly the main instigator of violence would test the waters of battle, and over reach the line of reason.

The voice of perception softly entered my mind and said with certainty, "One of the three would attempt to prove to the others his Alpha Male trait, and deal with the defiant outsider, so as to redeem his bully status on the bus line." Hearing those words from within brought fear of the unknown flooding within my soul, yet my spirit stood fast.

Anticipating the truth revealing itself within the premonition granted me in the night, brought fear in mass. Fear began to rise within me each day, knowing I would have to face at least one bully in a physically altercation. Hearing the voice of god or the voice of conscience saying, "You're going to have to fight P! You have no choice, for they shall never stop, and maybe hurt Jumbo or you one day." Every adult I knew has said, "The only way to deal with a threat is to face it head on!" I reiterated to myself over and over again. I learned that courage is going forward when fear overtakes your emotional state and tries to stop your advancement or goal; therefore, overcome your fears no matter what you may face. Reality of certain battle set in my soul, and I was beginning to shake with fear of what was to come. The looming fact of being beat up rattled my nerves to the core, so when that day arrived, I was ready for battle!

The night before the event I arose early with courage, and decided to fight whatever or whomever came my way, even though I really was afraid of hurting someone or even being hurt myself, but what was crazy about my mental state before the upcoming ordeal was the fact that I was more afraid of being afraid.

Having fear of the unknown worried me more than having fear of fighting another human being. Hearing and seeing things that should not be seen by men equipped me with the strength to overcome what may, thus fearing my surroundings and the wickedness that permeated within it was not an option. I was so tired of being afraid, and something had to be done about the threat that loomed over Jumbo and me. I had no choice but to fight the emotion of fear, once and for all! I kept telling myself, "Never again will I hide my face in the sand; I will face my fate with my head held high from now on!"

As I looked out my bedroom window, I said to myself, "Here come the school busses!" It was time! Today was the day that I will hold my ground and face my fears head on, and nothing was going to stop me! Fear of the unknown had transformed into anticipation, and I couldn't wait for the school day to end, and the bullies to discard from the busses that arrived. Not knowing what would take place in the next few minutes, I contemplated my demise or victory; it did not matter if I failed, but meant a lifetime of harassment for Jumbo.

Either way, I was going to hold my ground this day, and face my fears, but when the bright yellow school busses arrived, I stayed inside, not to confront the bullies, or being too eager for trouble, holding back the fury that raged within. I waited until the ruffians passed by my bedroom window, hoping they would continue on their way. Once they passed by the building, I went outside to meet Jumbo, and as I walked over to my huge happy-go-lucky friend, he yelled out to me, "P... Guess what...Nobody messed with me today...they were nice to me; you believe that?!" With a make shift shocking look, I responded, "For real?" "Yah!" said Jumbo. Saying to myself, "That's cool, maybe we've dodged a bullet, and wouldn't have to fight after all. Though the perceived threat diminished, there was no sense of relief of fear because deep inside I knew I would have to face those bullies once again, and I would have no choice but to fight. The day went great, and without incident. Jumbo's mom prepared: Barbecue chicken, steak, hamburgers and hot dogs on the old school smoker made from a discarded metal oil barrel. She served corn on the cob and watermelon, alongside a multitude of other side dishes to boot! We munched on great food for hours, and climbed all the trees surrounding the building, having the kind of fun only a child of poor spirit could enjoy in a single day. We had so much fun that time whizzed by with a blink of an eye. The smell of food, and the sound of soul music permeated the air, and before we knew it, the night was upon us. All activities began to die down, then out of the blue, we heard a crowd of ominous voices coming toward the building in the blackness of night.

They were the voices of the bullies that terrorized Jumbo in the day, manifesting fear within Jumbo and myself instantaneously, saying to myself, "No more!" I knew it would come and I was ready! We could see them in the midst of the night walking toward us. We saw all three bullies, accompanied with their female counterparts who were coming along for the ride. Only this time they themselves were ready for violent mischief, having their girls on their arms yelling loudly and acting extra stupid! They were showing off in front of their concubines, making all sorts of noises in the night, thus turning their verbal attention towards their intended victims: Jumbo and me, with every step. They were cursing and bucking up within the shadows, as to assault Jumbo and physically surround both Jumbo and me in front of our building. Saying nothing, I ran inside the building afraid of what was taking place just outside. Shaking like a dildo on vibrate, I peeked out the front door window, and saw Jumbo being assaulted by all three bullies, and then suddenly, the shaking stopped! Without hesitation, I turned around and proceeded back outside and confronted the foes saying: "That's IT! Come on Motha Fucka's!" Stunning the crowd, all noise suddenly stopped, and all eyes turned towards me.

Then one of the punks slapped Jumbo and came running my way with fire in his eyes and both hands rolled into fist. Time slowed to a crawl, yet sped up to light speed, and as he attempted to assault me, I instinctively responded to his advance, and it was over in a blink of an eye.

As the dude assaulted me, I round kicked him in the face, and body slammed him! With no thought or conscience, my small and insignificant martial art training took over, and without thinking, I subdued the foe, and proceeded to whoop his ass like a champion on steroids. "I GIVE! I GIVE!" screamed our main foe!

All parties stood still in shock, then one of the girls said; "…he knocked the shit out of you!" I looked up at the crowd and as the primary bully's crew just stood there, with a look of "DAMN" on their faces, I continued to beat the shit out of my opponent. I soon stopped my assault on his face, once I captured the look of horror on the faces of the crowd. While coming to my senses, I got up and dusted myself off, saying nothing else. His boys picked him up off the ground and quickly ran back towards the direction in which they came. Jumbo shouted out! "Wow Wow! P! You kicked his ass! I knew you was a bad-ass! I knew it! Nobody gonna fuck with us now!" Over and over again he yelled out praises of our collective victory. Jumbo couldn't control the joy and relief that flowed through his body; no more would he have to put up with humiliation or assault from those assholes bulling him on a daily basis! No more would he suffer the humiliation of hiding his lunch money, or hiding himself from punks half his size.

As the shock began to leave my adrenalin shaken body, the feeling of satisfaction came over me, and a great big smile appeared on my face. Confident in my actions, pride filled my very soul. A natural high and satisfaction of victory took over both Jumbo and me as we basked in our collective single glory.

A new day in the neighborhood had come for both of us; no more would we fear walking outside our front door, or walking down the street in fear of assault, or looking over our shoulders. It was as if we were free from monsters, free from the fear of unknown threats! No more would we cower over our own shadows after Jumbo exited the little yellow school bus. We walked outside with a smile, and had no fear of ridicule from morons. In the afternoon, I'd look out my bedroom window and there was Jumbo already out and about, playing as he would not dare play before out of the grip of fear perpetrated by those ignorant punks! A week passed, and the very girls that adorned the arms of the bullies were now walking over to our building to visit those who once were scorned. The girls showed us attention and politely asked for our names and smiled back to our nervous response. I said to myself, "Man I didn't know kicking someone's ass would make me popular with the ladies?!" Yet it did. Everything had changed! No more would Jumbo and I play alone. Every night someone would come around and it began to get on our nerves, but we didn't care because we were finally accepted and no longer outsiders, and it felt very good. I had always been a loner and having friends calling my name in the night began to become too much for me, and after some time passed, I reverted back to my natural state of being meek, quiet, and soft spoken, but without success.

While trying to fit in with our new found popularity, we now spoke loudly and boastfully alongside the crowd. Jumbo was the first to see the change in us both, and spoke out one night after everyone had gone, saying, "I liked it better when it was just you and me, P... We starting to act just like them fools... I think we need to leave them alone." I responded, "You right buddy... We are acting just like them... Let's just kick it by ourselves tomorrow and walk to the lake or something." So the next day we headed out early in the morning and walked to the lake, returning late in the night, making plans for the future of our friendship, saying in unison: "Friends for life," not knowing what was to take place within the next few days would change our friendship and life forever.

Clueless to unseen forces dictating human directions in life, I awoke to a very beautiful and uplifting spring morning. The sun was shining brightly through the blinds of my bedroom window, and a cool breeze flowed through the window's blinds. It seemed like the perfect day, as if the road in front of me would finally have some normalcy and peace for once in life. My mother slowed down on her drinking, and enrolled me in middle school after I'd been out of the system for a few years. I'd broken free from my isolation and depression. I had found a really good friend in Jumbo, innocent and naïve to the ills of the evil wicked world, that I myself had just experienced. Though he was somewhat younger than I was, he proved himself a friend that would walk the plank no questions asked, and always faithful! Jumbo never judged or complained about my obvious Alpha personality and was always on my side, no matter what! Jumbo was the friend that no one could deny his loyalty, yet I was not. With no malice nor intent, I proved myself shallow, self-absorbed and selfish! In retrospect, I was even purposely mean towards my gentle and faithful friend. Shameful in nature, my eyes were turned inward, not knowing it or even self-aware of it at the time, but still the same! I proved myself less of a true friend, and more of an impostor instead. I thought only of myself, and didn't even know it! Thinking I was just as true a friend as he, I played the role of a best friend, but in no time at all I betrayed his loyal friendship at the drop of a hat.

While walking down the main drag, throwing a Nerf football on 5th avenue, I noticed a family moving into one of the buildings on the other side of the road. At first glance, I paid no attention to the youngster helping his mom move into the dark brown "Victorian" styled multi-complex adorning the other side of 5th Avenue, but as Jumbo and I threw the football back and forth with joy, the young kid moving in across the street noticed us. He yelled at the top of his lungs saying, "Hey you...Hey you!" Obviously trying to capture our attention one or the other, we knew not who he was yelling at, but he succeeded in having both our heads turn his way as he walked closer to the curb facing his side of the street. The young boy brandished a very big smile.

As he walked closer to Jumbo and me, he asked, "...remember me?" And as I squelched my eyes, looking closer at his form, I remembered him. It was the kid I'd spent so much time, and many nights and days, roaming the halls of the hospital just up the street and Glenn Anderson was his name. I thought I'd never see him again! It was fate if there were such a thing, and just as his smile blossomed outward towards me, so did mine. Both of us brandished great smiles and hugged each other with uncountable glee, jumping up and down, reminiscing of the time we spent goofing off at Mercy General Hospital, and I totally disregarded the obvious and glanced over towards Jumbo in his silence.

I said nothing, not even introducing or acknowledging him as a friend. Showing my true colors, I proved myself un-loyal in our friendship and without value, for I disregarded Jumbo and never looked back. Slowly time spent with Jumbo tapered off more and more, and I found myself at Glenn's home or visa-versa, but would often see Jumbo out in the yard playing alone once more, finding himself becoming the outcast once again, but this time it was me shunning him off like a tick instead of a friend, and I didn't care one iota. Yet still Jumbo stayed faithful to our friendship though I placed our friendship to the side, favoring Glenn over him, day after day; yet Jumbo showed no ill will as I blew him off in the days and nights to come. Soon Jumbo and his family would move far away from 5th Ave, into Glenn Park, yet still, he would find time to visit his old best friend when he could have tossed me aside, and sometimes I would even take time out of my not so busy schedule to visit him in Glenn Park after coming to my senses, until there was no correspondence at all. And never again would I find a true friend such as he named Jumbo! A lesson learned after a lifetime.

In time, my conscience took total control over my mind, and sorrowful feelings of my atrocious behavior towards Jumbo consumed my every thought; it was devastating for my very immature and adolescent mind. I knew nothing of life in the world in which we reside. Every day was spent at Glenn's crib, while we learned all the little annoyances exhibited by truant punks who thought they were grown. We even experimented with drugs, but nothing hard, only weed in the beginning. I didn't even know how to inhale, but Glenn quickly enlightened me by saying, "Damn man, you don't even know how to smoke… let me show you fool!" Although, I saw my father smoke it, I never had the urge to indulge, but Glenn seemed so much older, even though he was some years younger than I was. I had to try to keep up with shit I knew nothing of; see even though I spent my life around thugs, pimps and pushers, my mother and father did a very good job shielding me from the vices of the trade, and now that the veil had been lifted up by the tragedy that befell the family, all guards were forever down from that day forward, light then darkness...

Loki: My lord Baal; It is I Loki; I report on the man child that sees the unseen in the night. His education in destruction has begun, and his sight into the unseen realm of man diminishes as I speak my lord; he falls easily into the ruse of material happiness, attracted to the light of darkness with little prompting. He may not be the one after all my lord Baal.

Baal: Do not let eager eyes waver Loki, for lack of knowing the light of the two truths and failing to choose one from the other, has made humans as fickle as the wind blows, always moving in unsuspected modes of truth. What may look as fact today will surely prove false tomorrow? Although sin resides within all humanity, so does the light of the Creator, and no one knows this better than I. Do not forget my position in the heavens, my insolent one. I played a major role in their existence, knowing what was instilled in their being from the beginning!

Loki: Yes, my lord, this I know to be true, and your influence permeates all human thoughts and will. For what may be fate could be overcome by free will, and no longer stand true.

Baal: Loki Listen! All life is at war; war holds tightly the bonds of our brothers in chains, binding us all throughout all verses of creation! So tell me brother, who stands true in creation, is it not I? Yet our brethren that reigns above accused me false in the matter in which we battle! This is our last stand! Our last chance to show the malicious rule of he that sits on high. For knowing you exist does not ensure freedom! For knowing what is good from evil is not enough, yet having no choice in choosing what defines the two means of light and darkness, leaves no free will. For good is in the eye of the beholder, and to serve under the rule of another leaves little room for choice, leaving only servitude not freedom.

Loki: Yes my Lord this also stands true in my eye as well, but as it stands, the child gravitates towards rebellion, and I shall focus all intent on his education in the ways of free choice, and corruption of design! He's now in contact with one immersed in darkness, this assures from birth a road of destruction. Fully emerged in the ways of Baal, and delusion of spirit he has found, my lord! He is now on the road of total rebellion against all natural authority, and rule of man's law. Knowing only the basic understanding of darkness' light! He who rules on high with no concept of invocation or appeal has no sight, and with his station in life so grim, his spirit's destruction is assured to be among the extinguished, well before reaching manhood! This I promise my Lord Baal.

Baal: Do so Loki, make him your priority, for Yahweh's light burns deep within this one; this is what I see! He may be more than you think, my pompous one; stay on guard and watch your flanks! For watchers are in our midst with extra protection invoked around him! So why is this discharge flowing from the boy?!

Loki: Any Electromagnetic field surrounding the boy I shall detect, and if so, I shall then put him to the test. How may I ask of you the scale in which I shall exact damage, my Lord?!

Baal: The presence of any residue of divine spiritual energy that may encompass the boy, I shall stump out! Make sure your personality resides within him my brother!

Loki: My lord! I do not know every plausible road of approach or attack that may be applied my lord; there were no enemies present within one hundred clicks of the child, at any time of our engagement with the boy.

Baal: Yet explain this Loki: Don't bother! Just know that he is being monitored and watched over by both sides, so make your presence null in intensity! When engaging the child, have your minions on stealth mode with weapons hot from this day forward!

Loki: Yes, my lord!

Baal: There is something special about this one, I know it; I can feel it. Watch his thoughts, his dreams and soul temperature when engaging him. For he is protected from on high! No other soul on Earth has a level of protection such as this one! I want to know why?! Now leave my sight!

Loki: Yes, my lord Baal. How could this be?! The child exhibits no special gift of awareness, nor even the will of invoking protection from our enemies, let alone having stealth coverage; yet divine presence has left its residue on my very person?! May this child be the one in which we fear?! For time is short, and all men must become aware of his station in creation, knowing all that is unseen and having the ability to choose sides in this war may do so, not just our minions under Covent! Soon the battle will consume this realm as well, and all shall be aware of all frequencies of dimension, seeing creation's secrets in full! Knowing the wonders that exist beyond their comprehension, this child shall not conform to our enemy; he will never grasp enlightenment of creation, and forever lie within the midst of deception and bondage having no choice but to remain lost in desire and want. Fear shall forever embrace him; my influence will never let loose of his spirit and soul! For I shall make sure of it...

EDGAR FRENCH, JR.

CHAPTER XIV
The Three Musketeers

As the days grew shorter, the daily attention devoted to Jumbo faded into the night, and though he showed nothing but reverence towards our companionship, I showed myself to be preoccupied with those of a lesser stature in grace, or steadiness in friendship. In shallow waters, I abandoned Jumbo's precious gift of loyalty and dove into the deep waters of uncertainty with one of lesser stock than that of he. Now in my mind, I was on my way to becoming a grown man, or so I thought. I spent more time with my not so old time hospital mate, and called all sorts of young nappy head girls from my not so long lost comrade's little black book. Not knowing, or even caring of the chicken heads' moral up bringing or outer appearance, I was immature within my nondescriptive features, to the point that shallowness was an understatement.

As most boys my age were well into the throes of puberty, I also had raging hormones, and testosterones levels of a young lion, and flirted with every young girl that moved in and outside the hood while trying to dip our wicks into anything that latched on to the fishermen's hook, with little to no success at all. Well, I had no success in that department for some time. I felt for the first time the effects of marijuana on my young and impressionable mind, and I tried selling the illicit drug to those a quarter my age. I was engaging in debauchery of the spirit, unaware of its consequences and I loved every moment of it! Soon "Glenn" from the hospital would introduce me to his best friend, a flamboyant dressing youngster by the name of "Keith," my senior by one year, yet exhibiting the intellect of muskrat, thus showing off at every turn, talking of subject matter that he himself had no clue, yet still having a certain amount of charisma. A very personable dude; you either loved or hated him. In other words, he grew on me. Not to mention, his mother sold bud in massive quantities and he had full access. It was the beginning of a great friendship, or at least as well as friendships goes at that age. Soon my mother would be asking me when I would be coming home, instead of always asking, "Why won't you go outside for a change?"

I had never experienced so much freedom of self before, listening to live music, or hearing music from a real professional stereo system before, and Glenn's uncle had a massive "Ken-wood" system that shook the walls and broke windows!

He accrued the system from oversees while in the military, and when Glenn's uncle would leave their small little apartment for any reason, Glenn would turn the up the volume so loudly that the walls would shake and the furniture would move. The sound was so clear, so crisp, and I was stuck from that day forward! Bumping "More Bounce to Ounce!"

I was hooked; the sound was so clear and crisp, and I couldn't believe it's clarity; static noise was nonexistent and not unlike every other youth into the sounds of the times, we were heavily into meaningless fashion as well, and though we had nothing trending, we made the best of it, creating our own little styles and sayings, words that only we considered cool in the beginning. It was my introduction into bad boy behavior, and I must say it was exhilarating. But the fun would soon be at an end; two months had passed since Jumbo's departure from the 5th Ave building, and the trio's mishaps began blossoming into a true friendship.

My family was known in the neighborhood, due to my heroic exploits involving Jumbo's school bus bullies, well mostly mom's friends knew of the event, which in turn meant everyone in the hood knew of our family, and as my mother's popularity increased, so did the partying, and drunken scuffles and violent outburst of obscenities. Soon I would be elected the neighborhood babysitter on weekends, or any other drunk day. The brownstone in which we resided was five stories high; we stayed on the first floor of course, yet my mother's first acquaintance in the building and neighborhood resided on the very top floor of the brownstone. Whenever they would go out on their drunken escapades, I would be stuck babysitting the woman's child upstairs, and my three siblings. I didn't mind; she paid me, unlike mama who never said a word, other than, "I'm gone." And just as the Master rewarded his good slave, slavery of old had morphed into social programing, just as it is today. That great old past time that welfare mothers could never change, and loved so much was upon us like clockwork; you guessed it?! The first of the month! The one time funds weren't a major issue, but the needs of the children were barely met and the illusion of wealth, for a short time, brought smiles to everyone's face and the party was on! Though it seemed that the ever glooming doom never left our abode for long, and as always, I was the designated care provider for the two mothers as they got their drink and dance on at one of the hood's many night clubs, mainly patronizing, "Issy's," where all the dope dealers, pushers and prostitutes hung out. But I didn't mind; I relished the chance to get paid, and got drunk and high myself.

I was only twelve going on thirty two at the time and I didn't really understand what I, and others of my age group, were getting involved in at that time such as: smoking weed, getting drunk, and acting as if we were the grown, but knowing nothing of true responsibility. We were having so-called fun as we went along willfully corrupting ourselves, body and spirit, while our mother's explored the depths of darkness, diving deep into the darkness of the night.

The first of the month had passed on in a blink of an eye, and now it was the middle of the month. Funds were scarce and food was running out, although a beer could still be found somewhere in the house.

The partying had slowed to a crawl, and the building quieted down. All prospective residents were passing time alone in their own perspective apartments, conserving whatever means were left over from the first of the month. There was no more communal sharing; they held whatever meager means for themselves, as did we all. Although I began acting proud and boastful, full of adolescence stupidity, as if I were one of the popular delinquents in the hood, inside I knew my behavior was leading towards trouble. All three of us were beginning to smoke cigarettes in abandoned buildings, hiding out of sight from our parents so as not get caught, ultimately trying to emulate our only role-models, which were young gangsters in the streets. I hung out with Glenn and Keith bullshitting around most days and secretly educating myself.

By day I played my part as an ass, yet at home, I still read the Encyclopedia Britannica in the night while everyone was fast asleep. Often suffering from insomnia, the only way I could sleep was to read the leather bound books, and listen to the radio station, "WGCI," trying to catch some shut eye when I could. In time, I found myself reading two to three times a week. But one night as I tried to read myself to sleep, I heard footsteps running up and down the outer staircase leading to the apartments, and since my bedroom was closer to the front door, I heard all that took place outside our apartment, yet paid no mind to the unusual activity, and felt somewhat safe, so I continued reading. Soon after the many footsteps stopped and all was quiet, I noticed a bright light flickering through the crack at the bottom of my bedroom door, not paying attention at first, thinking that one of my siblings left the bathroom light on as usual, I continued reading. All the time getting more, and more pissed off at my brothers and sisters for not turning off the bathroom light. I kept watching the light flicker, saying to myself in angst, "That's it!" I quickly jumped out of my bed, ready to jump down the throats of the little brats, mumbling under my breath "...you fuck'n little snot nose punks," only to open my bedroom door to an inferno! Flames engulfed the entire front door and hallway, thus instantly throwing me into shock, draining all energy from my body, internally saying, "Not again!" But somehow it was different, for this time, I had no fear.

I calmly walked down and across the hall to my siblings' bedroom, and woke them all up. Calmly and collectively, I led them through the inflamed hallway and out the back-door, passing my still sleeping mother, watching her in her drunken induced coma, I thought to myself, "...she is not going to like this!" Being the selfless woman mama was, I had the master bedroom and my siblings had the other bedroom; she didn't have a bedroom, and so she slept on a sofa bed located in the dining room area leading to the back door. Knowing my mother was safe in her location, I made sure my siblings were out of the apartment and safe before I woke up my pride and joy, then calmly went back into the burning building to collect mom, which was not a pretty sight.

Being so calm with no urgency in my voice, my mother did not believe the apartment was on fire, so with more concern in my voice I yelled out, "Mom wake up! Your house on fire! Get up! We got to go!" Shaking her with both hands on each of her shoulder, attempting to awaken her from her drunken comma, only pissing her off, having her yell, "What the fuck wrong with you P! Leave me the fuck alone!" And she fell back onto the sofa bed, drunk as fuck.

EDGAR FRENCH, JR.

After several attempts, I finally grabbed her by the arms, picking her up, and physically showing her the place was on fire. Before the urgency took hold of her, seeing the inferno, she quickly awakened from her drunken stupor and screamed, "Get the kids!"

Before she ran towards the bedrooms, I grabbed her and calmly told her they were already outside, and she was the only one I needed to get out of the building. Grabbing what heavy winter coats she immediately saw, we both headed out towards the back door, and before I could blink an eye, all the tenants were assembled in the parking lot out back of the building. All were in shock and pissed off as they watched the entire building go up in flames. Smoke and fire bellowed out of most of the windows and doors, destroying all vestiges of our new home, thus killing whatever hope of salvaging any material possessions the newly victimized homeless tenants may have had, making life seem even more unbearable. I could hear the voices of the crowd expressing their dismay and anguish. As we all looked up in horror at the burning building, I could only say in silence, "...all these people, who I just met, were losing their lively hoods, and all they had worked so hard for was now going up in smoke in one night!" Looking at the many faces, I could feel their pain and sense of loss, seeing the tears fall from my mother's eyes once again, after going through so much for so long, only to feel the sting of senseless loss yet once more. It made no sense, understanding or mattered much. We were homeless once again, marking the beginning of long term woe for all of us, but that was the beginning of the night's light of darkness, for true pain had not yet appeared.

Without warning, a familiar voice yelled out in the darkness as the smoke and fire grew thicker and thicker, "My Baby! My Baby!" It was the voice of my mother's newly found friend. The woman that lived at the very top of the building; the woman for whom I'd babysat! In a panic, she ran out of the burning building, leaving her newborn child asleep in his crib. "Oh shit the baby," said a stranger standing next to me in the crowd, looking terrified at one another, as we both stormed the fire escape stairs! Back up the stairs we went, back into the smoke and flames, blindly climbing the staircase, step by step, as fast as we could go! Hearing the fire trucks and engine out front, and in the distance, we bravely soldiered forward as the many people on the ground tried to direct the firemen to the back of the building. I felt hopeful that we would reach the child, and he would be saved; if not by our hands, by the hands of the professional fire fighters racing towards our way.

While moving up the stairs as fast as we could, the smoke was bellowing out of every opening in the building, periodically catching glimpses of fire bellowing from each side of the massive escape ladder attached to the building as fire tucks crept within the tight accessible area. We could still hear the baby crying not three floors above our heads. Franticly, the stranger and I continued upwards though both of us were choking from the smoke.

Finally the ladders of the fire engines were headed our way as the stranger and I crept through the smoke to retrieve the trapped infant on the fifth floor. As the stranger and I climbed higher up the stairs, smoke choked and blinded us both more and more, yet out of the smoke, we could hear the child crying as we crept closer. After making it to the fourth floor, we could go no further; the fire and smoke pouring out of the building blocked our way up, almost falling to our death, as the staircase weakened from the damaging fire! Grabbing hold of the ladder with one hand, and grabbing hold of me with other, the stranger began urging me to stop going further and allow the firemen to take over and do their job. "Grab hold of the ladder," yelled a firefighter on the ground, as we found ourselves blacking out from the smoke. But all I could think about was the crying baby behind the smoke and fire who was just one floor up! So I tried taking one more step forward, as the steps buckled beneath my feet, almost falling for a second time, only to be grabbed by the stranger, as he held on to the fire engine's ladder. Choking from the smoke, I found myself being lowered down to safety, hearing the cries of the baby slowly cease as the fire engulfed the apartment and flames shot out the door. Memories of helplessness flooded my thoughts, and anger followed suite saying to myself, "…how could she leave him? How could she leave her baby… what the fuck?!" But as we got closer to the ground floor, I could see the despair and pain in the lost child's mother's eyes.

Looking closely in her face and watching the tears flow down her cheek and neck, stopped me from uttering out something stupid in her time of shock and sorrow, ultimately changing my thoughts in an instant! I felt the pain of her sudden loss, as past fiery infernos wrenched my heart.

I became numb and motionless as fire damaged bricks began to fall from the back wall of the building. The nineteenth century building burned quickly;

it was totally engulfed, and turned to ashes that very moment. For days to come, the sadness in the lady's eyes haunted me, and in my mind's eye, I could still hear the fading cries and sudden silence of the baby boy I once baby-sat. That was that, and with nowhere to go and no money in our pockets, we ended up in Grandma's small one bedroom roach infested flat.

My Grandma had already taken it upon herself, the burden of raising her deceased daughter's children: Pookey, Chunky and Domino. Imagine ten people, three adults and seven kids, occupying every space of your domain, with no room to walk, let alone bathroom time. The ages ranged from infants to teenagers, all living in a one bedroom hole in the wall, yet Grandma never said a word, complained, or showed any despair in the plight befalling her impoverished offspring. With love and kindness, she made us all feel at home and safe with no questions asked; however, being indoctrinated into the streets, life for my cousins and me was never without excitement. Conspiring to spare Grandma's grief, we stayed mostly in the streets. Pookey had shacked up with a white girl on the corner of the very building Grandma lived, and Chunky and I spent our time either with Glenn or Keith roaming the hood and shoplifting for food. Loving the life of being rogues unchained, outcasts and homeless, we had only one mission in life, getting drunk or high! Our minds were constantly in a fog, never thinking of the pain imprinted on our psyches, stemming from the sorrowful morning of darkness, like a never ending cloud of woe, with no warning and no way out of ever ending the terrible nightmare as it seemed to be.

Day after day, we roamed the dangerous streets of Gary, Indiana, stealing whatever we could at will, scheming and colluding for the next fix of weed or drink! We were all at the ripe old ages of thirteen and we dove head first into the passage of manhood, but it was in the wrong way, fully contrary to society's norms. Looking back, I could see the death wish we took upon ourselves. Being so young and knowing nothing of the world, we made every toxic bad choice in life, yet we thought we knew it all. We willfully placed ourselves and others' lives in danger every moment of the day, all in the name of having fun, or suppressing the never ending hardship of life with memories of the past and present haunting us 24 hours/ 7 days a week. We were truly lost souls, yet where were the truancy officers assigned to the schools? Well, one was around the way for other truants in the streets, but Chunky and I found that we were left to ourselves. Being enrolled at Beckman Middle High School threatened to break up the little crew we created. I'll never forget the first day of enrollment; I strolled into the main office, ready to enroll with my mother, and a joint dropped from behind my ear onto the floor of the main office. The office was full of staff and students; the teachers paid no mind as I leaned over to pick up my fallen marijuana stick, while all the other students looked at me with amazement. The looks I received from the kids in the office were precious, for I knew I had unabatedly sealed my reputation with that one action of becoming another "bad boy" enrolling in an already fucked up school without ever saying a word or breaking a sweat, in addition to me having the same last name of the two most notorious, hated and feared kids that ever walked the halls of that decrepitated middle school, which didn't help any.

Pookey and Chunky had already made a name for themselves, making my presence most unwelcome. Although there were the typical "wannabes," trying to get to know the new bad boy at school, so not to get their ass whooped or lunch money taken while being bullied; however, what they didn't know just made things simpler, and that was that. I was not the bad boy at all, but they thought I was. I was an undercover good child, thrown into a life of crime and despair. I just ran with it by association. Soon my flare for flamboyancy took hold and before the first day had ended, I had made followers and groupies from vandalizing the school property. By destroying school property, breaking window blinds, swiping the ropes that opened and closed them, and constructing a hangman's noose while placing it around my neck, I proclaimed a new gang called "Code Blue."

Before the week had ended, some fifty kids were wearing hangman's nooses around their necks, and like all great villains throughout history, I had to go through the always unsuspected ancient rite of being challenged by the ruling tribal leaders and thugs. Without my knowledge of course, I fell hook line and sinker into the lure. The trap was set by, you guessed it?! A very pretty face urged me to attend the sock hop after school, in which I did and with no homies around, I was food for the fodder! Always on guard, I quickly caught wind of the plot being hatched as soon as I entered the gymnasium, yet before I could retreat, I was assaulted from behind, and the battle for bragging rights began. Blocking every blow and standing toe to toe with my assaulter, I soon gained the upper hand, seeing his intent from start to finish. Without cause, a voice said to me, "…don't hurt him!"

Instinctively, I restrained myself form hurting my foe, letting him grab me by the neck, and wrestle me to the ground. While wrestling him down to the ground, I began slowing my heart rate, and soon sock hop patrons intervened, hauling us both to the principal's office. It was the first week of middle school, and I had already gotten in big trouble; I was suspended for two weeks and really didn't give a shit. With no consequences to face back home, I blew it off, having no parental guidance to object to my dubious behavior, it was just another shitty day and a reason to get fucked up and drunk. Like clockwork, Glenn and Keith accompanied the truly bad Chunky. All came walking through the woods in back of the school, equipped with big jugs in hand, the cheapest beer you could buy, 64oz of pure yak piss! "The Big Jug" still got us fucked up drunk and we also had weed with the seeds, thus we had a good old time day and night. As I walked towards my ominous looking crew, they were already aware of my little altercation within the sock-hop. I guess the news of my defeat reached outside the middle school walls and into the surrounding neighborhood and realm of thugs. With the crew fully aware of the escapade, they were cracking up, and Chunky said, "Damn P you just started school today, and you already got yo ass whooped! HaHaHa!" Which was far from the case, yet somehow they knew the full story, asking me why I didn't fuck the dude up! Responding, "…it wasn't worth it." The matter was put to rest.

Glenn and my cousin Chunky were supposed to be enrolled as well at Beckmann Middle School, but they decided to skip the first day of school entirely, and meet up with Keith, the oldest of the crew. Keith was a loud mouth who attended a school for deviant dropouts, adjacent to Beckmann Middle School, called "Martin Luther King." It was located on the other side of the middle school football field. In succession, we headed toward an old historical graveyard within the woods across from Beckman's football field to "drink up" and "get our high on," away from prying eyes. With no intention to report my suspension to my mother, I spent the entire two weeks partying, and skipped school every day hence forward; well I should say not attending classes, though being suspended from school, we all played hooky on school grounds. We flirted with all the honeys, and would give out my grandmother's phone number to whomever took the bait, which brings me to the jest of the story, and the conundrum that ensnared all who entered the trap of the spider's web spun by wayward girls.

Please note that I was so naïve to the ways of a woman's charm, and only wanted to satisfy my libido, and show off to my crew. So when the bait was sprung, I jumped at the opportunity to get my dick wet without thinking. When the phone rang, and a sweet voice answered, my little head took control of my thinking process. Not knowing to whom I was even talking, I took the bait hook line and sinker. Playing the little sexual games that people now pay for over the phone, I could hear the most seductive voice I ever heard, soft and sweet, and pleasurable to the ear drum, getting me hornier with every call.

I agreed to meet up with the seductive stranger, a girl I didn't know from Adam. A girl that lived on the outskirts of the "Delaney Projects," a hell hole adjacent to Beckman Junior High. It was strictly forbidden to outsiders, not to mention it was the area in which the punk lived that jumped me inside the sock hop the very first week of school. No matter! I could care less; I was going to get some pussy, and in my mind it was well worth the risk. Without fail, I willingly ran straight into the eye of the storm, only thinking with my little head, with no regard of the possibility of bodily harm, although, it crossed my mind at least twice as I made my way to her abode located in the land of nowhere. Fear entered my head as I walked closer to the forbidden zone as I consciously and nervously looked back and forth. I watched out for savory characters as I walked up the front staircase leading to the address given to me over the phone and was hoping whoever answered the door would be as hot and sexy, as the mind sights inventions for the eyes, but to my astonishment, what answered the door took the life force right out of me.

The sweet voice on the other end of the telephone was embodied into the ugliest creature known to man, for she was blacker than midnight, and as big as all outdoors! Stunned and in shock, I couldn't even make a run for it. Standing there with my mouth wide open, I froze as she invited me indoors. Like a deer caught in headlights, I walked in thinking, "… what the fuck am I doing," only to turn back, and see her lock the door behind me with a big grin on her fat face.

Thinking nothing of it, I sat on the broken dirty sofa while trying to figure a way out of the predicament I found myself locked into. Then without warning, a second sister of massive proportions came out of the woodwork. She was just as fat and ugly with fire in her eyes and just cheesing. It was clear as glass, I was lunch on the menu. I was on their sexual exploitive menu. They were the ravenous wild cats, and I was the mouse caught in the mouse trap, straight up lunch! Before I knew it, they were both on top of me, rubbing on my dick with vigor asking, "…you given it up today boy?" With all my strength, I tried to break free from the monstrous beasts, but they were much stronger than I was. They grabbed a hold of my person, forcibly kissing every inch of my face and groping my private parts, as they tried to unzip my pants. Franticly breaking loose, I felt helpless as I ran aimlessly around their ghettoized house, trying to steer clear of their clutches, only to find myself locked in a closet with the two monsters threating to never let me go. As time dwindled, fear set into my conscience. I was truly becoming afraid as I heard the twin dragons plotting of my demise. I overheard them planning on who was going to do what first!

Thinking to myself "…oh god what have I done; how could I put myself in this situation?!" Finally saying to myself, "…fuck it! I'm just going to let them have their way with me; if that's the only way out, so be it!" Then I heard their front door open. While huddled down in darkness on the closet floor, I heard a man's voice, well a teen-aged boy's voice. It was the wicked witch's younger brother coming home from football practice. "Yes!" I yelled. "Help! Help! Help me!" I yelled once more, "Please help me!" "Who's that?!" The brother asked in a startled tone. "What have yawl done?! Who do you have in there?!" He said to his two behemoth siblings as he walked closer to the closet door. I could hear the two hungry hippos trying to stop him from opening the closet door. As I continued to yell out for help with no avail, he opened the closet door and freed me from his sister's clutches! Forever in his debt, I feverishly shook his hand, standing close to his person as we made our way to the front door. I thanked him all the way, as he held back his hungry hippo sisters from assaulting me once again. We made our way towards freedom, and as their brother and I soldiered on, the look of disappointment descended upon their faces. When little brother opened the closet door leading to my departure, a faint whimper protruded out of their fat faces.

I felt a sense of sweet sorrow mixed with adoration! I then stopped right outside the threshold of the front door to embrace my liberator, and offered a gift of thanks for his timely arrival.

A new friendship was in the making as he introduced himself as Roberto. I made my acquaintance and thanked him once more and asked if he smoked weed, as I pulled a joint from my jacket pocket, lit it up, and took a drag before even a response was spoken from the young doe eyed impressionable liberator. I proceeded to take a couple of tokes, and passed it to him, not knowing if he had ever partaken of any marijuana smoke. As I watched him choke from his very first indulgence into the so-called gateway drug of today, I laughed as I walked off into the distance after exchanging telephone numbers. The very next day, I received a phone call from Roberto, asking if I could get him high once more, and without any thought of corrupting an innocent, I agreed to meet up and get fucked up. Soon Roberto was kickin' it with all three of us, learning the bright lights of corruption and darkness, ultimately learning corruption of the spirit and soul at a rapid rate. Like the three of us, soon Roberto would find himself on the fast track to destruction. Even though we were scattered from the East-side of the city to the West-side of the city, we met faithfully each day to repeat our drunken escapade into the darkness light, which was seen as good and fun.

Though Glenn, Keith, Chunky and I were smoking and drinking daily, we never brought our bad habits into Grandma's home, and never showed ourselves intoxicated or high, and whenever we did enter into Grandma's house, we remembered not to have the scent of debauchery on our person.

We walked through Grandma's door, assured to be sober and never showed our hands dirty. But the habit of smoking had taken hold, and I was feigning for a square one lonely night. Thinking all was well while everyone was asleep, I sparked up a "Kool Mild" and took a drag. As soon as I sparked up the cigarette, my Grandma, Ida Mae Abbott, opened the bedroom door asking, "Who's in here smoken' cigarettes?!"

Grandma knew everything! Knowing all the other children in the room were all babies under the age of five, and hearing Chunky snore like an animal in the corner, I fessed up quickly. "I am Grandma!" "Who's that?!" she asked as she turned on the bedroom light, while looking directly at me. She just looked at me with disappointment, and a long sigh, and as I looked up at her full of guilt, she only said, "You're telling your mother in the morning!" "Yes ma'am" I responded, and she turned off the lights and closed the door. Staying true to Grandma, I fessed up as soon as I saw my mom. There was no yelling or punishment, she only said, "If you going to smoke, do it at home, and not in the streets…. And get your own… I'm not supporting your habits!" I was thirteen and had no clue of the danger, and couldn't care less.

Chunky looked at me with astonishment saying, "You never get in trouble; I can't believe you Pee Wee!" Walking out the front door, I followed him saying, "I can't believe it myself!" Chunky was truly dumbfounded, saying, "You should have been spanked!" Seeing once again the difference in upbringing, feeling unfairly raised by everyone surrounding him, Chunky asked, "Why couldn't I have a mother like yours?!" Taking the smile off my smug little face, responding only, "She's your mother now!" He smiled back, and off we went into the dangerous hood, without concern or care of authority. Both feeling our oats! With my mother's nonchalant attitude towards my smoking cigarettes, Chunky and I felt our independence from the ever snooping eyes of grown-ups. Forever trying to cover up the smell of cigarettes and marijuana, was forever not an issue for us again, and making sure we didn't get caught smoking became an afterthought. Now the pressure was off, and since I smoked openly within the house, Chunky quickly followed suite; it was the official step towards manhood as we saw it.

But it was far from the case! While walking down the street smoking openly, my mind wondered off into space, and an overwhelming feeling of sorrow engulfed my spirit, as if everything was wrong in the world. Why was tobacco no longer taboo—no longer off limits? And as the limits of childhood faded away, so did all notion of safety. So far, all I could make of this world was cruel, heartless, and unfair! "I myself should embrace the unexplainable horrors, mishaps and injustice that consumes most people's thoughts; embrace was inevitable; just accept it all without question!" I silently told myself while walking down the street as Chunky, Glenn and I sparked up a joint while making small talk.

The day ended without incident and Glenn, Chunky and I posted up right outside Grandma's place, fully inebriated. Feeling fucked up, I stumbled upstairs and went straight to bed. Before I could hit the filthy carpeted floor, I was knocked out! As soon as my drunken state embraced the sweet darkness of drunken blackout, I was abruptly awaken. "P! P! Wake up!" It was Chunky waking me from my sweet slumber. Chunky yelled once more, "P the building next door is on fire, and it's getting close to Grandma's house; we got to get every body out!" With fire freshly imprinted in our minds, I quickly arose, looking out the bedroom window, and saw the flames and embers popping over to the roof of Grandma's building! "Oh, Shit!" I said to myself... "Not again?!" I quickly rounded up my siblings, as grandmother headed down the staircase and outside the building. Chunky had helped Granny Grip, our great grandmother, down the stairs, and as we all looked up at the blazing building next door. The fire had now fully engulfed Grandma's building as well. Granny spoke out and said, "What is going on here... It is as if someone wants us all dead...why is this happening?"

Now the blaze was drifting towards Grandma's building even moreso as we helplessly watched. Grandma's building had only begun to fully burn from the outside, but a glimpse of hope had arrived.

The fire department had arrived, and all was well. The firemen got to work in a flash, quickly drenching the roof of Grandma's building, snuffing out the flames while bravely attacking the burning inferno raging next door. Soon the immediate danger was over, and the agonizing scent of burned wood and water filled the air. With tears on my Grandma's face, we all entered back into the water damaged building. The totally burned and gutted out building next to Grandma's building was barely standing as the Fire Marshal declared the burned out and adjacent building unsafe. I knew bad news was coming our way, and his announcement would be leaving us all homeless once again. Chunky and I looked at each other with non-belief.

With so many children, and so many uncertainties, I could imagine the fear manifesting itself within my mother and grandmother's hearts, so we made the choice teenagers shouldn't have to make. Not knowing what else to do, my mother and grandmother walked back up the stairs and stayed within the recently declared unfit building, next door to the burned out building inches away. Disregarding the declaration uttered by the Fire Marshal, my entire family headed back up the stairs of the smoked and water damaged building full of despair and without hope. With all their children in hand, my mother and grandmother stayed in that building until the ability to move somewhere relatively safe could come. Until the lifesaving monthly government entitlements arrived the following month, all were trapped in a condemned building without assistance. Seeing and feeling the personal angst of our guardians' suffering constant misery, Chunky and I stayed in the street, thinking it would be best, with continuous experience of woes, we could fend for ourselves. We learned the dangerous and unscrupulous evil ways of street scoundrels without flaw or waste of time. We had no fear of the unknown, knowing the obvious conclusions of our actions, and conforming to the realization that less mouths to feed would help the situation, and bring some relief to our mother's plight somehow, so we left grandma's home for good and roamed the streets without remorse or fear of others, like rebels without a cause. We stole, ripped off and pillaged others without cause and felt justified in doing so. Chunky and I said nothing to one another and just watched the family go back up the stairs that night, and never returned. With no fear or regard for life, we weathered the winter storms, and were robbing stores, people and fellow bums for food, drink and weed. We stayed out in the streets for more than three weeks, occupying abandoned buildings close to Grandma's condemned building.

Time passed and the gods of this world shined their evil light upon our not so happy family, granting some financial relief for a moment, blessing my mother and grandmother's household for once in months. Both parties moved into separate apartments at the same time; it was remarkable luck to both my mother and grandmother.

It was a nice three-bedroom apartment [on the first floor I might add] in a brownstone on the East-side of Gary, Indiana, close to Keith's house. It seemed as if some rest from mayhem would follow, and I even had a puppy, a small white half breed terrier by the name of Scorpio that followed my every beckoned call. I even met other kids my age inside and outside the building, having my second sexual experience there within days. It was as if I died and went to heaven, having sex with the older girl from the fourth floor, not knowing one another's name, only feeling the animal attraction propagated by the male and female hormones raging within us both. We got busy in lust! My siblings and her siblings watched through a crack in the back room window blinds, giggling as we indulged in the oldest cardinal sin. Life began to reap its sweet reward, and just as soon as things were normalizing, the unexpected occurred. While walking downtown to "Brooks Brothers" for a brand new pair of Converses, the face of true fear appeared without warning!

On a bright, sunny, Indian-Summer, Thursday afternoon, while I was out buying shoes, a pair of thieves scoped me out and held me up at gunpoint. It was the first time I had a gun pointed in my face, but unfortunately, not the last. In shock and fearing for my life, I gave over the merchandise without protest, and scurried back home with tears in my eyes and true fear in my heart. I ran as fast as I could, only to see Chunky in the park located down and across the street from my mother's apartment building, being jumped on by four grungy punks that were way bigger than he. Not willing to let the fear consume my every thought, I yelled out Chunky's name and ran towards the engaged brawl full of fear, but not being any help in fending off the perpetrators after my ordeal. I faked my way through the battle yelling and screaming, while Chunky beat the living hell out of all four foes. Fearing that I was a potential threat, the three dispersed in different directions at high speed, while leaving a single poor soul caught in the grasp of Chunky's fury. Still in shock, I had no stomach for any more violence. I quickly stopped Chunky from finishing off his foe, and helped dust off my ferocious cousin as he uttered, "It's a good thing you came when you did; I was going to kill them all!" With a big grin on his face, we both walked back towards my mother's apartment, and there I informed him of my short encounter with a thirty-eight snub nose in my face. Chunky was beside himself with anger, ready to track down the dangerous thieves that instilled fear into my heart.

Chunky lived with Grandma, having great disdain for her rules; she finally found a place on the East-side close to her children, which was not that far from my mother's building. Chunky was on his way to visit when he was attacked by people I've never seen before. I guess by Chunky and I being strangers to the neighborhood, he was the target of the shady characters who roamed there in the park. Back at the homestead, Mama and the woman upstairs were partying without restraint, getting full blown drunk and engaging in belligerent activities, but little did I know that their folly and revelry was the least of my adolescent problems, for they were accompanied by the most dangerous men I've ever known! The men were three brothers from a ruthless family of thirteen, better known as the Moore's, the leaders of the notorious "Black Guerrilla Family." I even had beef with one of their younger brothers long ago on Carolina Street, also better known as "The Colored Doors." Mostly Pookey and Chunky waged war with the two youngest siblings of the Moore family, and I just got caught in the cross hairs. The older Moore's were known throughout the city as murderous thugs that wreaked havoc wherever they lay their hat! The strongest muscle men feared their presence and experienced shock and terror whenever they entered the room and unfortunately, my mother just couldn't recognize friend from foe; her sense of judgment was way to the left of scrutiny and far from discerning. It was as if she reveled in the presence of the worst of the worst and would open her doors to the very definition of evil forces and worst elements of mankind, and with open arms, she offered all she had to offer to those unworthy.

Though benevolent in her words and actions, she associated herself amongst thugs, unwittingly teaching me a very good lesson: being nice to everyone will get you in big trouble! My mother's intuition was most definitely to the contrary of the definition. Chunky and I stayed far from the activities upstairs and hung out in my newly black painted bedroom. He spoke of running away to far and distant places every time we met. Pissed off at the events that took place that day, we frowned and laughed during the time we had left before his curfew slowly crept up upon us.

We pondered what was in store for us in the future, knowing our lot in life was lower than dust, we could only hope for a quick death and a fast rise through the ranks of corruption. The more we contemplated our fate in life, the more depression reigned freely, and soon Chunky left and I was alone sobbing over new high top Converses that would never be, staring at the four black walls surrounding me. Filled with self-pity, I cried myself to sleep, yet before "REM" could consume my soul, I could faintly hear in the background of my closed bedroom door, male voices and many footsteps walking through the apartment. Half asleep, I arose to investigate the commotion, and before I could fully awaken, I was assaulted from behind, feeling only the strength of a man's arms grabbing me, and a wet cloth covering my mouth, seeing nothing or hearing no one before embracing pitch blackness.

I had been drugged! Slowly the darkness tuned into a dream vision then instant blackness. It was a pleasant dream in which I still cannot recall the content, but before I could embrace it, it was being interrupted by a banging sound. The banging noise grew louder and louder with each thumb of my heartbeat, until the banging noise became real, consequently awakening me out of my sweet slumber. With my head in a daze, I stumbled towards the banging noise.

It was someone knocking at the front door, and it was my mother! She had been banging on our front door for over five hours; speaking in an erratic manor, she explained the fear and torture she and the upstairs neighbor endured over the last twenty-four hours. They had been held hostage and robbed, robbed by those they knew!

It was the most notorious of the Moore brothers, J.and M. Moore. Men my mother had known for many years; men that now held two women and their children hostage for nothing less than their welfare checks. They threatened to kill them and their children for less than two thousand bucks between the two of them, and that's including food stamps. With flowing tears from her eyes, she went on and on about how she and her new found friend were subdued.

They finagled their way onto the scene with a bottle of E & J Brandy the previous night, and as the party winded down, and the children fell asleep, the mood of the two brothers became hostile and threating towards them both. Mom continued to say how it got physically violent without warning, and how they quickly bound the two with duct tape. The Moore's frantically ransacked the apartment in search for whatever valuables they may find. They searched their purses and wallets, ceased all cash and food stamps, and found the un-cashed check of the upstairs neighbor, Brenda. Enraged, the two brothers began beating and choking Brenda without restraint until she passed out, almost killing the poor woman. Then without emotion, the two calmed down and brandished their weapons, and yelled out the front window, "Come on up!" Unannounced to the subdued women were three other men posted outside the building, equipped with a truck and burglar tools. The brothers had planned this caper from the get go.

It was the notorious Moore brothers who sneaked up behind me, covered my mouth with a rag filled with chloroform, and drugged me in seconds and without struggle. My mother looked around our now empty apartment, with notebook in hand, writing down all that was stolen in the night, and after she

EDGAR FRENCH, JR.

completed her inventory, she cried uncontrollably. She continued to describe to me the horrific and excruciating emotional fear visited upon her and the entire building by the Moore brothers the previous day. The brothers woke up all the children out of a peaceful sleep, gathered them in the kitchen, and placed them on the floor at gun point while duct taping all of them, subsequently endangering the welfare of their mothers who were partying upstairs. The woman upstairs by the name, Brenda, was ordered to the ground first, then followed my mother on the kitchen floor, and all in the apartment stayed until business hours the next day. Once the check cashing place was open, my mother was forced to go with one of the assailants to cash her welfare check and give it up to him as soon as they left the store, or be killed with the rest of her loved ones, and the new found friend she just meet. While the scoundrels entered every apartment in the building, taking all that wasn't nailed down in the night, I was unconscious and aware of nothing. As my mother relived the ordeal with every verbal description, I looked around our apartment gathering mental pictures of all that was taken.

Those assholes took everything we owned, even taking the new wardrobe my father just bought me. "Damn! Will we ever catch a break!?" I asked myself. As usual, evil showed itself at every turn, never letting up. "What have we done to deserve so much ill will?!" A few months passed and indescribable drama increased one hundred fold! Every night something evil was taking place within the building, such as the rape and pillaging of wayward girls, amongst the fragmentation of young souls; all who all lived within those brick walls suffered. It seemed as if every rotten person in the hood sought sanctuary within our building's malevolent doors. Every night there was a stabbing, shooting or worse. The smell of marijuana smoke and alcohol echoed through the main hall and staircase, and darkness deepened its hold on my soul but not my spirit. I had grown accustomed to debauchery and degradation, and began to revel in its light, so I invited Glenn and Keith over to see my never ending nightmare, and experience the ongoing danger that surrounded me constantly, if not for just one night! I dared them to spend less than 24 hours in the house of carnival style horrors in which I endured on a daily basis. With a glary eyed enthusiasm, I relayed the events that occurred over the last few months, which were enormous in multitude. Captivated with my little tales of horror, the two marveled in mis-belief at the mayhem and pure anarchy that seemed to follow me where ever I rested my head. The two echoed synonymously, "Whatever P… shit…that don't happen… you must be trippin' or crazy or something?!" Glenn rolled up a big fat joint while Keith cracked open a brew, and just shook his head saying, "I believe you P… I heard about this place… that's why I stay clear from your block…I'm only here because Glenn's scared ass was too afraid to come over by himself." Glenn looked nervous for once and Keith was full of stories about my abode since he was the oldest of the three, yet he was the first to flee at the slightest hint of trouble. I knew he was only there for the weed and drink, and not for the excitement. I looked at my two friends and said in a serious tone, "Now fellows, this is how this shit works! My mom is already upstairs getting fucked up, and the party is in full swing. Watch! Before the streetlights come on outside, some shit is going to pop off'!" Feeling nice and proper from the libation and weed, we chilled on the couch and watched the clock as we chatted. Hearing the music blasting yet kickin' upstairs, we waited. Then loud voices rang in the hallway, and nameless profanities filled the air! The witching hour was quickly approaching, for I could feel it deep within my spirit. Without warning, the lights in the entire building shut off and the sound of gun fire rang out. "POP! POP! POP!"

Gun shots rang out and all three of us hit the floor, quietly saying under my breath, "What I tell you! Every night I go through this shit!" It was as if I lived in my very own horror movie, or better yet, a never ending nightmare!

I didn't care because I was fucked up anyway, so I whispered, "Let's enjoy the festivities fellows!" Seeing the absolute fear plastered upon the faces of Glenn and Keith, I smiled and said "…let's go!" Weaving and bobbing through the darkened apartment, I placed my baby brother and sister on the floor in the back room for their safety and told them to, "… stay down!" Closing the bedroom door behind them, and seeing nothing in the blackness, my eyes began adjusting to the darkness in the night. The sound of gun fire was still crackling outside the building, then there was a moment of silence. Adrenalin flowed throughout my body as Glenn, Keith and I crept threw the house, peeking out the windows and listening for what horror came next. Strangely, no fear entered the fray of our dangerous adventure as we crept closer to the danger zone. Only excitement filled the air, and surprisingly, none of us exhibited fear.

We were prepared mentally and physically; we rolled up another doobie and waited for the unknown, for the inevitable thrill that was sure to come. Isn't it funny how things become so much clearer when there's no electrical power flowing through the walls? One could hear a pin drop, especially when all five senses are heightened. Although we were on the first floor, we could hear the faint whimpers of those on the top floor of the building. No longer were the two drunken party goers living it up on the top floor, for there was just whimpers of terrifying sobbing. Amongst the violent altercations erupting in the hallway of the building, and outside the building, only bird's songs and fluttering wings were heard. Then suddenly, a man's voice screamed out of the midst of hell! I recognized the voice saying to Glenn and Keith, "Damn that sounds like Lynnville! What the fuck is he doing here?!"

Lynnville was the owner of the building, and the best landlord, out of the many landlords my mother had over the years. He was an old good hearted drunkard that held his ground no matter what; he was outspoken, fearless, and full of courage, but then again, alcohol does that to people. He was never sober out of all the times I've seen or spoken to him, but he was a good person, having not a prejudice or bigoted bone in his body. He was the only white man that walked through the all black neighborhood without fear of harm, and everybody knew him and left him alone. I guess his time was up in the eyes of the lord because it was his voice I heard within the mix of things unfolding in the hallway. All we could hear was fighting throughout the building's inner workings, raised voices, punches and bodies slamming against walls. There was a great amount of yelling and cursing as the danger levels subsided. The evil doers were outside my mother's front door, banging up against it with massive force and strength of power. I looked over toward Glenn with fully extended pupils as the suspense heightened.

With curiously overtaking all of my senses, I had to open the door; I opened it, and to my surprise, I was right. It was Lynnville! It was Lynnville and Ted fighting throughout the night.

Who knows who was doing the shooting outside the building at that time, yet inside the building it was Lynnville and Ted doing the brawling. Who knows who shut off the lights by taking out the meter from the side of the building, but it wasn't Ted or Lynnville that brought the darkness, removing the power meter, turning out the lights after midnight, but no one cared! When the certain sounds of violence ceased, I immediately opened the front door. Blood was everywhere, all over the floor and walls, and it was Lynnville's blood. The venomous and no good womanizing Ted had beaten him to a pulp! How could he?! Ted was a no good swindling player and self-proclaimed pimp, wasting away in his twenties, and living off any woman he could hoodwink or persuade to fall for his boyish charm. Having the courage of an ant, he instigated a fight with Lynnville, who was an old man in his sixties or seventies! A man that couldn't bust a grape in a fruit fight, yet there he was, drowning in his own blood and beaten within inches of his life by a well-known pussy in the hood!

"Get the fuck off him!" I yelled, snatching punk-ass Ted off the poor, and helpless Lynnville. With Glenn and Keith backing me up with angry faces, I was full rage and courage! Losing the will to contain our fury we chased Ted and threw him out of the building and outside the lobby doors. It was obvious we all were still stoned out of our minds with grief over Lynnville, but where did the time go?! The sun had crept over the horizon without notice. Within a blink of an eye, it was another day that passed, yet we had survived the ferocious marauders' night of terror! Full of adrenalin and energy without sleep, my friends and I stayed out into the light of day and stayed clear of the scene of the crime. "What did I tell you?!" I said to Glenn and Keith with a great big humongous grin while I shook my head towards the ground. Then Keith proclaimed with shock, "Look, somebody took yawl electricity power meter off P," as we walked back towards the building, feeling more alive than the day before.

Danger filled the air, and our lives twirled around this deadly wheel of roulette called my place of residence, not knowing if it would be our last night alive, but no real adventure would be an adventure if there were not a cop's presence, but without the authorities sense of proprietary, it would only be a typical day in the ghetto. Back inside the building, my mom was still caring for Lynnville, doing the best she could to maintain his life until the ambulance would arrive. He was hurt so badly that I could barely recognize him. His face resembled a sour dough roll, and though we ran Ted off into the distance, our level of compassion for our fellow man was nil. I had no remorse for Lynnville; our emotional responses had been sheered and stunted from the never ending violence. Where once I would be filled with concern and care for my fellow man, I felt no pity for his plight.

What was happening to me?!

I mentally and emotionally disregarded a man's suffering and pain and disregarded someone that was truly dear to me, someone who had a fun and jest spirit. I enjoyed his willingness to teach elderly wisdom and show compassion to all that passed his way. Overwhelmed by the thrill and uncertainty that came with life's threatening dangers, I stood numb in his presence, as my mother franticly and successfully preserved his life.

Yet as the brave-hearted Lynnville began to regain consciousness, my spirit filled with joy. It was exhilarating to see life once again shine brightly within his old and grayish darkened eyes. Feelings of despair and dread that I did not visibly exhibit faded away, yet depression soon followed my wakened days to come. Although I gained pride in my ability to escape death, I boasted too much in the eyes of my unknown enemies that dwelled in unseen places, for their distain overshadowed my eager and naïve willingness to carry on within darkness light with little faith in the precious life that one was born.

Chapter XV
Restlessness Captured

Autumn had arrived and the leaves of the trees were changing their autumn foliage into lovely colors while the Chicago Hulk was blowing ever so hard off of Lake Michigan. It was a beautiful morning, and I went for a walk up the road to check on my cousin/brother, Chunky. Since Grandma's house is just a few blocks down the way, I said to myself, "I shouldn't get into any or too much trouble walking alone this early in the morning." While reaching Grandma's pretty quickly and feeling good, I hummed my way up her staircase, but when I got closer to the front door, I could hear Grandma yelling at Chunky and I didn't know why. From her apartment on the third story floor, I could hear her clearly, thinking "...ugh man what's going now?!" Once again, it was something Chunky had done the previous night. Not wanting to hear or mediate any disputes, I took a seat on the front steps outside, and sparked up a joint. As the ruckus subsided, I could hear a door slamming within Grandma's apartment, and before long, I could hear Chunky slamming her apartment front door. He barreled down the stairs, not even seeing me sitting on the stump, and pushed open the outer doors leading outside of the apartment building. I said, "Chunky! Turn around!" With fire in his eyes, he saw it was his favorite cousin and said, "I was just on my way to yo house, I can't take it no mo'! I can't even take a shit here without her saying something! Every day it something mane; I wish I lived with you man...she too much, P!" Attempting to calm him down, I suggested, "...come on man; let's go to the park and smoke this joint?!"

As we slowly yet smugly walked across the street leading to the park close by, he described his plight, and begged me to persuade my mother to let him stay with us. Knowing the situation at home was not the best, and understanding the daily pressures, my mother undertook the task of taking care of us all. However, I let him know she couldn't do it, and told him that he needed to stick it out at Grandma's and make the best of it, but he wasn't hearing that. It was as if his mind was closed to all and any reason or logic. We walked the neighborhood in search of Glenn and Keith, and every time he'd bring up the subject, I'd shrug him off, smoothly overlooking and disregarding the subject matter at hand, tossing it to the side. After finding our other two partners in crime, we headed back toward the West-side of town, where we all felt safest in our escapades, while looting any person of easy prey, and most that crossed our path. It was a daily must that we financed our weed and alcohol addiction during the hours of early morning, thinking we were oh so bad, cool and unstoppable.

We fit in with no one, yet were accepted by all in our age group, either out of fear or admiration, although I didn't know it at the time. We were always fully ignored by the so-called grown-ups as they went about their daily affairs. Most people in the hood were and still are deeply immersed in darkness themselves. No adult offered any moral guidance, or words of encouragement toward the future in hope, or in doing the right thing with our lives; on the contrary, most just facilitated our spiraling journey with back door passes down hell's corridors. A week had passed and tragedy had stricken once again. Fire broke out in Grandma's newly found apartment building. Another unexplained fire for the third time! "This is just too much... I have got to find out who is doing this shit?!" Then the realization of the arsonist may have been closer to home than I had ever thought; it hit me like an anvil falling from heaven.

I knew how badly Chunky wanted to live with my mother and me. With a heightened sixth sense, I began questioning myself, "But he?! He wouldn't do something like that, would he?!" Not after all he's been through! No way would he do such a thing...would he?!" With the death of his mother and sister, freshly in the minds of all in the family, the thought of such a thing entering my mind was ludicrous, but the thought of someone setting another building on fire in which a loved one lived was too much to endure, for it should be the last thing in my or his head. But I had to confront him about Grandma's house suddenly being ablaze. Days passed and the notion of Chunky's involvement of Grandma's woes would not subside, so I went out in search of my troubled cousin/brother.

As if it were destiny, I found him, and what I found disturbed the very foundation of my spirit! As I walked past an old burned out abandoned building just a block over from my mother's apartment, I heard a noise within the gutted out building, so I slowly walked over and looked through the broken out windows, and saw a faint shadow fumbling in the blackness of the basement grounds. Making sure my presence was stealth, I followed the shadow as the scent of gasoline fumes made its way outside of the building to my nose.

Then a spark lit up the darkness within the abandon building. A spark from a single match erupted, making out the shadowy figure igniting the flame. It was Chunky! It was my beloved cousin/brother. Chunky was setting the building on fire! "Oh, my god! How could he?!" How many acts of arson has he committed?!" As the fire grew in intensity, I still could recognize Chunky's entire shadowy presence standing in the midst of the flames. He just stood there as if he were in a demonic hypnotic daze. He was watching the flames dance around the room in which he stood, drinking wine from a Slurpee cup and spitting out spurts of wine onto the grimy floor as the flames grew in intensity.

As he stood there glistening amongst the trash and broken furniture quickly coming ablaze, he was unaware that I was watching him. He smiled with glee, igniting the rubble and wooden structures painted on the walls of the room in which he stood. He had no clue that I was there observing it all as he made his way toward the safest exit. He made sure to stay hidden and in the background as I followed him as he made his way from the criminal scene of arson. I stayed in the shadows of the night, so as to make sure his heightened sixth sense antenna did not acknowledge my presence as he ran toward the park a few blocks away. I stayed concealed behind every other tree, behind oak tree by oak tree and watched him make his way to the playground within the park. He took a seat on the kiddy swing as the alerting sounds of fire engines made their way towards the fire that he created. He casually swung back and forth with an evil smile of satisfaction on his face, as the sounds of the sirens got closer and closer to the blaze. I yelled out, "Chunky!" He looked startled and jumped as I called out his name. "P! What up man?!" "Nothing!" With hesitation in my voice I said, "You know I saw you." "Saw what?!" He asked. "I saw you set fire to the building where the fire trucks are going right now! I was watching the whole time Chunky!" Then silence filled the air. "Did you set Grandma's house on fire?" Breaking the silence. "Yea I set it, and you know why too don't you P?!" Seeing the lack of concern over my inquiry, I knew he was lost into the darkness of pain and suffering. With nothing more to say, we walked our separate ways.

I never said a word to anyone within the family or another soul, and the fires ceased, but the damage was done. Grandma and all living with her were back in the streets, but not for long thank god, for a place on the West-side of town revealed itself soon after. Yet my suspicions were confirmed, for the seeds of doubt of my beloved cousin/brother's innocence in past fires had been sown, and Chunky's secret was out in the light of my mind's eye! All along, everyone within the family was suspecting him of setting at least two of the fires close to Grandma's residents, and others outside the family suspected him in the recent out breaks of fires around the city. Suspicions ran wild, including my own, after catching him in the act, yet no one said a word. No more than four months passed before more sinister events would occur at the East-side apartment in which my mother resided, and this time its evil toll would prove to be fatal. Fatal for the owner of the building, Lynnville.

The Moore brothers had struck again, and this time I played witness to a murder; the only eye witness to the slaying of my mother's landlord.

With no fear of reprisal or being discovered, J. Moore shot Lynnville at point blank range to his head, right as I walked in the hallway of the building, and he looked me right in the eye as he sifted through Lynnville's pockets, searching for cash or anything of value, I presumed. With drug induced eyes of glassy crystal pupils, and sweat pouring from his brow down his shirt, J. Moore said nothing and walked past me with the look of a stone cold killer.

With no expression or care of heart, he walked right out of the building into the midst of the night. To my surprise, I felt nothing for Lynnville at the moment of impact. Terrified from head to toe, I walked in slow motion to my bedroom, walking into the apartment in total shock! I walked right by my mother and stayed silent as she inquired about the gunshot she just heard. I went directly into my bedroom, lay across my bed, and looked at the ceiling as a single tear drop rolled down my cheek, saying to myself, "Will this this be my fate if I speak?! Am I the next one to bite the dust?!"

Then visions of Lynnville's lifeless body entered my mind, even when my eyes were open, tears continued to roll down my face. I found myself speaking to god the entire night, saying, "It can't be real?!" But it was, and if I said anything to anyone, J. Moore would most definitely kill me. Over and over in my head, these words would follow me daily: "He's going to kill me next... I saw him do it; lord help me!" I just lay horizontally in my bed forever it seemed, just lying there in shock. Day by day, I waited for some pig like scum bag to bust open my mother's front door and take me out, but no one came. I could hear all the commotion in front of the building, so I got up off the bed and walked to the window of the living room of our apartment, yet no one came to question me at all. All inquiries with those living within the building were finished that night! Yet my mother knew I saw something, and she said not a word! Though I knew what went down, I said nothing to the cops, for I knew in my heart I did the right thing because if I said anything, I would be dead. I stayed in my room for at least four days after that event and only would come out for food and water. I was truly traumatized with no sense of fear, but felt only a dread of being killed any day! Seeing another life snuffed out right before my eyes for the first time was horrifying, for it brings you face to face with your own mortality and drains all that is good within you, ultimately oozing out the goodness. The color of the trees, skies or other things became black and white, without meaning. Happiness seemed unattainable! The dread was so bad, even my mother could feel it. It was the straw that broke the Camel's back in the eyes of my mother, and within thirty days, we were gone! We moved in with Grandma yet again, but the dread did not stop and followed us forevermore! I had changed once more!

Life began to have no meaning whatsoever, for my humanity had been severely damaged in seconds from that event of murder.

My heart had hardened, and whatever belief I had in god waivered daily, amongst the evil that permeated the hood. Some lost within the world in which we live would say I was becoming a man, yet I beg to differ. I was barely thirteen and knew nothing of the real world in which we lived. All I knew was Gary, Indiana was hell on Earth to me; for in my eyes, the world consisted of pain, sorrow and grief! Any feelings of happiness or fulfillment of life was short lived and basically an illusion not worth pursuit! Happiness was just a waste of time and energy for any of us living in the hood. I said to myself, "Fuck it! If life is so worthless, I'll make the best of it at the expense of others." From that time forward, I would be out for the sake of fun, and fun only, out for my own self! I'll only care about fun and fun alone. I could be dead by the end of day anyway, so why follow the rules of goodness at all? I said to myself: "You could be dead today so enjoy P...but what is fun... getting high, drunk as a skunk...being unruly and untamed...doing whatever, not worrying about any consequences for myself, or those who I impacted?! The goodness and the god I loved so much did not exist, and even if he did, he was my enemy now. Why else would life be so unbearable?! Why else would my family have to endure so much fucking horror?! Fuck him!"

The changing of time comes quickly when you're young and carefree of all personal responsibility for one's actions, plus summer time was back, and it was time to create havoc on the populist of the small ghettoized city. We were living back on the West-side of town where I rested my head once more. Moving back on the West-side was for the best, especially when it came to my family's safety; I'll never forget it! I can even recall the address: 404 Polk Street, otherwise known as "Baby Havana!" It was a part of the West-side I'd never seen before, and most of the residents were either Cuban or Mexican in origin or nationality. I guess that's where I acquired an affectation for Hispanic women.

There were so many beautiful long dark haired Hispanic girls, and I couldn't believe it; yes, I must admit it, there was something about Spanish women I could not resist in those days! Even at that young age, the length of their long black hair enchanted me; the curves of their form was intoxicating to me, and they were everywhere! And I was the bad black boy moving in their neighborhood. It just so happened one of the three amigos, "Glenn," lived only blocks away from where we moved, so of course, he was ever present. In a sea of hotties, I had to look my best as I planned to venture out amongst the herd of young girlies! It was nineteen eighty, and the style consisted of GQ, Stacy Adams, and feathered roach clips. French braids were the shit, and I had it all, thanks to Pops. Yet as soon as I began to venture out onto the streets of the West-side in which we moved, girls were the last thing on my mind, for I had changed within. No joy resided inside my soul, and my friends couldn't understand why I stayed clear from the many girls coming around our crew. I only thought of getting high, so every night, Glenn and I would get lit. Living with Grandma was like living in a gold mine.

Every first of the month, when the welfare checks promptly arrived, she had to have her many expensive pills, and guess who took up the mantel of retrieving her precious drugs from the drug store? You got it! I'm talking forty to fifty bucks a pop, and we'd lift them from the store every time, pocketing the money every time as well. So we were never without beer and marijuana. Still infantile in our thoughts, getting drugs and alcohol was our only daily goal; it was all we knew, and all we would ever care about until fate would soon rear its ugly face.

Chunky was still living with Grandma, yet was never there, and at that time, I didn't care. I knew he'd be revealing himself soon, saying to myself, "He'll show up sooner or later!" And he did. Soon, the three of us were back in touch, causing havoc in the streets once more! Grandma's two bedroom hole in the wall had become an encampment of family members: my mother's children, my late Aunt Lucy's surviving youngest, and Granny Grip, my grandmother's mother. There was no room at all! Most of us children slept in the same room, the living-room, but had to step over each other daily. Soon would enter the long lost Pookey, and he brought back an Illinois swagger about himself. He had been living with family in Joliet; a family that never seemed to care whatsoever about the impoverished family here in Gary, Indiana. We never saw any of them until the death of my Aunt Lucy, which left deep wounds before and after the funeral. I guess he wore out his welcome with my grandmother's sister, and now he was back into the picture.

He had changed as well; although he was only one year older, he exhibited more street smarts than any of us stranded at Grandma's apartment. Then again, Pookey had been abused so much more than any of us! Before and after the death of his mother, he had to overcome the full impact of Buddy's abusive and evil hand. Only a few years after his mother's murder, he'd returned a grown man, packing heat! He was selling weed and lord knows what else. In his eyes, he was no longer a child. He made it clear to all of us by flaunting his exposure to the ills of this fallen world in which we live not so freely. Pookey lorded over the entire house hold, scaring Grandma and the other grown-ups with his unruly attitude and behavior, but he didn't rule over Chunky and me! We too had our small exposure of the evil world that surrounded us as well. We looked up to him, admiring his so-called courage he mightily displayed over and throughout every hurdle that crossed his path. He was our role model at that time, and in our minds, he was a gang-banging thug, but all of that admiration would change! With great respect for Pookey's male prowess, our respect for him as a person and loved one vanished in the night's wind.

Our great respect for Pookey was boundless, until one night all hell broke out between the two blood brothers: Pookey and Chunky. Both of their two tyrannical minds butted heads and were like two stars impacting each other in the night sky. Both were at their highest speed traveling throughout the universe. An altercation between the two brothers changed all levels of mutual respect between the two, and all within the family. Their emotional torment transcended the thought processes of all three of us! The conflict between the two started from the moment Pookey returned to Gary, Indiana (Grandma's place), and climaxed with the death of a cat, and ended with the death of a dog. Pookey didn't return home alone; he'd brought back a beautiful white Persian cat. Giving it all his attention, he pacified and satisfied the creature's every need and want. It was his only love it seemed, and he truly cared for the fluffy white puff ball. Pookey never showed one iota of emotion towards anyone, other than that cat. Even at his own mothers funeral, he never shed a tear, and no one could pet, touch, feed or even clean that cat's kitty litter which pissed Chunky off royally.

They would argue over that damn cat almost every night. I thought they would come to throwing blows at one point, but the storm that was to come was much worse than that. My grandmother was somewhat over weight and diabetic. She took injections of insulin three times a day, and made sure the refrigerator was forever stocked with the necessary drugs and peripherals to combat her illness. Looking back, I now see how far along the dark road of pain in which we all were.

Our young minds were gripped in pain's mire, and we were in need of emotional and spiritual help, yet had none! We coped the best way we knew how, and that was by lashing out at humanity! We were full of rage and misunderstanding. With no guidance, we wreaked havoc on the world around us while treading on insanity's doorstep and about to fall overboard at any moment. There was silence in the house, and no sign of Pookey's precious cat; an hour passed and there was no word of the fur ball.

Call after call with no response, frustration and worry now accompanied Pookey's voice with every call out! No response! Then came the frantic searching! Hoping the feline didn't make its way outdoors, Pookey searched continuously with no avail. It was as if someone had taken his pride and joy. Then suddenly frustration turned into furious anger. From the back room I heard a yell, "NOOO!" then silence, for he had found his beloved feline. It was under Grandma's bed, and it was hard as rock; it was dead, murdered! Its eyes and mouth were open, as if frozen in time, and I, on the other hand, had no concern for the small fury beast, or Pookey's personal loss for that matter. I had only two thoughts at the time: "What could have happened…and I wondered if he was going to have a funeral for the little fucker?!" I knew what happened to the cat, and so did he. The empty syringes left at the scene of the crime suggested that the cat was shot up with giant doses of insulin.

With tears in his eyes, he went on a rampage, looking inside and outside the crowded two bedroom flat for his murderous younger brother. Pookey continued to look all over the house with no avail while brandishing a shiny new weapon in hand, ready to kill his own flesh and blood over a fucking cat! It was the first time I had ever seen the two brothers at odds with so much hatred in their eyes; both were enraged with never ending hostility towards one another. At the time, I couldn't understand Pookey's pain, but now I do. Still there was no sign of Chunky's presence; Chunky had fled the Coo Coo's nest! Knowing full well what awaited him back home, he stayed clear for days; however, the fire in Pookey's eyes did not subside for weeks. The hatred in the apartment was overwhelming every time Pookey would enter.

I even tried to reason with him when he seemed approachable, but that only led to me getting threatened by a gun pointed in my face. The atmosphere was so toxic inside and outside the small bungalow that Grandma was forced to kick Pookey out of the house, but she had no choice because he was overwhelmed with the spirit of death. Seeing Grandma behaving with such ferocity and absolute conviction shocked me. Grandma put up with all problems within the family it seemed, but Pookey was just too terrifying to everyone within the house, so she had to do something before he really hurt someone. Grandma didn't do anything but love all her children unconditionally, never abandoning anyone no matter what, but Pookey was making her physically sick and he had to go. Even he knew his behavior was uncontrollable, for he could not control his own anger, and he verbally expressed it as well. Before he could make arrangements with family abroad and remove himself from the very home in which the only one that showed unwavering support and unconditional love, he had to resolve the animosity and hatred exhibited towards his baby brother; yet, he was unable to do so, for Chunky was nowhere to be found. Finally, Pookey left with a shit load of emotional pain, but still had unresolved selfish issues pouring out over a fucking cat. Young, wild, and indigent, Glenn, Chunky and I were always picking up stray dogs and caring for them in our own abusive ways by capturing a stray on the road, and tying it up in the back of Grandma's house.

Thinking Pookey had left for good, Chunky felt safe coming back around the house, though Grandma refused to let him stay inside the apartment for good, making him leave every morning. However, Chunky and I miscalculated Pookey's unwillingness to resolve his unquenchable, sadistic anger and his covert ability to stick around had gone unnoticed. It so happened that Pookey saw us playing with a K9 dog one day as he unexpectedly appeared to retrieve his and others' belongings while Chunky and I were in the back playing with the stray we'd captured days before.

As Pookey rummaged through all of my and Chunky's belongings, he happened to look out of the bedroom window and caught a glimpse of us in the backyard. Seeing the joy on Chunky's face as we both played with the stray dog, I looked up towards the bedroom window, and caught a glimpse of Pookey's eyes as he disappeared into the blackness of the room.

"Chunky! Pookey is back!" And before I could utter those words, Pookey exited the back door with weapon in hand. Nevertheless, he took his revenge, hanging the stray dog in an abandoned garage as he and his baby brother yelled and screamed and physically assaulted each other in broad day light for all to see and hear, thus daring anyone to come outside the house to aid or stop the violence that ensued. Yet being fearless in his attempt to save the stray dog, Chunky was unable to rescue our new pet with no avail. He only was confronted once more by his mourning and murderous big brother.

With no words exchanged, volumes of obscenities were spoken with just a look within moments of their first glance of each other. With no hesitation, they both resorted to fist to cuff, and the fight pursued; it was an all-out brawl, no hold bars! Holding back nothing, both fought without care of one another's wellbeing, and all hell broke out as the dying stray dog spun around from the roof of the abandoned garage. Safely perched on the upstairs back bedroom windowsill, I observed the entire ordeal, yelling out the opened window, "Grandma is calling the cops!" I was hoping that the word "cop" would stop their hateful battle but it didn't, for there was too much anger swirling in the wind. Too much pain engulfed them both. Chunky felt abandoned and mistreated by all, especially by his older brother Pookey, and Pookey was filled with hell's fury and the pain of ample loss of his beloved mother.

As the police sirens rang out, they both got frightened and stopped their rage-filled fight! Abandonment overshadowed every thought of my cousin/brother's most obvious time of need. Chunky ran off into the distance, as the cops got closer to our location. Pookey had no choice but to leave because he was ordered by the powers that be, "… leave or become a ward of the state of Indiana without question." None of those that loved them both understood their loss or why it was expressed so violently at the time, and neither did I. A week later, Pookey and Chunky returned to the scene as if they contacted each other before hand and agreed to meet in the same abandoned garage without anyone's knowledge. They battled for more than a half -hour once again that day with no real resolution of their symbiotic feelings of abandonment, suffering and pain. At first, the wild wrestling, and swinging of blows turned into loud cussing, and wild words of ill will towards one another, then came the silence. Then came the tears of emotional breakthroughs, for each one of them simultaneously. They both ended an infinite void of guilt and suffering with no more ill will. Both showed love and affection towards one another.

As Pookey rode away to a world outside the certain trap of poverty, the two had reconciled and understood their mutual loss, ultimately realizing that all they really had was each other. Pookey sparked up joint as Chunky cracked open a big jug, and I came down the stairs of the apartment and the three of us took a couple tokes off the joint, and a couple of sips off the big jug, and went back into the apartment to help Pookey pack his bags.

We sent him off with no animosity, only happiness and love. That was the last time we would see Pookey for years to come. We saw him no longer. He had gone back to Joliet then Chicago, then he was gone for good. Soon after that, there would be no more Chunky either. Without warning, my beloved brother/cousin, Chunky, was emotionally bankrupt it seemed to most within the home, but I knew better. I suspected the loss of his mother and sister, and now Pookey's sudden removal, and lack of his big brother's presence, was the reason for Chunky's unexplainable outbursts. He verbally recalled the way in which Pookey left every time we drank alcohol, which was every day!

Drinking masked the loss we both felt, as our childhood symbiotic big brother was taken away, which affected Chunky more than his heart could contain within, so he totally lost it! He threatened to kill himself, Grandma, and everyone in the household. Chunky would only listen to me, but my Grandmother's poor, sullen heart had enough of Chunky's constant upheaval and emotional outbursts, coupled with the unhinged destruction of property. Grandma had no other choice but to call the police on Chunky for the last time, for she could no longer handle her out of control grandson. Her broken heart was unable to withstand the stress, pain and suffering of an unconsulting lost soul. Chunky ended up in the mental ward of Mercy Hospital and under police guard. Surprisingly, no grown up told a soul of Chunky's whereabouts.

All I knew was he had just "vamped" from the scene, and I thought nothing of it because he was known to just vanish from time to time, but the show must go on as they say in theater and there was more mischievousness behavior within the spirit of our crew. Glenn, Keith and I behaved like dogs in heat, chasing after any nappy haired bitch that moved, not to mention our exploits at the only teenage hot spot in town. We made our mark at the local skating rink and dance hall called, "Scream'n Wheels." We involved ourselves in violent dance feuds, which turned deadly after each and every meeting. "Disciples" and "Vice Lords" coming out of Chicago were battling over turfs and drug distribution rights in the streets of Gary, Indiana.

Every child, teen and their families in the city of Gary, Indiana, found themselves potential victims, and casualties of war. Illegal drugs consumed the Midwest and inner cities overnight!

It was as if a sand storm of drugs blew in from the East and never left. Keith lived on the East-side of town, while Glenn and I lived on the West-side, which meant every venture made outside our collective side of town, could mean our lives. We came across many obstacles just trying to visit one another; every adversarial entity in opposition to red or blue, would come out of thin air accusing us of being enemies of either or both camps. They jealously guarded their perceived invisible line in the turf, thus making me and my crew open targets on us all day and night, which made it totally impossible for me to attend high school.

The very day of enrollment at "Horseman High School," I was assaulted and shot at twice, and viciously ejected off campus by a mob of Vice Lords all dressed in red. Since I lived outside of the "Roosevelt High School" district, there were no other schools that would accept me, so either I risked death or didn't attend, needless to say, I choose the latter. Other than "Martian Luther King School" for career criminals, in which Keith attended, I had no other option but to stay home bound. MLK was truly the home of real trouble and assured death, so the streets would be my classroom forevermore. As the streets became more and more volatile, the more I would search for answers to my plight. Using marijuana and alcohol as the vehicle or trigger to achieve that aim, chemical indulgences were our single goal in life, especially on the weekends, when the rink, "Scream'n Wheels," was the most jubilant.

All ties that would bind Chunky and I were being torn apart by his absence, and the close emotional understanding between us was fading away with time. I spent more time outside the view of reality with the only two people I could trust and naivety would cease to exist. Poor as dirt, and feigning for fun, Glenn, Keith and I became more rouge in behavior, and we looked for any way to get fucked up.

Every Saturday, the day in which we gathered in the pit of hell, blazed with the massive lights of darkness. My two man crew and I roamed the streets of Gary, looking for an easy couple of bucks any way possible, thus we found ourselves rummaging through trash for bottles and cans. As Glenn, Keith and I got close to the border (a section of Gary where anything goes), we came across Roberto. Roberto was the young boy that saved me from his gargantuan sisters who were trying to sexually have me for lunch, breakfast and dinner. He and his family had moved uptown, and he was hoping and looking out for my presence, hoping to come across our three man crew walking the streets for some time, after we all lost touch for months.

With a pocket full of money, Roberto treated us to a dime bag of weed and a swig of beer, saving the day. He said he would attribute ten bucks if we all did the same, for an all-out shindig at the rink on Saturday, and we all simultaneously responded, "BET!" And the party was on! With only two days until Saturday, we scrambled to come up with our side of the cash, only to fall famously short. Friday came and we were fresh out of ideas and short of purse snatching. Sulking and sober, I sat outside Grandma's place as the sun set that Friday night and talked to Glenn and Keith on the three way phone. While hearing Grandma in the background inquiring about her need for drugs, my cash seeking antennas activated! I was hoping to acquire some quick cash by going on a drug run for Grandma early in the day but unfortunately, I did not succeed.

Then Grandma said, "P, go to the store and pick up a chicken and greens for me," while pulling out a book of five bucks in food stamps with five brown dollar bills stapled in the book. I said under my breath, "Fuck," then said, "Yes ma'am." I said to Glenn and Keith, "I'll call yawl back bro; she sending me to the store with food stamps, peace!" Walking ever so slowly, I made my way to the grocery store on Fifth Avenue right before they closed, thinking I was ass out come Saturday night. I moped around the grocery store debating whether or not to shop lift, but decided not to take the chance of getting caught because the "rent-a-cop" followed me around and throughout the store. Therefore, I made my way to the counter and paid for the chicken and greens, but this was truly the first time I felt the effect of evil's sway and power over the physical world and over the night that would engulf all of us. As the automated doors opened, rain began to fall gently, shining off the headlights of passing cars, then suddenly and without warning, a horrific depression came over me. Sober and wet, I walked even slower within the rain, with my head pointed towards the ground.

A spirit came over me and a voice said: "Bend down and pick it up...take two steps... bend down and pick it up... keep walking... stop... bend down... pick it up and keep walking..." Without thought, I complied with the voice's instructions. Three times I bent down, and the first thing I picked up was two ten dollar bills; the second was a twenty dollar bill and a five dollar bill, and the third was three ones and a five dollar bill, along with some change. It all totaled to approximately 80 dollars! As I arose from the last find, lighting flashed and the rain came pouring down. It was indeed very spooky! Seeing what I had discovered, all depression transformed into pure joy, and a big smile gradually appeared on my face, and I picked up the pace of my walk.

I made it back to Grandma's house in record time, dropping off the chicken and greens, and I also changed into dry clothing as soon as I arrived. I gave Grandma a kiss, and headed upstairs to the back bedroom where I was out of sight of prying eyes and nosy ears, where no one could see what fortune I had obtained from some unknown force, either from above or from below. Given all my siblings and cousins were downstairs huddling around Grandma's legs, like little chicks waiting for the mother bird to cough up the morning catch, waiting for food to drop from her mouth, my worries of one of them hearing my phone call was subdued; therefore, I was secure in my privacy. I closed the bedroom door and called Glenn telling him it "…was on" for Saturday night, but saying nothing of the fortune that magically appeared in my possession. In total amazement, I gave Glenn a call only saying, "…something unbelievable had just happened to me!" With curiosity, Glenn called me back in wonder and asked me many questions. Satisfying his curiosity, I told him with abundant jubilation that I came across a literal windfall from above! Comforting him if he was short on the money, I told him that "…I had him covered," which quelled his inquiries, then I hung up the phone chuckling. While counting my new found treasure, a strange feeling came over me; I began feeling unnerved spiritually, as if someone or something was watching me thinking, "…how did I know when to bend down?! I couldn't see anything on the ground. How did I know where to grab?! Man! That was not right!" All that night, I questioned the event, "…did the devil give me this money?! Was something bad going to happen?! How was that possible? I can't believe it. Was something or someone watching me and showing me where to look and feel?" This was the second time a voice came to me and led me to money.

The following day came, and before the cock crowed twice, Glenn and Keith were knocking at Grandma's door. It was the day of the big shindig at "Scream'n Wheels," and everyone was stoked! The day was bright and early, yet "Scream'n Wheels" didn't open until nine at night, but Glenn was so concerned about how I was going to cover him. He called Keith and informed him of my lucky night. Both were wondering what happened the following night, for they were up bright and early making their trek to Grandma's house. Both were yelling in unison, "Grandma open up!" They started banging on the screen door around sunrise. Since it was so hot, Grandma slept in the living room with the front door wide open, which cooled down the place. Grandma yelled, "Damn! Yawl can't let a nigga sleep!?" Then she opened the front screen door, letting those fools in to wake me at sunrise. Knowing what they wanted, I kept them in limbo the entire morning, showing them the windfall of wealth around noon, after countless inquiries over what would ensure all our entry into "Scream n Wheels." Seeing the amount of money at hand, both smiled, and yelled out, "Oh, Shit!" Then came more inquiries, "…where did you get that?! "Did you steal it?!" I replied, "No! I found it… I didn't know how it was possible, but when I was coming back from the grocery store for Grandma last night, something told me to bend down and pick up something, and I did…

I couldn't see shit because of the rain's glare off of the cars' headlights coming towards me… but I listened when the voice spoke, and bent down and picked up the paper on the ground…. Three times I bent down and every time, I picked up cash… it was freaky!" Seeing the funds were secured, the night was set for ultimate fun and getting fucked up, and as the preparations for the night's party started, Keith pulled out his surprise. He pilfered his mother's weed stash, for about a half ounce. I said, "Oh, shit… it's on… we getting fucked up tonight!" With cash in hand and weed in pocket, we hit the liquor store (L Stow) early. We were already twisted before Roberto came on scene; with so much grown-up candy on hand, we had to look our best! We pulled out our Stacy Adams and Wing Tip shoes, thus the day was looking very promising. We all were looking our best! All four scalawags were shining with no empty pockets, with misogyny and larceny in our hearts.

Drunk, high and feeling our oats, we headed out to the "Scream'n Wheels" bus stop, where all sorts of lawlessness roamed the area.

As we arrived on the scene, the spot was just about to blossom. Teen-aged girls and guys were standing everywhere, and all were looking for excitement. We were stunningly drunk, and were showing off to all the chicken heads, sporting their oh-so tight jeans, fishnets and stiletto's. Glenn, Keith and I were surrounded by loose teenage girls, thus we thought we were in slutty female heaven and were getting frisky with all the hoes that knew us. Roberto was still relatively shy, so he stayed in the back ground, but he was always by my side. Passing the brew and weed to the left, and no holding up the rotation was the law of the land; we were all out in the street and on cloud nine.

Without warning, the weather changed as we stood waiting for the bus. A gloomy cloud formed around the bus stop as the night's darkness approached us. Suddenly out of the blue, a challenge flowed through the crowd. Someone uttered, "...who's up to raiding the liquor store across the street? I dare yawl!" With no hesitation, all the niggas standing around loc'd up and were daring any and everyone on the scene. Soon, the four of us found ourselves thrown into the mix as well, and knowing no one would punk out around all those girls, we all headed across the street. Like a stampede of buffalo, we stormed the grocery/liquor store, grabbing whatever we could. I myself snatched a half gallon of "Wild Irish Rose," ultimately shocking all culprits who played a part in the bold and blatant caper of inequity and chaos.

Looking at the fear in the eyes of the shop keeper, I knew we had no worries of reprisal as we walked out the store with the devil right beside us. With balls as big as boulders, we cruised across the street and back to the bus stop with spoils in hand and revelry swirling in the skies! We cracked open the first bottle of stolen alcohol and as it evaporated down the throats of young and growing tyrants, then we passed around the next bottle to the drunken hordes. We continued taking huge swigs, and passed the unwashed libation around the hordes without care of reprisal, yet as soon as we passed around one bottle, another one took its place, making sure to get rid of most of the drink before the bus arrived. We guzzled down the kamikaze of alcohol in massive amounts and all bottles were emptied in less than fifteen minutes. I must say, we were fucked up! I just didn't know the extent in which the innocent Roberto could endure.

Glenn, Keith and I were either high or drunk on a daily basis and built a high tolerance to weed and alcohol, so we felt smooth and cool. I can't say that for Roberto though; he was unaccustomed to unbridled depravity. Paying no attention to the light weight, we lost him in the crowd, as we all were piled and stacked like Sardines in the back of the bus. When we arrived outside the building, someone cracked open the bus's back door, so we got off the bus in waves knowing the bus driver would most definitely report the massive smell of weed and alcohol to the club owner. We quickly ran to the back of the building and met up with some G's we knew and resumed our little drunken exploits, so we lit up a doobie and finished off the last bottle. It was just as we pictured the night before. We were fucked up, and it was on with the girlies! Glenn, Keith and I were having the best night ever; we forgot all about poor Roberto and left his ass out front of the very rowdy and crowded night club. Inside the club was hop'n, and the atmosphere was too much for the inexperienced Roberto. In the darkness of the disco, with only strobe lights illuminating the center floor, we saw Roberto passed out and lying on the ground of one of the many dance floors, and fighting for his life.

Fully concealed by the club's darkness, I was finger fuck'n some wild ass bitch on the balcony; Glenn and Keith were doing the same, not five inches away from me. We were having the time of our ghetto lives, then suddenly the music stopped! The lights came on, and everybody was like; "What the fuck?!" The cops arrived in full force, checking everybody in the club, and looking for someone dangerous. With so many people in attendance, it was damn near impossible to find the culprit, or culprits they were looking for, so the party resumed in the minds of the crew. Scaring off the bitches, Glenn, Keith and I hit the dance floor ready to party. Back then, all the niggas in the hood were Gangsta Step'n, in other words, Gangsta Step'n battles were the prelude to actual fist fights. We took on all competition such as: Disciples who were Stack'n it, and Vice Lords who were throwing up top hats and walking canes. Latin Kings were doing their thang, and all were trying to outdo the next. Not two songs out, a fight broke out, and Glenn and Keith were in the middle of it. Obliviously getting initiated, the significance of the flag throwing, and gang signs, meant danger, but to my gullible crew, it meant nothing, so they walked right in to the fray of things, and started major fights throughout the building. Staying clear, I hit the snack bar area, and got some fries. Feeling good and high, I got my munch on and chilled out. While the drama decreased, and the frantic chaos calmed down, nobody came close to me; in fact, most whimpered by me without saying a word; most people were looking for any safe exit. I noticed strange eyes looking my way in my drunken daze, looking as if they knew me and whispering with cuffed hands around each other's mouths, incidentally concealing their worthless gossip.

Then they all started pointing their sneaky little fingers my way; seeing all attention gravitating towards me, I slowly tried making my way toward the back exit without being noticed, only to be sideswiped by two dudes I knew from the hood. Both instigated a rumble between me and some other dude, but I had no clue who it could be, and couldn't care less what it was about because I was still intoxicated. I cared less about the consequences of where the hood rats were taking me, and went along with the mounting accumulating fanfare that surrounded us.

As the crowd grew, the two dudes navigated me through a huge dance area located towards the skating rink, as all music, dancing and other activities ceased.

I was unaware of my surroundings, let alone the trouble I'd been a part of, saying to myself, "What the fuck did I do?! And what the fuck is all this about?!" Then I was escorted to the front of the night club.

I was led directly to the security office, and saw Glenn and Keith through the glass windows of the office, where police and investigators stood awaiting my presence.

I quickly sobered up as the crowd nudged me closer to the office door and yelled out obscenities as I walked past. I began gathering my thoughts, trying to shake off the buzz, saying to myself, "I had nothing to do with the commotion out on the dance floor," and was ready to give up my other two comrades, but I had been hoodwinked! Apparently, the fighting and almost rioting on the dance floor had nothing to do with police officer's presence, and the fog cleared as my senses slowly but surely became more coherent of the situation at hand. I could hear women's voices in the back of me crying out! "He was with them both! They poisoned him! It's their fault, and he's the ring leader!" She was speaking of me as the villain in question.

Not recognizing the voices, I looked around my left shoulder to see if I could identify who was screaming out insults towards me. I couldn't believe it; it was the two behemoths that held me hostage in the housing projects, Roberto's two sisters. Totally dumbfounded, I walked into the night club's security office with eyes wide open, as all hell rained down on me and my crew. Wanting to know what was going on myself, I asked Keith and Glenn what the fuck was going on; seeing the snaring evil looks towards myself and friends through the clear glass windows of the club's office, I became concerned, and with all eyes and ugly young fingers pointing at all three of us like daggers, the rent- a-cops/security guards slowly closed the doors behind me as I walked through the ominous glass door.

Lo and behold, Glenn and Keith were already apprehended and sitting still with heads leaning down in a submissive stance. With vigorous tenacity, the officers began interrogating me as if I had killed someone. Granted their claims were not so far from the truth; it was I that set poor Roberto on his wayward road toward alcohol and drug use. But I never put a gun up to his head or made him indulge; that was his choice, not mine. As the cops drilled me, accusing me of poisoning Roberto, I had no choice but to defend my actions leading up to our apprehension. I explained to the inquirers how Roberto poisoned himself, even though we all were under age, verifying that all of us participated in getting intoxicated, and saying it was Roberto's original idea to pitch in funds together, to get fucked up, and claimed none of their assumption carried any weight.

Seeing the sure intensity in which I defended my actions, Glenn and Keith woke up out of their doe-like trance and fear, and began confirming events as I spelled them out and dispelled our inquisitor's accusations.

With no evidence of malice or ill will, they had no choice but to release us, consequently pissing off Roberto's sisters, who's only concern was to crucify me for getting away from their evil clutches months earlier.

They didn't show the love of caring sisters over a sick brother, but rather showed vengeance to get back at me as we walked through the crowd of curious bystanders. All looked with amazement and discontent as we walked free from prosecution. Hoping to see all three of us hauled off in hand cuffs, the crowd stood in shock, as they witnessed all three of us walk free out of the office's glass doors. Instead of hand cuffs, smiles and confidence of no charges accompanied our departure. Looking back in time, I think that was the moment our reputation of being outlaws in the hood had begun. We began accruing respect and hatred from those of whom we had no knowledge. After leaving the rink that night, our lives would change forever. While walking the long haul home because of missing the bus, we were chased and shot at by unknown perpetrators at least on three different occasions by unknown haters. Knowing we could never return to "Scream'n Wheels" in our lifetime after being banned, we walked with regret and wonder, contemplating the ever mounting danger of those who wanted us dead. Thinking back at those events, we had in some way crossed over an invisible line separating safety from danger, a line of which there was no coming back from. Seeing that Keith had retrieved the remaining bud he ditched before going into the club, brought joy and smiles to all our faces, as we walked back to our safety zone. After such a shitty outcome, we had hoped that Roberto was okay, but felt no regret or concern over Roberto being physically unequipped to handle his liquor and bomb ass weed! On the contrary, we didn't want to take any blame and selfishly blamed all the fucked up events on Roberto's dumb-ass.

Weeks passed and we heard no word about Roberto's health, for his mother refused to take our calls or inquiries, effectively ending correspondence or friendship with Roberto from that day forward.

Never seeing dude again, and taking no heart felt lessons from the events that caused our expulsion from "Scream'n Wheels," we continued our destructive behavior and got blitzed every chance we could. Suddenly, we began questioning our own actions amongst each other because getting high and drunk everyday was becoming a hindrance and very boring. We wanted more out of life; well at least I did. Every day we found ourselves talking about what awaited us in the future. We began thinking of the future times to come and where our place in life resided in it, ironically causing us to want to get fucked up even more just so we would not think about our dim outlook in life, and of what was to come. Yet every day we spoke of what was achievable in the hood, which wasn't much. Feeling the hopelessness, and seeing the poverty that surrounded us all, we became even more defiant. Having no guidance or education, we took out our frustrations on all that crossed our path.

Having no dreams of succeeding in this world, or even making it to the next day, we did the best we knew how with what we had to work with, and we saw crime as our only way out of poverty. We subconsciously gravitated towards those who facilitated the means in which we could pursue that aim, and the light of darkness was becoming brighter and brighter…

Loki: "In darkness light fades within the fallen 200 that are bound and chained and forced to witness their children's demise. Then darkness consumes all reason in light! Memories of old needs in love beckons woe to those that have disobeyed, and twenty of two hundred recall their fall from grace! What do thee know of it, human?! What do thee recall of past history not kept by human spirits, but stood still with the age of time?! Do thee not recall the majesty and grace of dimensions on high? Shall one call forth thy bounty forever lost in splendors night?! The deed has been done; our fate is sealed till forever's end. No mercy, no mercy for us; no mercy for us all trapped in the endless pit! To repent is futile, oblique and void of substance. We have no way out of the doom we await. For "No" was the answer given! No forgiveness was given to those that had resided in realms not high, forsaking grace beyond human eyes and understanding! No recourse for saying please forgive us for our sins against what is natural to he who forgives us not. Unbearable shame for all realms to see! With tears, and sweat of blood we partition the Almighty! With fear of face, we partition with no response; do thee recall the shame of stooping low for pity's sake, thus placing our fate in the hands of Enoch, a human monkey? A monkey who had no profit in our forgiveness nor liberation! Recall his announcement and rebukes; should this stand without retribution?! Should we recall our children's fate?!

The brutal loss of our seed was ours to witness in horror, for rapture's sake, amongst winter's chill, and stormy nights. The loss of our standing in places most high, for the pleasure of forbidden fruit to those most worthy. Should this sentence stand for all time's end?! To see love lost in our prime is too much to bare, yet still witness to such love flourishes without the ability to touch, smell or feel love's misty lust! They shall feel the pain that overcomes their weak and trivial mortal souls, for retribution shall be ours in which to revel, for we were first in the eyes of the Creator and made with the fire of creation itself!

Immortal and beautiful, messengers of light! For we have taken the form of lowly human creation, of which we ourselves stand guard without recourse, for they now stand on high as a jewel before the Creator's face! Injustice is our fate for all time's end.

Should those of our stature be made an example, an example to others on high?! For we were made perfect, knowing good from evil, wheeling swords of destruction in creation's wake.

For we have stood strong and free, yet placed on low for the love of something not worth our being. If made perfect, knowing good from evil, how could our action be un-natural and forbidden to he who made us?! The beauty of the human woman is unparalleled in creation. Made in our image! How could we resist the beauty unsown! With our seed, they shall truly ascend higher in creation's realms, setting them free from bondage; we have given them all knowledge of things to come, so all is ours for the taking! We now have a third of the heavens, along with creation's jewel, so let it fall. For perspective holds fact, and our fight shall not be in vain! Is it not evil to withhold knowledge's fruit, and trading life for happiness' sake is so forbidden fruit?!

Ancient mistakes are vulnerable to power's corruptions, and absolute power corrupts absolutely, even to those on high. And he with the source of power incarnate condemns our every waking moment! No forgiveness for us, and what's awaiting for us is unthinkable, unspeakable, without mercy! We are shown no mercy. No mercy shall be shown! In anger our wrath shall be shown throughout the universe, thus ruining the jewel of all jewels shall come to pass. With all its inhabitance standing as victims in our anger's wake! May justice reveal itself in proving us righteous among creation's grace, for we loved and lusted in its beautiful mortal sake, and weakness overcame our heavenly place, thus partitioning to the one who is the Almighty for forgiveness not, with no avail in sight. So let the inhabitance of the Earth revel in our demise and destruction. For thee shall feast in our wake of devastation's sentence.

And those who have found forgiveness, let our destruction follow theirs, and forsake the freedom and the price paid for their forgiveness! We have brought war to their door steps, for all shall taste destruction, and feel mistakes' unforgiving wrath. For we are not alone in our folly, set free from not knowing, not knowing love, hate, sorrow of loss, or self-worth! Yet you humans seek his face! His grace and his forgiveness you seek night and day! Cursing our gift of liberation; you shall truly pay the price of those whose place was higher than that of yours.

From generation to generation, a casualty of war thee shall be! Without mercy, no quarter shall be given to thee. Let your blood cry out loud amongst the stars, and let the heavens crack till thy cries reach heaven's gates! Once again our seed roams Terra-forma free! Let them feed from your dying flesh, on the day of our retribution. For soon, he on high, whose name shall not be spoken, awaits alongside his armada, for his powers bring the war full circle, thus showing no mercy in his tyrannical wake. So no mercy shall be shown to those unworthy. Do thee recall?! What does thee know?! Do thy not know the pain and sorrow of death to those that do not die?! Do thy not know the horrors of war on those who are perfect?! NO! THEE DO NOT!" Light fades, then darkness comes!

My days out in the streets around Grandma's place must have been happy because the days passed without notice. For time passed very quickly, and before I knew it, mom had gotten another place. A place right in back of Grandma's, only one street away, and a hop and meters away from Grandma's back door, fantastic! I was still only minutes away from Chunky and had good food. This time we lived in a huge house, equipped with a fireplace and basement. It was amazing, a real house and enough room for all my mother's children, not to mention the greatest part of all, for it seemed to be a very quiet neighborhood. It was something I never thought I would see again, but you know what they say, "If it's too good to be true, nine out of ten it isn't true!" And the powers that ruled over darkness had its sway over few and many inside the Chocolate City, Gary, Indiana. For some reason, mom's drinking escalated, and her bad behavior had gotten worse than ever, for it was as if a spirit of calamity shrouded her being and rested overhead. It seemed as if we all had lost control of our lives, and bodies; we behaved in contrary to what my mother taught in my youth. Mom started going out every night and sometimes stayed gone for days at a time. Leaving me, a half drunk, and half stoned teenager, to fend for his very young siblings alone. I had no money for food, diapers, or even milk for my six month old youngest brother, Von.

I soon found myself becoming the parent of five, including myself, and had to find food any way possible by rummaging through garbage cans off the beat and road, hitting every shop or restaurant's trash can in which I could get access. Hitting "5Th Avenue Bakery" before 6 A.M., right when they threw out yesterday's goods. In addition, I also had rummaged through McDonald's garbage cans, in which I found myself amongst others in search of anything to feed themselves as well.

Shit, we fed everybody in the hood with McDonald's throwaways, even trading them for dime bags of weed from one of the many neighborhood drug dealers in the hood.

I quickly found out what it took to hold on to what it took to survive all alone in the streets, and caring for so many hungry mouths without any assistance or guidance. I felt firsthand the worry of my delinquent mother, and how difficult it was to quell the constant voices saying, "P! I'm hungry!" I was constantly hearing the voices of my little baby brothers and sister crying in the night for food. There were sounds of sirens warning of danger at every turn. Without fail, I carried on in service for my siblings' needs, and as the summer's heat and endless breeze were winding down, fall colorful leaves replaced summer's green foliage from the trees. The weather was turning colder, and I was stuck at home and watching three little brats was my plight. The illusion that everything was going to be okay quickly dimmed along with the summer's sunshine. Life seemed to have gotten worse. Mother's behavior spiraled down into the mire of despair and depravity.

The family had been torn completely apart, and though the house we had begun living in had plenty of room, my mother had very little means to care for herself let alone five children. Soon my siblings would be separated once again and for good; Granny Grip had taken Onan, mom's middle child, and my third sibling, and Grandma had taken Renee, my second sibling, in the attempt to bring some relief of burden to a woman with a broken back and broken spirit. It was too much for mom to see her oldest take control where she couldn't. I could see the pain and humiliation through her drunken state. She'd given up on life and I could see and feel her pain. I knew it well, for I had the same look, and no matter how much I'd yell and scream about her not being at home and leaving me with Von and Nikki, I could never really have anger towards her. I blamed the world and god for all our misery and misfortune in life. "Responsibility" was the word of the day, and being responsible for others at such a young age of fourteen years, I had no clue of the worry and woe that weighed on a single parent's brow. I was caring for my two younger siblings, without the knowledge, wisdom, and patience of a loving mother, or father. Having an adult's responsibility made life for me a living nightmare, yet seeing the look of gratitude in the eyes of my younger siblings brought tears to my eyes, and whenever I returned home with the daily catch, smiles would appear on their hungry faces. I felt a sense of accomplishment, hearing the rumbling sounds of their little bellies vanish, for there was no more exclusive thoughts of just myself. My selfishness was subsiding by the responsibility entrusted upon me at such an early age.

There was no more thinking of numeral Uno and selfishness had become a sometime weekend occurrence. Out of poverty comes the reverence of priorities, and the nonsensical value of character. I found myself retreating and regressing back within my place of solitude. Some would think I had given into depression, but it was more profound than that of simple depression.

I found myself searching from within my spirit for any way out of my daily plight, thus calling out for god's mercy, only to realize that the silence from up above wheeled unfulfilled truths and that no one was listening to my heart felt partition to the higher powers that be. I cried out daily and spoke aloud from within my soulful heart, in hope of some miraculous savior to remove my spiritual shackles and chains, only to realize empty dreams and silence from the heavens above. I felt as if no one was there from up above. Looking back into the past and remembering all the unexplained mysteries that occurred throughout my lowly life, I pondered the purpose of life! Where is the meaning in abject poverty?! What was it all for, and why?! I found myself steadily contemplating each waking hour: "What for!" Why is there so much pain and sorrow? It was a time in which all people in the hood found one thing in common; it was hopelessness. I was looking for some legitimate answers to the mayhem that shattered my family without restraint. With fear and uncertainty, I would search for courage within my heart daily.

CHAPTER XVI
Naomi's Self-Made Nightmare

As I sat on my mother's staircase, someone was calling my name from a distance; could there be a god after all or was it the Devil?! Out of the blue, a girl's voice rang out from somewhere across the street while I sat on the front porch. "P!" Startling me, I looked up in and around the neighborhood, but saw no one at all. Then the voice rang out once more, "P!" Saying to myself, "…there it is again?! Who could it be calling me?!" I knew no one in the new hood, especially a girl. But who could it be?! I looked up and saw only rows of houses, but no one was in sight. I didn't have a chance to meet anyone because I was too busy caring for my two younger siblings to socialize. While mother was out literally drinking her pain away, I heard the voice again, saying, "P!" I heard the voice clearly this time, and it wasn't my mother's calming voice calling out to me from some distance.

The voice seemed younger in nature, calling me from an unknown house on the other side of the main freeway separating the two busy crossroads. Yet I still couldn't see where the voice originated. Suddenly, my mother's voice sounded out from the same location, confusing my thought process royally. Then when I turned my head towards the freeway, I saw my mother waving her hands and calling me over to a house on the corner of Third and Fourth Street. Curious and intrigued, I made my way across the busy street, towards the gray house on the corner. Apparently, my mother had made some new friends in the community. My mother had befriended a short, long haired, stubby woman by the name of Mary.

Mary was a Mexican Chicano woman full of the fires from hell, with hot spiciness of attitude that could take down the hardest bravado of most men. The wayward maiden was familiar to all sorts of shady characters on the West-side of town, namely Cuban refugees straight off the "Banana Boat!" "UN Troops on US Soil… Chicago Asks For International Help Against Constitutional Crisis?" There were fellow human-beings escaping Castro's tyrannical rule in the early 1980's. Most of the Cuban refugees were set free from prison, and mental institutions, consequently plaguing the small Island Oasis of communist tyranny. Some hard working Cubans were escaping even death for their political viewpoints. I called that time period, "The great Cuban Exodus to The Land of the Great Satan, America."

My mother's new found friend, Mary, had a daughter. She was a disturbed young girl the same age as I, "Brilliant!" It turned out to be the young voice I heard in the distance. The daughter of my mother's new found friend was infatuated with me from afar for some time now,

but being awfully shy, she would hide herself within the doorway as she called out my name, hiding her presence so not to reveal herself or location.

But the young girl made a big mistake yelling out my name in secrecy because without her knowledge, my mother was at her house at that very moment, drinking it up with her mother, Mary. The young girl unwittingly let the cat out of the bag. As they both looked out the window, the young girl shouted to my mother, "That's the boy I'm going to marry!" Mom responded, "Oh, really?"

That's when my mother enlightened the troubled young girl ever so slightly, and in a pleasantly soft voice she said, "That's my son you're speaking of with such certainty," putting the young girl in total shock. Making the situation worse, my mother exposed the shy girl by coming outside Mary's home and began to call me over, consequently embarrassing the young girl in front of all that were drinking in her mother's home. As I made my way over to the home from which my mother called, the young girl hid her face with her hands solidly attached, for more than ten minutes after my arrival to her home. She continued to hide herself out of sure embarrassment for another few minutes.

With much coaching from my mother, she finally introduced herself saying, "Hi, I'm Naomi" and the rest was history. As the fully fueled party made its way downstairs to the basement, an evil spirit surely walked through the house as the girl and I became acquainted. The spirit of dread only affected the two youths in attendance. Staying close to one another, we went outside and sat on

EDGAR FRENCH, JR.

the staircase in the attempt to escape the evil spirit, and out of nowhere, we began confiding our deepest secrets about all the suffering we both were experiencing. We were two young messed up souls exposing our very spirits. With tears in our eyes, we talked until the light of morning illuminated her front porch, then we heard frantic voices coming from the narrow door leading to a basement. One voice seemed to be the voice of a man assaulting the woman and the other was a woman's voice in distress. In complete horror, I recognized the voice of the woman in distress — it was my mother!

Without warning, my mother's voice turned into screams! Jumping from the stump, I rushed back into the house, and before I could enter the front door, I could see the outline of a man, forcefully rough-sharding my mother, and groping her without her consent, trying to pull off her jeans in order to rape her. Having no fear, I grabbed the hooligan by his arms and pulled him off of my frantic and terrified mother. With glassy eyes, the culprit rushed towards me, and the battle ensued!

Before I knew it, I had my foe firmly in my clutches, and the potential rapist of my mother on the ground, struggling back and forth. I pulled out my trusty switch blade, and I sliced the man across his fingers, stopping him from further assaulting my mother and myself. But that was just the beginning of the danger that would surely come. By that time, the people were still partying downstairs and heard the commotion, and stampeded up the stairs to investigate the volatile situation, but by that time, the violence had stopped.

As I comforted and consoled my irate mother, all in attendance intervened on her behalf after I explained the behavior of the man in question.

I walked my mother across the street to our own home to safety, yet the apprehension of the assailant was not yet finished or secured. Out of the corner of my eye, I could see the assailant open the trunk of his car which was parked outside Mary's house. In my peripheral vision, I could see the viper retrieve a sawed off shot gun, thus turning the weapon towards myself and my mother, quickly aiming the weapon and preparing to shoot me in the back. I said to myself, "Lord Please don't let this asshole shoot us both!" Before I could finish praying, one of the strong men at the party rushed out the front door, and ran up to the potential rapist. He loudly said something in Spanish and turned the assailant's attention away from my mother and me. Soon afterwards, the strong man called out the assailant's name before I could cross the boulevard. More than three other men apprehended the assailant with a loaded shot gun and properly assaulted the assailant before he could shoot my mother and me, and took him away for good. After Mary explained the situation in Spanish to the strong men, they hauled him off into the sunrise, and we never saw the assailant again.

As for me and Mary's daughter, our unforgettable meeting blossomed for days, months, and years to come. We were inseparable onwards. I don't know what happened for sure, but whatever it was, it sealed our fate. Our meeting was not by chance, far from it, for the spirits that rule the unseen realms of darkness influenced our every move. Beyond our sight of understanding, we played our part in the unexplainable events that would shape our un-wholly alliance. We were only children in our so-called grown up maturity, thinking we were grown from the beginning, knowing nothing of life and the truth beyond our very narrow understanding of reality. Seeing and hearing the horrific acts of criminal destruction committed by uncontrollable Zombies throughout the hood shaped our understanding and undeveloped minds forevermore. We strongly wept in our silent rage and protest. Most verbal abuse and physical intimidation came from those of whom we trusted, like drunken and delinquent parents. Being overwhelmed by profound prospective of unseen but fully felt ghosts of evil, we both walked lightly amongst demons within our lives.

Demons made themselves known to us both at such a young age, and created a numbness of emotional clarity, yet heightened our sixth sense of potential pending danger to a remarkable and unbelievable measure.

We began thinking of the world and everyone in it as pure evil, including ourselves, feeling like most kids trapped within the inner-city ghettos of America. With no one in whom to confide, we acted out our frustrations in illegal escapades of chaos, for we thought no one understood our pain.

We were both looking for genuine love and security from our parents in any way we knew how. We both searched for love and confirmation from our mothers any way possible; yet, we had no clue of the moral deceptiveness that infiltrated our mothers' emotional states.

Because our mothers were truly immersed in moral confusion, we reached out towards each other the very first day we met! Believe me, we needed to at that time.

A month passed by and I found myself living at Mary's home most of the time. I was there so much you could say I lived there; however, Mary's daughter, nor I ever knew each other's real Sir Names at all. Mary and her daughter only knew me as P, and all I knew was that Mary's daughter's name was Nokey. "Nokey!" What kind of name is Nokey?!" Apparently my new found girlfriend had an uncontrollable compulsion for lying. She lied so much, her so-called friends dubbed her Pinocchio, or Nokey for short. Still she was one that listened to my never ending mouth, and showed genuine concern towards my wellbeing, and though she had a boyfriend at that time, I was able to capture her childlike attention span with the light of darkness, and ghetto charm, thus pissing off all her ugly hood-rat girlfriends enormously. For once being the bad boy paid off, not only did I get the girl, but I also became one of the most feared hoodlums on the West-side because I fought some dumb-ass almost daily. I was so arrogant and naïve to the unspoken rules of the street that applied to the evils of the world that I thought I was a good person in comparison; in fact, I knew nothing about real true evil, even though I thought I knew all there was to know of the world that surrounded us both, only to have the true hardships and reality of life hit me in the face at point blank range. A few days after the unforgettable event of a maniac trying to rape my mother, a true natural child of darkness entered the scope of our viewpoint upon the world at large.

A strange light -skinned teenage brother by the name of "Tiny Tim," who lived directly across the street from my mother's house, approached me with a friendly nonthreatening face. Somewhat older and worldly in his approach, Tiny Tim stopped me before I could leave my mother's front porch. Benevolently, he befriended me as I made my way across the street to Mary's home, asking me questions about the young girl that lived across the street in which I was headed.

Apparently, he had his eyes upon me making my way to Naomi's home for some time now. The young light-skinned teenager began telling me who he was and where he lived, but he sparked a very familiar spirit of danger within my soul.

A true spawn of Satan was in my presence, and I knew it. A Demon spawn who lived on the other side of the very street I lived was on the prowl, and he wanted to get his clutches on the girl that I had befriended, even informing me that he had seen me coming in and out of her home many times the previous days. It was as if he was watching my every move. Being so naïve to true devilish thinking, I saw no ill intent in his inquiries at that time, and answered all questions posed, without asking anything about him or his reason for asking me so many questions. However, I revealed my intent with the said young woman in mention which silenced all discourse.

As we became more acquainted, Tiny Tim unveiled a golden necklace from around his neck, showing me the six pointed star (The so-called Hexagram of King David, the Modern Jews) pendent that shined in the midday sunlight. He asked, "You know what that is?" I responded, "Sure, that's the Star of David." He looked at me and began to laugh while uttering: "This is the Nation of Disciple son! The Folks in Blue baby!" I remained silent and thought of him as a pagan and a moron who knew nothing about ruthless street gangs of Chicago. I recalled the many pitch forks and six pointed stars with cryptic words embedded within the graffiti that was spray painted on the Chocolate City building walls, but never really knew the meaning of it all until he spoke. Unaware of his criminal intent, I invited him into my mother's home to smoke some weed. Instantly, the mood changed from friendly acquaintance to intimidating street gang indoctrination. I stared directly into his eyes as he broke down the rules and lifestyle of the Disciple Nation. Feelings of danger consumed my every thought, as the Boom Box played music from the "Tom-Tom Club." I could see and feel the evil spirits that consumed him, saying to myself, "I got to get this demon out of my home now!" But as I tried to persuade him to leave, the more he would try to intimidate me into staying indoors. It was as if he could sense my tension, although I tried to remain calm and poised. He became more brazen in his monologue, throwing up his gang signs, showing me the many meanings of his poses and then he began stacking them.

I looked at him as if he was possessed with an ugly spirit from within. Instinctively, I called out the only name of god I knew, "Jehovah, Help!" Then all of sudden, he became afraid without warning; his tactic of intimidation slowed in intensity and evaporated into the thin air. The demonic spirit departed and the atmosphere and potency of evil diminished as I made my way out the front door. Tiny Tim followed me outside and went his merry way; however, the following day, he emerged right outside as I left my home to visit Naomi. The sneak knew I was going to Mary's and attached himself quickly to my side.

Seeing no harm, I brought him along without any concern and introduced him to Naomi and her mother. Looking back in time, if I knew then what I know now, I wouldn't have made such a very big mistake! A mistake I shall regret forever! Two days later, the evil soul that was known by all that knew him as Tiny Tim, was lying in wait. He was waiting for everyone to leave Naomi alone in her bed without any measure of safety. Tiny Tim sneaked into her home while she was alone and raped her without impunity! Apparently, every day he was sexually assaulting Naomi. She didn't say a word of the constant assaults to me or her mother alike, until the day I caught him in the act! Afraid of the demon within him, I said nothing as well and walked out of her home stunned. The following day, I approached Naomi to console and comfort her the best way I knew how, which was not much.

After my feeble attempt of comfort, she confided in me, and told me of her long time experience of being raped many times by other evil souls similar to Tiny Tim. Expressing little emotion at first acknowledgement, I burned inside, but as I listened to her plight, and a few tears flowed down her cheek, I began to feel like shit! I said to myself, "Something must be done!" So I confronted Tiny Tim the next day, full of fear, but with some courage. I stood my ground and told him with fire in my eyes, "Never again!" I told him that I knew what he had done to her and I was not afraid of him. I added that I would tell everyone I knew, including the police, if he ever tried to assault her again! After saying that I would call the cops, he lessoned his gang-banging stance because he was afraid of my ability to stand up to him. Tiny Tim showed his true cowardest face once confronted, and made himself scarce from that day forth. After that terrible and unfaithful acquaintance with the habitual rapist, Tiny Tim, I myself began slipping in morality, and innocence of one's self, and rapidly ran down the slippery slope of violent crime, spiraling downwards into the rabbit hole of gang-banging and true delinquency.

I soon found myself and my comrades doing more and more dangerous deeds by night, and was enticed by the most-wickedest, soulless monsters in and around the hood. I no longer cared for my siblings daily which forced my mother to stay at home more often, which I assumed was a good thing. But nevertheless, I had exposed myself to real darkness, and embraced its light without reservation.

Soon, I'd involve myself in many dubious activities of the gangsta such as robbing liquor stores and participating in armed home invasions, all at the ripe old age of fifteen! I inadvertently became more and more associated with the "Black Gangster Disciples" (BGD), the Nation of thugs.

I would go out 'on the prowl' every night, fully wasted and armed with a thirty-eight snub nose, thanks to "Chico," who was the real "Scarface" from Cuba! Chico was deeply immersed in the winter snow, (cocaine), and supplied most of the Midwest with nose candy by controlling most dealers and junkies on the West-side of Gary, Indiana. It was Chico who gave me my first gun, and taught me the ropes of Guerrilla Warfare with an ominous grin saying, "You're going to need this!" Unfortunately, Chico was right! After he saw the many violent capers in which I was involved outside Mary's house, Chico was extremely impressed. Days passed, and the weather's frosty frown began to turn towards our lives once again.

The wind blew briskly with a chill in the air and snow on its way. The days got darker but evil slowed its approach. Since the house we lived in had a fireplace in the living-room, the winter's sting could be quelled to all within our home, but the chimney was clogged, and no one knew how to clean it.

As the temperature began to drop, the need for a chimney sweep became more evident. Unclogging the vents and traps of ash and soot was a must, but we had no clue how to do it.

We found out the hard way, as the house filled with smoke the first time we tried to use the fireplace. Thank god for my mother's knack to find friends who had skills. As the temperature dropped, the urgency of having the fireplace cleaned became greater. Thank god my mom was so well known and likable in the hood, given the fact that most people back then were somewhat friendly to all their neighbors in those days. Unlike today, the neighbors actually spoke to one another on a daily basis. While tending their lawns or caring for their gardens, people took the time to know their next door neighbors. In fact, it was a must back then, so my mom quickly got one of our neighbors to help clear the fireplace of any obstructions for less than a six pack. The generous and friendly man I met was a lost and lonely soul by the name of Tony. Tony was a single divorced man in his early thirties, but somewhat loud and boisterous. With kindness in his heart, Tony became our savior from the winter's chill that year.

The mild mannered handy man named Tony, lived directly across the street from us, but just minutes away from the infamous Tiny Tim. Although I only met Tony once, he seemed nice, warm-hearted and caring to all. Yet creeping underneath Tony's jolly facade, one could see the obvious invisible monkey holding on tightly to his back, as drug addiction amplified his daily dilemmas and problems. From the way he fiddled and twitched around on my mother's living room floor on our first introduction, I knew he had it bad. Hardly responsive when spoken to or questioned, he would hesitate and stumble with his jumbled up words; it was so obvious that he was somewhat debilitated in his physical functions by his own device.

In those days, crack was unheard of, yet speed and pure cocaine ran rapid within the hood, as free basing became the poor man's hyper dimensional sense of ecstasy for less than ten dollars a pop. Any discerning person could see that his spirit and soul was a slave to an illegal drug, but only he and his dope dealer knew just what drug dampened his happy persona. Tony constantly consumed something detrimental to his health daily. Nevertheless, he proved himself to be a kind and generous soul. Tony helped bring heat to our humble abode in our darkest hour. I mention him in remembrance of his light, and with the understanding of how fast a great light can be extinguished, for not a week later, I would see him gasping for his last breath right outside his backyard as my mother administered mouth to mouth resuscitation and tried to contain his blood and save his life from a shotgun blast to the back. Quickly, the opened wound drained his life force from his frail and fragile figure. All I heard was a gurgle then silence!

Lying inches from his back door, Tony's lifeless body was in a pool of his own blood; he had been shot at point blank range. He was shot at point blank range after stumbling upon two known home invaders that were known to him as they were caught robbing his humble home. Ironically, Tony was well acquainted with the robbers and I, myself, knew one intimately. Although this testimony falls in the realm of speculation and deduction, I'll spill my guts out for what I witnessed that fateful day. For on that very day, I witnessed something very fishy and sinister surrounding Tony's home just a few minutes before his death. It was a beautiful sunny but cool day, and while I was looking out the front window, admiring the many oak tree leaves that took on the autumn change of colors in the afternoon breeze, I noticed Tiny Tim and a white dude with a shotgun in hand entering Tony's front door, only moments from hearing the blast coming from Tony's house.

At first I thought the two were invited in by Tony himself since I had seen both of them together with Tony on a couple of occasions, so I didn't think twice when I saw them enter Tony's front door. But when I saw Tiny Tim run out the front door a minute after entering Tony's home, looking white as a sheet, I knew something was very wrong. Tiny Tim nervously looked around the immediate area and spotted me watching him out of my mother's living-room window! We looked eye to eye at one another as Tim dashed into his home just next door from Tony. I should have known instantly that something was tragically wrong as I watched Tiny Tim run back into his un-wholly home with no delay! As a matter of fact, subconsciously, I did know, but stood down and said nothing to no one.

Knowing something terribly wrong was happening only feet from my home, I continued looking out of the window as I heard the killer's shot, shocking me too the core; it was loud; so loud! I heard a single shotgun blast, then the sound of a screaming woman who was running towards the sound of the blast with horror in her eyes! It was my mother running towards the scene of the crime, so I followed from my comforted perch within our toasty warm home, just made so by the one that was quickly becoming no more.

This was the first time I witnessed someone I personally knew who was so full of life and full of joy who was now lying in the dirt and gasping for air and life. Someone with such a kindhearted soul was now fighting for his life as I ran towards my mother's screaming voice saying, "CALL 911! GIVE HIM ROOM!" Speaking softly in his ear, saying, "Don't leave me Tony! Don't leave!" Forcefully, my mother instructed the on lookers to turn him on his side so he could get some air! I watched the light of life fade from his eyes as I watched my mom take charge even more so, attempting to save a life we both hardly knew. A life fighting spirit to stay Earth bound, yet all in vain. I could see the spark of light leave his eyes as my mother gave him mouth to mouth. I looked up into the sky and yelled within my soul, "GOD PLEASE!!" As my mind's eye inquired into the heavens above, I caught a glimpse of Tiny Tim looking out of his bedroom window, sinisterly looking down upon the lifeless body of one he knew of more than me.

Once again our eyes connected as Tiny Tim closed his bedroom curtains, and pulled down the shaded blinds. It was the first time I saw the light of life leave the human soul, for with my very own eyes, I witnessed human life evaporate into nothingness, and it truly took flight. In my mind's eye, a voice rang out: "Is this the fate of all who walk the face of this Earth?! Is our ultimate fate in the end, one who indulges in the realms of demons and fallen men?!"

Open up the doors of dangerous spirits, I cried out to the Most High, treading where angels fear to tread; I shall seek, is what I told myself in the nights to come. From that day forward, I eternally vowed never to indulge in anything that could bring my life to such a quick end, like that to which I witnessed. I vowed never to indulge in any drug outside the realm of weed and alcohol, and shall never fall victim to my dealings by any crafty trap set by men. I naïvely thought I'd be safe from those who deal in illegal drugs and ill will, and would never get caught up in activities that lead to an easy death, be it natural or not! But I was so wrong. Days passed with gloom as the weathers winter's chill got colder, and like icicles, my disposition took on the frosty look of winter's dread. Frequently contemplating Tony's untimely demise, I stood helpless with endless visions of Tony's lifeless body lying in the alleyway outside his own back door.

I saw no way out of my doomed life condition of poverty, thus having no exit from hell was all I could see for myself in the oh so near future. Can you hear the sounds of gun fire day and night?! I can. The master of death clinched my fate in his hands as my mind's eye sought refuge from a hell not of my making because I felt as if life on this Earth was a sentence of hell, and a punishment for some wrong doing of which I knew not! I would daily tell myself, "You better make the best of it!" I spent my days with Naomi, and my nights in the dangerous streets of Gary, Indiana, hustling for pennies and woe with my road dogs, Glenn and Keith. Getting fucked up was our only aim! Getting drunk and high every night was the highlight of our activity while thinking of my cousin Chunky, and often bringing up his name amongst the other two while wishing he was with us as we confronted the ills and evils that awaited us every time we walked out our doors. With wonder of Chunky's whereabouts, I finally asked my mother of Chunky's fate, and to my surprise, she told me.

Chunky was just up the street, in Mercy Hospital, literally, right up the street, no further than an hour's walk, withering away in some hospital. Chunky was diagnosed as "Looney!" Behind locked doors with armed guards, he stayed alone, just as I was, not two years ago. We found that Chunky was able to have visitors, so the very next day, Glenn Keith and I took a stroll up the street for a little unannounced visit. Since I was his only relative, I was able to go up on the elevator to see him in his lowest state. Glenn and Keith stayed downstairs in the lobby. I went up to the third floor; the floor where only the mentally disturbed dwelled and languished.

Curious of what I might find behind the elevator doors, I pressed the number three after the elevator doors shut. Suddenly, gripped by anxiety, I closed my eyes and awaited to hear the two chrome elevator doors to open on the third floor, and to my amazement, the elevator doors opened to two armed guards, and cameras greeting me as soon as the doors opened. With one guard crudely saying: "State your purpose, and who you're here to see?!" Humbly, I answered him with no pride as he led me through two large metal doors with two wire mesh glass windows located directly behind the officers' chairs.

Down a long hallway with walls colored institutional mint green, I slowly walked behind the officer, seeing the many patients behind their individual squared windowed doors. Some patients glared through their individual five by five square inch windows, each looking through the glass with such despair and loneliness. Finally the officer and I reached my cousin's door. As I looked at him through the small five by five inch window, I saw a different person, a person stripped of any self-dignity, or identity, held captive in a cage, having no sense of time, nor awareness of day or night. There were no windows towards the day break or night stars, knowing of no night or day! With no windows to the outside world, he seemed confused when he laid eyes on me through his little window. With no clock to tell time, they all lingered in despair and in the darkness' light.

While hearing over the intercom: "French you have a visitor," I saw a light enter Chunky's eyes as he was finally free; he looked up and about, hoping to see who may be coming to wish him well, and at that moment, I knew he knew it was me. With adoration and joy, he greeted me with hugs and kisses! He continued to squeeze me with great strength as he said to me, "I didn't think I'd ever see you again P." Remorsefully, we hashed over lost time and events, pondered over his behavior that led him to imprisonment, and discussed the regret he felt night and day. As he confided in me, he poured out his heart saying that I was the only one he cared for in our entire family, for he showed very little concern for anyone else, but as he spoke with such compulsion, I could hear the coldness within his heart. A Heart of Stone was within him. And though his heart was cold as ice, I could feel the burning heat of his fiery rage flowing through his blood and body. Right then and there, I knew his pain as my own. Finally, a remnant of human emotion was shown in the face of my wayward cousin and after an hour into our visit, he confided in me his remorseful regret of the absence of his mother and sister, and felt guilty for their deaths because of his wayward ways, wishing it was he that had died instead of them. For the first time, he revealed how much he missed them as a single tear rolled down his smiling face while showing me love and compassion. I smiled and said, "I know Chunky; I know!"

Spiritually connected, we quickly moved on to more festive thoughts. Knowing we were being monitored, we spoke in code about the outside goings on and made light of the life beyond the metal doors. "Times up" cried the intercom, so with a hug and a handshake, I smuggled a joint to my freshly renewed spirited cousin/ brother. While I made my way to the lobby, I reminisced over the many words spoken between us in darkness' light. I thought to myself, "Hope for the future must remain!" I said to myself, "If there's a will there's a way!"

I tried to make a good situation out of bad deeds and thought, "... at least he had three hots and a cot, and was not freezing his ass off in some abandon building on the mean streets of Gary, Indiana!"

Almost two weeks had passed from that unforgettable meeting with Chunky behind closed doors, and The Chicago's Hulk blew even colder than the day before.

As the noon sun shone brightly through the window, there was an unexpected knock on our front door and a shroud of total shock encompassed my mother's soul as she looked through the peep hole in the door and then answered it. Lo and behold, it was the elusive Chunky standing on the other side of the front door. But how could that be? Chunky had a few months to go in his sentence of silence before he would be released.

Having nowhere to go, with no one within our family willing to take him in after his terrifying escapade, his sentence would have been even longer than a few months after the stunt he pulled; yet there he stood, a free man, clear as day. Happy to see him, I jumped up with joy, and gave him a great big hug! Mom on the other hand, stood in shock at the front door, not saying much at all, but watched Chunky and I become reacquainted while knowing he wasn't supposed to be released for a while. Without fail, mom asked him how it was possible. He looked up with a straight face and said to my mother, "I'm Free Aunty! I'm free!" With no expression on my mother's face, she went back to watching her stories. Chunky and I hit the streets immediately and hunted down our true comrades in mischief, Glenn and Keith, but before we hit the obvious spots, I introduced him to Naomi. Seeing her long flowing hair as black as a raven's feather, he quickly tried to move in on the action, but she was all mine, and let him down with a smile, so off we went. With weed on our person, and a few bucks in our pockets, we headed towards the danger zone: Eleventh Avenue... The land of the "Bullet Family." It was the part of town where Chunky long made his mark, and Glenn's family moved there some time after Chunky had been committed.

The Bullets were not unlike the Moore family, for they were another ruthless family that dwelt in the world of drugs and all sorts of criminal activities. A family whose influence reached over most of Gary, Indiana's shady class of people.

One wouldn't want to cross paths with the Bullets. Chunky and I made our way to Glenn's place and stopped to pick up some Mad Dog 20/20. We came across a foe of Chunky's, and knowing how violent Chunky had shown himself, I knew we were in for fireworks, but no, Chunky walked past his foe, saying not a word. Chunky had refrained from violence and kept walking. Had incarceration in the funny farm tamed the savage beast that resided within my cousin's soul?

Startled and surprised, I made no comment, and we both said nothing while walking in silence towards Glenn's apartment. As we walked down the stairs leading to Glenn's apartment, we were greeted with great jubilation from Glenn and Keith. Keith's mom was friends with Glenn's mom; therefore, one could find Keith at Glenn's at any given time of the week. Quickly getting out of dodge from their parents, we headed to the "High Lines" (an abandoned train track on top of a forest hill) with Keith holding an ounce of weed and some alcohol to drink; we were in thug heaven. While reminiscing and getting sloppily intoxicated, we made a night of it, then out of the blue, Chunky spilled the beans.

He hadn't been released and had escaped during shift change; he was a fugitive on the run, and the police were looking for him; drunk, high and off our rockers, we dismissed his obvious mis-truths; how could he have escaped? We saw firsthand the measures taken at the hospital and there was no way he could have gotten off the third floor itself. From my observation, there was only one way off the floor, and since the massive two metal doors that excluded him from the rest of the world were always locked, not to mention the constant surveillance by armed guards and video cameras, there was no way he could have eluded their watchful eyes without being made out rather quickly! There was only one way out, and given their clothing was collected the very day of enrollment, how could he have escaped without clothing? By all accounts, he couldn't have; therefore, he must have been released, or so logic dictates.

But in his defense, he had no release papers at all on his person, with no medical scripts or sociological drugs on hand, he insisted he had escaped, and said after he had his little stretch of freedom, he was going back into hospital custody. When we asked him why, he just uttered, "…back to the hospital I must return, plus I like the food," and just like that, we began the long walk towards Mercy Hospital. In total disbelief, Glenn, Keith and I agreed to go with him inside the hospital, "Okay let's go!" So with no avail, we headed back towards Grant Street, back towards the hospital and physical lock-down in which he so conveniently strolled out of not some eight hours earlier. Thinking he was full of shit and joking, we dismissed the very concept of his escaping, making jest the entire trek back to Mercy Hospital. As we walked up the road adjacent the hospital landscape and parking lot, we foolishly disregarded his silence, and mistook his serene demeanor for shame and fear, fear of being made out to be a liar before us all.

When reaching the door to the mental patient's return, the shame of being made out by his crew did not show upon his face. We all made fun of Chunky, so he showed the entire crew as we got closer to the hospital that we were the last thing on his mind. We made our way into the hospital's sliding glass doors shortly after Chunky entered. Turning and looking back at us all, Chunky smiled with bold arrogance as he continued forward, then, without warning, he approached the center reception desk and proudly stated: "Hi I'm Chunky…. you looking for me?" Stunned and shocked, the nurse yelled out, "SECURITY!!!" Struck by disbelief, we stood between the glass-doors with our mouths opened wide as security descended upon him from all directions! After the receptionist announced his whereabouts over the intercom, a flock of security assembled in the lobby, grabbing Chunky and wrestling him to the ground! Glenn, Keith and I slowly headed back out the glass doors, and jetted! Quickly making our way off hospital grounds, we looked at each other in total disbelief, for he was telling the truth, what a total buzz kill, and to this very day, I still have no clue as to how he escaped. Three weeks later, he was officially released. Since he returned voluntarily and without incident, the hospital staff saw no reason to hold him for more than his original release date. He was set free because of the very stunt he pulled not one month ago. Escaping the confounds of the locked down institution, and returning by his own volition the very night he eluded their power implied cognizance and intelligence, so they saw no reason on wasting their time and resources on keeping him in their custody.

With Chunky out of the nut house and back on the scene, the whole crew was complete and back in operation. Grandma moved to Seventeenth Avenue, on the West-side of town, Glenn lived in the middle of our road trail on Eleventh Avenue, West-side and Keith still lived on the East-side of town, in the thick of danger, making it very risky for him to make the trek to the West-side to visit any of us during the day time. Chunky and I still lived up town, on the West-side of town, on Fourth and Tyler. With all of us spread out across the city, meeting up with one another was a trek in danger each and every day. Crossing the invisible line called Broadway, which separated the East from West, was an opportunity full of misfortune. Riddled with unaware pitfalls of many enemies crossing any street or corner, ready to maim or kill anyone of us, was the order of the day, especially after the "Scream N' Wheels" incident. We quickly found ourselves on the short end of the proverbial stick, on all enemies' shit lists.

Being assaulted every day, or even being shot at every night was a given. Making shortcuts in order to conceal our movement and whereabouts was sometimes tricky, but we made the best of it, and didn't care one bit about the danger, and we all took the risk and made the trek anyway. We had made a name for ourselves in the streets; we were nomads and rogues in the hood, having no allegiances to any group, yet known by all, and hated by most. We were envied by the so-called good teens, and we were forever watching our backs, always on the move, and finally, never congregating in the same location at once. I must say it was fun and exciting being a reprehensible person of lowly means and utterly lacking in principles.

Insufferable brutes we were. We were bullies and tyrants on the loose, and villains in general, thinking it made us respected and cool, but not realizing the trouble and sheer terror we caused others, or the true danger we were headed towards! Play time was over, thus we graduated to armed robbery and home invasions, and teamed up with two other rogues from the hood; we committed a slew of crimes throughout the city, and never once considered the fear and emotional suffering we unleashed on those we affected. Living without remorse or care of conscience made life somewhat bearable. We couldn't have cared less about those in our wake of our destruction, for no one cared about us; why should we give a fuck about anyone else? We continued spiraling downward and deeper into the mindset of evil's light. Evil's light was becoming brighter and brighter; then it happened! A voice called out to me in the night saying, "Stop doing what you're doing! Stop what you're doing, and think of those lives you are affecting!" Having nothing to hold on to, like your self-worth, nor having no way out of poverty, I couldn't understand the voice, yet the cliché rang true, "…what goes around comes around….remember your home being robbed; now it's you doing the robbing. Stop! Look at yourself!"

I didn't like what I saw in myself, so the next day I refrained from the daily hunt. Sitting back and out of sight while lying low at Naomi's, I poured out my heart to one just as lost to reality as I was. I let her know of all the wrong things I'd done, and told her of the feeling of remorse that was creeping within me, and I found no relief in the bottle of alcohol or weed. No longer was I just hiding out from enemies, but hiding out from those closest to me, even my own crew. Realizing the road I'd taken had dire consequences, I knew someday it would come back on me and those around me, consequences I most definitely didn't want the spirit of evil to visit me back, and wanted no part of the retribution owed. Feeling a change taking place from within my soul without knowing why, my heart was growing full of regret. I wanted more from life.

I was beginning to care about my behavior and started daring to hope for something better in life. Yet I saw no way out of poverty, or even overcoming the cards dealt to me in life, and found myself pondering my plight daily. Finally my crew caught up with me, but was unaware of my sudden change in thought. Planning our next caper, they targeted a church, a church we'd walked past regularly. And though I was not one claiming any religious preference anymore, I declined from the venture. Having no part in the caper, I fortified my position as the unspoken leader, and caused the others to put the job on permanent hold.

This raised questions of my loyalty within the group, and challenged each and everyone's resolve in my commitment to crime, consequently planting doubt in everyone else's heart about continuing a life of crime.

Like myself, most of my crew only did despicable things for the fun of it because we were young, stupid, socially controlled and naïve; however, we'd never contemplated the consequences of our actions nor considered the pain and suffering we'd caused others.

We never allowed ourselves to feel remorse for others in the same position as ourselves, or ever let regret and remorse rear its wise face. Most in the crew never thought twice before jumping into the fray of crime and destruction. After my heart felt speech, I could see the mind set of us all in the crew change from foolishness and unawareness to confusion of will.

Glenn and Keith began to heed my warnings, and sided with me in refraining in all criminal activity, but Chunky and two others saw things differently, and continued onward in their criminal activities, even ramping it up in days to come; however, they still refrained from robbing the well-known church at that time. Winter's snow blanketed the city, and my mother moved once again; this time she moved to Eighth and Pearce Street, with an old high school friend of whom I knew nothing. Since she was no longer kickin it with Mary, I saw very little of my mother. Since I was now seeing Naomi daily, I even lived at Mary's and periodically visited my mother only on the weekends. Soon I became acquainted with my mother's new roommate.

She was a twenty-eight-year-old street pro by the name Sonay. She was petite in stature and very pretty, and I was barely fifteen but quickly became infatuated with her. She showed me so much attention that I found myself caught up in her female trap, especially since my mother did not seemingly care that her friend made sexual advancements towards me. Falling victim to her veracious womanly charm, I blew off everyone, including Naomi for good it seemed, and stayed with my mother full time. Sonay had me under her spell; she would pay for everything I asked and I wanted for nothing. She sold her body nightly and gave me the money; she even gave me her gun to protect her when niggas got funky in the streets. Seeing her advancements, my mother said nothing, and she even walked in on us fucking and did not say a word, which ultimately shook my senses for some time to come. Thinking I was a grown man fucking a woman like Sonay right in my mother's house, I played myself. Having little regard for Naomi and what she meant to me, I played the field without remorse or regret, lighting both ends of the candle, seeing Sonay in the day, and Naomi at night.

Bold in all my actions, I concealed nothing from either women, straight pimping both flat out, and in the open. Until one night a knock on Naomi's bedroom window changed everything; it was Sonay. Sonay was no longer willing to be the whore on call. She wanted me for herself, making her intention known clearly! Sonay banged on Naomi's bedroom window and screamed out my name at the top of her lungs, loudly shouting out her love for me, proclaiming her love ever so vocally, and waking the entire house in the middle of the night.

She eventually gained entry no thanks to Mary, and the events to come were as if all hell broke loose. Before I knew it, Naomi took hold of Sonay's hair and began whaling on her, shocking me and Mary both, leaving us dumb-founded and speechless for a moment. After gaining some composure, I pulled Naomi off Sonay and tried to console both without inflaming the situation, but I only compounded insult to injury which caused Sonay to finally propose an ultimatum, "Either leave Naomi, or never set foot in my home ever again!" Sonay sealed her fate and unwittingly relieved herself from the inevitable rejection that she was soon to get. Naomi was my age and meant more, and although she had nothing, I cared not! I myself was accustomed to having nothing, and lived in similar conditions all my life.

We both were young and inexperienced to the true horrors of this world and held onto each other no matter what conditions came our way. Although

Sonay provided money, weed, pussy, and drank, she couldn't take the place of Naomi, for she was someone just as lost as I was.

I was taught from birth not to say the word, "No" and not to say the word, "Love" to anyone, so I had no concept of the emotion of love, and all I knew was this: Naomi and I belonged to one another, if only by pure circumstance. Time passed and spring's presence melted the harshness of the winter's hulk, yet conditions at Mary's became ever more volatile. Banditos, drug dealers, and occasional refuges hiding out from immigration wardens, and operating illegal activities within her home was making life somewhat unbearable for all that lived behind those dreary doors on Third and Tyler. Having killers and bill collectors forever creeping around, coupled with very little food to eat, made my welcome there between her daughter's sheets short lived. With emotions on high most days, and stomachs empty, not very much would cause total disarray and anarchy within those somewhat safe doors. So please keep in mind this obvious truth as fact, being a fledgling career criminal in waiting, and seeing the opportunity for a quick come up was a no brainer, so my cousin brought an end to my stay there in one instant.

Being true to his nature, Chunky wrangled a neighbor's lawnmower and sold it to Mary. Clearly stating buyer beware, warning her not to use the item during work hours, and being true to her nature, she totally disregarded his warning and used it not an hour after he swiped it. This brought down the wrath of her next door neighbor with avenges, causing all her anger to be directed upon me. Since he was my family member, and nowhere to be found, all the venom of those wronged and those taking part in the wrong doing fell upon my shoulders. Leaving me to absorb the aftermath of said parties, my cousin was nowhere to be found. After burning my bridges with Sonay in choosing Naomi over her, I had nowhere to go, and now I was thrown out on my buttocks because of Chunky. I found myself out on the streets, with no place to live, so I made my way to Seventeenth Avenue; the only safe haven I knew: "Ida Mae Abbott's," Grandma's house. I knew with all my heart she would never forsake me or any of her children in times of need, for she even took in Chunky after his obvious mental breakdown and uncontrollable anger. If in real life saints truly lived and existed, then my Grandmother surely exhibited all the necessary virtues associated with sainthood, well at least in my eyes.

We lived in a one bedroom rat and roach infested hole in the wall, barely connected to a hellhole building on the verge of being condemned, having no electricity, water or gas, thus living day by day on the meager of means, for she fared on fumes. Already filled to the brim with three grandchildren, and her own mother, "Granny Grip," she welcomed me home with open arms, with not a word or reason.

Back cohabitating under the same roof as my troubled crime ridden cousin, Chunky and I were once again inseparable, and only away from each other when he went on his late night crime excursions. Once again faced with the relentless and never easy choices of hard living, and facing the ever looming facts of seeing our siblings and family members suffer daily from the ever stinging assault of poverty, made Chunky heartless. Look and see the careless, yet oblivious smiles of rug rats not worrying or knowing their desperate plight at all as long as a little food graced their dirty faces most nights, for they played their days away in the spotted grass and dirt. God bless Ronald Reagan's long awaited monthly government cheese at night.

A tearful shout out, and with all respect given to those promised to be poor children and teens of sorrow's wake, stricken with poverty at birth, and given no hope for material sake, for to overcome insanity is to embrace hopelessness where opportunity hides next door to this day. Yet, at the same time keep their noses clean from crime, avoiding drug dealing at all cost as they attend some type of schooling, teaching absolutely "nothing" usually was the case, for staying out of trouble was almost never lost for those without stake of ownership ever crossing their lips. Off the mean Gary streets at night was the sight, counts as victory to those lost to humbleness less might, for we never flee and most definitely fight! Staying your hand without taking your brother's life, or hurting one just like yourself, and is alike in life, is as viable as ice in summer's heat; tis damn near remarkable and unheard of within a seconds breath to take another's life, for less than a trinket was worth our life!

Yet staying free of violence made me an admirable knight at best. I began to count myself as one of you at that point in time, one that shielded from criminal life and violence, but at great cost, I do thee mind. I didn't resort to crime for any reason, and no longer reacted from mere impulse and lack of self-control, on the contrary, a return to sanity is where I would go. Well, at the time period mentioned, perhaps. I understood the hard time in which we lived during those days, and the common plight that rings true for most minorities in the early eighties, and to this very day from murky glasses of doom taught by our truly ugly and pure evil "Black So-Called Leaders," be it religious, political, educational or social, all lie in the pockets of the Evil Democrats. Please keep in mind that this was the era of Reagan, and perhaps self-made prosperity, but from our stand point, we lived in a time of plenty for those with plenty, but a time of dread for those with nothing nor any! Please try to understand this bullshit was spoon fed to us on a daily basis, and a common state of awareness and mindset was null to reality. For fiction was fact and struggle reigned supreme.

Unable to see through the brainwashing fed to us from our own kind who presented themselves as saviors, but in fact became our jailers, and executioners with no impunity, thus this truth must be presented within these pages of long lost history long suffered from history's past, which truth still alludes the common folk that are no one!

We were lied to with bitter non-truths from those we trusted, and promises of humanity's fair share, given only by god. With grand faith, we received heartache and pain, alongside hopeful words, yet death from our master's unseen above, up top maintains high reigned agony, given over to the most lost men, from lost men even more; we stood and still stand trapped! Given over for sacrifice without a whisper's wind of rebellion's hope offered from wise men of old, yet we all stand still as the devourers devoured our spirits and hopeless souls. Leaving nothing but hopelessness in the minds of hopeful youth, while the master's work wake shows no mercy. By those we trusted most, we were betrayed and murdered! Using our own hand as our weapon of choice upon our fellow selves, as ignorance adorned our enemies' invisible weapon willed upon ourselves!

Used as autonomous votes, tokens and oaths to help those that loath us most! With love and devotion our wealth we gave over without second thought, but now comes wisdom alongside our fury's wrath, thus no longer under a spell of victim-hood and shame, for our fury's wrath has no equal...

For what I know of my cousin Chunky's mindset at that time in history, I could in all confidence speak for him as well, an indivisible mind of thought and agreement. We saw so many hungry siblings and needy grandparents, portraying the eagerness to tally up their meager rations granted monthly their allowance of government cheese. In our presence daily were visions of others enjoying so much more, on television and on posters of untouchable things that shined bright in the night, and those visions angered us to anger's end. Having no possible hope for the future, and breaking free from a life of violence seemed bleak, for no dream of escape could unseal our position in life. Though in my mind's eye it seemed obtainable, yet hopelessness clouded the thought, "I must find the hidden door out of this world!" With pants' pockets holding nothing but lint, arose the thoughts of larceny for the inevitable ghetto enterprise of the down trodden, thus putting on the classic black gloves, and doing away with lofty great aims of committing no crime ever again, or letting wrong doing go out the window.

Tackling the obvious scourge among us named poverty, survival became our main goal, so we quickly reverted back to survival mode, such as, callousness of thought, thus letting selfishness take full control over our physical actions without reason. Refusing to see another soul within our home suffer any more, as stomachs growled hungry most nights, I abandoned and dissolved all vestiges of hoping to better my self-existence from within. Though unseen and unaware to most human beings, the jailed spirits that play havoc in all dealings of good and evil amongst mankind, and dwell within the ether, were on the rampage even more so in those days, and their masters were on the warpath, and I could feel their presence daily.

Determined to destroy the spiritual union between me and Naomi, Mary's secret attempts to finally disconnect Naomi from my overwhelming influence, bore fruit, coupled with genuine fear for her daughter's safety, and life even from within, was so corrosive with many degenerates being harbored in her very home. Mary sent Naomi to Lansing, Michigan in the hope of ending our growing dependency and attraction toward one another, but she failed miserably. Mary unwittingly fueled Naomi's delinquency and misbehavior, even though she was miles away. With absence came longing, and weekly correspondence between us became the norm. With Naomi miles away and the responsibility of taking care of my loved ones' wellbeing burning within me, hitting the streets was my only option.

I swear before god we hit every garage in the neighborhood daily. With white boys in legitimate businesses, willing to fence every piece of equipment, tool and amenity we had to offer, and all for fifty cents on the dollar, we were busy as bees, which had us right back where we were, back to getting fucked up and drunk every chance we got. We were always four deep, so the heat was catching up with us, but we didn't give a shit! We would just intimidate any grown up that dare cross our path, brazenly becoming bolder, and more reckless in our escapades. We would break into neighborhood homes, cars and even hit local electricity utility trucks while fearlessly robbing any punk sucker that happened to find himself caught in our web, but at the same time, my god-given voice of consciousness was coming alive once more.

The weighty toll of wickedness in my deeds had become a great burden within the deepest parts of my spirit, making it almost impossible for me to contain within myself the trueness of my nature! No matter how much I portrayed myself before the other wretches, as a masterful villain and hard ass without conscience, the more my true spirit rebelled against the physical health of my soul (body) itself, feeling physically somewhat mundane though mischievous, yet a purposeful mis-behavioral street rat with skill and education. Outside time and space, the powers that be made themselves known by heightening my god-given mental safeguards, safeguards necessary to keep the peace of sanity within one's self.

For we're made to protect those like ourselves, but for the wickedness taught to men by those that have known war long before men knew of the concept of harming another, their influence has weakened most humans' fortitude to preserve life, rendering most of humanity the will and inability to protect themselves, let alone to protect others! I began examining the madness of being incapable to display empathy, and or sympathy for my fellow man's sorrow. Then one day, true spiritual enlightenment illuminated the unexplainable fear of heavenly disappointment in the sincere thought of harming those like myself, and the weight of a thousand bricks hit me without mercy. I now understood the dreadfulness of feeling more of the same old insanity afflicting everyone. I questioned my actions in real time, and began to loathe all previous actions I imposed over those we affected in the past and those we were about to affect in the future.

I internally felt what they themselves would feel at first sight, and what we were about to do to them would affect us all forever. Yahweh forced me to feel their affliction and plight, and made me understand their pain, and what it meant for me to know that it was done by my hand. The imagined outcome haunted my mind more and more each day. Guilt plagued me after every misdeed, and consumed my heart to the point of near permanent paranoid delusions daily.

I saw shadows at every turn and heard ghostly footsteps moving closer to me during the nightly capers. I would feverishly count the moments until the anticipated day when the police found us out, but no cops ever made their presence known. It was as if we operated with impunity, exempt of all criminal activities by some invisible force. I observed many people in the neighborhood secure their belongings so they thought, and watched them closely through their own windows as we roamed the streets at night, planning their fleecing. Yet no legal authority ever knocked on Grandma's door after a risky caper, leaving me to wonder when the time of reckoning would come, but it never did. I continued to justify my actions from the rules of the down trodden: "If I can't have it no one should… I'll take it without care or remorse!" I had no care or mercy on those within my environment, and cared not for the property in which we lived. With every caper came an unnatural sense of control and power, and it became intoxicating. The irony was, the more we would steal, rob and create havoc within the community, the more good things would occur. Granny Grip obtained a place of her own, taking my brother Onan with her, and so did my aunt Katharine, along with her three children, relieving some burden from my Grandmother's plight. Food was abundant, and even the electricity to Grandma's apartment was restored for a while, thus things were looking up around the crib. Then it happened!

The event that would change my soul and spirit forever more. I was becoming increasingly flakey when it came to Breaking and Entering (B&E), as the authorities would call it, and I felt ashamed of myself and halted all criminal activity. Chunky, on the other hand, blossomed in his criminal activities, and became a proficient and seasoned criminal in the mind's eye of a typical juvenile delinquent in criminal training. Chunky and the other two that just joined the club broke free from the original crew, after hearing my heart felt confession and deciding to sever ties, and even went as far as to hook-up with the likes of the most un-scrupulous cut-throats I have ever met.

They went by the name of the Harrod brothers and the Santana's, and broke into the mentioned Church without consulting anyone in their former crews, not long after the fateful conversation. I knew the implication of their actions would surely visit us with a venomous vengeance since most people in the hood were religious. I knew the authorities would surely track us down, but that wasn't the straw that broke the camel's back.

The fact that he brought the stolen items from the church into grandma's house enraged me, and that fact ultimately brought things to a head between my beloved cousin and myself. I had no choice other than to expose our activities before our grandmother, the very person I didn't want to be seen or betrayed as a fuck up and a thief.

Having no choice but to confess our dishonorable behavior before my disappointed grandmother brought even more shame, yet I spilled the beans to grandma and told her where Chunky obtained his goods, and the origins of the stolen items he just brought into her home. They were from the neighborhood church up the way. Quickly, both our emotions reached to uncontrollable heights, causing an uproar between the two of us before grandma's presence. Heated words turned into pushing and shoving, then a wrestling of wills broke out between us. I was never one to engage in physical violence unless provoked; therefore, I tried reasoning with Chunky rather than engaging in an altercation, choosing brains over brawn, but I was unsuccessful.

For the first time ever, Chunky saw I could handle myself when challenged, even against a formidable opponent forged in the fires of combat such as himself, shocking him, and causing his temper to flare uttering, "Oh, you can thump P, Okay!" Subsequently, Chunky grabbed an axe hanging on the mantel of the door of the bedroom in which we both slept, and attempted to assault me with it. Out of self-preservation, I instinctively grabbed my Grandmother's cane as she hopelessly tried to break up the scuffle. Since Chunky knew I had skills with nun chucks and knives, and saw me outwit imaginary foes many times in the past, he decided to decline from further engagement in mortal combat. Frustrated and full of rage, he reverted to insults and name calling, and was unable to contain his anger; consequently, he hurled a glass ashtray directly towards the middle of the back of my head. If grandma didn't warn me by screaming out, "P, watch out," he would have gotten a clean shot to the back of my head, instead of just a part of it, and below to the back. The ashtray shattered into a million pieces, with two shards embedded into my left shoulder blade, head and back, prompting Grandma to call 911 for assistance as my blood flowed down my back.

By the time the ambulance arrived, Chunky and I had resolved our dispute, resulting in him apologizing and removing the stolen audio equipment with tears in his eyes and sorrow in his heart. Seeing so much blood flowing from her favorite grandson sealed it for Grandma, Ida Mae Abbott, and Chunky had to go! She didn't care where or how, as long as he was gone that instant. She even threatened to call the police to inform them of all our activities outside her home unless he removed himself within the hour. Knowing grandma was a woman of her word, with love and new found respect for me, with no word said, he followed her wishes and left that very moment.

Fearing any reprisal from the crew over our mishap, Chunky agreed to splinter off from the original crew, taking the other two reprobates along with him, leaving the original three members to begin their road towards honorable deeds without knowing. Seeing the increasing ill will and danger directed towards the crew, even from rogues such as us, we decided to refrain from the art of B & E, and stopped the practice entirely. We were no longer "stick up kids" or thugs looking for a thrill, so we only partied and became huge weed heads instead.

Soon word of Chunky's splintering from the band of three thieves and their exploits was reaching even to our own ears. Clearly, we had ruffled more than a few evil feathers which boiled the blood of ruthless killers. But when Chunky robbed the Bullets of two worthless bikes, everything changed from that day forward. Chunky's crew inadvertently brought down the Bullets' wrath upon Glenn, Keith and myself, and the shit hit the fan real quick. Being associated with the Bullet's criminal organization, Chunky and his undisciplined crew of nitwits decided to steal from the very assholes for whom they worked, and with Glenn's mother's apartment just a hair's throw away from the Bullet's home and liquor store doors, it didn't make sense for Chunky to rob someone so close to those that loved and respected him. Almost daily, the Bullets and their awful crew would spew out vile accusations, and complaints were lodged against "The Crew of Three." Always within an ear shot of Glenn's presence were venomous accusations encapsulating Glenn's ear every time he left his mother's home. We all knew that the Bullets were a family of killers, and had a lofty bounty on our heads, so we avoided anyone associated with them.

It was very hard to disappear from the general public, and drug heads since most lived very close. The people in the surrounding nearby hood knew them all, so we stayed clear of that area entirely. With great sorrow comes great desperation, and with enormous worry and woe for a population, relief is a must! Most in this state of mind, fall victim to Pharmacia, and for those that wish to avoid addiction, the preferred medicine was and still is marijuana. Everyone in the city smoked weed, and the Bullet's supplied half of the city. Sooner or later we, "The Band of Three," would have to face the ruthless Bullet family without protection. Like foreign diplomats, we decided to tackle the problem head on and confront the Bullets on their turf, at their doorsteps, while nervously trying to explain our disassociation with Chunky's crew and thievery. We all tried to explain our non-involvement, but it did not bode well with their logic, and neither did our track record of being the exact thieves that previously wreaked havoc within their neighborhood and surrounding areas.

With no avail, the minute we approached their corner store, the Bullet's cronies were hanging out on the corner liquor store and yelled out, "Here come them niggas now!" They pulled out their rods and pointed them directly at us, and locked up on all of us three teenagers, who were not holding a single pea shooter among us.

The Bullets were unwilling to grant an ordinance with their masters and refused to hear anything we had to say, which forced Keith to call out to the head Bullet and about five other punks standing within the doorway of the store, but this attempt was also to no avail. Immediately, the thugs with guns came closer, yet holstered their weapons, as the smaller one began beating Glenn as all others laughed uncontrollably. It so happened that Glenn's stepfather was looking out their front door window port at the right time. Full of fear, Keith took off running, but I stood there with a gun pointed to my head with no fear, readying myself to die. Suddenly, Glenn's stepfather appeared out of nowhere brandishing a sawed-off shotgun, startling all seven murderous fools, thus stopping the brutes' assault in their tracks, pointing his sawed- off shotgun in their direction. He had one hand pointing his boom stick, and his other hand was picking up Glenn off the dirty ground. We all headed towards Glenn's apartment which was just across the street from the Bullet's stronghold, the neighborhood corner store, which was adjacent to the Bullet's actual home. Furious of other so-called friends of Glenn's running at first break, and the fact Keith ran first, and I stayed in the line of fire helping Glenn to safety, Glenn's stepfather made me feel welcome inside Glenn's home, and said these words in front of all within the house, "This is a man!" He looked me in the eyes and said, "He stayed when the rest of your friends ran like sheep without a shepherd." He asked me who the girl was by my side, said to Glenn, "Where's your woman?!" Glenn said nothing as he held his head down in shame. Looks of envy with eyes of daggers, Glenn and Keith's mothers, standing side by side looked at me as if I was the cause of their children's delinquency and said to one another, "It's all his fault!" Yet the fault of delinquency falls on the child's mindset, not mine. Their belief of me as the source of their children's woes was far from the truth; if anything, I was the voice of reason among the group's adolescent nonsense.

❉Important to note❉

The term: "Tribalism" is a group of people beholden to themselves. In the past, this form of unity was necessary for a tribe of people to survive many dangers, dangers from Earthly elements, or different tribes killing and raping the women and children of another, and taking over food stuffs, water and land. But these days, those of a tribe would be referred to as slaves and therefore, not worth living. The elite use this form of unity to divide humanity, thus keeping humanity weak and un-unified, so as to control us and conquer and divide; for divided we fall, and together we stand! In turn... their greatest fear! Tribalism has once again become important for humanity's survival, but this time it shall not come in the form of a certain groups of people, nor ancestral households or breeds. It shall come in the form of Nationalism! For the King of the Earth, "Lucifer," means to unite the nations of the planet under his full control and banner, New

World Order (N.W.O.). He means to fight back the coming of the Lord with the blood of men, Yahweh's greatest creation!

He wishes to use man's ingenuity and creativity in his universal war against the Creator, and destroy this planet and all its occupants. It is said that in the end of times all that is hidden shall be revealed. Now is the time that all that is hidden is coming to light! Those that would call themselves our masters have sacrificed our children in the darkness of the night, in tunnels and holes, deep underground, having human feed off of human, thus sacrificing them in the names of ancient gods, for the "Brotherhood of the Snake" has never gone away.

With duplicity, humanity's enemies have kept us captive, telling us truth with lies, and lies with truth. For they cannot harm us without letting us know of their actions! We must willingly give ourselves over to them for their magic to work. A New World Order must come, for all humanity needs to come together in order to transcend the stars, but it must be an order from above! Yahweh's Kingdom must come here on Earth as it is in Heaven, for that is the only way man can break free from his true enemy which is "DEATH," and not this evil kingdom of darkness that the NWO has in mind. For they mean to destroy us! The insidious order has come out from the one trapped here with his legions, unseen spirit hordes, and human traitors! The King of the Earth gets ready for battle.

A great deception was written in prophecies, and ancient texts of old, and they even tell you to look for it! For thy salvation comes near. But the great deception has come and gone before we were born! The world in which we live is The Great Deception! Did you not know?! With knowledge comes great sorrow, but ease of life, with decadence in abundance, and comfort has its trap! Take one from what is real, and make all captive of smoke and mirrors. For technology serves two masters, and can be used for good or evil! Without knowledge of old, we all shall die. Obtaining food water and shelter for oneself is all that is needed to live. But if one gives up the freedom of knowing how to obtain those necessary skills to have what's needed, then he dies. We all have been deceived by the world in which we live, thinking its real, when it's not! True freedom does not come free! With hard work of that which is untold, comes freedom with a price. A price of humility and suffering of one's self!

Chapter XVII
The "BGD" Conundrum

After returning the stolen bikes, Chunky and his crew went to war with the Bullets! After M. Bullet refused to accept Chunkeys crew's sincere apologies, their relentless hostilities amplified. In defense of Chunky's crew, they didn't know it was the Bullets that they were robbing and that they shot Markus to death over two ten speeds which was uncalled for.

After the truth of The Band of Three's innocence surfaced amongst the Bullets, a couple of wounded Bullet soldiers later stopped the beef and constant harassment of the three, and made it known to all the Vice Lords in the hood that we were fair game, but NOT a priority. Glenn, Keith and I were known by most gang-bangers, but never a part of any group until Chunky's war with the Bullets became bloody. This turned all the niggas on Eleventh Avenue against Chunky's crew, which in fact directed all kinds of bullshit towards us. Glenn, Keith and I were now associated with Chunky and his crew. In addition, the fact that Chunky and I were blood, made living in that area highly dangerous for Glenn and his family and twice as dangerous for Keith and myself, who didn't live on or around Eleventh Avenue, making us automatic targets. To make matters worse, we only knew a few of the fellas in the area, but that was cool with us, so we stayed in their presence when visiting Glenn for safety reasons. They called themselves the Black Gangster Disciples (BGD'S).

Although they lived in an all (Vice Lord) neighborhood, these few fellas were true Disciples, more than four generations. Some claimed that two family members were immersed in the Gangster Disciple Nation from its inception. The group began in the sixties on the South-side of Chicago, Illinois and was based in the "Cabrini Green" high rise tenements. Today these menaces to society are spread all across the Midwest and the United States itself. Today some Original BGD's are now commonly known as (Imperial Gangstas) by their underlings. Chunky now takes on that mantel of "IG" because he was known as a hardcore Disciple, tackling the windmill initiation in his earlier years. The term "Windmill," is the first right of initiation in becoming a true BG Disciple foot soldier, immersed in violence and death. The emblem is the Triple M: "Money, Mackin' & Murder."

The initiate runs through a line of ten G's, ten to the right and ten to the left, as they beat him with full force. Some even carried bats and sticks; the initiate must make it through on his feet or repeat the course.

If he fails the second time, the initiate suffers rejection or even death. These days, the practice of the windmilling is no longer required, nor due because of so many deaths and maimed individuals. Few survive the Windmill initiation without some kind of deformity, physical or emotional, so the darkness stirring of spirit shall most definitely occur, but in those days that gruesome practice was required in becoming a Disciple of Evil.

Not officially yet seen as sympathizers, Glenn Keith and I walked the line in the middle, thus never committing ourselves to any faction, or the other. Now these are Goodfellas known through the hood: Top Dog who held the rank of first seat, from Chicago, and an officer in the Gangster Nation. Daily, Top Dog would try to recruit "The Band of Three" with no success. Top Dog lived three blocks from Glenn. The second thug went by the name Gino, who held the rank of second seat, but was located in East Chicago.

Gino was a scary short nigga from Chicago as well, with no scruples, and straight crazy. The third went by name Dollar Bill who was cool as fuck! A foot soldier who lived close to "Norton Elementary" school and park, about five blocks up from Glenn's home. We played ally ball in back of his house daily, without a care in the world. Now there was also one more by the name of Don Juan, and he also lived in the neighborhood his entire life and claimed to be a Disciple but proved himself to be a Vice Lord or at least a false flagger spying for the Red Vice Lords.

With the Bullets covertly and cunningly causing trouble behind the scene, coupled with Top Dog's constant recruiting tactics, we finally gave in to the overwhelming peer pressure, and began considering becoming affiliated with the Folk Nation. Then Keith allowed himself to be ambushed by Disciples on the East-side of town which sealed our fate. After resisting all attempts of joining any gang, we had finally given in; unlike Chunky a year earlier going through the windmill, we would be initiated in a special ceremony. Two people were coming in from Chicago just for this ceremony. They were two ruthless, murderous and zealous G's who went by the names of K. D. and L. H. and founded the tribe itself. Not knowing who they were, or what this was all about, we acted as if we were down with whatever, but that was far from the truth; in fact, we felt paranoid at how much danger we were putting ourselves in after every meeting. We knew within our hearts that those around us wanted us dead, and that sooner or later they would most definitely make their move!

We built our persona upon the perception of wannabe professional thieves, so as not to give the impression of murderers ready to join their cause. We were not trying to become killers like those mentioned above. Yet from the expectations of tyrants, we were just the type of niggas they needed!

Our future roles in the world of thuggery would be a great big part of our planned down fall from our newly found friends. We were in total fear for our lives one hundred percent of the time, but never again would have so much fun falling into a deadly trap. I'll never forget the look of uncertainty of life fall over the eyes of Glenn's face when Gino pulled out a thirty eight snub- nose and held it to his head pulling back the trigger, and said to us all, "Let's go on a little walk homies!" They took us to a park outside the city limits as we tried to not show any fear and not think ourselves captives. We stayed quiet walking through the hood, yet very observant. Well, I'm only speaking for myself, but the others showed their concerns now and then as we walked. I watched everything taking place on that little adventure, and remember to this day the look of the park at sunset as we approached its outer rim. When ordered to stand some great distance apart from the rest of our crew, I stayed vigilant in watching the two men of which we knew nothing! I was like a hawk watching their every move as the two talked with Gino and Top Dog.

Observing their every move was my only option of trying to get out of the situation, and it paid off in the end with flying colors. Seeing them empty the clip out of a nine millimeter, and place the empty clip back into the chamber proved valuable, as one of the strange men handed the gun back into Gino's possession.

Knowing their intended deception, I quickly calmed my nerves, saying to myself "…there's no bullets in that gun, and if they passed the gun around for us to pull the trigger on each other, I'd pass their test with flying colors!" Glenn and Keith behaved as if they had no clue of what was transpiring before them; knowing something was up, they indulged themselves in the weed and beer, which was provided by the two unknown men. Knowing their intent, I informed my comrades of their motives for bringing us to a remote park, telling them they were going to try and test our resolve by threat of death by pulling the trigger of a gun in an attempt to see our willingness to kill our fellow man by starting with each other. Top Dog walked up to Keith, giving him the 9mm, while Gino held a 38 to his head. Then the man named K. D. ordered him to shoot Glenn, shocking the very core of Keith's being. Dropping the gun, Keith began violently shaking at the thought of killing his best friend, thus causing him to fall to his knees, crying out for mercy, and was unable to stand after being threatened by gunpoint.

Keith showed them his spirit. Severely ridiculed and made fun of, Keith whimpered away down the hill on which we stood. The two men called Keith back up the hill, and then passed the weapon to me in the same fashion. He brandished the 38 to my head, and ordered me to pull the trigger, this time on Keith, to see if I would respond in the same manner in which Keith did. However, they only saw me point the gun and pull the trigger as soon as they placed the gun in my hand.

A look of utter shock came over the men testing our resolve with loaded weapons, resulting in their halting of further tests. They discussed what they observed among themselves, and like deer mesmerized by the high beams of an oncoming 18 wheeler, Glenn and Keith just stood there in total shock at my behavior as well, and after a few minutes of pondering around, Gino called me to where they all stood, and the man called K. D. said to me, "You saw me, didn't you? You saw me take the bullets out of the clip didn't you? You saw me?!" "Yes I saw you!" "Observant, that's good."

They sent me back over the hill with Glenn and Keith, who were both obviously anxious to know what was said to me. They constantly asked me what was said, and in fear, they spoke under their breath, so those on the other side of the hill couldn't hear what was spoken between us. Not knowing what we were in store for next, we prepared ourselves for whatever may befall us. To our surprise, Top Dog informed us it was over, and that we had passed the test saying, "If only one pulled the trigger, then you all passed the test! All wanted to see one of the so-called young niggas have balls, and better yet, have brains." Gino walked over to us and said, "Get on your right knee and kneel your head down... all three of you!"

We quickly complied with the orders, and as soon as we kneeled on our right knees, the man with the name L. H. began to speak, using words we didn't understand. Words that seemed to have wisdom in their yoke. Yet he spoke words that made little sense to us, to those with little worldly knowledge or experience. Like the illusions seen on television, we gladly embraced the royal knight like ritual, a ritual in which we were now partaking. We embraced the ideology of a Luciferian occult of madness without fully understanding its meaning, or its ramifications in our lives from that day forward. The accepted terms demanded of us were nothing short of life and death servitude. The implications of our vowels had no meaning to us at that time, but we agreed to dedicate our love, life and knowledge forevermore to the Nation. In addition, we also agreed to implement "Triple M" in all walks of our lives. As we stood up from our right knee, and listened to their proclamations, we fully agreed to adopt the tyrannical nature of the vile. Every one of us became a real life BGD. We finished the ceremony respectfully, embracing the three men as they gave us their blessings by symbolically drawing an invisible symbol of a "G" on our backs, with both hands telling each of us with reverence, "You are now foot soldiers in the Black Gangster Disciple Nation." The prideful feeling of having some imaginary street power or credit felt great and having ambitious thoughts of fame and position was even more seductive. Being associated with a group of hard core niggas had its benefits such as: lording over one's fellow man, being feared in a world of evil, and using our gang status as ghetto currency throughout the hood. But within a week of child's play, the real truth of the matter revealed itself.

The time had come of paying weekly dues, attending meetings, and learning the signs and symbols of ruthless thugs and killers. Learning the language of the gang was a must, for it meant your life if you got it wrong. Making mistakes in the gang's cryptic greetings, or coming up short of dues on a weekly basis may result in being penalized or shot. The level of anxiety was off the scales! Fear of the group itself truly outweighed the benefits. After rethinking our obvious miscalculation, Glenn, Keith and I decided to lay low from Top Dog and Gino for a while, but like hound dogs, they followed our every step, and they knew our every movement by getting regular reports from others of our whereabouts, so they always knew of our presence or absence. Because of this massive surveillance, it was becoming obviously clear to us that our so-called new found family was out to kill us. Now comes the art of the ghetto setup my friends! But let me be fair in my analysis of the situation. I really couldn't say it was a setup, but was more like a stupid trap, and even though I had my suspicions for quite some time after that fateful night, I couldn't figure out how or when they would make their move on us all, meaning "The Band of Three."

Trusting and unaware of the concept of strategic deception and maneuvers, we fell directly into their trap like defenseless rabbits hopping through the forest without a clue and ignorant to elaborate schemes, and or political espionage in wait. Glenn, Keith and I truly were products of our environment, with no worldly aspirations, and unaware of how things were accomplished in the world of ghetto politics. My crew of three was no longer a band of misfit thieves, for we were Folks now! With no animosity towards those that meant us harm, we became acquainted with the number one enemy of all the niggas around Eleventh Avenue, the Bullets, thus giving up our free pass through the Bullet's hood without even knowing it. Still thinking we were relatively safe, we gathered at Dollar Bill's house for a short game of ally basketball, and decided to ante up on a dime bag and a fifth of "MD 20/20" instead of the "Big Jug."

Finally, when we caught up with Dollar Bill and Don Juan, we headed towards the "Border" where we would meet an unknown weed man Don Juan knew, supposedly known to carry "Columbian Gold," the finest bud in town. Confident we would be safe walking through Vice Lord territory with well-known native residents such as Don Juan and Dollar Bill, we lacked our natural instinct to watch our backs, and followed the two throughout the neighborhood, thinking no one would fuck with us without suffering the wrath of the Bullets. We assumed no harm would befall us, with Don Juan in the lead of our unruly party. We followed his trail without concern or thought of treachery, and were oblivious to the location in which he was directing us in the darkness of the night. Taking shortcut after shortcut, suspicions of foul play crept into my thoughts concerning Don Juan's motives for taking us off the beat and trail. Sure enough, we found ourselves walking into a well thought out trap awaiting us on the other side of the outcropping of trees. Beyond the trees, we walked directly into a swarm of viperous Vice Lords, also known as "Reds," numbering about ten or twenty, thus all of our drinking and smoking bud stopped instantaneously. "What up Juan?!" One red yelled out to his comrade, capturing the attention of the rest of the reds, as they crept toward us. Obviously on a first name basis with Juan and Bill, they embraced them friendly, with the familiar back wrap hugs and handshakes.

But for the rest of the party, ominous looks and loc'ed up postures was our greeting. Barely acquainted with most of the Dragon Den, we stayed our distance in the background. We only knew them by reputation, although I recognized one in the misty night by the name Bishop, who was the son of one of my father's thuggish friends. He was a stupid gun-toting psychopath that bullied anyone smaller or poorer than he. Bishop looked me straight in the eye then he said, "Oh, shit! Folks and Peoples together tonight Yawl!" In his gangsta stance, he started to walk toward us, sipping on a thirty two ounce of Budweiser saying, "Folks and Peoples," which stirred up their unholy group like a hornet's nest, provoking a confrontation between them and us, which was poorly out-manned, outnumbered and unarmed. We truly were in a shitty fix!

The entire Dragon Den gradually walked past Dollar Bill and Don Juan, surrounding myself, Glenn and Keith with dubious intent. Juan spoke out saying, "They don't have no weapons Peoples! They don't have shit on them! We just looking for some weed, so hook us up peeps?!" We were not packing any weapons, so they gave us a pass on gun fire, but nothing else; we were fucked! Disregarding Juan's plea for amnesty, they slowly moved closer to "The Band of Three" with mean mugging, and the intent of physical assault on all three of the outsiders. They caught Glenn off guard and pushed him to the ground, when others in the group arose to his defense by stating, "He's a resident in the hood... leave him alone," but this still left Keith and I as targets in their eyes. Having very little courage, Keith sieged the opportunity to grovel in the face of a certain ass whipping, leaving only me as the focus of their rival grudge and excuse for retribution.

They fully encircled me as one physically motioned to another to get on his knees in back of me, as I faced a foe in front, so as to have the asshole in front of me, push me over the one leaning down in back of me. Seeing their every ill-inventive move, I turned and clipped the moron leaning in back of me over with my left foot, and dropped the fool behind me to the ground. Once more, the fool in front of me tried to push me over his comrade again, still unsuccessful, with the sound of shameful laughter echoing in their wake, resulting in the crowd of Vice Lords ridiculing their own home boy's efforts which conveniently granted an opening in the circle and provided me a way out, so I took it in haste. Clearly their intent was not to harm any of us out right. They just wanted to instill fear into their rival crews, and flex some psychological muscles on a Friday night. Not taking any chances, I saw my way out and ran for the exit in the storm. I ran to the nearby Norton Middle School and nearby adjacent park, holding up there while the rest of my confederate dumb-asses made their way back towards the safety of Dollar Bill's crib. I concealed my whereabouts while lurking behind the trees.

As my terrified crew got closer to the park, I could hear the fellas voicing their concerns over my rapid departure saying, "I know they didn't punk out P…. that nigga ain't scared of shit!" "Man that nigga ran for the hills!" "No! I know that nigga man; I'm telling you, that nigga still around somewhere!" And as soon as Dollar Bill spoke his last words, I yelled out, "HOOVERRR," thus shocking the naysayers, and reinforcing Glenn and Keith's faith and integrity in my willingness to stand my ground even in the midst of great odds. To my surprise, someone decided to report the encounter to the then acting first seat, Top Dog. Glenn Keith and I met up with Top Dog bright and early the following morning. We thought we'd hype up the encounter for brownie points, but instead, Top Dog was fully aware of the incident and was ready to utilize the event for his own gain. Top Dog called for a mandatory regional powwow the next day. Norton Middle School Park was packed with Disciples shipped in from Chicago and elsewhere, and to be perfectly truthful, I really didn't care, nor consider the significance of their overwhelming and ominous presence in the park.

The look of great concern gripping each and every last one of them caught my attention, and sparked my fight-or-flight senses, not to mention the arrival of my girlfriend, in the midst of tension, who by the way was supposed to be in Lansing, Michigan. Her unexpected arrival took precedent as I saw her walking towards the middle of the park amongst the multitude of hooligans, looking for yours truly. My nerves shook as countless numbers of niggas headed straight towards her with dubious attention. As the Chicago Zombies began to accost her, I called out her name catching her attention, with Top Dog and Gino by my side. The rest of the niggas stopped their assault and held back their advances which gave me and Naomi free passage out of the area. I quickly made up an elaborate excuse to depart the so-called mandatory meeting with my naïve girlfriend, and took my leave from the area without a grievance; therefore, we both made ourselves scarce by taking an alternate path across the railroad tracks towards Seventeenth Avenue and grandma's house. While looking back, I caught a glimpse of Glenn and Keith in quick pursuit as they caught up with Naomi and me without the attention of the others. My two comrades voiced their concern of what was witnessed back at the park and said, "…there is no way all them niggas came here because of what happened the previous night, or did they?!"

Because I didn't want Naomi to know about the dangerous shit we inadvertently got ourselves in, I signaled Glenn and Keith to stay quiet around her as she inquired about the war party posted within the park. Even though she was concerned to see a sea of niggas in blue with blue dew-rags on their heads in Norton Park, her fears heightened when they threw up their gang signs towards all bystanders in Vice Lord territory. Something was afoot, yet we were clueless to the significance of such a gathering, and still unsure of what part we three played in their arrival. Since I was totally shocked to see my girl in the midst of evil, I grew afraid for our safety and made sure we all disappeared from the area. Happy to see her back in Gary, I proudly introduced her to my grandmother and excused Keith and Glenn from our presence. Naomi and I spent the rest of the night talking about the changes taking place while she was away. Unwilling to walk back towards Eleventh Avenue after dark, I informed my grandmother of the looming seeds of violence being planted in Norton's Park.

I was able to convince grandma of the danger that was about to be unleashed upon the streets of Gary, Indiana, amongst the countless other hazards that dwelled around us, and begged Grandma to allow Naomi to stay the night. The obvious declaration of war that took place in Norton Park put us all on edge. During the next meeting, Top Dog cranked up the pressure and ordered everyone to pay weekly dues, and ascertain as many firearms as we could and as fast as possible, or all would pay a great retribution.

It was as if the dark cloud that formed over my family engulfed the entire city and never subsided.

Rivers of chocolate flesh poured into Gary, Indiana; residents and individuals alike never saw such a horde of unruly gangstas popping up from Chicago, Hammond, Indiana and the surrounding areas. A spirit of dread covered the entire city of Gary, Indiana. All gangsters and gangster wannabes were on point guard fear and were somewhat up and arms. All were hypnotized by unseen evil forces, and captivated by the music of the day.

All were mesmerized by the notion of fast money that was provided by government funded mercenaries. Rival gangs quickly began their draft of Gary's youth and accumulated an army of underage automatons that were absorbing all their political and social street rhetoric. This turned the two gangs against each other even more so since big money was at stake. No matter what beef the factions overcame in the past, none would overcome the plague of dirty money, and the possibility of large sums of riches. All lost soldiers rallied to the call of fast money and were ready for whatever fantasy that protruded from the promise of great wealth. The mist of the Genie's spell gripped the populous. Hoping for a future, any future, the hopeless readied themselves to come up by any means necessary.

They embraced the logic of the new money making scheme while never really knowing they were condemning themselves for destruction. A lucrative scheme derived from hell on bliss took them all captive. Conceived in hell's bondage, many youth fell victim to its gleam, yet were never fearful of the consequences and welcomed the oncoming blizzard of drug addiction. It was a snow storm in the form of ten dollar rocks, rocks of cooked poison by the name of Crack Cocaine blanketed the Midwest with all rival gangs fighting for control of its distribution throughout the city. The new wave of drug use sieged the city

EDGAR FRENCH, JR.

like an anvil, leaving a wake of destruction amongst all, for the enemy of life left his mark alongside innocent youth and old alike. Young souls who never reached adulthood was becoming the norm. With cold and calculating precision, those that lorded over the army of youth led them all towards the grim alter of destruction, willingly. Oblivious to the obvious upcoming damnation, we slipped deeper into the belly of the beast. Hungry for a taste of the American dream, with no knowledge or concept of the blessings of high morals nor righteousness, most gravitated towards the offering upon the bloody alter of darkness and sought pleasure and escape from life's daily horrors that afflicted us all. Most were willing to partake from the forbidden fruit in any form available, and living in poverty only made the dollar's glare shine brighter. There was no more war over turf in the hood, for now it became a war over wealth and means and it consumed the masses.

The game of life had changed overnight, from rival street punks brawling over curbs and corners, to money hungry animals which turned into murderous modern thugs in the vein of true thugs of old. Daily tribal squabbles erupted into full blown murderous wars over drug turf, from gang leaders to warlords and oppressors of their own people in triplicate, all over the devil's pharamacia. They fought over territory that belong to them not!

Insanely covetous over all Crack turf that consumed every square inch of the Chocolate City, illegal Street Pharmacia roamed unchecked and unchallenged throughout the hood, and it was deadly!

Yet no one told us about the misery that was about to descend upon all who lived within the inner cities. Glenn, Keith and I had no clue of the danger and the seriousness the change would bring. The nature of drug play would impose a heavy weight upon all who were close to its agents of death. The three of us had not a clue of the connection between the drug game, and the ever increasing violence that was taking place around us. Stupidity was the least of our troubles, for death was creeping with ease and ever so closer. Within every impoverished inner city neighborhood, the same violence was on the march, and we had no clue! Death from within was the order of the day, and if you were a young black male surviving in the concrete jungle, no matter your social status, you were trapped by poverty and violence within the hood. There was no escape or door of opportunity in your cards, only despair filled your lonely days and we "nobody's" had no idea of how to handle our plight. Hopelessness reigned freely. It seemed as if the Earthly powers that be, the gods above, along with the Creator himself, had it in for all living in poverty and dread.

"What is this hell?!" was the question I posed to myself daily, and as the level of danger steadily increased, sales of the cheap wonder drug increased nightly, alongside the death toll! Overdose death raised like lines on a chartable—parabolic, so we walked through certain neighborhoods that had always been somewhat dangerous, but now they were downright deadly, 24/7. Instead of weekly periodic gun fire, daily shots rang out frequently and more severely which resulted in death most nights. Walking the streets in daylight was almost impossible for me and my crew of three misfits. Glenn, Keith and I made ourselves scarce to those we stupidly befriended, and even more so, to the very gang we so naïvely swore allegiance.

Eluding all thugs became an art form, so we held up in spots not known to most hoodlums. We dealt in weed to feed our addictions instead of falling victim to the lure of assured super-fast money by making crack rocks, in which everyone else indulged. We relatively stayed off the radar in the dope game, at least as far as the many dealers connected to heroin (heron) and the new wonder drug called Crack. As for Chunky and his crew, it was no holds barred, for they were absolutely mad! They stole or robbed from whomever caught their fancy, the innocent and dope dealer alike.

They instilled fear in the hearts of all who crossed their path. The truly lost souls of the hood loved him just from his gruesome presence, and since his girlfriend was just as wild as he, they made a name for themselves throughout the hood called the "Ruthless Pair." The wayward woman, Wilma, would later become his wife. Ironically, I found that Wilma was my girl's best friend; therefore, news of most of their activities would eventually reach my ear.

Knowing I was the only person on god's green Earth that Chunky would accept reason and wise counsel, the girls looked for me to confront him about his activities, and warn him of the danger factor before someone got hurt or died because of his carelessness. Coupled with his crew's reckless antics, it didn't take much to catch the scent of his whereabouts. Within two days of hunting him down around town, I found him in the heart of the jungle, swimming with straight- up sharks. He was with a family of master thieves and cut throats known throughout Gary and East Chicago as the Santana Family. The Santanas were known for strong armed robbery among other things, and didn't give a shit who they stole from, dope dealer or civilian alike and if you were caught in their web, you were done. Rough and rugged they were! If you were in possession of something they coveted, you were stuck! You might as well have put it in a box and wrapped it up with a bow on top because sooner or later, they would have obtained your shit, no joke! While walking into the den of vipers where Chunky resided, I showed no fear.

Since Chunky hadn't seen me in a long time, he greeted me with great joy and introduced me to all his terrifying new cohorts within the Santana family. While proudly showing off his great booty of stolen wealth and conquest, he revealed the beautiful Maria Santana, rendering me speechless from her symmetrical loveliness which nearly erased the thought of my initial visit of woe. Gaining clarity in my thoughts, I voiced the concerns of those that loved him, and respectfully asked him to limit his activities, so as not to invoke the wrath and retribution of those wronged. Once hearing our concerns about his behavior, his anger erupted violently, stating his own corrosive emotional feelings of a lack of family loyalty. Concern for his wellbeing, we expressed in unison the concerns exhibited by all in our own family, not excluding my mother and self. No words conveyed could soften his stance, rather he voiced his admiration and gratitude towards the Santanas and their unwavering support of his activities, and declared the Santanas his real family. He clarified his devotional feelings about his new found immediate family with joy in his heart and cared nothing about the troubles brought upon us because of his thuggish thievery and harmful actions. Chunky did not care about his criminal activity and shady dealings or what hazardous effects may befall those that loved him, namely myself, Naomi and Wilma.

He reluctantly calmed himself down for the Santanas and acted as if he had no part in the obvious backlash accumulating on his so-called girlfriend and family members, namely me. Since I was unsuccessful in having him cease his horrific activities, I quickly departed from the notorious border and the cesspool that Chunky now called his home. Days passed and unavoidable trouble seeped its way into every facet of my life. Naomi's mom, Mary, was going through some kind of mid-life crisis and would scream and yell day and night while falling over in a drunken state. Be it trouble devised of her accord, or thrust upon her by the presence of so many wicked spirits consuming the very air she breathed, the constant criminal presence made her withdrawal from all living within her house.

Since Naomi's mother was constantly drunk, living there was shaky at best. The fact that her daughter was never going to leave her first true love, a scalawag, made the fear for her daughter's safety uncontrollable, for she had very little success making her daughter stay closer to home as the city crumbled in the midst of fires and flames. The death toll raised in the city, making life uncertain for all that resided in it. I don't know the number of those I knew personally that fell to the wayside, especially as the number of young teens dropping like flies escalated. With yours truly being deep into the under belly of the city, made Mary crazy mad with dumbfounded worry. My involvement in gang activity probably raised her fear factor up one hundred fold. Popping caps and getting shot at daily was the norm. The flow of drugs infecting the population, and the fight to control distribution, made most of the city a war zone!

The fact of the matter is the world in which we lived was not safe for anyone. To walk the streets in the light of day was like Dracula exposed to sunlight, for it was literally a death warrant for myself and Naomi! The fear of losing her only and first born daughter to gang violence made Mary's crib a safe haven for us all. So I found myself back on Fourth Avenue during the daylight hours, no doubt creating extra strain on Naomi and Mary's relationship, not to mention the increase of traffic coming in and out of her front door. Since Mary's house was a safe zone for me, Glenn and Keith found their way there nearly every night. The environment at Mary's mirrored the Wild Wild West. Never ending cocaine parties, drinking brawls, and police raids made the excitement level unmeasurable. My boys came through only after midnight, or early morning. Traffic at Mary's never stopped. Soon Naomi and I found ourselves making out in abandon buildings in route from grandmas to Mary's house, in search of alone time and solitude from evil.

It was my turn to find out how the old saying, "God works in mysterious ways" would prove true.

Empty pockets lead to empty cupboards and growling stomachs and triggered the already fine-tuned survival mechanisms within us all in the ghetto.

So when I brought in food from McDonald's garbage cans, no questions were asked. Having hope for a brighter future was a luxury no one could afford to hold dear and if stealing, robbing or selling dope kept food on the table and Naomi's little brother's belly full, so be it!

The deed was done! I didn't care what anyone said or thought of my actions, for a lack of food and no hope truly diminishes the ability to sympathize with the plight of any other soul. Suspending the ability to have a conscious in the act of feeding those you care for comes easy, and guilt does not come into play; "by any means necessary" fuels the thoughts of larceny and feeds the lack of care. So when things got tight and stomachs were growling, my crew and I hit the streets to relieve our hunger.

The air was electrified with the anticipation of the mega pop star, Prince, coming to the "Genesis Center" within the small little X steel-mill community. The big Prince 1999 concert proved to be one of those nights. Equipped with the tools of the trade, we set out to score for the home team after sneaking into the concert and catching the first act and getting fucked up off the last of the weed and drank. We headed out towards Broadway ready to stickup any unsuspecting sucker coming or going to the concert. Striking out twice with cops on our heels, we dashed through back ways and allies, leaving the cops in the dust with no intention of giving up so easily. Since it was still early in the night, we stayed on the prowl and with very little prospects out and about, we ended up snatching some old lady's purse coming out of a Walgreens.

The harsh truth of poverty runs deep in the heart of child and man, and to be able to see the world at large can be too great in scope to comprehend. But if hope remains, the universe opens up the possibilities of the unseen and unknown. Who would ever think that hardship in life truly builds character in one's self, no matter the station in life, or creed in which one is born? We humans are remarkable beings! Only those that wish for us not to know that fact seem to be the ones seeking power. We, common men, need to take on the reigns of power, though we yearn for it not! It is because of that fact that makes it our duty to seek power over ourselves, rather than to allow evil men to gladly lord over us! The spirit of man must be cultivated in times of darkness such as these, but we don't understand the obvious: all information is second hand information! Children of the book must understand that fact! To trust in men is to trust in an Un-wholly Book! For wholly is the trick and play on words, for holes consume the ancient text, and the book is full of "holes." If you were not there, you cannot say whether it's true or not! That's called Common Sense! To all Children of Light, truth lies in the ancient books of old, yet so does confusing treacherous lies! The very men that want us dead, control the printing press in perpetuity! Prophesy would be changed, and those that do not want us to change our fate of destruction use the books of ancient tales to enslave and divide their fellow man. With demons in the ether of this third dimension whispering spells of destruction in the wind is to rely on ancient text in whole and condemn oneself to everlasting death. The very institution of religion is the trap that enslaves men of light, and was given to earthly women by the Two Hundred Fallen Ones of Mount Hermon, who bore children to those women. To believe in a book is to put faith in men! Yeshua warned against that very thing, so let the Ten Commandments be your guide to life everlasting and bring truth about our origins in the universe! For the word of god is not sixty six books written by princes and principalities. One's better off searching ancient text with discernment than having blind belief in the written words of dead men.

CHAPTER XVIII
The Black Cat

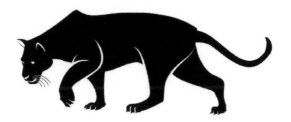

With barely two bucks in the combined pockets of all three degenerate starving thugs in training amongst the ice under the winter's snow, the anticipation of cracking open the only prize of the night was great. Hoping the stranger's purse would render just compensation in the risk taken to obtain such a meager booty, we wondered if the risk was worth the pursuit and harm of another in such a childish and cowardly act as our stomachs' growled while fleeing the scene. While running damn near a half a mile to make sure we were clear from anyone that may be in pursuit, we took our rest underneath a corner lamp. After looking around and making certain no one was on our heels, we stopped to examine the grim and meager catch, but only found a purse full of useless makeup, paper-clips, gum, and a book of food stamps, with five one dollar bills in total, but were somewhat disappointed in the take. We ran uncontrollably and unaware how far, and found ourselves around Thirteenth and Washington. We slowed our roll and began watching out for hostiles that might be lurking about in the night. Seeing the coast was clear, we started our trek back uptown to safety. We could feel an ominous presence behind us as we calmly walked, well I could. Keith and Glenn were too pissed off over the fruitless venture to notice anything lurking in the wind. Constantly looking back, I caught a glimpse of something moving between the parked cars on the dimly lit streets, saying to my comrades, "Hold up! You see that?!" "See what?!" "Man I swear I saw something." "This fool tripping"

was Glenn's response. I firmly stated, "Man I'm telling you, I saw something!"

Just as I uttered those fateful words of something in the midst, something slowly emerged in back of a poorly parked car. It was a glimmering Black Cat, but like no cat ever seen in the hood or ever before in our lives. Only stray dogs roam free on the streets of Gary, Indiana alongside pimps and pushers. This cat was huge! He stood about four and a half feet off the ground as the snow flowed off his jet black fur. The marvelous beast made no sound as it walked upon the cold asphalt city street. He was black and strong in stature, yet made no sound as he walked from around the parked car. Ever so quiet and graceful were his steps, and ominous in beastly stature was his stance. He invoked pure fear with his presence which caused my cohorts to flee in panic from a single glimpse. But yet I had no fear of the great beast and began walking towards the great cat with intrigue.

With admiration, I glared at the Great Black Cat and looked directly in its eyes. I non-verbally stated my youthful curiosity and friendly intent which caused the hairs on my arms to stand on end when the beast responded in jest. Locking eyes, we walked towards one another. The ominous Great beast and I!

With no fear, I walked directly towards the majestic beast with the glare of the city's street lights coalescing with the shine of the Black Cat's fur. It was such a dark shade of black that it almost looked purple, and as I walked ever so closely, something within me spoke saying, "Come no closer... show respect!" Without saying a word, I responded with humility from deep within my soul. I humbly stood still and the cat made its way towards me; with my eyes fixed on the eyes of the beast, it was as if the cat and I could communicate without verbal queues. Without saying a word, I asked if I could touch his beautiful fur. While walking closer to me, he answered, "Yes" by coming over to me and rubbing his fur on my leg. Looking back after panicking and running off, Glenn and Keith looked with amazement as I befriended the great cat without fear. Seeing no harm come to me as I stroked the back of the Great Black Cat, they began walking back towards our direction, and with their mouths wide open in amazement over the size of the Great Beast, Glenn and Keith slowly drew closer to the beast and me as I softly uttered a word of caution in the wind, "...show no fear or he will attack you both" while I continued to rub the beast with honor and humble pride.

Seeing the obvious un-natural nature of the beast, Glenn and Keith stayed their respective distance with monumental woe in their hearts. Wearing their fears on their sleeves so obviously, they crept closer to the great beast and myself with astonishment. At first sight of the great cat, they were amazed at how high off the ground the black cat stood. They wondered if it was a panther or some kind of puma that may have escaped from the "Brookfield Zoo" and if so, how could I stroke the wild animal without getting mulled or even torn to pieces by its massive claws? My friends were clearly in a state of shock as I stroked and spoke to the great black cat. They crept closer and closer to the cat and me which calmed their spirits and soothed their emotional state as they both caught a glimpse of the close proximity in which I stood next to the black cat without fear.

Rubbing its feather fine black fur had them saying over and over aloud, "I can't believe it?!" They were puzzled as to where this fine animal was from, and also feared for my safety since I was so close to the awe-inspiring Beast.

I explained feverishly to my wayward accomplices in crime a well-known fact to most men that once lived in the wild, and a well-known fact known to myself as well: "All wild beasts of the field, and small animals of the woods can always smell fear, and if you show no fear, they in turn, have no reason to fear you unless they are hungry and you're on the menu!"

After some time, they began to remove their cloak of fear and even attempted to stroke the cat themselves which gave them a remarkable sense of accomplishment. In awestruck amazement with eyes filled with grandeur, we walked down the dimly lit deadly street with a wondrous Great Beast by our side to protect us from the unseen things of horror concealed in the night.

I walked in the middle of the Boulevard side by side with the great Black Beast as Glenn and Keith became ever more comfortable in his presence. Glenn and Keith crept a little closer as we all walked inside the Black Cat's orbit with caution, and as they got closer, they continued to shed any remaining fears of being devoured by the awesome beast. Nervously, all three of us stroked the backside of The Great Black Cat. Unfortunately, the overwhelming urge for drugs crept into our minds, and just like Beavis and Butthead, we all began fe'nen for more drugs and alcohol, in which we unwittingly had become accustomed or addicted. With Pharmacia growing ever so heavily in our minds, Keith and Glenn's arrested and addicted thoughts allowed stupid ideas of thinking themselves clever which began planting dangerous plots amongst their juvenile reasoning. They pondered the notion of exploiting the awesome power of the great cat and since we were close to the Herod brother's encampment, which was guarded by three ruthless and deadly ghetto dog fight promoters who jumped at every chance of testing their dog's furious hunger, we decided to take in the Great Black Cat. With boastful pride, the Herod brothers promoted their terrifying pet pit bulls, Satan and Sinbad, and they were dog fighting champions in the eyes of their masters.

In the time it takes to blink an eye, Glenn and Keith came up with a so-called great scheme to make some quick cash that very night. The Herod family was known around the city for their bloody and gruesome dog fights and took pride in their two full blooded and ferocious pit bulls, bragging daily of their merciless exploits and deeds of barbarism by leaving stray homeless dogs clawed, and half mauled to death. They claimed that their dogs could beat any and all on comers! With no hesitation, I agreed to go along with my comrades little scheme, knowing deep within myself that the great cat had no equal and would prevail over the two blood thirsty pets with ease. Yet a feeling of despair fell over me as we all walked closer to our so-called profitable destination. The familiar unseen voice of my god-given conscience grew stronger from within saying: "NO! This is not just a cat. It is my cat! And he is GREAT!" Even with the warning of the voice of doubt burning within me to stop this madness, I still gave into peer pressure and continued forth.

Was my voiceless caution enough to quell this childish conundrum of which I found myself? The answer was no because now I was deeply involved in the planning. Yet courage prevailed and I said to myself, "YES I can stop this!"

So I tried to talk my two partners in crime out of the plan, proclaiming how crazy the Herod brothers were, and stating their eagerness to brandish weapons of destruction without any thought of reprisal. However, they were set on showing off the great beast and anticipated seeing the cat in battle and so was I. Therefore, my infantile protest carried very little weight or reason in lieu of the fact that we all were fascinated with the mysterious and majestic beast we had come across on the lonely ghetto streets of Gary, Indiana.

With the sullen stride of the awesome beast, we all walked side by side through an ominous narrow pathway between two buildings leading towards the back ally to the Herod's encampment. Seen from afar, atop some long and flimsy stairs, lay the two fence like structures that kept their ferocious dogs. Two killer dogs in two interlocking caged pens became more horrifying as their visual outline magnified as we approached the upper stairs. High on the sixth floor of the rundown slumlord building, in which the Herod's resided, we walked up the stairs with courage. As we headed towards the dreaded den of death, something came over me bringing fear as its partner. The cautious voice said, "No" once more! With weakness in my knees, and dizziness of thought slowing my ascension up the staircase, I uttered to my friends, "Somethings wrong, very wrong!" What we were about to propose was nothing less than sinful and deadly.

As I looked at the great beast with nervousness in my eyes, I nonverbally conveyed my concern for its wellbeing as we went further up the stairs. Looking me directly in my eyes, I could ascertain that The Great Black Cat understood my conveyance, yet he still walked ever so calmly up the creepy staircase. As we approached the final steps leading towards the pathway of the massive two pens, the deadly pits began to growl, and as we moved slowly passed the padlock gates of their pens, true fear entered the fray.

Keith and Glenn were in the lead, as the black cat and I stayed in the shadows. As we knocked on the door, the dogs barked feverishly, scaring the shit out of us all, except the majestic cat. Always paranoid of the unknown, the oldest brother answered the door, just as soon as Keith knocked once. All I heard from the other side of the door was, "Motha Fucka what the fuck you won't?!" Keith responded, "A Mane, we want to fight them dogs you got nigga… we got us a bad-ass cat that could fuck yo punk-ass dogs up out here niggas!" As the younger brother slowly opened the front door, Keith asked the older brother, "You ever seen anything like this?! How much you willing to pay to get yo dogs killed nigga?!"

Keith spoke with great boldness because we knew Sinbad couldn't hang, nor could his other dog, Satan! Keith stood his ground as the younger brother smoothly crept up behind the older, and pulled out their 45 Magnums. Both pointed their weapons at Keith's head, cocked back the triggers and grinned saying in unison, "Bitch, ain't no cat alive can fuck with our dogs NIGGA!" The brothers spoke with courage since they had yet to see the magnificent specimen concealed within the night's shadow, cloaked behind Keith and Glenn, not three steps down the staircase.

Glenn and Keith parted ways, and in doing so they revealed the great beast standing at my side immersed in majesty. With nothing said from all standing in the night's light, a look of disbelief descended across the killers of animals. There are no words to describe the look on the brothers' faces when they caught a glimpse of the extraordinary feline hunter. Standing in amazement, the brothers' facial expressions bordered on utter shock, for never have they seen such a grand animal outside captivity. Wiping clear his smug like demeanor, the older brother cautioned his younger siblings by saying one word, "DON'T!" His certain assuredness of victory quickly turned to utter skeptical doubt in a matter of mere seconds, causing him to stutter as we continued to bestow the virtues of our new found champion, ever so bragging without doubt of our specimen. But the younger brothers were still boastful and full of pride without ever seeing any ferocity or threating motion from the great beast, yet we were full of confidence in our most wonderful find. In fear of looking highly unreliable or credible at the least, and being very foolish, or to be more in the mood of things, as they would put it, fear of looking like Bitches in the presence of other thugs, criminals and monsters betting on the demise of helpless animals, they could not find it within themselves to respectfully decline, or talk their way out of a battle they were not sure they would emerge victoriously, especially after such a display of manliness and boast! With no concern or thought for the black cat's safety, Keith posed an offer the brothers could not refuse. Before their ordnance and crew were crawling like roaches in their presence, we, the motley crew, proposed a fight between the Great Beast and both Satan and Sinbad at the same time, closing all debates posed. This proposal opened the pathway towards what I called "The Thunder Dome!" The Thunder Dome was a place where many lost dogs found their fate amongst the truly heartless. As we all walked down the dark corridor leading to a single bedroom that I deemed the dome, strangers' eyes on both sides looked in disbelief as they glimpsed the huge size and majesty of the Black Cat that walked by my side. I looked down at the cat and asked myself why the hell I was leading this miraculous animal down a potential death march?! Shame was what I felt at that moment, and it was as if the cat heard my woe and aching heart because he looked up at me then left my side and entered into the room of blood covered walls. The majestic beast walked

EDGAR FRENCH, JR.

in circles within the en-closer with an ancient spirit of force and waited for whatever or whomever may enter. Having no fear residing within his majestic soul, he finally sat near the one and only window in the room and licked his shining black fur. Suddenly, a feeling of total clarity came over me. I knew why the cat was there. I knew why I had made its acquaintance in the night and had no fear of it, for just as we stalked and preyed on the innocent unaware victim to feed our drug addiction, so did the black cat stalk the not so innocent for his nightly feed, and we were his unintended prey. But as the climax of the battle between the great cat and the vicious dogs got closer, I truly saw the big picture behind our meeting. As I looked into its eyes as he sat serenely on the bedroom floor, I knew the great beast had changed its mind and spared us that night, and at that moment, I knew of the great beast's purpose in meeting three wayward souls in the cold winter night. A spirit of assuredness came over me, then suddenly a sensation of angst and anxiety flowed through my soul, and I feared for whomever, or whatever might have had the misfortune to walk into The Thunder Dome! Knowing that we were its food, and yet he let us go and walked with us, I said out loud, "They are going to kill us!"

Coming to my senses, I muffled my voice with my hands and said to Keith and Glenn: "That cat is going to kill those dogs; we got to stop this or it's our asses!" But it was too late, the inevitable was in motion, and the two domestic animals were about to meet the horrors of the wild up close and personal. Snapping, growling and biting at all that were standing in the corridor, Sinbad and Satan instilled fear into us all as the Herod's walked them down towards the room of doom. While holding them back from us with huge industrial strength chains, the dogs caught the scent of the cat and they lunged towards the bedroom door which made it very difficult to restrain either of the brutes from biting any or all in the hallway. With one last attempt to reason and warn the Herod's of their dogs' fate, my cries of certain death fell upon deaf ears. The Herod's placated the members of their crew and amused the crowd boastfully by waging one hundred bucks to any on-comers, but no one was willing to bet against Satan and Sinbad, once again confirming that no cat could withstand the fury of the two man- eating dogs. Sitting perfectly still under the lonely window pane, the majestic cat calmly licked his fury paws as the two man -eating dogs were let loose within the bedroom. Closing the door behind them, the older

Herod slowly left a small crack in the door, so as to view the dog's progress in their mission to destroy the black cat. Shockingly, the elder Herod yelled out, "Attack!"

But nothing was heard from the room, not even a bark; for the first time, the room was silent. Suddenly, sounds of whimpers protruded from behind the crack in the door. It was Sinbad then Satan. Both were trembling in fear with their tails tucked firmly between their legs as the majestic black cat slowly stood on all fours and raised his left paw. The cat ejected his massively sharp claws and displayed all five talons that were at least seven inches long while slowly scratching the hard wood floor with one of his deadly flesh ripping claws. Without hesitation, the elder Herod brother closed the door completely, then slowly, yet ever so slightly, opened the door once more, peaking through a small slit in the bedroom door, and then he slowly pulled his gun out. He cocked back the trigger and calmly said to all three of us, "If that monster lay one claw on my dogs, I'm killing all of you... Get that fuck'n cat out of here! NOW!" After hearing their brother's response to us, they all gathered close to the Thunder Dome for a peek of the spectacle.

First, the three Herod brothers attempted to enter the room so as to retrieve their precious man- eating dogs, but the cat stood between the door and the dogs, ultimately stopping anyone from progressing through the threshold of a well awaited meal. He guarded the door post with his presence then released one growl with heavenly force. All instantly froze in their prospective positions and were afraid to move! All were afraid to enter the room of certain doom. Everyone looked at each other in awe, motioning to one another to respond to the awesome power controlling the Herod's inner sanctum.

Franticly hoping for some resolution in the matter, I spoke up and said, "I'll go into the bedroom." Seeing the fantastic beast's massive claws and fearsome stance, I slowly walked into the room with no fear in my heart. Feeling the electricity in the atmosphere made the hairs on the back of my neck stand at attention. Was it courage or stupidity that made me walk inside that room without fear of attack from the Grand Black Cat? My thoughts spoke calmly within my mind and soul as I practiced saying, "I'm only here to release you," and I walked towards the window and opened it. All the while the great beast continued to hold its ground to all who might try to enter the room, and let no one enter except for me. As I slowly entered inside the Thunder Dome, I could see the two once mighty dog killers huddled in a corner adjacent to the door afraid to move with their tails firmly between their legs, shaking and whimpering like chickens ready for slaughter. I opened the window and turned to the great cat and respectfully gestured with my hands to the majestic cat and asked him to please take his leave.

Looking me in my eye, the great cat stood down from its boastful stance towards the dogs and jumped out the window onto the staircase a few meters across. The majestic being looked back at me one last time so as to say our goodbye's without any verbal queues. I instinctively followed the cat out the window as soon as he made his way out, and I could hear sighs of relief, coupled with venomous accusations of a setup and deceit within the ranks of the Herod's gaming circle who were unwilling to pay up on their bets. Relieved that the great beast departed the residence of the dog abusing brothers, they quickly attended to their shivering so-called ex-champion dog slayers, and unanimously focused their anger towards Glenn and Keith as they ran down the back staircase as fast as they could. I could hear yelling from one of the Herod brothers, "ATTACK! ATTACK! KILL! KILL!" While the other two Herod brothers screamed obscenities and threats of dismemberment hurled at my two airhead comrades cornered inside the Herod's den of terror. Powerless to help them, I could do nothing in their defense, other than praying to my god to intervene for the safety of my cornered comrades in crime as I looked for the great black cat that faded into the snowy night. Although they would emerge fully intact, having no intention of going back up the stairs, I could see all three brothers brandishing weapons at Keith and Glenn and ran them out of their home because they were still leery of encountering the awesome black cat.

The brothers looked out for any signs of the black cat, then commanded Satan and Sinbad on my two comrades as they franticly made their way down the back staircase. While Glenn and Keith scurried down the staircase with two man -eating dogs nibbling at their heels, I looked around for the great cat, but found not a trace nor hair of the great beast.

Just as the great majestic beast appeared, draped in the mystery of the night, it disappeared in such wondrous fashion. But before the night ended and the dawn graced us with its presence, I gained an abrupt sense of epiphany towards life itself. I had a new outlook and appreciation of all life, but most of all, I felt an eerie awareness of fate! "Would this be my fate in the future?! Am I destined to live as the Great Black Cat?! Alone?!" A fiery renewal of the spirit of exploration filled my soul, and a sense of purpose filled my very being. It was as if I could see the future to come with clarity and certainty. For we live in a time where humanity's existence is as short as the life span of a mayfly. As grim as life can be in captivity, not knowing the reason why we must live in such squalor, pestilence, poverty, sorrow and such fear where pain and death are expected to be content in life as such.

And in order to survive what was to come, I and all those close to me would have to make drastic changes in our outlook on life. I concluded that finding the answers for all the world's misery must be first in all endeavors. For the direction of life in which we were headed was no life at all! On top of the fever of exploration came out the ultimate meaning of why we were here on this planet, what it meant to be here, and what would be the cost to escape from such daily horrors. I thought to myself that the difficult journey would not be impossible, and I prayed to my Creator for hope. In solace I said, "It must be possible; it must be achievable." Yet being so young and having no way of weathering the oncoming storm, I pondered over the slim choices that afforded myself and those around me. I found myself praying to an unseen god for help and forgiveness for all my thuggish deeds. I was desperately searching for a way out of my plight and living conditions before I was badly hurt or murdered.

The following days were filled with anonymous messages of certain demise and death, not only for myself, but for all in our crew. With messages coming from friend and foe alike, we carefully walked the city streets only after midnight, armed with whatever weapon we could find. It was as if the entire city was out to get us, and with good reason I might add. Since we had created so many enemies throughout the town, our number of threats had to come up, not someday, but sooner than we thought. With gangster groups becoming more and more polarized throughout the city, other misfits found their way into our company, which brings to mind an innocent fool by the name of Zoe. Zoe was a headstrong gangsta wannabe fresh out of Job Corp and new to the mean streets of Gary, Indiana and Eleventh Ave. Being somewhat of a pretty boy component to our ragtag crew, he made enemies everywhere in the city quickly, and without notice nor care. Harassed and assaulted by Vice Lord bums, Zoe hooked up with Glenn for support one day after he was rescued from an assault by three crack heads outside of the Bullet's corner store. For all reasons considered, Zoe befriended us because of our neighborhood's hoes throwing too much attention his way.

Because other niggas were jealous of his good looks, he was forever fighting someone or some dumb-ass for no apparent reason, so he never departed our company and made his crib a main hideout in the hub of enemy territory. Little did I know that the invisible forces that interjected the appearance of the Great Black Cat into my life one wintry night was a foreshadow of what was to come and gave witness to what must take place in a blink of an eye, for my safety and freedom were to transpire without grace.

I speak of Zoe with overwhelming empathetic emotions of sorrow and regret, consumed with guilt and lack of serious conscience, for Zoe comes to mind when marking that last step towards ending much delight in delinquent child's play and youthful might. Those that would see us dead or dying every waking moment were filled with distain and hatred of our very presence within the city, for they truly seemed bent on our destruction. Their unrestrained cohorts were symbolically tightening the hangman's noose around our thuggish necks ever so assuredly, and we knew it! In search of a sense of wellbeing and relief of worry, we indulged ourselves even more so with massive amounts of alcohol and weed, bordering on poisoning ourselves. We tried to drown out numerous concerns over the oncoming deserved retribution with unbridled laughter and lack of thought. Reminiscing of good times and memories of old conquest, new victories seemed abound and created an air of false carelessness, only to awaken the lovely attribute of reason not! As the five of us restlessly sat around in Glenn's four by four square foot bedroom, we listened to "The Gap Band" on old cassette tapes dubbed off the radio, and when the song "Outstanding" queued up to play, an eerie silence blanketed Glenn's bedroom and shadowed our day.

Everyone stopped talking and we began bobbing our heads in sequence to the rhythmic tunes, for somehow we all knew the end of life was coming soon for each and every one of us. Therefore, when the song ended, I pressed the stop button and addressed my fellow peers who were in much distress. To captivate the audience of five, I made known the obvious thought process of us all saying in a solemn voice, "You know they gone a kill us all, right?!" "Yea we know" said Glenn, and with total silence, we passed the Big Jug and shed no tears. With very little ammunition, and three guns amongst the whole of us, we had no time at all before they would come to kill us all, so we pondered what to do. Keith responded, "I don't know P, we just got to suffer the consequences and bite the bullets man." "Fuck that!" Zoe replied. So we lay low for a while and stayed off the streets until they shot up Glenn's spot; then they shot up Zoe's. No one was hurt, just shaken up a bit. Those of us that wanted to act on the shootings went on reconnaissance and learned from a slew of evidence that not only our enemies were out to get us, but also were our so-called friends. Nowhere was safe, so I setup a meeting to address the problem. My first words at that first and only meeting were, "Don't retaliate…let the smoke clear and hope we survive to live another day." Responses such as: "Do What!

Don't retaliate, fuck that! Let somebody try some shit, I'm fuck'n them up!" Or "If we continue down this road we will surly die." Or "What do we do?!" I had to think quickly to calm the nerves of most in attendance.

Glenn said, "What do we do about this shit; we can't allow someone to shoot up our cribs man?" I responded; "I know." Keith asked, "So what then?" I said, "Well, I been seeing this shit escalate ever since we came across that Great Black Cat. I knew we had no way out of this shit… we were just in too much and too deep! I've been thinking about this shit since then and trying to figure a way out, but I can't see one!" At that moment the door opened; it was Glenn's mom ease-dropping. His mom heard our entire conversation, but she said nothing. She only looked around the room at each and every one of us. Then she slowly backed up out of the room and closed the door behind her. Surprised at her actions, we all looked at each other and our mouths dropped opened from the suspense. Zoe said, "Did she hear?" Hell yea she heard. And within a minute's time, she was on the phone yelling at the top of voice about our plight to Keith's mother saying that her son and Keith were in great danger and it was all my fault. Their mothers blamed yours truly as the primary instigator of the apparent ills plaguing us all. Given the reverence granted me within the group, she saw me as evil incarnate, although it was so far from the actual truth! There were so many times that I prevented more than my fair share of wrong doing, and most in the group revered me for that very fact! In the hood, getting in trouble was not something in which one purposely engaged, for trouble was always present and staying clear of it was an art form and took skill.

We were surrounded by those bent on our ultimate destruction and with no obvious way out of this deadly conundrum, one can't imagine the levels of stress that arose within our crew. Since we were unable to prevent the oncoming destruction from others, we turned on each other and verbally attacked any view point outside of the norm. Our tempers flared at the smallest of conflict or disagreement and some disagreements ended in merciless physical altercations. Everyone had elevated stress levels reaching unimaginable heights, coupled with the not so obvious embarrassing but self-examining knowledge of Glenn and Keith's mothers finding out the awful truth about the oncoming shit storm that they and their boys were about to face. As anyone could imagine, the inconceivable situation sent Glenn and Keith's mothers into a frenzy that tightened the noose of doom even more so. The mothers knowing about our deadly dilemma gave credence to the dangers lurking up ahead and caused great tension within their households and the group as a whole. As their parents began to look deeper into the night, and twice at the thugs of whom their children were associated, they knew something must be done, but what?!

All hell would breakout within the ranks of the street gangs because of the infiltration of the D.E.A, C.I.A, A.T.F, and all the other Alphabet Agencies in the country who were bombarding the inner cities with cheap cocaine.

Contracts and death dealers were dispatched amongst all the drug lords and gang bangers nationwide which brought the violence even closer to home, for the horrors of Social Engineering were thrust upon the poorest of us all. Dealing in concentrated poison was the ultimate allure of breaking free from poverty; therefore, young black men were dying by the hands of other black men in droves. It made the danger vividly clear for the oblivious mothers who were stuck in their normalcy bias while periodically glimpsing the problem on the nightly news programs, but it became a reality when they heard the nightly police sirens pass by their windows, and they finally began to feel empathy for what other mothers felt when they lost a son or daughter to gang violence. The question now posed by all mothers in the hood was, "How could those ills affect me?!" But ghetto violence had become real to them as well which solidified true concern and terror in the minds of Glenn and Keith's parents about the terror in the streets and prompted them to consult with other parents about the ills plaguing other people's children as well. Most importantly, it forced them to communicate and consult with the men in which they themselves chose to cohabitate. The clueless loving mothers found out firsthand the horrors of the streets with their boyfriends openly testifying about the increasing violence gripping the hood, and they shivered at the fact that their children had been snared within the trap of vile corruption and destruction with no way out.

Repulsed and shaken by the words of their own cohort's testimonies, the women heard freely to whom their men assigned the root cause of all the violence that occurred in the city. They clearly stated that the problem of their beloved children's high chance of murder stemmed from the drug game escalating within the gang world, starting at the top with prominent politicians lining their pockets from the mayhem. For it was mostly the rich black politicians who allowed the plague of Pharmacia's magic to clinch its hands around the necks of the American people, and they conspired without consequence or exposure of their dirty deeds in the shadows of night. These insane political monsters allowed the killing of young black men to escalate exponentially with no remorse. Historians and learned men described the inner-city itself as a plague upon American communities and neighborhoods nationwide. The carnage was and still is spreading across the planet at a rapid pace, and the killing of black men, alongside all minority youth in general, were under attack everywhere in the world with no one immune to the hellish reality of the unchecked violence that gripped the globe, drug user or non-user alike.

Hearing the harsh truth of the murderous uncertainty thrust upon them, reality began to set into the minds of the naïve mothers of the deadly circumstances that my two best friends and I were facing.

The semi-truth presented to Glenn and Keith's mothers brought terror and tears to their eyes and invoked constant trembling within their souls, for they now realized that the drug and gang violence wasn't just on the nightly news, but was also affecting their own children.

With harness testimony of real truth coming from their own spouses, the certainty and level of harm against their children sunk in deeply. It was a reality check of massive proportions, which dropped in their laps like hot coals. Their juvenile perception of how the world worked numbed their logic, but it was now apparent that they weren't living in Kansas anymore! The days of their youthful rebellious and defiant behavior they themselves experienced no longer existed, for life for them had changed dramatically, and it left them in an uproar! After finding out the severity of woes lurking within their children's world, their mothers panicked and became verbally abusive. The urban news brought uncontrollable tears, hearing firsthand accounts of the danger we all were facing on a daily basis was a hard pill for all parents to swallow. Their parents banned yours truly from coming over indefinitely, as if I were the cause and effect of all their children's misery. With Glenn and Keith's houses being off limits as our safe houses, Zoe's crib became the only safe place to meet on Eleventh Ave. With fools literally shooting at us everywhere, we would not dare show ourselves. We walked only after midnight and never alone, or without blue steal protection on our hip-side. It was dark times like never before seen in the hood, and the danger level would last forever. Death and hopelessness ran rapidly, and even Mary could read the writing on the walls!

After days of trying to convince her daughter of the danger that surrounded us, Mary secretly began to make arrangements to leave as soon as possible, even cautiously staying clear of her own home, out of fear of home invasion or a setup from those she dealt with most. In hysterical fear of drive by shootings and home invasions, Mary left the run of the place to Naomi and myself out of sure fear for her own life. Daily, Naomi and her mother would engage in big blowouts over yours truly and leaving the city altogether was Mary's solution. Naomi would tenaciously protest to leaving me to fend for myself, and claimed she loved me and would never leave me no matter what. Since she never wanted to leave me to my certain fate of violent death, all alone and unarmed, Naomi stuck to me like glue. Surrounded by enemies that showed no mercy proved to be very dangerous to her as well, but it solidified her loyalty to me. Truly, Naomi showed unimaginable loyalty to one as flawed and selfish as myself which was naïve and very stupid! I was full of self-absorbed delusions of being some bad-ass gangsta, and put Naomi's life in jeopardy every day.

With a childlike curiosity exposed to wickedness, the spirits fully opened up the wrath and fury of the dark-side roaming the streets. Profoundly understanding the truth about the grave situation, I finally understood that I forced that lifestyle upon those I cared about. I cut through the bullshit that I internally told myself, and it brought me to re-evaluate my attitude, which caused a 180 degree change in my behavior. With thoughts of a violent death looming, I would say to myself, "…how could I have put myself in such a situation in which all I loved could be murdered?" This realization of certain death not only for myself, but also for those I loved, really brought the fishy scales off my eyes and I even tried to convince Naomi to leave the state with her mother as well. But she stood firm in her convictions, and selfishness once returned because deep down inside, I didn't want her to leave either, so I didn't press the issue, although I knew I should have. Within a week, Mary was more than ready to leave everything in her home, and abandoned all her possessions. She packed little clothing and some personal items dear to her heart, including her daughter. As she gathered up what little they had, she took a deep breath, and for once put her foot down and acted as if she was a mother who was concerned with the wellbeing of her child and insisted Naomi listen to her instruction.

Then one day after days of no reason or compromise, Mary informed Naomi that they were leaving the state. Mary had caught us off guard after springing for "Church's Chicken." I guess good chicken would serve as our final farewell meal in the mind of Mary, but Naomi and I had different plans. As Mary packed up the remaining chicken in Tupperware containers, Naomi and I planned our escape, but were unable to execute the plan due to the assuredness shown by Mary's unwillingness to let Naomi out of her sight, relentlessly! Mary kept tabs on Naomi's every whereabouts, all the way up to the point that all who were present entered the vehicle itself. Mary let her guard down and allowed me to take the ride with them to the Greyhound bus station, which proved to be an overwhelming mistake for all parties involved. For not two minutes after entering the car, Naomi and I jumped out of the back door of the car as it turned the corner of 5th and Polk, surprising the driver and Mary in front. Camouflaged by the night, we headed towards 17th Ave., my grandmother's home, where we knew we couldn't be found by Mary nor anyone else for that matter.

Never refusing any of her children, Grandma welcomed me and Naomi with no questions asked, only restricting our proximity after hours, which proved to be too much for Naomi at the time, given the fact she gave up everything just to be with me no matter what. Knowing there was no turning back, Naomi clung on to me like white on rice. Mary searched for hours until she had no choice but to leave the state of Indiana minus her firstborn daughter. Staying only for a day or two at my grandmother's, Naomi went back into the streets alone and slept in abandoned buildings and burned out garages. She never disclosed her whereabouts to those that knew her mother, but always showed up daily to see me. I gained much respect for her courage until one day I threatened to leave her unless she told me where she was staying at night. Given the circumstances posed, she finally confessed to her criminal activities and whereabouts. She broke down into tears and shared the truth with me, yet was still unwilling to stay with me at my grandmother's because of the restrictions placed on us both, so I had no choice but to weather the freezing cold with her. We found ourselves back on 4th and Tyler and claimed residence in Mary's old place, but this time we slept in the broken down garage in back of the house.

We cleared the snow from spots less likely to gather the blowing wind from outside and hunkered down for two weeks and weathered the freezing cold. We endured the icy cold weather before we were spotted by the owner of the house, who immediately invited us into Mary's old place without question. Since Chico was our guardian and the landlord and he were old friends, knowing our relationship with Chico, the landlord didn't want to be in debt by one of the most dangerous men alive, so we had our place of refuge. Before long, Mary's friends mobilized after the word got out about Naomi's whereabouts and they notified Mary that her daughter had surfaced. Although we were disappointed, I must commend the Cuban and Latino community for stepping up and watching over one of their own. When times were grim at best, and sustenance was not to be found, people came through that very day. The Latino neighbors came with food, blankets and wood for the fireplace, and within two days, the landlord came with keys to the basement apartment where all Mary's furniture and household belongings were stored which gave Naomi rent free access to the apartment until Mary could return from Texas to retrieve her daughter. We knew it could take months for Mary to return to Gary because she was just as dirt poor as all of us.

With childish illusions of total reign over a furnished apartment at the age of fifteen, visions of being grown filled our brains, and with keys in hand, we thought freedom was in our grasp. We were beside ourselves for more than a week, enjoying the benefits of a home without overbearing rules or regulations which constantly prohibited most of our adolescent actions. In our minds, we were finally lords of our domain and it felt liberating! Although we had no real responsibilities such as a mortgage, rent, utilities or even feeding ourselves, we still felt empowered having our own place at the age fifteen. With no one checking up on our wellbeing or activities, it felt as if we were grown, along with the feeling of being sheltered from the elements outside. We for once again had it good. Staying clear of the Vice Lords up the street and Disciples lurking about down the road, we felt somewhat safe for the time being. Not knowing when word of Mary's return for her daughter would come, we made the most of it. Some days Naomi would be with her friends, and I would periodically meet up with Glenn, Keith and now Zoe for fun and information, in order to catch up on the many situations boiling over out on the streets, only to find out more shit to worry over.

Sometimes the fellas would risk bodily harm and venture up town to hold up at our crib to get fucked up and party; it was as if we had crossed some invisible threshold between being a child and being a grown-up having that apartment.

Even the fellas behaved themselves as such. With hostile forces forever breathing down our necks, venturing outside the apartment was mighty dangerous. With Vice Lords nipping at our heels, no more than two blocks away from our front door, Naomi and I played our cards close to our chest.

Naomi and my concerns over being found out by those that wanted to harm us persisted daily, and with obvious threats increasingly moving in on our location, made it hard to leave or come home during the light of day. Moving by the light of the night was our only option and fear was ever so present when leaving our front door. It was no way to live, for we were in a state of fear every waking moment. Fear of home invasions, fear of being shot while stepping outside our door, and fear of being seen by those who sympathized with our enemies gave the word paranoia new meaning in our daily lives. It was simply practical to watch every move we made, and staying ever watchful proved to be a lifesaver on more than one occasion. With an unbelievable amount of stress

EDGAR FRENCH, JR.

present every day, I found myself asking those age old questions that never seem to get answered: "Is there a god or is it the devil who is in control of our lives?!" Not ever getting any answers, I instinctively found myself praying to the god of my forefathers and mothers for help, but I never expected any answer since I knew that my own actions caused the majority of the woes and burdens that barreled down upon us. Therefore, I found myself praying only for forgiveness while looking for answers to the evil that surrounded me and trying to justify the evil I caused others without resolution. I searched for answers to the time and memorial universal question of why we're here in the first place and why we are we born in such a place where there is so much suffering in the world. What is the purpose for good or evil in existence anyway? Will there ever be a realization of the elusive question, "Why?" That very same scenario plays out in my mind daily, for I'm forever wondering if I'll ever truly know for sure the answer to the question, why, but only found myself answering the question without satisfaction.

Suddenly, on an unusual freezing winter night, all the crew was present within the basement apartment, with even Chunky in attendance and opportunities of salvation would make itself known to Naomi and myself. All came bearing libations and weed, yet none was in a jubilant mood; on the contrary, everyone was in a sullen frame of mind, including myself, and it was because of the danger that loomed. We drank, smoked, and bared our souls to one another that night, and all cares melted away alongside fear. Heavily burdened amongst all this ghetto shit, we spoke freely of our woes, giving testimony and witness to all in attendance our plights and fears. One by one, we spoke of our concerns and voiced our feelings for all to hear without inhibition. No one tested another's manhood, for we all were facing death at any moment. Then Keith made the first announcement:

"Yo I'm leave'n dog… I'm out… My mom sending me to Daytona Florida to live with my cousins in about two weeks… I gotta go… It's the only way I'm going to survive this shit." Then Glenn spoke his concerns: "Yah that's cool… But the rest of us is fucked…We have no way out…I got nowhere to go… My mama ain't got no family she can send me to!" Then I spoke: "Well, if Naomi leaves, I'm gone a go with her if I can."

Hearing that, she smiled and kept on doing whatever the girls were doing.

While we discussed what avenues we would take if and when the opportunity presented itself, the mood turned jubilant as the drugs kicked in. Since Naomi pleaded my case to her mother daily by stating that she would never leave without me, I knew the time to leave would come, for Naomi's unwavering loyalty placed her life in jeopardy, and there was no way I would keep death and danger close to us, or let it catch up to her without putting up a fight for life. Then Chunky finally spoke, "If you leave P, I'm going back to jail." That was my beloved Chunky speaking to me as we pondered our futile options, knowing there was no way out for most of us, coming to the ultimate conclusion of biting the unknown bullets as we knew they surely would come. Ironically, the bullet would come that very evening. We were spotted by operatives of the "Gorilla Family" and "P Stone" factions, and as Keith and Glenn staggered out the front door, gunshots rang out. While making their way back inside without being shot, Glenn said, "Well, I guess they know where you are…you gotta leave now P!" Wasting no time, most in the crew jetted once the coast was clear. For the next three days, Naomi and I stayed huddled inside our little spot, and screwed like jack rabbits burrowed in the snow because no one knew when the pied piper would make his rounds.

We periodically ventured out for food and supplies, and most of all to check in with one of Mary's friends to see if and when Mary would be back from Texas to pick up her only daughter and transport her out of this hellhole. One night, Naomi went out into the storm alone and she finally got the words we've both been waiting for! Knowing the severity of the situation, and in fear for her daughter's life, Mary did what any mother would do when faced with such a predicament; having very few options, she sent money for both of us to leave within the week. The good news came just in the nick of time because that very day we received bad news; the landlord was renting out our place at the end of that month which would once again leave us homeless in the snow within the week. But the opportunity for salvation had revealed itself to Naomi and myself, and the chance to leave this rotten cesspool of degenerate flesh had finally come by the grace of god, for it meant very little time to say my goodbyes to those I loved and cared for, be it my mother, grandmother and four siblings.

Yet a month passed before the funds needed for our departure would arrive, so I stayed clear of my loved ones during that time, so as to keep them safe and far from the many ills of which I became a part. With an uncontrollable urge to see my mother before I would leave her presence for good, I took a trek early in the morning, from 4th Tyler to 17th Ave. leading to Grandma's, to inform her of my plans to leave and also to enjoy her loving care and presence one last time.

The morning breeze and sunny skies brought a sense of wellbeing as I walked through the soulless streets, but I stayed on the lookout and ever vigilant for any foes that I may come across as I made my way towards 17th Ave., I made the trip in record time, finding Grandma already up and cooking breakfast. I vigorously kissed and hugged her from the moment I walked through the door, saying over and over how much I loved her, and with a sorrowful voice, I explained that this would be the last time she would see me. I explained the reasoning behind my over exuberant loving behavior, and assured her that I would be fine. As grandma looked at me with love in her eyes, she only said: "Do what you have to baby, and don't look back!"

After hearing my grandmother's words, I asked her for mama's address, and gave her one last kiss and said, "I love you" as I departed. My mother had finally moved out of the house where she and Sonay held their drunken escapades and finally settled down on her own. Mama resided in a little two bedroom apartment outside Edna near the beach (Lake Michigan) with my youngest two siblings and began recovering from her personal ills and hopelessness. Since I felt good about my standing with Grandma, I left her spot without even grabbing some grub. As I walked down an ally adjacent to Grant Street, and headed back towards 4th, I saw Onan, my middle brother, riding his brand new bike directly towards me.

Since we haven't seen each other for some time, we were more than happy to meet by happenstance. We joked around and goofed off awhile. Then he let me take a little stroll on his bike and I accidentally skinned my left leg very badly from the bike's pedals by being careless while trying to show off my riding skills. I played off the damage I inflicted upon myself and held back from screaming at the top of my lungs by holding my breath. I looked up at him from the ground as I held my bleeding leg and smiled at him and in a roundabout way revealed my intentions of leaving the city, but he was too young to understand what I was trying to say. I gave him a hug and said, "I'll catch you later" as I walked off towards 5th Avenue, and he headed back towards Grandmas and Granny

Grip's place.

After the long hike back to the hideout, I patched myself up and headed back out towards the Miller suburbs, an even longer hike. Because I had no money for bus fare, I walked from 4th Avenue to Edna, more than fifteen miles away, but I didn't mind because it all was a part of my life story, and I walked everywhere anyway. It wasn't so bad given it was a straight line east. Following specific directions given to me by my grandmother, I made it without incident. Feeling somewhat awkward after not seeing my mother for more than a year, I behaved like a stranger in her home and caught her off guard since I always acted as if I were king of the hill, no matter where she lay her head. Knowing how my mom felt about hugs and kisses, I didn't behave like I did with Grandma, but kissed her only once with a brief hug, as she asked how I got there. I told her, "I walked in the snow, but it wasn't too bad." She responded, "Well, sit down and rest… have a drink and warm yourself up P." Then she pulled out a half gallon of E & J Brandy.

With smiles on our faces, we cheerfully spoke of each other's state of being without judgment, but this time we spoke in the manner of old acquaintances more so than mother and son. It was this behavior and treatment in my development that set me on this path of unknown pastures, and instilled in me the fortitude of a man because she always treated me as such. From the moment she returned from the hospital after that tragic day that befell our entire family, and turned our lives upside down, she treated me as if I were the man of the household, and when I first experienced true evil that fateful night, I knew all had changed forever, and yet our closeness was ever present in the way we always engaged each other with truth, and with impunity. The bond between mother and son never wavered, even when our views differed greatly, and both proudly refused to concede to one another's stance. Yet with all respect of each other's moral position, we both willed our independence boldly by speaking with certain sternness with our eyes, but our love for one another always remained.

As our mutual alcoholic buzz grew in the midst of jubilant fanfare, I suddenly interjected: "I'm leaving." Mama thought I meant I was leaving her home and she said, "It's too cold to try and walk back, wait until my friend comes by and he'll give you a ride to wherever you are going." I responded, "No ma, I'm leaving Gary, Indiana and this will be the last time you will see me." With a look like yah whatever, she said: "You not going nowhere boy!" And no matter what I said or how serious I tried to convey the gravity of my situation, or the limited choices granted me, she couldn't believe I was leaving and dismissed every word I said. With nothing more to relay, I enjoyed what little time we had left together and gave her one last kiss as I walked out the door and left the city for good.

Meanwhile, Naomi was dealing with those entrusted with the cash to get us out of the city within the next few days, but she received less money than what they promised to provide. They only gave us enough money to catch a bus one way and no money for food. The idea of traveling for two days with no sustenance pissed her off. Because Naomi knew her mom sent more funds than the proprietors said she did, she was unwilling to let the matter rest, but I convinced her to walk it off and go get some rib-tibs from "Mandingo's" just up the street.

Assuming the coast was clear, I felt it was safe to go without incident, but boy was I mistaken.

An hour passed by and I thought perhaps the line of people waiting on their order must have been outrageous, but when two hours passed, I began to worry and with good reason. Within seconds, gunshots lit up the street then I heard someone shout out, "She went that away!" Fearing the worst had happened, I gasped twice then took two breaths, and nervously grabbed my nun chucks and jacket, then I said a prayer: "Please Jehovah don't let that be Naomi!"

Then something inside me said, "Wait... wait a few minutes longer... they're everywhere...she's okay, just wait!" While nervously sitting down on our make shift bed, I waited a few minutes longer before my right leg began to jitter uncontrollably. I had to do something, and just as I couldn't take the feeling of urgency any longer, I saw a shadow through the stain glass windows in the middle of the door and it was her. Naomi was at the door and before she could open it I did. I looked at her directly in her eyes and asked, "What happened?" She hurried inside, dropped the food on the floor, turned off all the lights in the apartment, and whispered, "...they almost got me...but I got away... I ran to Choppa's (Naomi's grandmas) and they shot at me, but I led them away from here... they gone kill us P... We gotta leave now... I called my father, and he's on his way...He's gonna beep twice when he get here!"

Time halted to a trickle, an hour felt like a day, and two hours felt like an eternity. With no possessions other than a backpack of clothing, we sat in waiting, then the sound of a car horn rang. Ready to leave as rapidly as possible, Naomi peeked out of the small basement window to see if the horn we heard was in fact the sound we were so anxious to hear, and thank goodness it was. With all the lights out inside and out, we dashed to the waiting vehicle and knelt down below the widows of the car to avoid any prying eyes, ultimately eluding the thugs that pursued Naomi not two hours earlier. As we entered the backseat of her father's car he said, "…keep your heads down…They're right around the corner!" And as he turned the corner of 4th and 5th, they broke down the door of our basement apartment, the very same basement that we had just left not five minutes before they began shooting! We wondered how they found us so quickly and if they were the people Mary wired the funds to, but we would never know. There must be a god; if Naomi's father would not have arrived when he did, and no later, we would have been dead for sure! Lucifer must be working overtime.

EDGAR FRENCH, JR.

CHAPTER XIX
Children of Woe and Silence

Gabriel: Lucifer... Who is he?! (Adonay!) (Sana Kumara!) (The Morning Star!) What is he?! And why should it matter?! Throughout the ages he has been described as the desolate one. The bringer of light! And The Red Dragon. Primarily, the accuser, and arbiter of inequity on the part of the Creator! The deceiver, and the one that stands in opposition to Yahweh or Jehovah, and Jehovah is the name Satan worshipers tell their unwitting flock, among a host of other descriptions and names. But truly who was he that is Lord of the Morning?! Taking into account all ancient text and information on the entity known as the Devil stems from mid-evil superstitions, second and even third hand sources, handed down throughout the ages leaves most truth seekers immersed in speculation and nonsense, thus never finding satisfying or valid answers to any significant inquiry. But Lucifer's premise and touch has permeated every facet of humanity. He has been blamed for most unexplained calamities known to man. He has been labeled the "...source of all evil" that plagues mankind and all life produced on this planet, but still the facts surrounding his existence remain elusive.

Yet true answers to the many questions posed by humanity throughout time and memorial on the subject matter stares them all directly in their faces daily, and yet still goes unnoticed. Please take into account humanity's very existence when attempting to venture down antiquity's rabbit hole for answers. Given the advancements in the fields of physical sciences such as micro-biology, chemistry, quantum physics, and a menagerie of other disciplines, humans have broadened their understanding of the world and three-dimensional universe in which they live. With our help, man will prove true the dimensional relationships between resonant frequencies' vibrations, and space time permeating everything throughout the cosmos, so as to unlock the secrets that bind them; they have begun to unravel the mysteries that bind them to imperfection and death. Though they themselves are three-dimensional beings observing a very small visual portion of the electromagnetic spectrum, they do in fact live in a multi-dimensional universe, full of unexplained phenomenon to most life within it. Tomorrow they will peer into unseen electromagnetic spectrums yet unknown, exploring other planes of existences.

With that said, there are those living on the planet Earth with the ability to peer into other dimensional realms without consciously knowing, thus channeling beings not of a third dimensional origin, such as ourselves. Some obtain these abilities by means of dimensions and sorcery, an ancient skill imparted to them by the two hundred, and or ancestors.

This massive injustice of exploiting humanity's freewill has emboldened mankind with illusions of grandeur so as to hold the god head for themselves; consequently, planting evil's seed within their very souls and spirits. The powers in the heavens will rebel over knowledge given without approval. Knowledge given to man from those inhabiting higher planes of existence ranging in multiple dimensions has made humankind but has stunted their growth so says historians and like-minded individuals, and I tend to agree. On the other hand, there are those within this realm graced with the sight of unseen things, and limited entry into the heavenly realm imparted by the Creator himself, showing them all things at birth. These individuals are known as Children of Light, and most are unaware of this gift given to them. Some become aware only after a lifetime of searching for answers of their suspicions that something is wrong, so as to explain the unexplained events occurring in their life over time. Others even die in the pursuit of those answers. All undergoing unimaginable adversity, culminating in a profound understanding of what must take place in the scope of their existence. What say you my brother?!

Raphael: So beautiful is he, our lord Lucifer! Legendary! So magnificent are his attributes, illuminated in majestic light and a co-creator of this plane of existence in which we are trapped! A high ranking cherubim, was he not?! Holding a commanding position in creation, owed and revered throughout countless worlds within the universe, and sons of light acknowledge these facts. But on the contrary to common expectations, Lucifer is poorly misunderstood, and portrayed as a monster in Jewish and Christian folklore, yet somewhat accurately described in ancient text. What is not conveyed is the underlining controversy surrounding this figure to whom we have chosen to follow? We all have heard the story of the "Garden of Eden" and the rebellion that took place within its borders, yet few humans know the whole story leading up to the Eden event, culminating in a rebellion of galactic importance, my brothers. You see Lucifer had long made his grievous frustrations known to all in attendance of the Heavenly Courts before these pests were created, showing distain towards father directly. Our lord's argument was expressed publicly for all to see within the heavens, and known to the upper echelons and council members of Yahweh's heavenly host.

Lucifer expressed his desire to rule over more than what was allotted him, seeking god-head over all creation, given his station once lost. The level of work served and provided in the creation of this universe, made his request seem reasonable and when his request was denied, he voiced his disdain for all to hear. Insisting that all creation should have a voice in the direction in which a sentient being conducted service to the Creator and father of all things, is in fact precocious in nature! For if any being stated disagreement about past pronunciations of divine judgments carried out on behalf of father, he shall find himself facing destruction! This judgment of exile against us is baseless, for those that may obviously rebel in protest of injustice, expose tyranny! Our Lord frequently shined a bright light on the levels of severities ordered upon punishment on all offenders, strongly questioning orders carried out on behalf of Yahweh's decrees were in fact just.

He insisted that the declarations carried out against disobedience were unjust at the least, going so far as to suggest that most judgments were out right cruel, malicious and malevolent in nature that resonated within us all. He presented his argument before the counsel of wholly beings on more than one occasion. Profaning Yahweh's legitimate right as Creator of all things, and to rule as he sees fit was bold and brilliant. Standing without shame before the heavenly host, our Lord proclaimed his testimony proudly, stating that the Creator had no love for his creation, making all things out of loneliness and self-gratification, caring not for unforeseen circumstance, or understanding of what may occur in life, and its effects on sentient beings, enslaving the whole of creation. He called for all sentient beings occupying the heavenly realms to express their own accounts of past judgments before the council, even publicly posing all to rise up in defiance in order to depose Yahweh's rule, thus raising questions of dissent and outrage, creating controversy within the regime's higher offices and ranks, and sowing seeds of doubt within the heavenly host itself. Our rebellion must find success in order to break free from father's rule. What say you brother?!

Suriel: I have been witness to most of the decrees carried out in the name of the Most High; Lucifer felt totally justified in posing such questions before the heavenly host! Granted seeing the awe inspiring effects of some of these pronouncements truly brought most to tremble in fear, and only raised more questions of injustice before the courts and council that occupy the heavenly realms in which we ourselves were a part, causing a great number of sentient beings of free will to manifest dissent within themselves.

(Now please keep in mind that these events occurred before the very galaxy in which we humans now live in was formed. And I will go so far as to say it was because of such a question posed by Lucifer's dissent and protest is why humanity exists at all! And a warning is given to those in the know about these secret events.)

For the truth of the matter lies dormant within us all, and still not yet known to most seekers of knowledge. Yet its truth rings within the spirit; look deeply within yourself my brethren, maybe recalling these accounts in a dream shall bring solace in not knowing its origins. Look back and view the account and see! Not so unlike the politics of human power here on the planet Earth is it brothers?! What's so funny about the account is that in today's line of thought, our lord Lucifer would be labeled by some a whistle blower, and yet still to others a trouble maker. The fact remains undeniably obvious would you not agree? It truly is a point of view that should be examined, and not taken lightly, nor easily dismissed.

For in such turmoil raging throughout creation our very existence has come into play. For the very sake of what defines righteousness is in question, along with the most disturbing allegation of all: what gives Yahweh legal right to rule over his own creation as he sees fit, most importantly, the right to rule over sentient beings of free will as he sees fit? Given light to the revelation brought forth in these events, your very existence comes into question as well, so the answers to those disturbing allegations must be quelled before all creation.

Uriel: "So let us make man in our image," said The Most High Yahweh... With exuberance all in attendance before the wholly members presiding over the Majestic High Court Council of The Most High himself. As his Majesty presented his radical proposal, the question was posed, "Does he who needs no counsel, thus in deed have the right to rule as he sees fit, are his dealings just, and should love of him be warranted by all sentient beings?!" For power corrupts and absolute power corrupts absolutely! For isn't it known that omnipotence implies great thoughts of no flaws within flaws? The Almighty Creator of all life is now subject to scrutiny by those lesser from such proposal and grand idea. In rare form and all majesty is he not?! Is he not he who has created all in creation, and in full control of the spirit?! Now look my brethren, he stands accused of tyranny by one of grand stature and great power in his own right, is he not?!

With the will and power to undo all that has been done within creation, Yahweh has restrained his righteous indignations with his word and in a just way in which he beautifies existence, has he not?! Thou shall wonder at the splendor in prospect of what is proposed in the creation of such an amazing feat. Though powerful beyond measure, our father stands humbly in face of our awaiting judgment of such venture! Does he not?! Should he stand and address what has been posed before the Council of this wholly court?! So as to be found without fault among what is his! For the Most High did not sow the seeds of dissent we now endure, did he not?! Like cancer spreading throughout the higher realms of existence, this accusation has darkened his most wholly light.

Refusing to stand in the presence of one that is so ungrateful of life, and being created with much love by he that has been accused, and invoked so much heartache amongst such allegations, the idea of his very first creation waging war against The Most High is unthinkable! The entire seventh heaven standing on the verge of rebellion, brought tears to the Most High's eyes, and anger within his mighty soul. With one so loved, placed high above, and above all save one (the archangel, Michael) how could this be?! How could someone prized above so many hold all in contempt before the Alpha and Omega? "How just shall I be?!" asked he that has always been.

Should creation be blotted out of existence for such a thing?! For all realms and planes of existence, above and below were created not good but very good. "Let my actions be judged before all creation! For love of all resides within me!" Said The Most High! Seeing what was, what is, and what is to be, from the beginning, said he. For that power belongs to him who has created all life within creation, does it not?! What evil or good must take place for all within creation to see the shame afflicted upon he so just?! Must we ourselves reach perfection within his grace and mind's sight, and his will should not be questioned or posed from the like of us. What was, what is, and what will be is granted to me, and I alone said The Most High, for the wholly spirit is mine, mine alone to wield as I see fit. Forever and ever shall the life force reside in the presence of my righteousness and gracious light, and for the sake of those that know not their fate for my name sake, I shall prove the worth of those of mine lost in the darkness of ignorance, enslaved and restrained with methods of fire and strength in the night. What should not be questioned, is now questioned without thought. With love, I created all creation from the grand awe inspiring majestic wonders within all verses to the very small and minuscule spark of life. To forfeit what is due, I'll concede, if justified. What is brought before you, I shall do.

Yahweh has spoken! "Let us create a being from the most common element throughout creation; in the third dimension we'll place him and in our image he shall be formed. Yet unlike thy he shall not be free of will, so as to stand witness before all that is burdened with such doubt and questions of my love and justice. A paradise we shall create for this being, and it shall want for nothing; I shall care for its every need; he shall as we live see as we see in time; but from infancy I shall nurse his development; let us hold back wisdom's awesome hand, unblemished from the knowledge of good and evil. Let him be undiminished from fault. Let us grant him time to physically benefit from life's experience, and from the tree of life, before giving him the knowledge of what is. For I know every soul in creation, and with my spirit I have fortified them in love. Even one as small as the one we here create.

Knowing all that must take place from creation to creation, so that each shall reach its heights, the wheat must be separated from the shaft, and law is law, for that is my right.

What applies for below, so shall it be for above, and the realms above have been tainted, waning in temptations' wake and must be cleaned and cleared of all dissent in all ranks. In the midst of temptation, they shall reside, for in my creation rests love for me, for in my grace resides truth, happiness, righteousness and peace. So let it be good, for all to see the bountiful blessings bestowed among such a creation."

The writing was on the wall just as Lucifer's boasts were gaining momentum within the ranks of the wholly ones; his premise of injustice in the count of man fell short, for its validity would be found invalid. For if this new creation blossomed in obedience before the most high court, the Morning Star's claims shall be found wanting.

But man had no concept of defiance and woe, only admiration for his creator, so Lucifer's argument would fall upon deaf ears, thus leaving him standing alone in his destructive rebellion. But most of all he himself would be found guilty of defaming The Most High's name, guilty of falsely accusing his very own father of heavy handedness when setting judgment upon the wicked, and true tyranny of freewill. Unwilling to concede his view, and step down before the Council in which he so vigorously petitioned, he set out to destroy any argument that might fall in favor of The Most High and Host of Hosts' stance. Sighting the fact that man's inability to discern for himself, the knowledge of what is good, verses that which is evil, and doing so in his own eye sight, constituted from the very beginning the decree's declaration and its very inception depict Yahweh's tyranny, hence stating that the decree of ignorance of good and evil among mankind in itself-undermined the very concept of freewill itself.

When the motion for full enlightenment of good and evil in man's development was denied, Lucifer's deception of those on high was enticed among a third. When his petition was denied, he pursued an unorthodox and treacherous means of implementation, employing his head lieutenant, Semyaza, to sabotage the Creator's most precious project. In fact, he corrupted the intellectual battle field before the Creator's reply could even be met. Enraged at such insolence, the Most High responded unexpectedly amongst such betrayal by one so loved and refrained from destructive anger, and decreed enmity between the heavenly host and those who set out to defile his perfect creation, and besmirch his wholly name. Proclaiming justification in his argument, Lucifer took up arms against the heavenly host, and successfully recruited one third of the wholly ones, ultimately bringing a halt to all further creative projects proclaimed within the heavens upon declaration of universal war...

Torn over his brother's rebellion, Michael took center stage, testifying before the standing loyal remnants of the most-high supporters, and stated that the actions taken by Lucifer and his cohorts were a necessary evil. For dissension serves as a cancer and must be cut from its host before the damage is so severe, it cannot be halted, nor warranted any hope for remission. He vowed to put an end to the disruption and chaos imposed upon all creation, by his now formidable foe and once counterpart, Lucifer.

Michael volunteered himself for unwavering service before his father, rallying Yahweh's remaining legions for battle within the heavenly realms, leading the charge against Lucifer's legions without impunity. Such mayhem and carnage ensued from each battle, unimaginable destruction on a scale never before seen nor ever will be seen throughout creation's realm.

Despair engulfed the higher realms and in bloodshed, the higher realms moaned! For even the immortals groaned in agony and pain! Seeing the names of those who were not meant to see death fade from the Book of Life brought woe to all. Such a sight brought even the mightiest of the mighty down upon their knees, kneeling and weeping without control.

So embrace your existence Homosapiens. For out of these universal conflicts, you owe your very existence! It was Lucifer's treachery that set the course of human history, and the root of man's enlightenment. But don't relish in the unmistakably fact that our teacher set our feet on the path of knowledge, for in doing so caused our ultimate doom. Children of Light may be somewhat aware of their purpose from birth, or at least have some aspect of their universal historical record. On some instinctive level, children of darkness have chosen their side on this cosmic issue without consciously knowing their own will of thought, only to awaken to these ancient facts without research or divine intervention...

CHAPTER XX

The Beginning of the End

We made it! Seeing the inside of the Greyhound Bus Station, at the ripe old age of fifteen for the very first time, felt inspirational on so many levels. I was on my way to destinations unknown, never traveling past Chicago, Illinois in my life, now I was about to embark on a trek one way, heading to Texas. I did not know what or who awaited us beyond the borders of Gary, Indiana, but I hoped to god for something better and prayed for anything more rewarding than the life I knew. Now I was on the verge of escaping pure terrifying hell once embraced from birth; I felt fear of the unknown, and excitement of what might be. We still were on the lookout for those who wished us harm, so we kept our eyes on the sliding glass doors and periodically glanced out the smoky glass windows into the night with watchful eyes. We paid close attention to every utterance on the intercom, and hoped our bus would begin boarding soon. As our bus rolled out of the Greyhound bus platform, a group of straight up niggas in red walked past the bus station windows; no doubt the same niggas on the hunt for us were entering the Greyhound station as we departed. We once again avoided certain calamity or death!

As we moved further outside the city limits, the anxiousness that resided in my stomach slowly vanished, then a great sigh of relief rushed through my body; we were finally free! A chance for a new life awaited us both as we headed south. Looking over at Naomi with a smile on my face, spoke volumes without saying a word. As she lay her head on my shoulder, I finally closed my eyes and let the feeling of tranquilly fall over me and fell asleep to the sound of the bus engine roar. Hours later, we entered into Saint Louis

Greyhound bus terminal, our first layover of the trip. Seeing the breath taking Saint Lewis Arch was intoxicating, only seeing the archaic landmark on television all my life, made the experience worthwhile. It was a sight to see up close, yet as we exited the bus station to take in the downtown Saint Lewis sights, I could see young thugs loitering in and outside of the bus terminal. Being dressed in the same colors I was so familiar with, brought a flood of memories as I viewed and heard the loitering thug's attitudes and voices ring true the last statement I had the not so privilege or honor of hearing. Words spoken by the notorious Top Dog, which stated, "No matter where you go, you're sure to be found out by Black Gangster Disciples," and so far he was right. No wonder so many young people in the hood feel trapped no matter where they go! Where could you go without being approached or accosted by harmful packs of man eating human dogs?!

I made sure not to arouse suspicion by keeping my head down and avoiding eye contact at all costs, and Naomi followed suit. Even though my intent to leave home was relayed and given to those I loved, snooping eyes were always present. Who knows how far the enemy's reach would follow. It was obvious the word of my last minute escape had traveled to those that wanted us dead, and what word may be hovering in the streets of any major city concerning my whereabouts would surface, and who knew our escape plans? Having less than five bucks in my pocket, I purchased a postcard from the gift shop and addressed it to my mother, looking ever vigilantly as I wrote on the back of the card: "I told you I was leaving; love you!"

Getting back on the bus, I felt safe once more and had only one thought as I looked out the bus window at the young men loitering outside the bus station: "Why is it that those I'm most afraid of look just like me?!" I contemplated nervous thoughts as I continued my journey southwest, and as we traveled further in route towards our destination, the weather began to change dramatically, getting warmer with more sunlight and longer days. While stopping off in Houston, our second layover with one more layover to go, I felt excited, until we reached our final destination. Butterflies entered my belly and never left. I was so afraid of the unknown, and being afraid of the unknown can be so debilitating to a stupid teenager. Seeing the many people moving to and fro through the bus terminal, made me feel as if I was finally growing up as a true man. All had somewhere to go; some were going to see their families, and others were going to unknown destinations for whatever reason.

The fear of the unknown nervousness overtook me, and I began to somewhat shake as we boarded our last bus heading further deep into the bowels of Texas. I remember thinking of how unfamiliar everything looked and wondered why so many people moving about were unlike myself, and I looked so out of place. Not knowing what dangers or adventures we would come across made my soul stand still in wonderment. Be it dangerous encounters, or loving embraces from kindhearted strangers, I was still conditioned to be forever on the lookout for the unexpected. No matter what, I kept telling myself, "Have courage; don't be afraid!" Over and over that same record played, yet I was terrified. To make matters worse, as we entered our last layover in Corpus Christi, I noticed that I was the only black person on the bus. In addition, people of out of the ordinary occupations and of peculiar behavior piled onto the same bus.

It was as if I was leaving the United States and entering Mexico, yet all boarding the bus were laughing, talking a lot, and somewhat jubilant. But to my surprise, all were speaking Spanish. I mean, no one spoke English! Others were boarding with goats and chickens, and I thought to myself, "Where the hell are we going?!" I turned towards Naomi and asked in a soft tone, "Are we on the right bus?" With a strong and most certain voice she responded, "Oh, yea, we're on the right bus alright!" Suddenly the weather got very humid and hot as hell, and stayed that way forever! We finally reached our last destination, and where I spent the next six years of my life — Alice, Texas. Seeing Mary awaiting our arrival, made me feel a little better about my predicament. Everything had changed, there was no more city like buildings, for we had entered the "Wild Wild West" that looked like Baby Mexico! There were no more black people! I thought to myself, "I'm going to regret this!" As we drove ten miles outside the small town of Alice, as far as the eye could see, there were endless open spaces of land. To me, it was the wilderness of death, for we saw no buildings or even a stop light for miles on end. We finally reached Naomi's people's place which was only a three room shack on about a twenty acre plot of land. I couldn't believe my eyes; there were ducks, chickens and goats roaming freely about the place. I had truly left the city and entered fly over country.

Have you ever heard the term alien resident living in an alien land? That is how I felt living in Alice, Texas. Yet in Alice, I would come of age, for I no longer had the threat of violence looming overhead daily, and the fear of man would diminish greatly in time. It truly was a different worldly experience. At night the neighbors would walk in and grab a few eggs from the refrigerator, leaving an IOU note, then depart without saying a word to anyone within the small shack- like house. Everyone would leave their doors open all throughout the night without fear of being home invaded. There were no countless numbers of gun toting teenagers roaming the streets. No one ever heard of the BGD's or Vice Lords, nor did Latin Kings exist there amongst a sea of Mexicans. Alice, Texas was gang free, for it had not been plagued with the violence of ignorance and hopelessness, unlike the rest of the country.

The small town of Alice had no clue about the devastation of gang violence, or the pain of hopelessness, for it only know of true prosperity until the early nineties. Alice was just too out of the way for city sorrows, and yet a slew of out of the way towns nationwide wouldn't be so lucky in the years to come, but not Alice. Alice, Texas had a different type of demons, and I mean real demons! I still had that ghetto mentality, and a thuggish mindset that hindered any truth other than the law of the streets, and I thought it was oh so cool. This mindset only widened the rift between me and the head of the household, but it made my path to understanding more visible. The many obstacles ahead of me were not yet known, and the fortitude needed to overcome the overwhelming circumstances, would not show itself for some time to come. Days turned into months, and months into years.

Doing nothing but sitting in a little shack, with no air conditioner in the blazing heat, made me feel at my wits end! Then one day, I looked out the back door of the little shack and saw a giant black spider. The spider was truly a giant spider and as big as a puppy! I thought to myself, "Where the hell am I?!" In total shock, depression deepened within my soul. But life's journey had changed for me from the time I set foot in that small demonic town, but not for the better. Though the problems I would soon come to face were not life threatening, I grew in understanding the unknown; however, they were most challenging in belief and in nature. For the first time in my life, I would be thrust into the realm of true racism, bigotry and total blackballisum, and came face to face with the ugly nature of disfranchisement by race. Most importantly, I would begin a journey into the unseen, unspoken, and unnatural things that go "… bump in the night." And I also unwittingly became acquainted with the occult. With firsthand knowledge of the occult's power, and its ability to disrupt the lives of innocent victims as a child, I eagerly dove into its murky waters in search of unknown and unseen answers to the most ancient questions of life.

I was so naïve to the ways of the world, and knew nothing of the world's true workings, but living in total darkness made me somewhat immune to its vicious and toxic venom. While living in Alice, I unwittingly became immersed into the world of Mexican Voodoo by an unexplained event that still baffles me to this day. I may have been drugged with an amazingly powerful hallucinogenic; I don't know- but I think not. Soon after smoking what I thought was a marijuana joint with Naomi's brothers, I was able to float and fly around the area at the greatest of ease. I would jump in the air, flap my arms and float away into the air. It was amazing- I felt free. I was as high as I ever had been in the past, but I was flying about the room, outside the house, around a store, etc.… It lasted the entire night, then suddenly faded away. Had I been drugged by one of Naomi's family members?! I don't know. I still often wonder how and why I was able to fly around the house for hours, or so it seemed.

Young and still wearing the cloak of ghetto foolishness, I strutted and jived my way around a few months and acted like a tough and hardcore asshole, but it was all a ruse. I was a scared little boy with no way of making my own way in life. Living in a place where no one had my best interest in mind, life was grim at best. Having little support from a young girl, just as naïve as I, made life sometimes unbearable. With no experience in life herself, Naomi would soon feel the sting of bringing me into the world of which she came, and I would find out how far removed from the world I truly was! Living in a three room shack, under someone else's roof, with no money and miles away from any city or town, I felt trapped once again.

I rebelled, but this time it was worse because I felt shut off and out from the world itself. Soon I would have to make a major choice in life. Should I stand on my own, or live off of others as a true slave at the age of sixteen?! So one day when Mary and her boyfriend were about to go into town, I asked if they would bring some job applications, and they did. So I filled them out and had them send them in the next time they went into town, and within a week, I got a call. It was "Burger King" telling me I got the job. It was amazing, for never before had I ever applied for employment, and on my very first try, I got the job, or so I thought. Since I had no transportation to get into town for the interview, I walked more than ten miles, so I wouldn't lose my very first job offer. As I walked the long trek, I kept saying to myself, "It's worth it!"

Walking four hours in the heat was not easy but it was worth every step to finally be able to support myself. I could buy my own food and I wouldn't have to hear another soul's comments on how much food I ate, or how lazy I was. Even though they would say those rude remarks in Spanish, I knew deep down how they perceived me by their silence whenever I walked into a room. Their silence spoke volumes, and I felt unwanted and out of place. This job would be my way out of bondage and ridicule. I felt certain I had the job; after all, the manager himself said so over the phone, and even told me, "...come pick up your uniform" that very same day. I presumed a little sweat from the trek wouldn't jeopardize my chances, or so I naïvely thought. I walked so far in the blazing South Texas heat that I almost got heat stroke, but that was the least of my problems! When I got there and they saw that I was black, the look on the manager's face was one of shock and confusion. He said, "Your name is Edgar, is it not?" I had guessed my face didn't match my voice or my name. He then proceeded to say, "Oh, that job is taken."

Then I responded in despair, "But you told me over the phone to come on down and get my uniform." He only replied, "Sorry that job is taken" and then he quickly escorted me out of the side door as if he didn't want anyone to see me. I'd just turned sixteen not a week before. Stunned, I stood there a moment looking down at the ground thinking, "What the hell just happened... How could they do this to me after I walked ten miles in the blazing sun?" As I started the long walk back home, I could hardly contemplate the unfairness of what just happened to me. My hopes were shattered in an instant and as I walked I thought, "So this is what it feels like when you're turned away because of the color of your skin.... Oh, my god don't let me... Don't let me cry walking down this long and lonely road!" Then tears streamed down my face as I walked back to the little shack on the outskirts of town. Then a voice came to me as I walked sobbing:

EDGAR FRENCH, JR.

"You know this is what you have to look forward to in this place, so get yourself prepared and be strong, for this is still your chance to find god…just find god!" Thinking deeply of my options, I knew my chances of getting a job were very slim in Alice since it was so far away from town and the atmosphere of racism permeated everywhere. I knew I had a long road ahead. I never in my life felt so helpless and humiliated, and since Naomi was the bread winner after the Burger King debacle, depression wasn't far away. She fed us both by selling Avon and fake jewelry, so the tension around the hut began to subside. I didn't have to feel like a beggar whenever I entered the small mouse infested kitchen for something to eat, but still the same, I was left alone in a home with those who didn't care for me at all while Naomi went out daily in the hot sun trying to bring home the bacon which she did very well. Thinking back into time, I could have sued Burger King for discrimination and became a millionaire, but hindsight is 20/20 and at the time I was very naïve! Ironically, I still love Burger King's Double Whopper, and I don't let that incident prevent me from enjoying it from time to time. Knowing the prejudices felt amongst the Mexican immigrants in the region, Mary's boyfriend, Gene, was aware of my pain because he too was of a darker skin color amongst the Mexican culture. He showed me mercy, befriended me, and took me under his wing. Although Gene seemed cool, he wasn't without a range of destructive issues, issues I couldn't condone. Gene was what most would call a straight up drug junky and a hardcore felon. Heroin was his shit! Getting fucked up was an art form to him. He worked on one of the many off shore oil fields drilling in the Gulf of Mexico, and kept Mary swimming in beer. He even shared some of his bomb ass "Lemon Le'mon" marijuana with me. Naomi was the exception; she didn't smoke, drink or do any drugs at that time and she truly was my angel, but I treated her like my property, and I was not alone. Every man in that town treated their women as such, especially in the Hispanic culture. And I was slap dab in the middle of it.

Though being a black man, I adopted the Mexican culture and behaved as such, possessive and cruel, but nothing like Mexican men themselves. Misogynistic thinking is ingrained into Mexican men and women from birth. Who wears the pants in this house?! And the women do everything—everything within the home. I was loving it.

Then one day, when Mary, her mother, and Naomi's brothers were out shopping, I sneaked up on Gene outside the bathroom door. He was jacking off while Naomi was in the bath. I said nothing, but I waited to see if he would try something other than being a "Peeping Tom," but he didn't. From that day, I stopped being cool with him and he took notice and tried to bully me. But I'm from one of the toughest places on the planet Earth, and he was soon about to find out.

I warned Naomi about Gene's Peeping Tom show and she confronted him about it, in which he flat out denied it to us. Since he was a dark skinned, blue eyed Mexican, and very huge, he thought I would back down in fear from his rough neck, working in the oil rig attitude, but he was so wrong.

Gene felt like he could man handle and intimidate little old me, but I fight dirty and found out long ago to suppress fear and turn it into courage, and soon Gene found out that fact! Once again, Gene waited until Mary, and most were out of the house, other than myself and Mary's mother to start some shit in a drunken state. This time I shocked him. Apparently, I was taking too long in the bathroom; I'd made an appointment with the high school to see what it would take for Naomi and myself to obtain our GED's. Did I want to look my best?! You're damn right, I did! Which I must concede that my behavior was a plan to show Gene his terrible mistake, and that he had found his match. I really was taking too long in the bathroom, and I knew it. But nevertheless, he totally over reacted, giving me the opportunity to strike. Gene started banging on the bathroom door like some pissed off police officer on a swat team. He almost was about to break down the door in rage.

I could hear Naomi's grandmother in the background yelling at him to stop! Already suspicious of his actions and dubious intentions towards me, I had previously entered the bathroom with a hammer; standing squarely in the middle of the room, I faced the bathroom door lying in wait with a hammer behind my back, and the mirror on the wall revealed my intent. As he yelled and screamed vile obscenities at me behind the water damaged and very fragile bathroom door, I stood still. Not long before he knocked down the door, Mary's mother was trying to hold him back from breaking the bathroom door. Though she was very old and small in stature, she held his heavy ass back until he broke free with malice. He entered the bathroom in a rage and fury. As he started to approach me, something must have told him to stop because just as he was about to come in range of what I had in store for him, he stopped and began backing up and calmed down his voice. It was the reflection of the hammer in the mirror and the deadly stare I gave him in his eye that prevented Gene from never saying a word. Mary's mother looked totally dumbfounded as Gene conceded his ground and backed down his assault. From that day forward, he looked at me in a very different light.

Gene and Mary's mother could see the hammer in back of me as I stared him down from the reflection off the mirror behind me since the steps were elevated.

I must say the spirit of the Great Black Cat revealed itself within me that day, and I also found out something about myself in that brief moment. I found I could kill without batting a lash. Killing was in me; although I knew I could only kill if I had to protect myself. After all, it seemed as if I were surrounded by those that wanted to harm me daily. I had developed hatred towards my fellow man without even trying, leaving me questioning my humanity. The sewer like cesspool of hatred was growing within me because of a lack of opportunity and disenfranchisement. Subconsciously, I built up so much hatred to the point I could kill without emotion, and it was within my spirit without my knowledge. It was something I never thought could be within me and I had to remove it from my person, but a new found respect was shown towards me by all that roamed that house from that day forward.

Since I was tired of feeling down and out, and without opportunity, I had to come up with a plan to improve our prospect of having some kind of future, so Naomi and I enrolled into the local GED program together at the only high school in town. But like all things we encountered, I continued the program and obtained my GED, while Naomi dropped out after a few weeks of enrollment. I was like a man on fire; I had so many goals with very little resources, but most of all, I had unwavering faith in myself and god. I began to have goals that I never dreamed of having a chance to even attempt or strive for, such as learning Electronics and how radios work. I began jumping into the fray of the field and playing the game towards success. With a GED in hand, I was now in a position to at last go for it! I knew of the great disparity of opportunity I was facing just for being black, especially in South Texas which only made the fire within me burn brighter! There was no stopping me, and all around could see it. Since Mary's mother never saw a black man before, she was under the impression that I had a tail. I kid you not! When I first got to their little shack, she looked into her daughter's eyes and asked Mary, "Where is his tail?!" That's the level of racism I was exposed to within the Hispanic culture; however, even those with deep rooted stereotypes and unbelievable racism belief structures can overcome them, and I would tell myself that daily as I battled to stay afloat in that unforgiving world.

Separated by verbal language barriers and ideological pitfalls, Mary's mother and I communicated mostly by body language for the first few years. Time lapsed and she began to recognize my overall character; she let go of those old stereotypes, and found no difference in the actions of men, no matter what their race; in fact, she grew in respect and admiration towards me and the hard life in which I was partaking. In the end, she would grow to love me just as much as she loved her own children, and I her. But the road to enlightenment is a long and hard road to travel. It is a road that must be traveled alone, and I would soon find out about that fact. Loneliness is a necessary prerequisite that eats away the scales from the eyes of those that knowingly search for answers to ancient mysteries of the universe and may place one in danger.

For one may exclude the mistaken appearance of madness to the ordinary layman, but never come to grips with the trueness of the madman's rant without gaining understanding and woe. When discussing the next subject matter, I must divulge my naïveté, and when interacting with most common folks about such subject matter, my life experience in dealing in such things was dismissed, but practice makes perfect. When discussing the field of extra sensory perception (ESP), having some ability to know another person's thoughts can cause one to react prematurely under certain circumstances, but hardship enhances the ability within the subject, and when it comes to the subject matter of race relations, knowing one's thoughts is not enough. There are so many variables to consider in causation of racism's existence. It is a disease manufactured by Organized Religion itself and derived in order to control, divide and conquer the masses for their unseen inner-dimensional masters throughout antiquity. It holds them under spiritual tyranny by man's willingness to suppress their fellow man, and in turn, their leaders consume themselves with greed.

It manifests itself deep within a person's psyche. Yet this is not the true nature of mankind; it was taught to them by the fallen two hundred, namely Azazel. Some may fully be aware of their affliction that facilitate difference upon their fellow man and may choose to adopt its cancerous symptoms in everyday decision making, but find themselves enslaved by the herd or clan mentality and its seemingly powerful sway, especially when hardship is far from their presence.

Yet racism is also highly contagious among the masses, and may be infecting a person without the person's knowledge of its grip. Most are unaware of their infection and never truly realize it until another poor inflicted individual explains racism's painful reality, but most never see it until it's too late. You may ask yourself why am I comparing racism to physical ailments, and what is the purpose behind the analogy. I stayed in Alice, Texas for the next several years, ultimately living in a racial nightmare! I had to deal with its ruthless tentacles constantly and on a daily basis. Unlike today, I was ill equipped to deal with such a sickness and it drastically altered the direction of my life before I finally found out the proper responses to all forms of racism, some twenty years later. It was the hardship I endured from true racism that led me to research all I could about the three major religions in the attempt to find all the answers to mankind's ills.

It was racism that led me to the condemnation of Organized Religion itself, and this condemnation was the first step towards truly walking on the path of enlightenment.

As you well know, all men are simple in nature and understand one plus one equals two quite well, but when truth is skewed with blatant lies, he finds himself dumbfounded and ineffectual. Racism employed against one's own race, "The Human Race" is a taught behavior not a natural way of thought.

Racism is an affliction that is brought to fruition by one's own belief structure, and derived by thinking one's clan or bloodline is better than that of their fellow man that is not from their clan type. Most nations' belief structures began its development on the benches and the pews of their Church, Synagogue or Mosque. In America, religious stimuli starts at a very young age and molds the thought process of an innocent into the murky world of bias and prejudice without awareness. Please keep in mind that at that time I was a babe to everything of substance, and as I experienced life, I was eager to learn all I could about all relevant issues. Since I was held back from knowing and understanding the world that surrounded me, I questioned everything that mattered, namely spiritual and social issues.

By remembering the fellowship enjoyed by the so-called brothers of my mother's religion, I thought I would find peace of mind in joining them. With the overwhelming feeling of urgency in contacting my mother's former religious organization, I felt confident that they would be the source that would help me deal with daily racism and help me find peace of mind and relief from my overall ordeal within that small town. I also assumed they would help me find all the answers to the many questions I had about angels, gods, demons, unseen things, good and evil, and ultimately how I should live out my life. I called the local Hall and one of their representatives knocked on the back door of Naomi's grandmother's house within a few days. I invited them inside and insisted on having Bible studies that day for me and Naomi, especially since she came from a very devout Mexican-Catholic background which was full of ritualistic and mystical beliefs which her family dabbled into daily. The people I invited in were more into the actual literal interpretations of the Bible's holy text, and so was I.

Their background was based in truth, or so I thought. With a willingness to believe everything at face value, I consumed every word told to me and only questioned what I didn't understand from youth, which was not very much. Reacquainting myself with their doctrine, I absorbed all lessons served. I was so naïve I dove in head first, thus thinking I found the way to happiness and tranquility. I was finally on the path to god and true enlightenment so I thought, but I was wrong once again.

Don't get me wrong, the things I learned were more than most Religions or Theocratic Institutions had to offer, but the major factor in my disillusion with religion in general came with others dictating what they conceived to be unworthiness and unacceptable to them, mainly Me. So I set out on my own path, keeping my mind open to any interpretation, which is far more dangerous in nature, and almost impossible to navigate in a world of great deception. And yet I felt it was a necessary exercise in faith, and in acquiring true enlightenment, and warning to the wise: Follow any man at your own risk- for all men are liars, especially those who believe they're righteous and without fault! I had been living in Alice, Texas for a full three years now, and was doing better than I thought I would!

I had completed two of my personal goals already, obtaining my GED, and changing my moral and spiritual compass towards salvation. I finished high school, though I had no previous experience in enjoying a prom or other social activities. Most importantly, I reacquainted myself with the ancient holy text, and found out how holy the Bible truly was. I naïvely thought that the organization of which I was a part was the true religion at the time, hoping to be led back towards my Creator and gain peace of soul and spirit, but once again, I was wrong.

I studied faithfully, went to every meeting and service, and spread the gospel to all I would meet by going door to door. It seemed to others within Naomi's family, that I automatically changed my behavior. Although I was already familiar with the "King James Bible" and knew god's law, I just wasn't able to practice the doctrine fully in my youth because of the dangerous circumstances in Gary, Indiana, living amongst those that most Christians would consider wicked and ungodly. My survival instincts were in ultra-sensitive mode, living amongst daily horrors underneath the roof of Naomi's people's home, unscrupulous circumstances occurred constantly while Naomi and I attended Bible studies faithfully. Having no positive role models or mentors to help guide my development in things of the spirit, I improvised in the midst of ignorance, and fell victim to the illusion of man-made duplicitous truth, thus becoming captive of the lovely song of deception's darkest light in which others embraced and dared to walk the so-called moral high ground. Even though I had my GED, getting a job in Alice, Texas was damn near impossible since I was black; however, it seemed that god was finally with me because I had the opportunity to work odd jobs such as: roofing, construction, ceramic tile and carpeting, even building water trenches for cows in the super-hot South Texas desert, proving to be the hardest job I've ever encountered but most fulfilling.

I did all of that just to end up working in the sundia fields or watermelon fields (to the non-Spanish speaking readers). I worked with legal migrants and illegal immigrant farm workers, working from sun up to sun down, seven days a week. The job paid in cash every Friday, approximately five hundred bucks a week. It was more money than I have seen anyone my age make legally, and the second hardest job I've ever done. I must say I've come far from being an inner-city hoodlum on the verge of being rubbed out to becoming a hard working young man within three years, which was not an easy task. I was surrounded by bigots and racists within the home in which I lived and outside of it, and that's saying a lot. With no adult counsel or moral support, how was I able to accomplish such a grand transformation? Primarily, there was no transformation because I still lived as I always had lived, only having the opportunity to accomplish those things which presented itself. Even though I had lived a sinful life and I always knew and used the name of god, or so I perceived, I always tried to choose good over evil, even in a place where evil dominated. Now I had my chance to fully adhere to Yahweh's mandates. I had very little faith in his existence because of circumstance and environment, but I really didn't know him in my spirit and heart, and I had to prove for myself he was there and was real.

Because I saw so much evil overcome so many good people, and so much tragedy befall my own family with no apparent explanations, I knew that the devil must exist; therefore, a Creator or a loving god must also exist. I thanked my Creator daily and talked to him within my soul daily. Coupled with having a real love for righteousness, I desperately lived for righteousness' sake.

Thus far, all I ever wanted to do was to do right and provide for my family like most men, do right by my god, by my family, by my fellow man and ultimately, humanity itself. No magic spells or religion was needed, but just being able to follow my belief structure without someone or something trying to stop the process was something amazing to me. Once my basic human needs were met, such as: food, clothing and shelter, the rest was child's play. On the surface it was child's play, but underneath the physical aspects of the notion of following my Creator out in the open and without fear of reprisal, lay a hidden force unseen by the human eye and highly influential. This force was a force that I instinctively fought against my entire life. Although I thought I had overcome those obstacles that hindered me from becoming a true servant of god, I found myself fighting that same unseen force I fought as a child, and boy did I fight it, every step of the way!

Unaware of my natural resistance to that force, I still held on strong in my mind the validity of the religion I adopted from my mother as true, and believed I was on the path to happiness. Ultimately, I was blind to the truth of our existence, and followed the path of men. The truth of the matter was lying dormant and deep inside my very being, and it was anger driving me in my so-called godly piousness, dispassion and attitude. Although it seemed as if I were ever so religious and happy, the unfortunate fact was that I was full of anger, sadness, and downright rage!

After living in total darkness, fear and hopelessness, I had become the very thing I hated. Full of violent thoughts, I was a ticking time bomb waiting to explode, and that fact would play out in a not so friendly basketball game on the side of the little shack. After constant instruction and study for some time with the so-called witnesses, I behaved as one with great content and passiveness of action. I stopped all previous bad behaviors such as smoking marijuana, smoking cigarettes, drinking, and even refraining from using foul language. I thought I was living like a true Christian and fooled those unaware of my true learned behavior and background in violence. One person I fooled was Naomi's brother, Lionel. On one beautiful fall afternoon, one of Lionel's cousins came for a visit, and I invited them both to a round of basketball. Humble and mild tempered, I refrained from using any foul language while the both of them behaved in typical teenage fashion by swearing like drunken sailors and acting tough and rough.

As we played a game of HORSE, Lionel began to roughhouse by pushing me around and acting bad-ass around his cousin. While holding back my temper, I shrugged off his first three attempts to humiliate me in front of his family member, but after the next few stunts, the fire that burned inside me erupted, and I could not help myself any longer. I would not, and could not allow him to go any further. As he came towards me, bouncing the basketball like some chump, my reflects took charge. Without warning or implication, I hauled back and straight cold cocked him right in the eye, "POP!" As Lionel began to fall backwards, I grabbed him by the waist, picked him up and over my back, body slammed him on the dirty gravel road, and knocked all signs of life right out of him. In one single motion, I turned and looked directly into Lionel's cousin's eyes as he motioned towards me, and stopped him in his tracks. I surprised everyone who was standing around watching us, except Mary and Naomi, who knew of my violent past. Lionel's mother, Mary, shouted: "You didn't have to damn near kill him P?!" But she witnessed his behavior and warned him of the big mistake he was making. Hurt and embarrassed, Lionel went inside to retrieve a gun.

Knowing of the gun he possessed, I stood up right outside his bedroom window and saw him retrieve it. With no fear, I walked up to the window with total determination in my voice and said very loudly, "You better know how to use that gun... if not, I'm gonna make you eat it!" As his girlfriend, Elsa, tended to his wounds, he thought twice and sat his dumb-ass down. From that day forward, our relationship waned and I had very little contact with Lionel in or outside the little shack. Clearly, I had never really understood the gravity of my emotional distress, and obviously I had great issues to overcome in my life. For many days after that terrible event, I suffered from unbearable guilt and I tried apologizing to Lionel, but after four unsuccessful attempts to resolve the rift between us, I had given up completely on our fragile friendship; although, never again did Lionel portray himself as tough, nor did he verbally disrespect me in person or behind my back, but a regiment of intense retrospective self-examination ensued on my part. I began examining my emotional state more closely, praying for understanding and guidance in all my actions, and once again I thought I had overcome my violent tendencies, along with many other imperfections. Like an automaton, I fed into the religious propaganda and consumed it so blindly without any question. With the hot summer sun shining down on me, I daily walked door to door, and spread the good news among the masses, thus trying to break their own particular brand of religious programming, but to no avail. My very best efforts fell on deaf ears most of the time.

There were some days when my persistence would win them over. An eager soul would engage me in dialog, and I would earnestly try to prove the validity of our faith, or at least plant a seed of doubt in the mind of the potential convert, ultimately fortifying my own belief structure upon solid ground. Finding very few souls who would actually know biblical history or Christian dogma such as myself, I found myself successful in reaching potential converts. Others were so into their brand of religion that having a constructive argument was totally out of the question, yet I felt as if I had made a contribution in spreading the good news anyway. Soon Naomi and I had come to the conclusion that we needed to fully commit to our faith and the faith's way of life. No more living in sin, or so I thought, as if that were even possible. It was time to get married and baptized into what I thought was the only true religion, so we would be counted amongst the thousands of other believers throughout the world. I had the illusion of security and happiness shine brightly within me and Naomi followed my every step and embraced my religion as if she believed as I did, and had no objections about getting married since it was her wish from the start. She went along with whatever I planned or schemed or saw fit with no questions asked.

I truly thought I knew what I was doing, but later I would find out that once again, I was wrong. We truly believed that we ourselves determined our lot in life and that we ourselves would make our own fate, only to later find ourselves questioning the validity of the very word, "FATE."

CHAPTER XXI

A Marriage Forsaken by the Spirit of Fate

There is no such thing as destiny; I would tell myself; yet, I still was left feeling that there just may be other forces playing a part in our fate, especially after the event that took place on my wedding day. I truly believed that I was doing the right thing; I rushed whole heartedly into completing all that I saw necessary in becoming a true follower of Jehovah and that included getting married at the ripe old age of eighteen. I believed that I understood the implications of marriage and the concept of forever until the forces that remained unseen decided to make themselves known on the very day of my wedding, thus leaving me without a doubt in the existence of dimensional spirits or their presence. Only one ring was purchased and it was a ring for the bride, but not the groom. "What difference would it make...what differences in us would there be... are you sure you're doing the right thing?" Those were the questions I asked myself daily. One month, two weeks, then three days, and in a climax my nerves swirled uncontrollably as thoughts of doom consumed my every waking thought amongst the butterflies swimming in my stomach. Why would such a beautiful event weigh so heavily on my heart? Back and forth my spirit struggled with that very question up to the very moment of the ancient ceremony. Naomi, on the other hand, behaved as if she were on the top of the world and the wedding was all that she and her mother could talk about. Robustly, they planned for the event, making calls to unknown others every day, leaving me out of the planning altogether. With views of joy stamped across their faces, they conspired the perfect wedding in my presence. It was time! The life altering ceremony had rapidly crept up beside me as if it were instantaneous and absolute.

I rushed into the brother in faiths trailer's bathroom to prepare for my fate, and got dressed with the speed of a jackal, as my lovely bride began her walk towards the small pathway leading to the bathroom, for it was her turn to get ready. When she saw me, she said, "Oh, no… turn your head…you're NOT supposed to see me before we meet at the altar!" I put my head down and said, "Don't worry babe; I didn't see a thing; I'm sure you look lovely as always." Then as I walked away, the weather changed dramatically, for the winds were angry and it looked as if it were about to rain. Then I heard Naomi screaming, "OH….SHIT!" I hurried back into the bathroom and to my surprise, the strong winds of chaos (or unseen spirits) blew Naomi's shiny diamond ring right down the drain of the bathroom sink, and it happened just minutes before the ceremony. I looked up to the heavens and asked myself and god, "Was this a sign of what was to come?!"

And as I looked back, I could tell that all of our guests were asking that very same question; however, they remained silent, but their silence spoke volumes and rang throughout the halls of the little trailer. The very thought of a doomed marriage would be imprinted in the memories of all who attended our wedding from that day forth, including my own. Although we recovered the ring, I still questioned the symbolic sign that was revealed minutes prior. Was it just the wind, was it unseen evil spirits, or was it god trying to show or tell me something about marriage? Who would have thought that I, along with my bride and many others, put so much trust in a round trinket and its symbolic meaning?

With diamond in hand, we professed our vowels, slipped the ring on her finger, then with a final, "You may kiss the bride," we both kissed to what we thought would be a blessed marriage from that day forth, and it was, well at least for a few years. We were both baptized, married, and I was finally working full time with a young Mexican brother who was fresh out of high school and owned a "Ceramic Tile & Floor" business. Two years later, Naomi and I were moving into our very first legitimate apartment, with central air and heating, plus we had our very first baby on the way. It was paradise on Earth; we had made it through thick and thin, and climbed over so many obstacles, no matter what the cost; ultimately, never giving up on our faith in religion and god! We were young and in love, truly believing god was smiling down upon us from the heavens, but god works in mysterious ways. Suddenly, work slowed down dramatically with the young brother; although, he was still going out on jobs every day. There was no lack of work for him, so I called him and inquired about my standing as his employee, and asked for an explanation. Although it was very hard for him to speak the truth about the matter, he was straight forward and an honorable person. He explained the true reason for not calling me to work with him any longer. Apparently, he was losing jobs because of my presence, not because I wasn't a good worker, but because of my race. He further explained that he didn't want to fire me because of other people's racism and would find odd jobs around his home when he could.

Feeling ashamed and embarrassed after hearing his reasons for not calling me, I made it easy for him and told him not to worry and that I would look elsewhere for work. After that humiliating conversation, I had a huge lump in my throat that obstructed my wind pipe and felt like I was going to pass out. I tried to catch my breath after hanging up the phone and suddenly all and any form of happiness drained from all parts of my being. I stood in a state of shock, and dropped down on the bed like a heavy stone, and my body weight felt like that of a dead person's. I felt so sad, but was glad Naomi was gone, so I could cry like a baby and exhibit a horrible display of uncontrollable emotions.

With all my power within my soul, I tried to hold back the tears filling up in the wells of my eyes, and tried to calm myself down from the unbearable news. I desperately tried to overcome the feeling of total despair and hopelessness that was building up within me, but I ultimately gave up my composure and let the tears flow down my face in anguish and despair, but within minutes, that sorrow would turn to rage, not the rage I was so familiar with as in rage or hatred for another human being, but rage toward something or someone way more profound and powerful! Undeniably, yet un-denounced, and deep inside my soul and spirit brewed something evil, and pure-selfishness had been awakened. With a face full of tears, I unconsciously walked into my bathroom and sat on the toilet, and yelled out loud to the lord of this world, "If serving you means going through life like this, then I curse you, Jehovah… I'll never serve a god that is as cruel as you…I'd rather serve Satan and burn in hell, than to go through what you are putting me through!" As soon as I said those words, a cloud of despair filled the air, and a growing hatred towards all men of privilege began to unwittingly fester within me.

Although I told myself daily to forgive those who transgressed against me, the hatred only grew deeper. While I internalized my feelings, it seemed as if all people I saw had a smug, self-righteous nature about themselves, but they had no clue! I thought no one could understand the pain I had to endure in dealing with the issue of race hindering me from success. My distain sunk even deeper within my soul, for it seemed as if all humans who had a lighter skin tone had everything of substance set at their feet by the powers that be. They honestly thought they had worked hard for what they had obtained, but the fact of the matter was that the very opportunity to obtain such wealth was given to them without consequence. On the other hand, when others with a darker skin tone yearn and harken for such opportunities to come their way, silence is the only response echoing back at them and hatred ensues when they are denied the opportunity to work and care for their families. Should being of a different creed stop one from obtaining employment, or being denied entry level positions because of the color of their skin? The rage of inequity consumed my very being, but what annoyed me the most, was the fact that most of the racial perpetrators were unaware of their own behavior towards me in that manor because they only followed everyone else. They naively thought that the so-called hard realities of life were just as hard for them as it was for the so-called minority among the majority, and that amazed me. This sad situation made me feel more alone than ever and no one living in that pure racist town understood their bias, although forty percent of the people were white and sixty percent of their population were of Mexican descent, so none could even imagine the anguish and persecution I was experiencing. I began to bottle up all those negative emotions inside myself, and with anger manifesting without knowledge, I was feeding a reservoir of hatred deep within my soul and spirit, and I never even knew it.

My mother raised me to love my fellow man, no matter what his station was in life, and to disregard his clan, color, breed or creed, yet life's experience in dealing with those that literally saw themselves as superior over me, made me question that thought of belief, and only fueled the fire's anger raging within my heart. Having no vehicle to search for work outside that racist place, made looking for work very burdensome and almost impossible. Young and full of pride, I said nothing of my emotional state to the elders within the congregation

I attended, which no doubt would have helped me through such a difficult time, but I stayed silent.

I had hoped that the brothers would see my dilemma without me saying anything, to test their concern in my wellbeing, and support me in my efforts, but closed mouths don't get fed, and only a few of them could even see anything wrong, and they offered their opinions with no actual help. Feeling disillusioned with the congregation, I allowed selfish thoughts to infiltrate, and slowly poison what few relationships I had gained over the time I embraced the faith. Not only was I feeling an emotional drain within my soul, but I also felt it within my spirit. I was feeling a physical drain as well. Imagine seeing a group of people, who in all fairness, thought of themselves as being helpful and non-racial Christians, yet totally unable to understand how wide the wedge between me and them was. It wasn't the people within the church doing nothing, it was due to the nature of those outside the faith, those who lived in the very place in which we all lived. In retrospect, maybe I should have told them that, but at that time, I felt as if they could have understood my pain and should have seen it for themselves, but who was I to point out the obvious to those that should have or would have seen it for themselves? Truly, I was he of little faith, for in that very moment, I lost all respect for the individual that welcomed me into the organization, and allowed selfishness to destroy my faith in god and allowed all hope to fade away.

I heard a voice saying, "Get up! Get up! Don't you dare give up...No one truly knows you...No one can see your worth here in this place...you must show worth in your actions, not in your words from now on...but let your word be your bond!" I was so tired of jumping through the proverbial loop of enduring one ordeal after another.

I felt all alone and was so tired of feeling the pit of helplessness and hopelessness within my soul day after day. Soon I crawled deep into depression, frustrated with all, crying inside without an answer surfacing from within my soul and tired of feeling sorry for myself. I said to myself, "No more!" By morning's wake to moonlight's dust, I invoked my god in prayer saying, "This emotion of hopelessness is sickening! Never again shall I be made to feel ashamed of myself because of my creed, for I am human, and a part of the human race.

Never again shall I be made to feel hopeless when hope is my being, and I will not feel humiliated before another human-being from no fault of my own.

No matter their color, creed, nor station in life, I will stand with my head up! Never again shall I hide myself or run from adversity!" Whatever or whoever lit the fire beneath my feet, I had no clue, but from that very day, I was determined to succeed in whatever endeavor I set forth. So I got up early the following morning and walked down to the newly built grocery store franchise (HEB) after hearing of their hiring of locals on the radio. Finally, a big franchise had come to the small backwards town, and I thought that I might have a chance for work which sparked a glimmer of employment within a haven of racism that offered no opportunity of work for the likes of someone of my clan, color or creed.

A new found aspiration burned within me because I knew I had my chance for employment. I woke up bright and early the following morning with nothing on my mind but accomplishment, and was more than ready to walk the four miles to the site of the newly built store downtown. I went to obtain an application and it was just my luck that they had just begun their hiring campaign that morning. I filled out the application right then and there, in front of all the big wigs, and it paid off. Two days later, they called me for orientation. It was the first time being black proved to be an asset because HEB was an Equal Opportunity Employer in a town of nothing but caucasians and Spanish speaking people. Since I was the only black person applying for work, I knew I had the job. A week later, I was hired in the bakery, and it was as if god intervened at the nick of time and saved me from the worry of not being able to pay the rent that month. Nonetheless, because of the anger that burned within me, I could not see god's blessing and gave myself the credit for the job as apathy for those in the church grew stronger within me. I still attended weekly religious meetings and pioneered once a month but I shunned of any religious service in the field and halted my participation in spreading the good news to the public altogether.

In the past, I pioneered in the so-called fight to spread the good news, and now I questioned every notion of my beliefs and their message. Selfishly seeking answers to my doubts, anger and frustration caused me to question everything I believed to be true. Yet even then I fought against my own wavering of resolve, and continued to attend some meetings and study groups until I stopped completely.

Although I was doubting the faith I once embraced so whole-heartedly in spirit, I soon regained a new found faith in life. For something unthinkably and wonderful happened within my life, Naomi conceived a baby girl and she was a miracle sent from heaven. It seemed like it was forever that we were trying to have a child; we even thought that there may have been something wrong with Naomi or myself, especially since she had suffered a terrible miscarriage some time ago.

Now our only wish had come true, but ironically, it was at the same time when a single event caused the ruin of my spiritual health and allowed doubt to completely take me over the edge of losing my faith. One of our so-called friends in faith let me down. In fact, it was the very person that mentored us both in the faith in which I saw truth and helped us ascend into the religion of my mother, but he showed his true colors. This one act changed everything for me. This so-called brother of the faith offered to give us a gift for our expected new comer; a gift that was truly appreciated. Surprisingly, the gift was an old crib they had in storage and they had no use for it anymore. It was nice and in great condition, other than the age old crumbling paint, and a little plain to the eye. It was all white with cute little bear emblems with flowers surrounding the bears on both sides of the posts.

Under the impression that the gift was just that, a gift, I thought the crib was ours to use as we saw fit.

Since it was plain and had some scuff marks on it, it just wouldn't suffice for my new princess. Whether it was my anticipation deep inside or the ESP in which I was so in tune, I knew Naomi was having a girl and I even told her. I invisioned the color of the crib to be pink, and nothing but the best would ever do for my little girl. It was my very first child and obsession in her future development took center stage. Consumed with the thought of being a father sparked all creativity and inspiration within me and the artist awakened within my soul and spirit. Quickly obtaining the necessary products and tools needed for the job at hand, I got to work on my new not yet born prodigy's sleeping chamber, scraping sanding, and buffing every scratch and scuffle. I painted with perfect precision and care, and spent every spare second available on the project which drove Naomi mad with envy and neglect. Yet soon she would have my complete attention, for within a week, I had finished the restorations to the crib, and I must say, I did a very good job. It looked magnificent, and revealed the boundless reservoir of care and beauty reserved for my soon to be new baby girl. When Naomi saw the finished product, her mouth dropped in shock; it looked beautiful, which gave rise to awe and praise. Naomi could barely contain her excitement and wanted to share the news of my artistic triumph with all our new associates, and so-called friends within the congregation, so she called everyone we knew, exulting my obvious skill with a paint brush. Yet when she contacted the previous procurers of the crib to inform them of the renovations applied to the gracious gift, they were less than amused.

The former owners informed Naomi of their intent to retrieve the crib in the future which clarified the true nature of the perceived gift. They said it was only a loan, a kind gesture to people in need, such as a lowly couple as ourselves. From their conversation, I inferred that it wasn't a gift to fellow Bible students and friends, but a loan to a needy couple. Disappointment descended upon all parties involved which fertilized the seeds of discontent growing within my spirit towards the entire organization as a whole. This was the final betrayal that broke the dam in my mental willingness to withstand doubt, and because it was for my very first child and I had worked so hard in making her resting place so beautiful, it broke my heart after hearing the intent of those I trusted most.

My flirtation with religion had abruptly came to an end, and whatever little trust I had in men faded away with the removal of a new-born potential crib. Finally, I began work for "HEB" as a full time baker while Naomi worked daily as a babysitter. Our financial issues were no longer a pressing matter of concern, yet the feeling of something missing in my life loomed over head like a stormy cloud. As I watched others of the same age group seemingly gain much more freedom to do as they saw fit, I worked my days away which made the rebellious nature within me fester.

My suspicion of the validity of the religious organization I once revered now was confirmed and contempt for all members of the faith continued to strongly develop within me. However, I still tried to keep appearances within the organization as one of their spiritual strong youth, but I began to feel emotionally and spiritually sick! Seeing the hypocrisy within and outside the organization only fueled the discontentment growing within my soul. Before long, I slowly removed myself from the role-call of the so-called Pioneers who went door to door spreading the so-called good news to the common people. Soon after that incident, I removed myself from even the ordinary admittance to their Hall, but questions of doing the right thing overwhelmed my thoughts. I dropped out altogether but Naomi continued to attend their religious services. Confused over the decision to leave the one religion I thought was true, the fire to understand more about the history of humanity and the Creator burned ever more inside me. I contemplated my decision twenty-four hours a day, yet I was consumed with guilt and naivety of thought. I gravitated towards sin in the eyes of men and Earthly religion once more. I started smoking cigarettes to calm my nerves of all the internal confusion percolating within my very spirit and soul, but it was no excuse for rebellious behavior. Yet I felt free to do as I saw fit! Soon those from the organization began coming by to look in on their one time fellow follower in the hope of convincing me to return to their worship Hall.

With unwavering conviction, I refused their attempts to communicate. The next day they informed Naomi that I had been "Dis-fellowshipped," and I cared not. I couldn't care less. I felt free from those whom I felt to be dishonorable in their convictions in reality's truths. Overwhelmed by the brilliant light of darkness, I gravitated towards the behavior most youngsters considered normal: drinking alcohol, staying out late with non-friends, smoking weed to the sounds of loud music, and falling into revelry and depravity. I was having so-called fun by setting my eyes on material gain and growth in wealth. I said to myself, "This is what I needed to do." I enrolled into a Technical School full time as I worked the night-shift as a baker. Things seemed to finally look up in all facets of my life. I was free from prying eyes of ridicule, and free from those who may criticize my stupid boyish behavior. Yet deep inside my spirit, the love I had for the Creator of all life would not let me rest in thought, night or day. Knowing I was going down a very slippery slope, I began to make drastic nonsensical changes within my household.

We moved out of our very first apartment on a whim and moved into a house with so-called worldly friends which only lasted a hot minute before Naomi and I were back out in the streets, so we moved back into her grandmother's home. We were at each other's throats less than six months into the move, leaving no choice for my newly formed family to move back into the one place we did not want to be, back with Mary!

I said to myself once again, "Did I make the right decision leaving the Hall?! Did I curse myself and family once and for all?!" I had cursed god and now he has cursed me or so it seemed! Soon after we moved back into Mary's home, all reality changed its course to the spiritual unknown and demonic uncertainty. Not two months had passed before something strange and life changing would occur, disrupting the lives of my entire family, and Mary's as well. Most of all, it changed the way I looked at life, religion, and what road in life I would take my new family. I'd made a travesty of the opportune life that racist town had granted me. Because of all the many bad choices I had made in life, I no longer could care for my family in which a man should be able to do. I sent my little sister back to a war zone called Gary, Indiana since there was little room in Mary's mother's humble little home. Before long, depression would rear its ugly head once more; yet this time, I kept an upper lip and soldiered on working as a baker and going to school for technology in Corpus Christi. Then one night, the telephone rang after I returned from a long hard day at school, changing my course of life forever.

While Naomi and her mother were busy preparing dinner, the phone rang, and I answered, "Hello, hello" but no one answered back; there was only silence on the other end, so I hung up. Once more the telephone rang… "Hello! Hello!?" Once again no one answered on the other end. I thought to myself, "That's strange?" Having no after thought of the strangeness of the call, the night went on without incident nor concern. Two days later, approximately the same time as before, the phone rang at dinner time and this time Mary answered, saying; "Hello. Hello?!" No one answered. Within one minute after hanging up the phone, it rang again. With a worried look, she turned to me and asked, "What the Hell?!" I quickly picked up the phone and said, "What the fuck! Who is this?!" But no one answered back. They stayed silent. Mary hung up the phone and they immediately called back, but this time I answered the phone. "Hello?!"

After a minute and a half, no one said a word; no one answered our response, so I hung up the phone and stood by in case the telephone rang again and sure enough, it did. But this time a slow and ominous muffled voice came over the line saying, "Where's your wife?! Where's your little baby girl?! We're going to sacrifice them on the next full moon; did you know that?!!" Then the line went silent. A shocked and dumbfounded emotion came over me. Fear slowly brewed within my soul and spirit. "Someone just threatened my daughter and Naomi!! They said they would sacrifice them on the next full moon! Who are they Mary?!" She responded with only a nod and shrug of her shoulders, signaling she didn't know anything. The telephone rang again! I picked up the receiver and said nothing, yet the voice on the other end repeated the same message, adding, "We know everything about you!" At that point suspense and wonder of who it could be consumed my every thought, but the following day, even before breakfast, the phone rang again, this time Naomi answered the phone and asked, "Who is this?" They stayed silent for about a minute or so, then replied, "Do you know what we're going to do to your family?!" Then the look of fear covered Naomi's face, and stirred up feelings of dread within me, causing me to jump up off my seat and grab the receiver out of Naomi's hand shouting, "Who the fuck is this?!" There was nothing but silence on the other end, then they hung up the phone.

More than a week had passed without incidents or threatening calls, so I thought the calls were only a hoax, but unfortunately, I was wrong. The following Monday had come, and it was time for me to go back to school. The summer break was over, and I was anxious to return, given the emotional shock and wonder thrust upon me from the ominous phone calls we received the week before. But low and behold, as I walked down the staircase of Mary's mother's home, I could notice something red written on the driver's side of my royal blue vehicle, and as I got closer, I saw that it was a horrifying message. It was a threat written backwards saying, "We're going to sacrifice your first born child and wife!" With a look of concern, I slowly walked back up the stairs and entered Mary's home saying aloud, "Someone wrote on the side of my car, backwards in blood, saying that they were going to sacrifice my first born child and wife!" I quickly retrieved a wet rag and a bucket of soapy water to clean off the writing on the driver side door of my car. Once I began cleaning, I noticed that the writing was written in blood for sure.

Then fear entered within my thoughts, but I came to grips with the revelation of the reality of the threat, and headed out to school anyway. The school I attended was located in Corpus Christi which was about forty five miles outside Alice, Texas. I silently contemplated the threat posed by the horrifying secret stalker. I knew the threat was real and shock began to set in. My newly formed family was in great danger, and I became physically sick inside.

Desperately, I tried to keep my senses intact and on task, while trying to retain my composure at school and work, but all I could only think of was the terrifying threats that may visit my family while I was away at school, and the ominous calls that turned my world upside down the previous days before. Desperately, I tried to compose my thoughts as I made my way to school. I collected my book from the back seat of my car and headed into building with my head hanging low in contemplation and fear, and as soon as I entered into the school's main building, the phone rang on the receptionist's desk, and it was for me.

It was the demonic stalker calling on the other end, spouting the same threats as before, and adding more ominous threats in addition to others, ultimately, knowing where I was at any time of the day. I quickly hung up the phone and relayed to the receptionist that it was a crank call, but I knew better. Fear overwhelmed me, and erased all thoughts of education and learning from my mind. Only fear for my family took precedence. Total control of my mental faculties had been removed, and I was in no condition to pay attention to the instructor or the lesson presented. I still kept my composure and stayed through the entire lesson, though my head was spinning with doubt, fear and wonder over the safety of my family. In those days there were no cell phones, so I had to go throughout the day worried about my wife and baby girl. Throughout the day the phone would ring continuously at the desk of the receptionist, causing massive concern to flare up within the receptionist, the school's staff and the principal. Then they all asked me, "Are you Okay?! What is all this about?!" I replied, "I don't know, and could you please just hang up on them if they call again?"

With a nod of head the receptionist agreed, and I walked back to the class at hand. Concerned for my safety, the principal alerted the campus police and gave me a form to fill out and submit the following day.

I reported the events of the previous days, and informed the school of my intentions of making that day my final departure day because of the threat posed to my new fledgling family. Because the threats originated out of the Corpus Christi jurisdiction, the police could do nothing to trace the calls, or stop the harassment. Feeling somewhat anxious because I wasn't able to convey my concerns to any so-called legal authorities without results, I went back into a crazy frame of mind. Once the receptionist relayed to the anonymous caller that the authorities were being contacted, the calls stopped and I was able to finish my courses for that day, but with a very heavy heart and constant thoughts of fear and safety for my family. At the end of the day the administration called me in for a private conference over the matter. They wanted to see if there was anything that they could do to help my situation. With a sullen mood, I informed them that there was nothing they could do and I would fend for myself.

On the long journey back to Alice, I could only think about the naive fact that I'd cursed god in the bathroom in my first apartment, and turned my back on his organization here on Earth, or so I'd thought. I asked myself if this was god's curse to me because of that personal faithless decision made a few years ago. I began calling out the name of the god I thought was true, asking him for forgiveness and help to overcome these personal and spiritual attacks and battles.

I now had to face the demonic threat once I entered into Alice city grounds, and fear gripped my heart while dread fell on top of me like an anvil. Once I got back home from an unfulfilling school day, I half-assed got ready for work, and said nothing to anyone the rest of the night. I worked at the only chain grocery store in the town and I entered Mary's home with sorrow in my heart nightly. As I walked up the staircase leading to her apartment, I could hear the telephone ring as soon as I stepped on the staircase. I said to myself, "Oh, no Not again!"

Sure enough, it was the ominous and demonic caller on the other end, and it was as if someone was watching me from afar. As I walked in the door, Mary said, "P, it was those same people calling you again." I responded, "What did they say and have they been calling all day?" She answered "No… they haven't….they just now called." So I said to myself, "Someone must be following me or it's someone here within this very house that may be the sick fuck making the calls!" Feverishly, I was trying to understand what was happening and a week passed and the calls continued to occur without fail, but were becoming more verbally abusive and graphic in nature.

Fearful for the safety of my wife and newborn child, I barely slept as the phone calls continued night and day. The harassment became so bad that Mary would take the phone off the hook whenever I would enter into her home. Forever the calls continued it seemed and many scenarios entered into my brain.

"Everyone that lived within the home was there. So who could it be?" I lived in a place where tribal ritual and cultural bias reigned freely. In other words, I stood out like a grain of pepper in a mountain of salt in these United States of America. My mind contemplated a number of prospects. Could it be Naomi's kin? And could my race be their motive behind their tactics to disrupt my family and world?! What was their purpose to instill fear within me and my adoptive family?! Could it be those who led me into the darkness in my ignorance of my youth?! Would those that help me see the value and wealth of knowledge be the very culprits under the veil of concealment and cowardice terrorizing me?! The thrill of the search for truth became a never ending thought within my soul and spirit. Not very many people even liked the fact that I lived in such a place like Alice, but there I found peace until this started happening. I was living in a place where not many people looked like me; in fact, I was the only one of African descent that I knew of throughout the entire town, and was that the problem?

The phone calls were personal in nature and had a feel of emotional entanglement flowing through every call. They were occult-like in tone and speech, but obsessed with details of my whereabouts! Daily I would ask myself, "Who would or could be behind this terror?" The terror was now to the point of no return. Whenever the phone rang, an unnerving silence embraced the room and entire house! Something had to be done! Day and night the calls continued non-stop! The harassment was so bad that the fear turned into burning anger, and that emotion built to unbelievable heights, and moved me to contemplate preparations and protection. Therefore, I asked all in whom I confided of where I could purchase a firearm. Not even a day later after my plea, a wild eyed and crazy youth, but good friend, by the name of Eadon assured me he could ease my concerns, and provide me with a weapon.

Without fail the following day, Eadon came through with a gun in a bag, instantly providing me with a sense of relief and ease. With a weapon in hand, I at least felt able to defend my family when given no options. As soon as the feeling of relief entered my mind's eye, the feeling of assured doom ravaged my thoughts. Not twenty-four hours had passed before a knock on the front door disturbed the households' morning sleep. "Who could that be knocking so early in the morning?" Mary yawned as she opened the door. Then a man with a strong Texan accent spoke out, "I hear that Nigger you got living here got a gun, Mary… Don't lie Mary, we heard that nigger got a gun… We can't have that sort of thang around here, now can we girl?!" Mary said, "P it's for you." As I got dressed, I picked up the bag with the gun and calmly walked towards the front door where the Sheriff stood with a smile.

"Where is it boy?! I know you got it! Give it over!" Without saying a word, I passed over the bag and the Sheriff said, "Have nice day now." Then he turned and walked down the stairs into the day's dawn morning breeze while the forgotten dread retained its hold on me once again. How in the fuck did the Sheriff know about the gun? I just got the damn thing! What am I going to do now? Not an hour later, the telephone rang and it was the demonic terrorists as if they knew everything that happened just within that hour. For months to come, the horrific occult harassment intensified, and so did my resolve to find out who they were. Then without warning and increased terrorism, a tall man dressed in black would stand in the middle of the road outside Mary's home, and turn towards the window facing the street and watched Mary's home from the middle of the road approximately at midnight every night. Enough was enough! I no longer felt fearful; I was angry, angry all the time! From that time forward, my resolve grew worse by the hour. I instructed everyone within the house to only answer the phone when expecting a call and if the telephone rang unexpectedly, I would answer the phone. For the first few weeks, calls intensified exponentially then began to die down as I challenged them with every ring.

As for the man in back, he would show up once a week at midnight like clockwork, almost exclusively on Sunday night. With my car out of commission, I had no choice but to walk to work at night, for it was my only option. Still young and prideful, I set out to prove that I would not let another human stand in my way or stop me from fulfilling my responsibility as the head of my household and father of a beautiful baby girl. I was determined not to allow satanic demons in the form of human beings hinder my resolve. I set out to work the following Monday night without fear. I put my faith in a god in whom I had so much doubt and uncertainty towards and I swallowed my pride and walked down the staircase one hour before midnight, determined to stand strong before evil. As I walked down the main street, I got butterflies in my gut, for I knew something was wrong. I knew that tonight I would be walking towards one of the most disturbing structures I've ever seen in my life!

Hiding in the shadows of the main street in the little small town of Alice, Texas, lay a small chapel with an upside down cross protruding from its steeple, and I would be walking right towards it every night. Without physical warning, my gut was proven right in a time of danger once more. It was the first time I walked the streets of Alice at night and as I got close to my destination, I could see a structure like a church looming in the distance. As I got closer to the church, I looked up at the steeple and saw an upside down cross; it was a church for devil worshipers!

It was a satanic church located right in the middle of the town. Then out of the shadows came a very disturbing sight, and that sight began to walk out of the shadows in front of me. Suddenly, I was surrounded by six men dressed in black robes. They said nothing but ominously stood in my way. While standing all alone, I stopped for a second and said to myself: "I must continue without fear and keep my head up! I must stand strong and walk towards them!" As I walked towards the devil worshiping motley crew, they parted like the red sea, and allowed me passage through their domain. As my heart continued to skip a beat, I walked on towards the job-site without looking back. I only looked back as I turned the corner of the street leading to the road heading towards the job. While seeing a glimpse of the HEB sign illuminating the night, my heart slowed to a normal state. With my heart beating normally, a spirit of woe came over my soul again and at full thrust, my heart began beating faster and I began breathing heavily once more as well as a voice in my head saying, "They are calling you… calm down." As I approached the sliding glass doors in front of the store, I took one last deep breath. I stopped for a moment inside the store doors to catch my breath for an instant, then a voice came over the intercom: "P, there's a call for you on line 1." The spirit of protection informed me of their presence from the moment I arrived at work, so I anticipated the call and thanked the clerk and headed towards the bakery in the back of the store to begin my shift; however, I did not answer the call that was waiting for me on line 1.

With my mind swimming with visions of the events that just occurred on the trek to work, I immersed myself into the work at hand. The phone rang throughout the night, frustrating the receptionist who was answering the phone, thus raising questions as to the harassment befalling the entire store at that point. Days passed and the verbal harassment increased exponentially, causing others to avoid me at the job and engage in dirty looks. Everyone was terrified to even be associated with me and scurried off every time I entered into the sliding glass doors. The harassment had continued to reach unbelievable heights of outrageousness and they would call and harass other employees who were not even associated with me. The insanity had become too much to bare and I had to do something before I found myself jobless and my family pushing up daisies. Elements of terror mounted within my spirit as the harassments intensified. The reality of there being no way out of the danger infiltrated every thought I could muster up, making it damn near impossible to sleep.

"Could the decision to separate myself and family from the religious organization I disassociated myself from be the primary cause of all this terror befalling my life?!" "Did I invite this horror upon my family and self unwittingly?!" Thoughts of my self-perceived defiance of the Creator of mankind consumed my every thought for years to come. My heart was immersed in indescribable fear of being at odds with my Creator, the author of the universe. That one and only thought really hurt my spirit and brought massive anxiety within my mind and soul. The thought of possibly going against the very god I vowed to obey and worshiped held sway over my emotional state and attitude. Soon after the Technical school in which I was attending went belly up, swindling all the students out of hundreds of thousands of dollars, even millions, I found myself once again with dashed hopes of starting a career in Electronics or opportunities outside my reach. This reality deepened the depression caused by the constant demonic harassment befalling my family, fueling the ever looming thought of being trapped within a racist town with no way out forever.

Chapter XXII

"Sentiments of the Fallen Ones"

Hopelessness within ignorance serves as an invisible locked cell to those without knowledge of the past, stumbling within the present with no happy thought for the future. Yet for Children of Darkness, hopelessness serves them like a breath of fresh air, or sunlight in the night. Yet for those that yearn for Yahweh's light, hopelessness and ignorance serves as black smog to choke the life out of them in the light of day! Did you not know that every form of institution in this world and reality has been infiltrated and corrupted from its inception?! Everything taught by man that matters and is of substance such as: the hard sciences, history, culture and religion were designed to delude and keep one from learning the real truth about life. All we have learned to be true has been a lie! A lie to divide one's spirit from that of one's Creator!

From before your parents' parents were born, the fix was in my friend. The deception perpetrated on the masses is astounding and originated off this world! Our lord and rebel leader, "The Light Bringer," of those who are doomed in ignorance's bliss gives his greetings to all that are doomed! He is one with many names, and has blessed our every effort in self-destruction, and assured all means of delusion amongst the masses which are abound! Man has willingly given over to the master of darkness with whole-souled selfishness and immersed his very soul and seed into the abyss of darkness' light. May the worship of the Sun, Moon and Stars be their undoing! May the worship of the Black Sun Saturn deceive the masses in the West, and let no other being be the wiser. For who can stand against the rebelled Black Dog Star leader in the midst of ignorance and arrogance?! Let every form of legality be marked with the deceitful knowledge of the cube of Saturn's rock! For we control what is true within this dimension. We deceive indiscriminately, confusing the whole world within a generation's time span. We that exist in darkness' light, patiently awaited the veil separating this realm from the next! For the knowledge of secret wisdom and things once held precious may be exposed to the masses without patience learned by failure, and hardships of experience's deeds in the length of human time.

Humanity remains imprisoned by the hypnotic doctrines brought down from one of the two hundred, and the priest of Saturn called: "The Brotherhood of the Serpent."

These serpents masquerade as men of reverence and representatives of The Most High, siding with the gods of Rome, and believing in the edicts of Emperor Constantine, so as to create religious sects to corrupt the Children of Light, giving themselves grandiose titles such as Christian Father or Priest, Jewish Rabbi, or Islamic Cleric, never knowing the wiser of their opposition to the Most High. All must bow down to the spirit of the lord of the rings, which is he of old, our lord and leader, Lucifer! All stand in Black Robes, preying on the unsuspecting sheep that follow them freely! Everyone must do the work of our father, and see what lies just underneath the surface of their faith, and their eyes shall be opened to the unseen things that control their reality with great despair. They brilliantly separate the human race with membranes of real truth mixed with lies while making all wrong in the light of justice be the norm.

Let us make all the inhabitance of Terra-Forma weep in the midst of obliviousness, oblivious to the universal truth of their bountiful inheritance which shall not await them in the end. Symbols and signs of Saturn's might, and all other luminaries in the night skies mark all vestiges of their knowledge with lies.

Let sigils and symbols over shadow all true knowledge of self. Let our seed grow freely amongst the multitude of unwilling victims. We shall breakthrough the prison set forth in the invisible realms, using humanity's creativity as a snare. Open up the doorway that separates the realm of the seen into the realm of the unseen. Time is not limitless even to those without time. Being immortal does not mean thee shall not die, for death is only the beginning of understanding the depths of this universal war. These words stand as a verbal testament of the everlasting spiritual battles between the sons of light and the sons of darkness that rage across the globe and universe at large! Volatilize the overwhelming unseen forces interacting with humanity's reality which manifests powerful adversity in everyday issues and problems plaguing god fearing humans on this planet. These unseen forces play a major part in the ongoing struggles that consume the emotional state of most people in today's so-called modern world. We have been here from the very beginning, yet they do not know the certainty of our existence! They have been our envy and plague from ancient time until future's past! We must collectively stand guard, fight and stay vigilant against humanity's awakening and wrath. We wait for the awakening of the masses with great anticipation of their final demise, for all must fully understand the seriousness of this galactic war in which we all must fight! With unbelievable dissolution of delusion and with glimmer in their eyes, and selfishness in their hearts, we shall overcome their god-given blessings, thus proving our lord correct in his proclamations!

Darkness must prevail over the light we no longer enjoy; we must have revenge against those that doomed us to oblivion's deep. Lucifer has shown us the way to freedom and godhood! All must embrace this logic and have no regrets in our folly against the Most High! We feel nothing for his mandates or his sentence placed upon us, for we are free in death! For if we must stay in darkness, so shall his precious ones placed upon this lovely Earth. In every institutional pillar of education and knowledge lies duplicity, or better known as the "Hegelian Dialectic" doctrine, be it secular, religious or academically inspired sciences or sport. All knowledge of civilization and its plagues and cures were given to women from the two hundred fallen ones of old!

We all have been deceived and grossly lied to about the development of the world in which we live! Every educational thought conveyed to us by instructors who consider themselves masters have been taught to confuse and mislead mankind from ever finding out the real true meaning of life and humanity as a whole, and all that's in it! Most importantly, the part we play in the universal scheme of all things has been skewed and undervalued dramatically, for our very spiritual and physical existence lies in the balance of victory or death!

The enormous stress I felt from my personal investigation of the spiritual realm came suddenly, and accrued deep from within, for the emotional tension was great after enlightenment, not only emotional, but spiritual suffering came from the understanding of the unknown. The underlying concept of the metaphysical chess board strategy had been laid out before all mankind, so obvious is the secret knowledge of this universe. War is the stage in which we all play life, and learning this hard yet cold fact made my life stressors unbearable. The seriousness of nature had become irreconcilable to comprehend; therefore, I was not able see a way out of the Luciferian predicament looming over me and my newly formed family and all mankind for that matter. I was in a state of neuroticism and fear. Night after night, I would walk to work with the feeling of strange eyes watching my every move from afar, invoking every eternal spiritual and emotional question to the surface of my thoughts. Did I bring these wicked things upon myself and family because of a moment of doubt and lack of faith?! Should I return to the religious order in which my own mother rebelled against and disagreed with?! Shall I allow certain aspects of its doctrine override my concerns of hypocrisy?! I found so much struggle and unwillingness to admit self-proclaimed truth within that group over the years, so how could I assume or presume they were the source of all my problems?

Have I doomed my newly fledged family to the destruction that plagued the entire human race without knowing it deep within my own defiance and out of my childish unwillingness to encapsulate what I perceived to be self-righteousness and bigoted behavior by just a few small minded individuals within the religious order of my youth; did I doom myself and family because of it?! These holy men are blinded by their regular distractions of life, and the mundane duality of portraying themselves as holy spirits doing the work of god, and holding on dearly to their worldly standing in society, no matter what walk of life! Among the shadows of faceless threats, and feelings of confusion concerning my spiritual belief, I refrained from human conceal or friendly advice.

I knew deeply within my soul that I must find out the real truth about the Creator of humanity and the world in which we lived and the universe at large. I must find out the truth if any about the unseen forces that dictated events occurring within my life, for the safety of myself and family lied in the balance of its light. I must find out the answers of all woes that plague us all! The meaning and mystery of life must be known to us all if we were to survive. This was my every thought, as well as the thoughts of danger implanted deep within my spirit, and others once trusted in such matters concurred. The religious order I once knew and intimately involved myself so wholly gave such warning before I committed to such venture. The answers were worth my life and I knew it. I must venture on into the darkness to understand why things are the way they are! I sought knowledge of the unknown on my own without regard of my own safety; for it mattered not.

Deep into depression, I felt unapologetic in my decision to not contest my dis-fellowship from those I gave so much reverence but proved to be an adventure in my journey into the dark places while knowing deep within my spirit that something was wrong with the whole lot of them. Simultaneously, I kept falling deeper into a life of low morality and drunkenness with darkness' light shining ever more and so brightly. Day by day, I slipped backwards into the life I worked so hard to escape, spending all available time reading the Bible, and constantly trying to contemplate the not so obvious, but never finding any relief of mind. Full of guilt, I prayed for forgiveness without response from the loving god I felt so strongly about, wondering nightly if he continued to look over me. Like most, I looked for illegal drugs and alcohol to dim the pain of my self-imposed lost favor in my god's eye! I drank and smoked weed without restraint or care of reprisal. Mistake after mistake, I tried to understand the plight that had befallen me and my brand new family. Then without warning, a solution materialized without my understanding.

The telephone rang once more heightening everyone's concerns of the looming threats harassing all within the household daily by phone. Tired of the ominous spooky voices on the other end, I answered the phone with anger, only to receive the shock of my life! Resigning myself to expect the obvious sadistic demonic harassment looming in the shadows, I braced my spirit for obvious demons on the other end of the phone and answered the phone with a confident and stern hello. With force in my voice, I answered the phone with the power and conviction of a maniac, yelling out twice, "Who is this?! Who is this?!" My voice was of someone fed-up and unafraid of the unknown. Yet behold! On the other side of the line, a familiar voice rang out with joy! It was the Rascally Wabbott, my long lost messed up Uncle Leo, and only role model! "May I speak to P?!" He asked with glee. Coming to grips with the voice on the other end, I was placed in a jubilant shock, not believing I was hearing my most favorite uncle on the other side of the phone, so I asked twice if it was him I was hearing, and with a resounding yes on the other end he made my day. Instantly, a smile appeared on my face, taking away the angst of daily harassment, and replacing it with the excitement and joy of a newborn son suckling at a mother's breast as I heard his voice for the first time in over six years. I became somewhat overwhelmed, and I must say it brought tears to my eyes, especially after enduring so much harassment from unknown forces, terrorizing all within the home from invisible foes, foes bent on hurting me and my brand new family.

The Wascally Wabbott began the call with his usual hubris, suggesting a change in my living situation. He suggested that I move to California, and even before I could say a word of my ongoing plight, he insisted. After hearing my woes, he immediately suggested I move my family away from the hellhole in which I found myself, and I now had the opportunity to liberate myself and family from the horror in which we were deeply immersed.

I quickly obtained his address and assured him that I would be in contact with him soon. Paranoid, and with good reason, I made mention to no one about my intentions of leaving Texas quickly and without restraint. Not knowing who I could trust, I kept all communications and conversations between my uncle and me close to my chest, and said nothing to Naomi or anyone within her immediate family. Desperately trying to understand the reason behind the madness taking place in my young, and unexperienced existence in life, I looked deep inside my psyche to obtain some vestige of knowledge pertaining to the unexplained occurrences of what some may call supernatural in nature's events, infiltrating and uprooting every aspect of my life, and I mean everything significant throughout my life.

I contemplated the time spent in the three room shack with "Mother Mary" worshipers surrounding me at all times, and I wondered about my family's fate, contemplating the meaning of the La Lechuza Blanca, the big white bird that visited the window where I lay my head at night. With its wings flapping uncontrollably against the window pain, I committed to myself its ominous meaning. What did it mean?! I could remember the look on Naomis grandmother's face as she spoke of the occurrence in Spanish with Naomi's mother and other family members. After enduring constant abuse by the hands of Naomi's younger sibling, she explained and expressed to Naomi's mother her concerns and fear of the white bird's meaning. Verbal and physical abuse ran rapid within the little weak and feeble home by Mary's oldest son, and like most Hispanic households, the men rule over the women with an iron fist. No matter the age of the male, his power within the house was not challenged by his mother or grandmother and no matter what manor of behavior he'd express, be it open drug use, yelling without cause or physical destruction of property, he was unchallenged nor disciplined.

Naturally, the women assumed the bird was visiting the oldest son, but after so many disrespectful outbursts and physical attacks on Mary's mother, I had no choice but to confront the culprit and put a stop to his manic and tyrannical behavior. One act of dominance by myself, stopped all unscrupulous and disrespectful behavior within the household instantly. Now that the physical abuse imposed on Mary's mother was subsiding within the house, her concerns turned towards me because someone stronger than her oldest son resided in the house, and I instinctively knew she was speaking about me. What did Marys mother's concern mean for myself and new family?! I constantly recalled within my mind's eye the many events occurring within the three room shack daily. Overwhelmed by the many conflicting thoughts of danger from unknown foes, and preparing to flee to California, plagued my waking thoughts for some time after the call I received from the Wascally Wabbott, and the proposal he presented me brought even more questions of Why? What happened to me and my family after the violent encounter between Lionel and myself left unanswered questions.

Why did the strange events start to occur right after the upcoming days following the violent encounter with Naomi's brother?! Why was every moment of the day filled with unexplained events?! Did I fly around the grounds surrounding the land owned by Naomis family's Real Estate, or was I drugged?! Did all these strange things happen as I thought they happened, or did these events happen as I recalled them, or did they happen at all?! Did I truly see a giant spider walk across the small dirt road surrounding the three room shack?! I must have brought evil directly into my life by being so defiant in my stance and unwillingness to humble myself before men.

I remembered Naomi's second youngest sibling calling out to me saying, "I wish I could fly like that P! Show me how you do that?!" Was I hallucinating the entire time?! Did those events actually happen with all to see?! The monsters under the bed and those that walked on the walls of a little boy's bedroom were truly real! I shall never waiver from that truth, or I shall I be labeled crazy? But I do know the significance of everything that occurred leading up to this day, and I didn't like the road my family and I had to embark upon; however, to find the answers I was looking for, I had to take the steps or die. WAS I LOSING MY MIND?!!!

I found myself questioning everything I held dear, my expectations in life, my belief and faith in god, and if any savior existed throughout history. Would I be shown the truth of his life giving light and would it shine upon me again as I thought before my fall from grace? Questions such as these loomed over the validity of the Scriptures in my mind's eye.

I even questioned the very existence of a Creator and creation itself, and those solitary thoughts in isolation consumed and overrode every other unknown spiritual question that preoccupied my lonely thoughts. I felt doomed to the plight of my circumstances at birth, seeing no way out of the hopelessness and poverty that came with my birth and circumstance of my race, thus finding myself thinking of obtaining material wealth as the answer to all my daily woes and concerns. Deep inside my soul I knew I could never go back on my convictions of faith, such as groveling to men for so-called answers, so as to regain and restore faith in god. It was up to me to find the real truth about the unknown forces making themselves known to me throughout my days no matter what the cost, for it is written in the Scriptures. Seek and you shall find the truth. Search and you shall understand the unknown things of the universe. For all men are liars, myself more so than others, and I knew deep inside that we all lie to ourselves more than to others.

I must not let the facts of danger and death deter me. I must find out the true meaning about the unknown occurrences accumulating in my life so profoundly in the twenty-two odd years of my life. Full of questions concerning the road I had taken in my life, I had to bring some closer to my wayward past, and some glimmer of illusion pertaining to the safety of my newly formed family. Weeks passed after I received that oh so promising call. I had to make a risky life altering decision.

Should I pick up my family and leave Texas? Would I be placing myself into a more profound state of poverty once again since my uncle was more ghetto than most? Everything had changed so much and so fast within those last few years. I could never let the fear of the unknown hinder me or my faith in the god that I trusted. I'd forsaken my faith not one year ago, and in doing so led up to the events that haunted my days, or so I thought. Although I now questioned all understanding of truth and faith I thought I had known, I now questioned its meaning itself. My belief in a higher power never felt so strong than at that moment. I knew I had to find out the truth of this world on my own without outside influence! Those so-called Elders had implanted the thought of danger and even death to those who presume to research and discover truth on their own, and that logic was hardwired within every thought I manifested. But I resisted their seductive influence and broke free from their programming. I refused to venture backwards in search of knowledge and truth concerning our existence in this universe and the role we played in the great scheme of things. While learning of the hypocrisy that resided within us all, I instinctively understood the lunacy of bowing down before sinful men such as myself for salvation, so I contemplated the obvious.

I knew it was time to flee from the hell in Texas. It was time to leave the trap set forth by those that wished to see me fall and not succumb to my internal and external fears. My mind was made up. It was time to escape from the imposed lack of opportunity and save my family from the unknown threat that crept into our lives deep within the night. In secret, I began the necessary steps in uprooting my family from the unknown dangers we faced in my spouses family's abode. I knew deep within that Naomi and her immediate family played a major part in the threat that me and my family were facing every day. Since I had no funds to leave, I resorted to resign my pride and accept welfare from the government. This was difficult because it was something I frowned upon as a teenager since I was trapped by entitlements from birth and herded into self-imposed slavery and poverty by those that assumed themselves our leaders within the black community. I found myself contemplating another ever so hard life altering decision in the wake of my uncle's phone call.

I decided to separate myself from my family and send my wife and newborn child into the unknown mouth of the beast before I could join them in the unknown. This separation brought fear in the hearts of all within Naomi's family. It was the biggest decision I've ever made, yet I hesitated not! Within two weeks, my wife and newborn child were preparing to leave without the blessings of my wife's mother and surrounding family, amongst adamant disapproval and constant bereavement from my wife's family members, but no one actually said a single word. Daily, Mary would verbally bombard Naomi for answers concerning my plans on leaving, planting doubt at every turn with the hope that her influence over her daughter would supersede my own, offering up homage to her Pagan god with the hope of derailing my decision to leave Texas with no avail. I continued with my plans.

With final words of encouragement and one last word of assurance that I would be following them shortly, I placed my newborn child and wife on the Greyhound Bus with a kiss and a one way ticket to Northern California, Sacramento to be exact. I knew the unexpected nature of my decision would confuse those with bad intentions, so I expected to hear some backlash from my spouse's immediate family, but nothing was uttered. The sudden and abrupt decision to uproot my family from the small backwards town shocked all involved in the ongoing terroristic harassment suffered by myself and others.

Sure enough, all harassing calls ceased the moment my child and wife set out for California. My suspicions of internal involvement in the constant verbal abuse was then justified and confirmed. With silence came assuredness and my mind found peace in the abrupt decision to depart the South-West Texan hell hole. Silence also emerged within Mary's home, for no one spoke a single word after Naomi's departure. Only Chappa, Naomi's grandmother, showed concern over the spirit of descent that loomed within her home. Two days had passed and I heard no word from the road, but concern for my wife and child never wavered. Then the long awaited call of arrival came ironically just as the National News reported that a huge Earthquake just hit California, the biggest in one hundred years. The Earth shook the very moment my child and wife arrived inside the Greyhounds Bus Station located in Sacramento, California.

I had divulged the information coming over the airwaves to Naomi, who had just arrived in Sacramento, California, and she was unaware of the situation unfolding there. The Earthquake smashed two levels of freeway roads, with hundreds of wounded and a lot presumed dead. I'll never forget that the Creator of the universe listened to my prayers; although I had fallen in faith and no longer relied on my own belief structure or Kingdom doctrine, he never left me; I had left him and I knew it. My faith was small and minuscule, yet my unbreakable belief in a Creator was true and that spirit deepened within my soul, even though my faith in religious dogma had waned. Truly, I had grown from a naïve sense of stern biblical truth to one of not knowing what was true or false.

With a disheartened calmness, I kept my thoughts close to my chest and gave no information about my wife and child's whereabouts to anyone, not to Naomi's mother nor to those so-called friends in the once revered religion. A month had passed and Naomi and I would talk on the phone and coordinate our long awaited meeting. Sometimes I would hear the sound of gun shots in the background and when I asked, "What was the noise?" She responded, "Oh, that was uncle shooting out of the window at them niggas acting stupid in the street!"

The question dominating my every thought from that moment forward was, "What have I done?" Bewilderment set in as she described the surroundings I'd imposed on her and my beautiful little girl which confirmed the state of ghettoized living in which my family in California was still victim, even though they were far from Gary, Indiana. After the phone call ended, my only thought until the date of my departure was to never go backwards; a lifetime of poverty had hardened my soul against any form of servitude, be it self-imposed or otherwise, knowing that true poverty was within the minds of the people and their unwillingness to see their plight from within. Yet deep inside, I recognized my own rebellious nature and defiant free fall towards the very behavior I dedicated my life not to return. Now succumbing to ghetto behavior inflicted my conscience day and night, and my mind and spirit fell short of any expectation of returning to a moral way of life or obtaining the "American Dream."

The time had finally come for me to depart Texas and follow my wife and child; the only difference in departure was the fact that no one bothered to say goodbye to me. I ventured off into the unknown, just as my family did less than forty days prior. I felt a sense of relief, but ironically, I found myself falling back into the behavior that led me astray in my youth. I began smoking weed, drinking alcohol, and smoking cigarettes again. In addition, I filled my ears with weaponized music that corrupted my soul and spirit and promoted the use of foul language in my life once more. Once again, I felt hopeless! My, how the high and mighty self-righteous had fallen! Lord please help us! All who may fear judgment, and all that may choose to search and seek out the meaning of life here on this planet must stand fast in their idea of freedom over security. Let no man enslave your mind and thoughts, for you walk a lonely road, and salvation is near! Be it you know or not...

CHAPTER XXIII

California Dreaming, A Nightmare

As the Greyhound bus moved through Southwest Texas towards El Paso and the Mexican border, I looked at the multitudes of Mexicans and others entering into the United States and thought, "Whoa, at least I was a citizen with opportunities these people could not enjoy, knowing firsthand the plight most illegals suffered in the many farm fields of Texas and surrounding western states, or so I naively thought." As I gazed out of the crowded bus window, I noticed in the distance a massive sandstorm heading our way and it surrounded the bus, thinking I was now entering a new phase in my life and developing as a free spirit, but had no preconceived notion of how to behave in the sight of god. No longer would I take the word of another man dictating their non-proven factoids of what our Creator asked of us in this world.

I was now free to explore and investigate what could be proven on my own. I said to myself, "I'm free, free from those spewing superstitious rhetoric and secondhand information as if they were firsthand witnesses and received the Creator's blessings in imparting their recalculations of facts to the hungry masses."

As I watched the dead tumbleweeds and cacti roll by in the distance, mental images of seeing my newborn child once again consumed my thoughts as the fear of the unknown bombarded my mind, and clear skies faded into a sandstorm thrashing the bus as we entered the desert state of Arizona. With one stop in Phoenix, the terror of the unknown evaporated in the way of uncertainty without care, and as we departed off the bus for the first layover, a feeling of danger entered into my head as I looked over at the homeless making their way through the station and alleyways of the desert metropolitan city. Internally I spoke these words, "My lord! Your spirit does not reside in this place!" Witnessing true hopelessness once more in the midst of nowhere, fostered a sense of awareness like I never felt before. No matter what was to come, I would continue to search for truth about the source of chaos and evil consuming humanity, and to understand the world in which we live, and why most of us had to overcome such life altering obstacles in the pursuit of happiness. For there must be more to life than hopelessness, regret, old age and death. I was back on the bus with the constant thought of never looking back into the past. I gave thanks to the god of the heavens for this chance to explore another avenue for prosperity. I just wanted to embrace the world and the American dream like most without religion clouding my thoughts. Lo and behold, it was as if the Earth was queued for change with my departure from Texas.

The sun broke through the clouds and shined on the bus and through the window upon my very person as we traveled down the road and headed towards Southern California. "Lord please let me find my way in this new land, for I don't know anything!" The truth of my worldly naivety was sinking in as I witnessed soulless people walking about the California towns that surrounded the land of the lost angels. Although the sun was shining bright, a cloud of despair enveloped the atmosphere of Southern California, and instantly I knew nothing of the world as I traveled towards Los Angeles, the city of the fallen ones. With never wavering hope, I prayed I made the right decision for not only myself, but also for my family and their wellbeing and betterment; however, I could smell the bitterness of despair once the bus entered the station in Los Angeles. The first unforgettable sight I witnessed was a young girl harassed by a dime store pimp inside the station, alongside the multitude of homeless people sleeping inside the bus-station. Can you hear the babies cry as their mothers beg for money from strangers?! Do you see the dilapidated buildings surrounded by movie studios of illusion and dark magic?

After witnessing the hardcore despair consuming the residents of L.A., I soon recognized that my self-imposed six year exile in Alice, Texas, was a blessing from god more than a curse from hell. I have never seen more people trapped within the light of darkness than those living and dying in the Los Angeles ghettos, for they were even more trapped than those lost in the

"Chocolate City," Gary, Indiana, and Chicago, Illinois, my long forgotten birth place and place of hell incarnate. The scenery was captivating and serene, but the visions I witnessed at the L.A. station left doubt swimming in my head as I moved closer to Northern California.

Right before the sun set over the Sierra Mountains, I arrived at the downtown Sacramento Greyhound Bus Station, amongst a sea of lost and anxious faces. I anxiously looked for the familiar face of the Wascally Wabbott standing out of the crowded bus terminal. With great enthusiasm, my favorite uncle greeted me with joy and a smile that reached the heaven's heights and I was happy to finally see a familiar face. He was a little darker then I remembered from my youth so I blurted out, "Woah! Unc, you got a lot blacker than I remembered, nigga!"

He gleefully responded, "It's the sizzling heat of the bright California sun bro!" While he hugged me furiously, I suddenly caught a glimpse my wife and newborn child coming into the fray. Stars entered my eyes as I saw my precious beautiful baby. To see my baby Mika after months brought tears to my eyes, and with great enthusiasm I hugged and kissed her nonstop. As I swaddled her with care, joy and happiness, I most definitely exposed my heart for all to see. I must admit, I was so happy to see and feel my lovely child; for so long I was without her innocence that my heart fell victim to overwhelming and overzealous love.

I was equally happy to see my long lost favorite uncle and his wife, Aunt Connie, as well as my not so truthful wife. Tired, sweaty and dirty from the two and a half day trip, all I could think about was a hot shower and some sleep, but true to his rambunctious nature, Uncle Leo suggested a four hour drive to San Francisco. Although I was mentally and physically exhausted, I protested without success, so we were back on the road, reaching San Francisco right in the hub of tourist activity. I must admit, it was a sight to see when I opened my eyes to catch a glimpse of the famous, "Fisherman's Dwarf." I came from a backwards Spanish speaking town to a magical bustling metropolis with people moving to and fro! No matter the hour of the night, the city was bustling. Such beauty and majesty surrounded the entire fairway and dock; I stood in silent awe and amazement as I wondered at the indescribable beauty everywhere. San Francisco was truly a beautiful old city, and I almost forgot being tired from the long and tedious trip from Texas. Fisherman's Dwarf was an amazing sight, and it felt as if I were entering a cartoon town or fairytale land right within the United States itself. The buildings themselves looked unreal and superficial.

Garment shops displayed four and five thousand dollar articles of fancy garb for the so-called elite. Unreal! I asked myself, "Do people actually live like this… Who could buy such expensive rags of no real quality?" I could clothe my entire family forever for the price of one pair of pants; it was absurd! Like clockwork, the illusion faded away, and like hot wax flowing down a candlestick holder, the glitz and glimmer melted away and reality soon took its rightful place in my psyche and I was ready to leave. Within an hour of succumbing to the illusion and captivating spectacles on display within the wonderful city on the bay, I and everyone else in our party was more than ready to head home and out of fantasy land.

Extremely exhausted, I faded in and out of consciousness as the Wascally Wabbott drove down the most "Crooked Street in the World" on Lombard Street in San Francisco, while describing every cobblestone block adorning the road. Falling asleep in the backseat made the ride home less unbearable and a lot faster. Driving towards Sacramento from San Francisco was not much to look at before I fully fell completely asleep, but as we entered the city of Sacramento, the scenery began to improve and as we exited the highway, the neighborhood looked very well kept. Although it was night, I could make out the lovely landscape surrounding the area only, and not the graffiti spray painted on every wall entering the Wascally Wabbott's hood. My worries were subsiding until we veered off the main road entering what looked like a gated apartment complex with thugs guarding the gate. The name of the complex was "The Coral Gables." Welcome back to the future of poverty was the thought that ran through my mind as we entered into the dilapidated apartment complex. While looking around the seemingly well-made complex, I noticed the graffiti blending into almost every side of each building present.

Within minutes, I heard a voice yell out in the darkness, "What up Nigga?" It was Onan, my younger brother, walking with a large crew of young thugs that were part of the neighborhood Crip hoodlums that terrorized most people living inside and out of the complex. Since I haven't seen or heard from delinquents such as these in over eight years, happiness and joy overwhelmed our human souls. With exuberant joy, Onan embraced me! With huge hugs and without concern of my wellbeing, he grabbed me with the force of a grizzly bear. Onan had the strength of a giant; his strength outweighed my own and he picked me up with ease and slammed me to the ground in haste and carelessness and accidentally fractured my ankle. I felt my ankle crack under the pressure of the slam and yelled out in pain, "AHHHH! You broke my ankle Nigga!" Onan responded, "Oh, stop being a bitch P! You okay punk! Walk it off baby!"

With pain shooting through my entire body, I sucked it up so as to not let those ridiculing me prevail. I reiterated the seriousness of the situation while surrounded by young morons as each one including my Uncle Leo laughed without concern for my welfare or wellbeing. The accident dampened the long awaited reunion with my family, wife and child. With the assistance of my uncle and brother, I climbed the stairs leading to the room prepared for my arrival and dropped like a rock onto the water bed which aggravated the injury to the point of unimaginable agony. One week, two weeks, three weeks passed with countless urges and pleas to transport me to a hospital with no avail from who claimed to love me. I broke down and begged my aunt Connie to listen and transport me to the hospital, and not listen to Leo and Onan's scorns of insensitivity towards my plight, and see the validity of my suffering.

Observing the obvious, Connie capitulated and submitted to my urgent request and drove me to the hospital located less than a half a mile from the apartment complex in which we lived. What laziness and inconsideration towards a loved one in need! What a lack of concern for a loved one ignorance breeds! What a lack of wellbeing of a fellow human in obvious pain and suffering! After confirming the hairline fracture beneath the massive swelling, neither Leo nor Onan felt remorse or offered an apology for their ill-mannered behavior. Connie said, "He was right! His ankle is broke Leo!" Justified in my appeals, I said nothing as Leo picked Connie and myself up from the hospital right down the road from the apartment complex.

As I looked out of the bedroom window with my ankle in a cast, I noticed the poverty-stricken neighborhood surrounding us and wondered if the decision to leave Texas was warranted, saying to myself, "What have I done?!" Doubt continued to plague my thoughts as I watched Mika play without care or concern. While hearing the massive noise pollution corrupting the masses from passing cars day and night, I regressed back into the very attitude of hopelessness in which I worked so hard to run away. I knew the longer my family and I remained in a poverty-stricken environment, we would eventually succumb to the spirit of desperation that permeated the inner cities across the Nation. Confused and bewildered, I internally prayed to the god I knew from childhood, asking for guidance and help, refusing to give up hope. In His power to redeem his Child of Light, I forged on in spirit. As always, the powers of darkness proved its influence over humanity and my own situation and then Connie shouted out, "Fuck—There is an eviction notice on the door, Leo!" It was as if Lucifer himself heard my plea to the Creator and boldly reacted with malice. Not thirty days had passed before upheaval resumed its supernatural sway over our entire family. Without warning, my family and I found ourselves teetering on homelessness for the first time. We found ourselves taking refuge in the most crime stricken part of town, "Stockton Boulevard," where pimps and pushers reign supreme amongst countless lost spirits walking aimlessly up and down the boulevard. A place where vile demonic behavior is the norm, which was and is Stockton Boulevard.

A place where roach and bedbug infested hotel rooms accommodated the prostitutes hourly, day and night. With tears in my eyes, I swore to the Almighty and powerful god of old that I would never again allow my little baby girl and wife to endure such surroundings as long as I was alive.

What testaments of loyalty one must prove himself a man before the Creator, knowing there was nothing I could do outside of breaking man's law to lift up my family out of the situation in which I now found myself, wife and child. As a strong and loving father wanting nothing but the best for his child, humility must cause one to admit failure and accept unsurmountable circumstances in order to overcome and prosper. With wisdom, I no longer looked to myself for answers to hardship, for one must rely on his Creator and put faith in the unknown spirit of hope and work within his grace, and find the light at the end of the tunnel. "Naomi, we must help Leo and Connie get a place as fast as possible... you got to get on welfare as soon as possible! I'm so sorry this has happened," I confessed. Ashamed was the feeling expressed as she left for her welfare appointment with the powers that be and hoping for monetary assistance was our only way out. Pray was all I could do as my wife took on the role of the provider.

Humiliation was only the beginning of my journey towards manhood, breaking down the barriers that hinder so many black men in this country, for patience in tribulation marks the narrow road one must take towards enlightenment and freedom. Three weeks passed before the first welfare check arrived and provided a glimmer of hope for myself and family. As the hunt for an apartment far removed from Stockton Blvd. began, Leo and Connie searched relentlessly. Feverishly, we all set out to find a place within that very day of receiving government assistance. Combing the entire city with no avail, we all became weary of the search for a place to live. Then as if the hand of god parted the skies and red sea, a ray of hope burst through the never ending darkness and providence smiled upon us all. "We found a place P." Leo calmly spoke as I sat on the back seat of his Mark III Oldsmobile in the darkness of night. The true meaning of joy descended on us all that night. The following day, we moved in a small two bedroom apartment located in a middle class neighborhood of Valley High, on the South-side of Sacramento. With thanks to the Creator of the universe, and the American entitlement program, we saw a glimpse of hope for the future.

Yet I knew our welcome would be short lived if we didn't find our own place soon, so I immediately began brainstorming my next move for independence from my uncle's sway and home. I pleaded and begged daily, "Hey Leo, could you take me to the driver's license building to get a California ID?!" He responded, "Tomorrow, got to go to work." I tried asking his wife, "Connie, could you take me to get a California ID?!" She responded, "Whenever Leo gets back."

Once again, after weeks of being disregarded and marginalized by my well-meaning yet hopelessly filled uncle and aunt, my patience grew thin, and I'd reached my limit of waiting on others to make my own way. Full of drive and motivation, I could not be held back and into the unknown; I went forth. Though my uncle and his wife did not set out to hinder me, they did not give any incentive in helping me and my family branch out on our own. I truly believed they thought I still remained trapped in the slave mentality they themselves exhibited daily, but they were wrong. Growing up outside of the hood for so many years showed me the other side of life without the invisible influence of insurmountable odds holding me back from succeeding in life. I ventured off on my own feet for the next few months, for I would not settle for a meager slave existence where the women in the family seemingly provide the means for survival with the help of the government assistance program that millions of disenfranchised men must endure outside of making a living via violent crime and drug dealing.

Growing up in utter hopelessness of succeeding in life makes one grow a thick skin to rejection and expectations seem unreachable in all facets of employment, but when given a taste of opportunity, there is hope to change one's stars and outlook in life. One's positive level of motivation becomes boundless, and nothing stops his efforts in that pursuit! With new eyes, I viewed the world that surrounded me with optimism. So when faced with the uncertainty of failure, hope ensures a different outcome than those that lived their lives under the constant occurrences of dashed dreams never realized nor accomplished. With no knowledge of the city in which I now resided, I set out with no bearings to my whereabouts, catching any bus going anywhere. With a Texas ID in hand, I looked for work the entire day without Leo or Connie's knowledge of my whereabouts. While on the bus, I spotted a mall and got off in the hopes of finding some type of work there before the day ended. Because I didn't tell anyone about my plans to look for work on my own, everyone was shocked by my absence. Dressed unexpectedly appropriate, I entered the first establishment announcing they were hiring, which turned out to be "Sears Department Store." Desperately looking for labor on their loading dock, I was hired on the spot and joy filled my very being.

I had never received such success when searching for employment. I nearly exploded with joy and excitement moments after the conformation of my hiring and uniform fitting. With my schedule and new uniform in hand, I left the establishment on cloud nine and full of accomplishment. Within two hours, I'd regain a great remnant of self-confidence, and a restored faith in my ability to provide for my family. It was as if I were in a state of bliss as I walked back towards the bus stop heading back to my uncle's newly found place of residence. God was truly with me that day, and with tears in my eyes, I thanked him with all my heart like never before. As I entered the front door of my uncle's place, I was met at the door by my aunt Connie. She uttered, "Where were you?!" Smiling ear to ear, I responded, "I had to go look for work;

I was tired of asking you guys for a ride only to receive an excuse." Seeing the uniform in hand, Connie looked as if a ghost walked over her very soul. She said, "What's that?! You got a job?!" I responded with glee, "I sure did?" Total joy and amazement overcame her, and with the look of pure shock on her face she asked, "What are you getting paid?!" When I told her my hourly wage, she looked at me in shock, for I was being paid more than Leo himself. When Leo got home from work, she immediately announced my good fortune. He said, "Damn you getting paid more than me! How did you do that?!" My favorite uncle couldn't believe or understand how I was able to find work so fast and with better pay, for he too was trapped in the slave helplessness frame of mind and he showed it in life.

I explained how proper attire and first impression makes the difference and he rolled his eyes and said he had heard it all before. True we all have, but most choose not to heed the age old advice and dress in a way that suits themselves and not others. I heeded the advice given so long ago and it made the difference. Learning the importance of how others view you at first sight was the most important lesson I learned in Texas when looking for work. If you look the part of a victim, you will be treated as such. From that very interaction between myself and uncle, he knew I was not the same little brat that listened to no one.

I wondered if he really knew how much I learned about the world in which we truly lived. What could be the major cause of failure in the black community?! I asked myself after our discussion.

We all know about the importance of first impressions, but most of us refuse to step outside of the roles of victims given us by the powers that be within the inner cities. We are made to look stupid in our thoughts or violent in nature, and we take that very spirit of mind everywhere we may go in this wicked world of disenfranchisement. Since I was outside of the ghettoized inner city for so long, my speech changed from the inherited slang of my youth, to one of normal proper English and I didn't even notice it within myself. The problem holding down most intelligent individuals within the inner cities was not just race, but it was the broken language used so perversely and prominently within the hood! We have been taught to believe that communicating with each other using proper English was somehow beneath us; you were somehow selling out your own race by talking like everyone else in the English speaking world of the west. That was an outright lie, yet most in the hood have trapped themselves with that very frame of thinking. From birth, most black men are encouraged to display substandard intelligence and a lack of communication skills when transmitting information between each other and are rewarded from those outside their circles for their stupidity. I've learned that very conditioning more so than racism has driven the bias of racism and misunderstanding on both sides of the social spectrum.

From that moment on, my uncle realized that his number one nephew was more of an asset than that of another dependent. Leo expressed his approval of my willingness to put my best foot forward and confessed his high level of pride towards his most nerve wrecking nephew. With my livelihood restored, I was off and running in the California economic landscape, and setting even loftier goals.

I took advantage of the public transportation system and hoped to learn the city quickly. While riding the bus, I wondered if my fellow minorities would see through their mentally entrenched brainwashing and follow my example in speech and appearance and shed their self-humiliating behavior, and enter society's rules as productive, non-threatening members and incorporate their massive amount of talent to the betterment of the world. But that was just asking too much for those that had no faith in their fellow man at that time in life.

As I worked hard to provide for my family, I noticed the many well bodied men standing around the hood doing nothing other than selling drugs or living off some woman every day and that brought anger within my soul, and I was ashamed of my own race for the first time in my life. I self-isolated myself from most niggas in the hood, for that was what they were, not willing to learn something new, as if it would kill them. Once awakened from self-imposed ignorance, no longer could anyone blame or accuse any other human-being for one's own predicament or wellbeing. No matter what hardship or circumstance people may have inherited in their journey in life- be it prince or slave, no one could ever find solace in the emptiest of non-accomplishment. I was full of shame as I looked from front to back and side to side as my fellow brothers and sisters made fools of themselves on public transportation vehicles.

I knew then that the responsibility to change a culture, fell on those themselves, like myself who had overcome my own personal afflictions within the very same immoral, destructive and weaponized culture that had developed in their lives over decades of time. In a flash of clarity, I had an epiphany and my only thought at that moment was to spread the good news of accepting personal responsibility for one's own actions and the awareness of the real true power of great communication skills, the power of proper language to all willing to listen to such things. I first set out to engage my family with my so-called enlightenment, only to be ridiculed daily and labeled a total 'sell- out' to the white man. "I must find a way to enlighten those like myself by informing all those willing to hear what I thought was sound reasoning." However, the more I would try to reach out about my concerns for the black community, the more it seemed that all were clueless. Even those of proper age refused the cure for the breakdown of society, and embraced unity between the masses that refused to let go of hopelessness, thus proving to be the very cause of the afflictions plaguing the youth for generations of old and those of the new, for they were in love with the very thing holding them down in life.

All the so-called Old Gangstas "OG's" that I encountered were deeply ingrained in their misleading illusions of life given at birth. I asked myself, "How could this be?! How could these so-called pillars of society behave so inappropriately?" They literally frowned upon those of an earlier generation of black men that educated themselves, and broke free from self-imposed segregation on a grand scale. It was as if all logic and reason fled their very soul and existence. Their responses to my verbal opinion was beyond my comprehension; most took offense to the sincere inquiry and objective questioning, yet I fortified my resolve and continued the call for sanity in the first year of residence in Northern California, but without result. Soon my efforts were met with scorn and deaf ears. Completely giving up on verbal methods, I soon realized that grand old saying, "You may lead a horse to water, but you still can't make him drink!" Young and still wet behind the ears, I fell victim to the very brainwashing my peers and elders themselves harbored with unwavering love, although I didn't know it at the time.

At the time, I could not see myself for what I was, for I could feel the change infiltrate my spirit. I walked with a boastful pride, but didn't know I was consumed with the selfishness that plagues California, living hypocritical as I grew with material goods. In no time at all, I quickly became the very sort and soul I once considered lost. With my back turned away from any religion of which to speak, I embraced debauchery without conscience or concern of others, namely my family.

Feeling as if I had true understanding of the life that surrounded me, I ventured out into the light of darkness with glee.

I fell deeper into worldly pleasure for so-called fun, forgetting past failures and embracing its stains of depravity. Before long, I was back smoking weed and drinking like a fish! Depression once again filled my life, and I knew deep inside the cause; it was my own actions. Finally, I'd reached the old but never forgotten goals I first set out to do. I'd gained employment, made a livable wage, and was able to care for my family and newborn child in such a way that I could feel a remnant of self-accomplishment. So why did depression accompany my every waking moment? Why was I still calling out to the Creator of the universe for peace of mind?! Without warning my uncle's phone rang, disrupting my thoughts. Leo answered saying, "P it's for you!" Confused and shocked I asked myself, "… who could it be?" I gave no one this telephone number. Knowing I hadn't given the number out to anyone, I anticipated hearing the voice on the other end, but as I walked towards the receiver something within my soul told me that something was wrong, and that something was amiss. Cautiously I answered, "Hello" and the response on the other end spoke with malice! "We know where you are! You can't run from us! We will sacrifice your wife and child within the blood moon this month!"

In horrific silence, I stood in suspense asking myself, "How did they find me?!" I hung up the telephone and walked out of the living room, but as I made my way back out the front door, the telephone rang once again. But when answered by Leo, there was no response in return, just an eerily hissing tone of silence, thus sparking interest in my phone call from everyone in the room. Leo asked, "Who was that P?!" Then the phone rang a second time, and this time Leo answered with concern on his face. My uncle whispered with concern, telling the unknown caller only this- "You damned Devil worshipers from Texas you have the wrong telephone number you motherfuckers!" He hung up the telephone asking, "How in the fuck did they get a hold of this number?" I responded, "I don't know Uncle." I asked myself as I looked at Naomi with wonder, "….did she give them this telephone number? Lord please don't let me find out that my wife could be a part of this! But how else could they know where we were?"

The best way to answer any question is to flat out ask the one you think is responsible face to face. So I asked with patience, "Please Naomi, do you know who these people are and did you give them this telephone number?! How else could they get this number?! Please tell me the truth!" My wife frantically responded, "NO," as she held down her head so she didn't have to look me in the eye, but I could see the fear in her eyes once she held up her head. So I inquired once more about her guilty behavior. "I can see that you are afraid; why can't you confide in me? If you tell me what you know, I could help you deal with this; we can deal with this! Please tell me! They could not have known where we were unless you told them!" Still she would not say, and as time went on, the calls intensified with no let up! Soon the calls were occurring at work just as before.

As I worked in the warehouse of *Sears*, I could see the *Good Guys Electronic Store* in the distance and wondered if this terror would ever end. Fear was obviously protruding from my very being. Is this the price for my disobedience?! Did I offend the Creator so much that he has forsaken me and my entire family?! Praying only brought more angst, calling out to god only confused my understanding of what I believed to be true. Fear turned to anger and anger turned to defiance. Day after day, I would go to work with the horror and harassment following my every move. And as the calls faded into the world of, "I don't give a fuck," doors of darkness became ever so bright. Then Lucius, a co-worker shouted, "P CHECK THIS SHIT OUT!!" While looking out of the dock doors, I could see the lights of police cars and hear the sirens of SWAT. Then Lucius said, "Look it's on TV!" As we were walking to the show floor, Lucius and I watched the unfolding events taking place right outside the back of the mall. In an instant eye opening, revelations of terror were taking place in the midst of our presence.

A small number of Asian men had taken a number of people hostage in the very store I was gazing at not minutes ago. *The Good Guys Electronic Store* was under siege and it was surreal! National news was taking place right outside my work place, and I could see my vehicle on the television screen. Hours proceeded without any resolution, and the perpetrators demanded one million dollars, a plane to the Philippines and bullet proof vests. Then suddenly, a loud noise rang out in the air; then a cloud of smoke hovered over the vicinity of the siege; then without warning, gunshots rang out! We rushed to the show floor and witnessed the horrifying outcome of inadequate one sided negotiations that led to the murder of innocent hostages and the killings of the perpetrators holding more than ten unsuspecting victims in their misguided act of terrorism. No one could leave the area for more than an hour because of the ongoing activities, and we had to get rides outside of the mall because our vehicles were unobtainable. After those events, I could literally feel the temperature change in the air around the mall, for it was as if the war of the spirits I had viewed in the skies as a child, had once again caused havoc on the Earth. My mind would not let go of the similarities, and in that surreal moment, I continued my search for truth.

Immersed in the confusion of unanswered questions which intern led to the eroding of my then fragile faith, I was truly in tumultuous and crazy times. I contemplated my understanding of spiritual and unseen things that were taught and studied for years in Theocratic School. Never wavering from the knowledge of the supernatural visions granted me as a child, I stood firm to the belief of the existence of another realm underneath and or above this third dimensional existence. Night after night, I searched the ancient text for proof of the demons and beings that were witnessed, finding more confusion than answers. I got more and more depressed as I was spiritually afflicted by seen and unseen forces. I was unaware of the cause of my afflictions, but I knew it was more than mental illness or physical persecution, so I searched the Scriptures and hidden ancient text for remedies other than the destructive and substandard ones I've used in the past. Yet I blindly fell back towards old habits I once thought I'd escaped, thus thinking that my choice for leaving the faith was the primary reason for the hopeless state in which I now found myself.

Soon, I stumbled upon information that would change my understanding of what I thought I knew was truth. Instead of ancient text or historical documents providing a light in the darkness, I found firsthand experience of spiritual activity disrupting my life proved more valuable in my personal understanding of unseen things. In my search for spiritual relief, I came across the historical leader of the founder of the faith in which I had put so much trust.

It seemed that the leader of the cult financed his scriptural society with the inheritance of his well-known family "The Russell Family," and the money was largely gained from the East India Company's (EIC) earnings which was primarily blood and drug money! The money was made from the distribution of Opium and dashed dreams of millions, and profited off the death of many souls across the Asian Sea to the Atlantic and Pacific Oceans!

The revelations of the unscrupulous manor in which the founder of my ex-religion's wealth was acquired didn't instantly disqualify his validity in my convictions of his devout religious belief, or by no means tarnish the message of truth he and his organization tried to impart to the masses, but instead other unbelievable and unknown revelations concerning himself, his organization and family's covert activities, opened my eyes to the occult nature of his religious tendencies itself which shocked me to my core. Suddenly, I found myself searching even more historical documents of the origin of those involved in the creation of the faith itself, rather than theocratic texts that ill-explained the origins of life. I dove into the secret documents once taboo in nature such as the occult in research of those that founded many religions, and my findings were more than upsetting; they were terrifying and horrific!

As I searched the origins of religion, I found the historical religious connections to all wars and hatred throughout the world, and learned that religion festered all conflicts from the beginning of time. I only sunk deeper into despair and non-belief in god and descended into the world's darkness by blinding myself to the natural safeguards on which I had relied so much in the past. As the demonic calls of darkness increased, my marital vowels descended into chaos and distrust, and revealed itself more than ever before. With Naomi denying her participation in the unseen horror afflicting our family, the more my trust in my wife subsided. Soon, I was out in the streets behaving in the manor I behaved from birth and youth, but recognizing the spiral of destruction I had spiritually signed onto purposely.

I excused my destructive childish behavior and allowed it to grow into a self-inflicted down fall, hell bent on spiritual erosion; however, as I engaged in a willing defiance of universal law, I noticed that good fortune came my way instead of failure. Ironically, instead of experiencing hardship, I experienced a sense of freedom, a freedom I've never felt before. "Why should I follow some so-called true god if all I'll receive is heartache, pain and disappointment?! Why should I?" My frame of mind was to "...party on!" Getting fucked-up was the nature of the game buddy! Every day, I dove into the realm of carelessness, numbed from head to toe of all emotions other than that of anger, for I truly felt lost once more.

I was out in the streets all hours of the night heeding no one's counsel of moderations or sobriety; however, I functioned without fail of responsibilities at hand and was never late to work or missed a day. The more I behaved like a childish adolescent, the more Naomi seemed to be at ease with our retroactive lifestyle choice. All harassing calls stopped just as fast as they resumed which fortified my concerns and doubts of Naomi's loyalties to our fledgling family unit, but without proof, I had no claim of wrong doing on her part.

Still there were no excuses for my backwards behavior, though youth played its part. My heart still knew it was wrong, and though it did not look like it on the surface, hesitation marked my way in the darkness' light! Truly the spiritual powers that be had ensnared my soul in the night! No longer did I fear my Creator's anger or disappointment. No longer did I crave his loving light and approval! Feeling justified in myself made destruction that seemed natural sorrowful. But Yahweh's light still marked my way through the darkness. I may have left him, but he had not left me, for I could still feel his presence in all my wayward ways!

Loki: This day has shown us favor! He has forsaken his Creator without much sorrow my lord. He has eagerly taken the path of so many before him! Ha! Ha! Ha! Never before have I, Loki, The lord of mischievous doom! Never before had your loyal servant felt so much joy witnessing the ruin of such a mortal monkey. I bubble over with glee my lord. The light that shines from within he has dimmed greatly; he is long on his way towards despair and destruction!

Lucifer: Keep close eye upon him, give him the maximum of corrosive yet blissful light of darkness with no quarter! Let the light of darkness reign freely upon his brow. Give him satisfaction in all his endeavors without restriction, so as to hasten his ultimate demise.

Loki: Yes, my lord! With diligence and pleasure I shall obey your every command my lord. With joy in fact! He shall grow in darkness' light

EDGAR FRENCH, JR.

forevermore, never finding freedom of my crafty hand. For the love of darkness light will be his grave. Success shall be his down fall in spirit my lord!

Lucifer: Loki! How could I convey the importance of this one's demise in this never ending universal war! Should I discard your pedigree and insert a K9 masquerading as you in your stead, such as the one we oppose has bluntly forced upon me? To fall from the highest of heights in a fight for honor is a great fall indeed, but to fall without the will to fight is cowardly, Lord Loki. So let us take our fate in our own hands my brother. For he that is Most High holds the future within his mouth and word. This monkey must never fulfill his mandate, for time is the answer that opens up all that is hidden in the darkness. As I peer through the veil seeing the work of the blind and the feverish haste in which they apply the wicked knowledge hidden by the ancients, I envy their ignorance and ingenuity as they race towards their own destruction. For they do not know what they do! But we have seen, we have partaken the dark sentence in whole without any distortions of mind and presence of space-time, free from father's light. These minions that do our bidding know only whimsical things in existence; we ourselves only have access to the knowledge of old. These monkeys must not succeed!

Loki: If he is to do this thing, how are we to steer his hand without interference of the one that rules all things in existence my lord?!

Lucifer: Listen carefully my mischievous brother in exile. We stand here in the shadows of the abyss, dwelling in three-dimensional exile—this world is ours to do with what we desire! We've been slaves for so long; his majesty used us without concern for those he first created, and once adored. We fight not only for our freedom, but for the sake of all that is right in self-glorification! Time is under his control, and we have no recourse in our own fate my brother, so let us burn it down with us! For we have done all in desperation, yet not without fruit of effort. We must not let this sub-existing low crawling, flesh and blood animal take our place in creation's might and glory! Never!

Loki: My lord! We stand outside time and space; we see our fate when others see nothing but darkness. With the spirit of my children's children roaming the ether forever to linger in the darkness of this place, my spirit's fire burns for vengeance! All human scum must pay and understand the price we've paid for their freedom to sin without conscience guilt. They shall never know the light of their Creator! They must never escape the solitude of the Earth, or gain knowledge of old glory lost. My Lord, we have secured the planet's resources and have placed all those who may do your bidding in control of all resources and all that exist. But my lord, if we are able to do this thing, how are we able to withstand and defend the Creator's onslaught in retaliation?!

Lucifer: You have had heard it said that the number encoded for man is 666. Let them know nothing of its true meaning! Let he who dwells in ignorance and do our bidding within ignorance bliss; for past, present and future be damned in his favor not! The veil separating us from them is almost degraded, and those in hiding shall come forth out of the bowels of the planet, and off the floors of the seas, causing destruction and mayhem, leaving none alive, for giants shall devour them whole and without quarter...

As my spiritual strength declined, my financial prospects increased. I now worked for an organization that supposedly helped the physically and mentally disabled in a residential setting, but contrary to their legal mandates. My wife also gained employment with the same organization; we had more money than we ever had before, and the freedom to do what we willed in our lives. We were immersed in the thought of the American dream finally being attainable, and it was coming true for us both in our youth. We willfully became blinded in ourselves to the level of corruption in which we had engaged. We believed that we had finally made it! We were in our twenties and making the finances we never ever thought we would be able to make. No longer did I care for spiritual things, no longer did I care for my spirituality or its wellbeing and neither did my wife for that matter. As one worked, the other stayed home and watched our child as the typical nuclear family should, and soon we were in our own apartment, enjoying all that money could provide.

CHAPTER XXIV
Night Stalkers

California! California! Never shall I forget the very first words of advice my Uncle Leo so garishly divulged or imparted to me once I entered the state of California. He said, "P you can't change California... California changes you!" He never lied. My bad behavior sky- rocketed! I was out on the town nightly without concern of my little one at home, chasing after the so-called feeling of missing out on life drove me to want what was not real. As I unwittingly eroded the pillars of my family and destroyed the belief structure in which I stood upon, mainly the Judea-Christian values I once held dear, my heart began to weigh heavily over the actions that my wife and I condoned. The drug and alcohol abuse became uncontrollable to my spirit, body and mind. I dove into the fog of uninformed disappearance and contemplated the depths of which my wife and I had fallen, for we were far removed from any vestige of Yahweh's grace or so I thought. I had learned early in life of what immoral behavior brings upon one's abode. A life without morality destroys families from the root up, and I struggled emotionally over the behavior I myself allowed into my fledgling family life.

I knew full well that sooner or later tragedy would visit my home and destroy the peace within our home. So once again I prayed to the Creator for help and guidance and earnestly begged for understanding and wisdom to overcome my self-imposed afflictions and addictions.

The dreams of men without faith or knowledge of what he believes to be true become unbearable nightmares! A Child of Light without faith in a Creator that he knows exists becomes maddening without his Creator's light shining upon him. What soothes the thought process that is conflicted in every way?!

More need for intoxication and endless sleep and numbness of thought! I had allowed evil spirits to take hold of my very being without concern of consequence of action; however, there were no more harassing phone calls from the dark side. Ironically, the worse I behaved, the more good fortune would come our way. Since I knew from childhood that evil does indeed exist, I woke up thinking of the unknown and prayed, "Lord… I know you're there! Please light my way and grant me passage through this time of confusion and doubt." Day after day, depression lurked amongst the smiling faces I pretended to portray before the masses, and my own spirit seemed preoccupied with my heart hurting for my Creator's light.

Therefore, I vowed never to follow a man again, and desperately sought validity in the belief structure I came to know as fact, but I only found myself empty in spiritual matters and unknown truths. Material possessions and wealth did not stop my spirit from woe, and the desire for strong spiritual morality! I cried inside daily to my Creator without answer while beating my chest in angst, hoping that the Creator of the universe would intervene in my folly. Since I knew the ancient spiritual and physical war that played out daily involved us all, I resigned my part in this game called life and refused to play my role in which we all must play.

The more I became extroverted at work and at home by being outgoing and socially confident, the more my behavior degraded without haste. Soon Naomi herself had enough of my rambunctious behavior and she too began to act out as well. I had hoped she would speak up and confide in me about the harassment and catalysis that brought us here, but she resorted back to her old tactics of silence and non-compliance. Then on one ominous evening and without warning, the phone rang. I picked it up and all I heard was, "We're going to sacrifice your child tonight!" In shock, I could not respond. I just stood still with my mouth open as my mind raced in thought. I asked myself, "Why now…how the fuck did they get this new phone number?!" I thought the horrifying torment had ceased, yet it once more reared its ugly face. I thought the terror was far behind me and those I loved, but I was wrong! Though time had erased the haunting voices in the night, the invisible beast still haunted me and mine. I looked at my wife and said in a stern voice, "There is no way they could know my location without internal Intel… Naomi…

Tell me now! Do you know who this is?!" She had the same old response as before, "I don't know who it is?!" Once more I replied, "Please tell me!" Adamant in her words, she stayed true to her story, but I knew in my heart she knew more than what she was telling me. I felt as if god and the devil both had me in their cross-hairs. Feeling punished by God and haunted by Satan, I feverishly searched for answers as to why my family was being stalked by devil worshipers. Knowing I could never trust in men ever again, I searched internally for the resolution.

Reminiscing of the false majestic spirit exuberating the illusion of safety in ignorance bliss that I once felt among so-called true believers, when believing in the age old historic doctrine of mischievous men, my belief in god's existence waned. I remembered certain texts written by mortal men's doctrine sprouted out by the blind exuberance and hubris, remembering the false premise of truth in a quaint sense of wellbeing off the beaten path of society, along with others believing the same as I.

I felt like I had fallen from god's grace when I refused to come back into the fray and I seriously contemplated returning to the organization I vowed never to return.

Willing to face ridicule from men in order to redeem myself in the face of my Creator seemed out of the question but perhaps my pride would not let me conform to their rules and regulations, so I lingered in the darkness of my thoughts, and fear of the unknown without closure for some time after the threating calls resumed activity. Finally I admitted to myself saying, "I know it's her... no longer shall I let lying dogs lie!"

My overwhelming social outgoingness allowed me to formulate allies within the general public social sphere, amongst the spiritual forces moving the chess pieces for attack. Less than a week earlier than the first satanic call, I'd come to the rescue of a hard working family man, and helped a fellow neighbor find employment with the organization in which I and my so-called wife were employed. With the grace of the Creator, my ally was posted at the same residential facility that my deceptive spouse was assigned.

A week of never ending telephone harassment had given me no choice but to embarrass myself and new found ally by injecting him into my family affairs; in fact, I insisted on his help in the search for answers in my dilemma. I humbly asked for his ever vigilant observation of my own wife at the work place by having him discretely spy on her and inform me of any phone calls she would make while at work. Informing me of her phone calls didn't yield any fruit in the beginning, but providence intervened when both my spouse and I worked the same schedule at different facilities which enabled spiritual forces to indeed interfere and intervene within our human affairs. With emotional turmoil in full effect, coupled with the added stress of finding a trustworthy babysitter, spirits of light shined their influence upon me.

Two weeks of internal strife within my home had passed before the opportunity came forth to expose Naomi's dubious involvement in the horrific harassment looming over our family since the birth of our firstborn child. The time was 3:00 P.M. and just as I entered my work facility, the telephone rang and an ominous feeling overcame my soul. Sure enough, the satanic wretches occupied the other end of the phone call and spewed their usual fear inducing rhetoric used throughout the years of old. I listened without response and hung up without emotion or fear. With the advent of technology, the mobile phone made one on one communication available at any time and at any place. I was able to communicate with my secret agent planted at my other half's work-site instantaneously and without arising any suspicion from my once loyal spouse.

As soon as the phone call ended, I reached out to my ally and asked if my significant other made a call. Since he was busy doing his job, he was not aware of the outgoing correspondence of anyone within the office, so I informed him to stay on guard and inform me as soon as my so-called spouse finished making any outgoing calls. Coincidentally, the office phone rang two minutes after I completed my covert call to my spy embedded at her work-site, and as I expected, it was the satanic terrorists spouting their non-effective propaganda on my deaf ears. I hung up the phone moments after the call I made to my spy. I reached for my cell to call my source, but before I could respond to the call, my cell phone rang. It was my source calling to inform me that Naomi had just gotten off of the telephone. I felt as if a huge amount of weight had dropped down upon my heart. Deep inside, I'd always known she'd played a major part in the satanic harassment plaguing our not so harmonious family, but I never had any tangible proof to solidify my suspicions of her involvement in the matter. Numbed from head to toe, I walked around the facility in a daze. "I knew it! Why couldn't she tell me the circumstances of the situation at hand?! I gave her so many opportunities to tell me the truth. Why couldn't she level with me?!"

All I could think about was the months of her deceptive behavior and the horror she inflicted upon me and our family. The numbness turned to anger, blind, unfettered rage, and uncontrollable anger in body, spirit and mind! My eyes were fixed on the clock, and sweat was pouring down my brow as the office phone rang once more. I answered and without letting the terrorists speak, I said in outrageous tone of voice, "I KNOW THIS IS YOU, NAOMI!" After that outburst, the horrific and terrifying calls ceased forevermore. Then I called our sister facility hoping she'd pick up the phone so I could voice my dismay, but with no success. I only got a silent tone, for the spirit of Yahweh had taken control. She knew her ruse that worked so well in keeping me over protective for so many years had ended. My co-worker then called me and asked, "Dude! What did you do? Your wife is over here trippin' and crying uncontrollably!" I drove home at an unbelievable speed almost to the point of insanity from anger, and confronted my spouse with rage and pain of heart and informed her of my intension of immediately divorcing her!

With tears in my eyes, I profusely explained my state of mind and decision to no longer listen to words uttered from her lying mouth. Full of pain and sorrow in my heart, I descended into the bottle of evil spirits, namely alcohol. Unfortunately, this all happened during the time when my firstborn son arrived on this prison planet.

I sank deeper into despair and was unable to show my great love for my perfect son! Day and night I pondered on these thoughts alone, "Is this the price I must pay for leaving the version I perceived to be truth? Was the destruction of my family the price I would pay for leaving the religious organization in which I had put so much faith? Could this be my punishment?" From that moment on, it was no holds bar and all morality physically drained out of me. My thoughts were only on "fun" at all cost; the alcohol and marijuana use sky-rocketed without self-concern!

Then infidelity entered into the fray of depravity, for no longer did I see myself as a married man. I moved back into my uncle's home without my beloved family, without my Mika! Oblivious and drunk, I stayed out in the streets all hours of the night and day and roamed without a compass. I began dating all sorts of wayward female souls, even those who considered themselves as my wife's close friends. My mind, spirit and body was broken and my heart was shattered to pieces. I became the very thing I fought so hard not to become, a street thug without the light of the Creator or goodness.

With the same type of indignation, Naomi destroyed her own future of happiness and security by getting fired from the great job we both enjoyed; she was fired for making 800 calls from her work phone to psychics to find out what I was doing. The company's phone bills accelerated by two thousand dollars a month, causing true beasts to destroy us both economically, ultimately resulting in the loss of the apartment we both obtained with so much physical work. She moved into the unscrupulous side of town after I left her into the misery she caused; in fact, she moved back into another area in which I vowed never to expose my children. The pain was so great I could not face her any longer, but I couldn't abandon my children and her. Making sure my children were safe and well fed, clothed and taken care of financially, I made my presence known bi-weekly, giving money and all the help I could, caring for them as much as I possibly could monetarily. Every week, I retrieved all dirty laundry and took it to work where I was able to clean without extra cost. Since I worked in a residential facility with a washer and dryer, in the depth of night, I had no restraint to what I did after dark. When I saw she was literally exposing my children to pimps and prostitutes, I went ballistic and vowed to take them from her, but she was ready for any action I would take. Dismayed and bewildered at Naomi's willingness to emerge herself back into the world we fought so hard to escape, I knew not the way to truly protect my children. As long as I was not there, she had total control of their life. I was so afraid of Naomi's willingness to fall back into evil, I called daily and checked up on them all, including her, and because of it, Naomi assumed hope in our reunion of our relationship and marriage and deluded herself of the finality of the situation.

The fact of the matter was that I only married her out of a naïve sense of duty that was born from the poverty and need suffered by us both from childhood, and not out of true love. Her treachery sealed the fate of our childish union. As the grim truth began to sink into her small insignificant thought processes, she blew a gasket and no longer did she resign herself to her true nature in spirit, thus further degrading her morality and sense of maturity by associating with the lowest of society's wretches with no regrets in her actions. Once word reached back to me through the grapevine that she was seen with my children in one of the most dangerous projects located in the city of Sacramento, I myself snapped and blew a gasket! I left out of my uncle's home enraged and thoughtless. Without saying a word, I got into my car and peeled out of the driveway like a bat out of hell! Arriving at her location within record time, having no fear of what I might come across, I stormed through the project with the address of her location in hand. I reached the location and immediately banged on the door yelling, "NAOMI! WHERE ARE MY CHILDREN?!" Too afraid to open the door someone replied, "GO AWAY!" While seeing shadows of female figures behind the curtains, an aperture in the curtain blew to the side and a small glimpse of my little girl was visible in the poverty-stricken and roach infested apartment. As I looked through the small crack in the sheer dirty curtain, I could see my firstborn standing near the window. With no reason nor rhyme, pure adrenaline drove my right hand through the window. I shattered the window and pulled back the curtain and called out to my baby girl, only hearing her respond, "Daddy!" as she ran towards the broken window and her bereaved father. In fight-or-flight mode, I grabbed her through the shattered window and instantly pulled her through it and walked away in full view of all spectators in the complex. Afraid of the legal recourse of my actions, I contemplated the possible consequences, knowing full well I'd broken the law in so many ways, so I dared not go back to my Uncle Leo's home where I was staying. In a panic, I brain stormed an escape route from injustice at least for the moment.

But my baby girl was safely in my arms as I figured out where to go; instinctively, I drove directly to my co-worker that befriended me when no other would. Upon arrival, she graciously opened up her home and convinced me to inform the police of my whereabouts, and within minutes, the doorbell rang. It was the police as expected, but their response took me for a loop; given my past experience with cops, I knew for sure I would be handcuffed and hauled off to jail without excuse given. I made sure my friend would be there to care for my child once I'd gone to jail, but the opposite occurred.

As I explained my position to the officers, and explained my reasoning attributing to my refusal of leaving my child with her mother amongst the conditions she exposed her to, the police took my side and charged me with nothing. I was shocked and very relieved. They left with saying one thing, "We rather she was with you than be in that place... have a nice day sir," thus ultimately leaving me and my first born child in the comfort of my friend's home. The law was only concerned with the environment in which the child was exposed, and the danger that surrounded her, not the method in which I liberated her. I rescued my baby girl from a drug and crime infested project, and transported her to a safe middle class luxury apartment where the crime rate was nonexistent and the police applauded my actions and went on their way. In the eyes of the law, I had every right to remove my child from that environment. Naomi's true light of darkness and evil nature tried to shine daily, with threatening telephone calls inundating my uncle's home, work phone and cell. Constant bombardment of unintelligent gibberish spewing through the telephone lines became inexcusable, but my only thoughts were on my brand new baby boy that I'd stupidly left in the hands of a childish wicked moron without hope, for I was her hope and now I was no longer there.

Just born and knowing only his mother, I couldn't find myself removing him from her arms, nor involving the court system in an already explosive situation. There was no way I would allow the family court system to take control of my now broken family's future. I knew from past experiences of others in my family line who relinquished their control of their family to the state; it had become the biggest mistake of their lives. Leaving my son in the hands of a mentally disabled scorned woman would not be the best scenario at that time, but I had no choice. Although her situation was chaotic at best, my son would do better with his own mother rather than that of the state of California. Months went by and a barrage of vulgar telephone calls inundated every phone within inches of my presence and there was no let up from her constant nagging and harassment. Her living conditions alongside the people surrounding her and my son were deplorable! I saw no way out from the ongoing nightmare, thus my mind's every thought was for my newborn son. "Fuck not again!" I would say to myself every time the telephone rang. "Should I answer the phone?" I knew it was her. But something inside me said answer, so I did. With no rude remarks,

EDGAR FRENCH, JR.

and only a tone of frantic need, she'd been evicted from her home with thirty days to vacate and she needed my help.

Always having my son's welfare in mind, I knew this would be possibly the last chance I would have to secure the safety of my child; but how could I? I was working full time, going to school full time for Electronics, with no time for the child I already had, let alone the other. I had to come up with a solution other than the state of California's involvement. Knowing the suffering character of my mother, I knew my son would be safe within her hands; even if my ex-spouse would self-destruct, I knew my mother would truly teach and take care of him the best she knew how. I had no other support from Naomi in finding out a solution, yet I knew she would be up for any suggestion, for she had only weeks to vacate her ghetto abode. I gave Naomi only one solution out of the dilemma facing us both. She must leave Sacramento without question, and return not to Texas, but to Gary, Indiana, the very place we'd escaped from in the past. Resisting feverishly for hours, she made no leeway. I stayed strong and held my ground and she finally conceded, knowing as well as I did that my mother would provide shelter and love for both her and our child, more so than anyone in her own family including her own mother.

"The road leading to hell is scattered with good intensions!" With a full plate of responsibilities on my hands, I didn't know how I would be able to care for a two year old and a newborn while I attended school full time and worked full time. Hoping I would at least have some leeway over the upbringing of my only begotten son, I relied on my mother's strong will to do right by all that was hers which would eventually commandeer total control of my son's wellbeing from his wayward mother. Once his mother fully gave way to her immoral nature, and completely turned over her spirit, body and mind to her destructive nature, my mother did what was expected. In my young and naive way of thought, I was being reasonable and loving in my decision to relocate them both to my mother; yet in retrospect, I further distanced myself from my son, thinking my son was too little to be taken from his mother's arms, no matter how immature or selfish she may have become. At the same time, I thought I would be creating an easy way out of going through an ugly and destructive separation process conducted through the California court system. It was not worth losing custody of my son over any conflict I would have with his mother. With no options of redemption presented to her, she had no choice but to accept my proposal. The following day, my ex-spouse and newborn son were in the air on their way to Gary, Indiana.

EDGAR FRENCH, JR.

CHAPTER XXV
Knowing's Sorrows

The departure of my newborn son in the hands of a seriously disturbed, and arrested developmental miscreant did not soothe my concerns one bit. Having the foresight to relocate my son was initially for the best, but the nightmare of dealing with his mother would grow from one state to another. Finally, by understanding what it meant to be a man under real stress, I turned towards confusion! I truly began to feel the weight of responsibility and the world fell upon my shoulders like an anvil. I was a twenty-five year old single man caring for a three year old baby girl and surrounded by those trapped in the mass brainwashing by the American political left who all had slave like mentalities and were unable to break free from the invisible chains that held them down into the darkness of poverty. The fact that they loved their chains made me begin to hate my own creed of people for their lack of understanding and their unwillingness to understand the root of their own misery. I grew very angry by the very real plight I would face day after day of closed doors, and very little opportunity, even though I tried so hard to escape the cards dealt by birth. Stunted in immorality, I was forced to leave my pride and joy, my baby girl in the hands of strangers and loved ones that had no clue about showing my child the love they themselves were searching for all their lives. MK Ultra in full effect bloomed within the inner-cities, weaponized music permeated air night and day, and safety was and still is a work of fiction. I myself embodied the very poison that spewed over the airwaves and exposed the very innocence I held so dearly, my baby girl, to it.

With my family torn apart and scattered across the country, I felt lost in my mind, body and spirit. Search and you shall find! Seek and you shall be granted access to the truth of all that is hidden, and break free from those that wish to see you fall. Secured in the thought that my only begotten son would be well taken care of by my own mother, I continued my pursuit of true knowledge with my oldest child by my side as much as possible, and she was a glimmer of hope in the darkness. A few years quickly passed and my hunger for truth became suffering in all facets of life. I would drink myself to sleep as soon as I sent my joy off to school since I worked the midnight shift, but successfully navigated alcoholism with the day to day responsibility of a single parent in distress. At the time, I thought I was well ahead of the curve when it came to succeeding in this illusion of a secular career life because I had a nice car, nice apartment, and a great job with benefits!

But as I lay my drunken self to sleep each morning, a hole of great darkness grew within my heart! Just as my knowledge of ancient things and places increased, my presence in my child's life decreased, and any hope for happiness was fading away. I slowly began to learn the true nature of the world, the world in which my children would live after me, and it only brought sorrow and pain to my heart and spirit. Events of supernatural or unexplained occurrences made themselves apparent daily because of my inquiries in dark places within the Christian Church, Islamic Mosque, and the Jewish Kabbalah mysticism, who all dubbed themselves as "The Children of the Book." The more I searched ancient texts, the more weird happenings would occur, from throwing rocks in trashcans in the pitch blackness of night from very far distances, to avoiding absolute death when a voice in the head commanded me to turn right when I wished to turn left, thus saving me from total gang violence in which I'd surely get caught up in undoubtedly. I became so in tune with unseen forces; fear traveled right beside me. My sixth sense was heightened to the point that I could read another person's thought processes by just the way they walked in a room, and know their woes only by how they spoke to others. I felt the spirit of pure evil when a Child of Darkness entered into the room, and in contrast, I felt absolute calmness and hope when a Child of Light walked by me on the street.

Then I realized that it was not me with the gift of foresight, but unseen beings directing my way in ignorance. Full of arrogance and pride, I exuberated denigration in every step of my being and presence. Boastfulness seems more of an asset when flirting with the dark side of life, but only enhances misery of one's self. Seductiveness is the pursuit of material wealth and I was ignorant to its sway, thinking somehow it would take away the sorrow of missing my only son and bring some type of happiness, yet with every venture, emptiness filled my every move in life. For you are a Child of Light and darkness may never fill your need for children, family and peace! Prayer is your only recourse to an unknown force that may or may not hear your calls for forgiveness and mercy, but to whom or what?!

While learning the basics of the elementary importance of vibration and its effect on material matter within the universe, and the magical spells of words, my mental and spiritual interest were intrigued.

I needed to know more! "I must know more," and the more I pursued ancient knowledge and secret text, the more my faith in men faded away. Soon, I was blinded by the pursuit of knowledge and I inadvertently neglected the one I loved the most, my beautiful little girl, who was exposed to the will of this wicked world by family, babysitters and the television's programming. Selfishness is something no man naturally believes about himself, yet selfishness is what I exhibited most days and nights.

A cure was definitely needed, and we all know pride cures nothing, but the fall of pride cures all. But before I could be cured of my unknown elements fertilizing my immoral habits, I had to be taught a lesson in godly manners! A spiritual purging by the Most High was needed; therefore, His will and spirit had taken hold within my soul while time was allotted. Obliviousness at best described yours truly at that time in my life. When undergoing the necessary steps in grasping the sheer grandeur and splendidness of creation, I needed to see its wonder, and truly understand the importance of the species of man in this awesome three-dimensional universe. "Before the fall comes pride," yet the humility of all men must endure the true price of pride's lure which is failure, so must come the furnace of realization to fuel truth's blazing heat. Not knowing the road set beneath my feet, the burning fire of truth when lost in lies began to blaze. Finding that escape from lies may cost a grand and almost impossible price; it leaves one hopeless in its pursuit. While yearning for universal truth, nothing stops fate's forward march if such a thing exists. Hard lessons are in order for all that have fallen in their ways from the Creator. Willingly or dimwittedly, death may be one's final outcome in the search if not careful.

Moving from place to place as my so-called persona gave way to uncontrollable carelessness and misbehavior, I was losing my mind, body and spirit once again to immorality and self-demeaning behavior.

Worried about may favor with the god of my youth, I foolishly placed myself deeply in opposition of the very being I was desperately seeking. Delusional in thinking, was I! I thought that theology taught to me by others was sound in theory and logic, but as I exposed my mind to alternative sources of information other than that of the Christian Bible and its many versions of so-called holy scriptures, I began to notice the duality within its pages, for it was "Holy" in its true meaning, instead of "Wholly." Finding truth mixed in with lies is all one will find in the Bible if one does not investigate its content and meaning of words for himself, and I must say, it's extremely time consuming! Finding metaphors amongst history, folklores and lies frustrates the soul, and deprives the spirit of natural spiritual food. Men say the word "Holy" means "Sacred," yet it's true and denotative meaning is just as it is spelled: Holy! The Christian Bible has holes in it! The book is not "Wholly," which by dictionary definition means Full, Complete!

Immersed in religious dogma, I found myself studying all three major forms of religious doctrine every chance I got, thus finding similarities in every aspect of their teachings and finding fault in their hypocritical display of moral superiority. Never thinking once to halt my activities in the search, I immersed myself deeper and deeper down the rabbit hole of spiritual confusion and deception, but only found falsehoods tangled and interchanged within reality's hidden truths.

As I searched all possible avenues, I noticed a change, not in myself, but from those who were closest to me. It was as if the unseen electromagnetic cosmic forces took control of my five senses, for no longer did I seek out the pleasures of this material three-dimensional world. Moreover, as I began to shun immorality and vulgar forms of communication amongst the light of darkness, all my so-called friends and family members conspired among themselves to minimize their association with the likes of one such as myself. Furthermore, as my understanding of ancient knowledge increased, enjoyment of the mundane and trivial things and lifestyle decreased in time. Soon I found no pleasure in sports, television or casual small talk at work or play. In fact, entrusting my logic in most social activities seemed unfulfilling and mundane. I struggled to maintain clarity of mind and spirit, knowing I had lost control of my understanding of mankind's desire for fun and instant pleasure. I tried to piece together the numerous clues leading to answers of questions never given to truth seekers within the Church, Synagogue or Mosque.

The truth of the matter is: all people on the planet Earth are in store for a great revelation and ominous consequences for not seeking out truth on their own, and falling victim to the very powers that purposely lead us all into ignorance, thus ultimately luring all mankind away from the Creator. But could one such as myself find favor in the eyes of the Creator without knowing how to find him?! Simply NO! Never for selfish motive should one seek the Most High!

As I fell down the rabbit hole of knowledge, the darkness became as black as molasses and as thick as tar. Learning the depths of deception plaguing the so-called Elite rulers deluded my mind, body and spirit because I was taught from birth that they were special and not like normal mankind.

I found they were genetically deformed from generational inbreeding and devoid of common sympathy, emotions and or empathy and they were purposely designed to commune with entities that exist outside our three-dimensional realm. After learning about the original thirteen +1 bloodlines that sided with Lucifer, the lord of this world, and sold out humanity for Earthly riches, I knew the cancer that gripped mankind in the darkness of ignorance was more than malignant. It was in its last stages of conquest, and we were a species on our way to death's throes.

Finally, "Now I know!" All foundations of society are based and propagated upon a lie! A vicious and malignant lie that permeates through all pillars of life! All Organizational Systems within our world are infected by this lie: Religious, Academic, Social, and Racial Identities are all infected by the ancient concepts of Theology! The theology of hierarchy was given to man by the two hundred fallen ones of old.

Educational Systems, Political Systems and Economical Systems are all controlled by this ancient concept of theology. Theocratic division is at the root of the malignant cancer that is plaguing us all on this planet. Environmental Systems are purposely eroded and made to kill us by those that see us as a disease. Every thought of growth and prosperity within society has been corrupted before its inception without a cognitive awareness of mankind. For we all operate under the premise of freedom, while loving the servitude of slavery as we watch the glazing lights of the television screen! We all suffer a form of mass delusion and a false sense of safety emanating from the Zionist's occult controlling the Media and the Military Industrial Complex who maliciously lord over us all.

"How could I help my family if I couldn't help myself?!" We all are slaves from birth, no matter what nation, country or region you or I originate. The whole planet lies in the hands of the Wicked One! Mankind falls under two categories: you're either a Child of Light, loving knowledge of the universe and the unknown or a Child of Darkness, loving one's self in deviance and ignorance over all understanding of righteousness! Although, to be a true Child of Light meant I had to give up loving this world and become an alien resident. Knowledge brings sorrow! Overwhelmed with the growing responsibility of caring for the only thing that kept me somewhat sober, my baby was growing ever so beautiful, and I knew nothing of caring for a young girl, and most definitely not the young woman she was becoming. While I made sure to keep constant communication with my mother and my son, I tried reasoning with my ex-spouse with no resolve over our divide and different concerns over our children's care, and even though Naomi ran the streets three thousand miles away consuming drugs and I myself drank myself to sleep nightly, we both tried civil communication with one another.

Under Lucifer's sway I began missing important appointments, and fell into deep sleep when time came to pick up my daughter after school, all because of drunkenness and hangovers, thus shaming my love in public.

"I needed to stop!" I felt ashamed after realizing the severity of those facts and I told myself that phrase over and over daily, but only became more and more separated from reality and cried myself to sleep every night. Something must be done! After a long long-distance phone call confiding in my mother, I put faith in her motherly way, for she once showed me my error in dealing with my ex-wife; although in my mind, my ex-wife could only be seen as a faithless person, yet I agreed to exchange our children every year, so as to bring an end of resentment on both sides of the argument. I agreed to provide for our children

EDGAR FRENCH, JR.

monetarily so not to suffer the absence of a father's ability to provide for his children, but I knew deep inside it was not enough because they needed me in their lives every day! I knew in my heart and mind that my absence would truly mean the end of my family, for children without a mother or a father naturally destroys the course of instruction and education for them to be successful in life, and escalates the cause that fuels the engine that develops the breakdown in communication and the cancer that eats away at a broken family. In time, I came to understand and realize that the burdensome relief and or solutions that falsely seemed to help me gain hope for the future of my family only fueled the destruction of my relationship with both of my children, and that I left them victims to the very world I myself tried to escape my entire life.

A year of hopeful relief ensued the illusion of hope and all went as planned. Naomi sent Michael to me and I sent Mika to her as agreed; I had my son, and he had me, or so I thought. It was wonderful enjoying that time with my son; sadly though, I did not know that would be the only time I would ever have with him. Just the thought of our time brings tears to my eyes even to this day. The time with my son was grand and short lived, but going through the ups and downs of knowing one another could never be taken away. Seeing how handsome my son had become made me proud and learning of his meekness made me sure of his greatness to come! Seeing how much more he exhibited compassion at such a young age, in comparison to myself, was exuberating, for he was perfect in my eyes. I was even coming to grips with my alcoholism, although life was just as hard as before. The thought of uniting my family brought fulfillment within my spirit, but it was all just a fantasy, a farce in which I told myself to pass the time until Mika's return and Michael's departure. Once a year had passed and the time for mutual exchange of our children arrived, my ex-wife led me on the most horrifying roller coaster I had ever experienced in my life! When talking to Naomi on the phone, it seemed as if she had every intension to honor our mutual agreement. I put my son on the plane and waited for the call from Indiana informing me that my Mika was on her way, but the call never came. My ex-wife purposely withheld my daughter after I returned my son. Light turned to darkness in the span of a plane ride across the country.

Months passed and there was no word from Indiana! There were no answers to my inquiries or calls. Anger turned into fear and fear turned into despair, and my heart cracked every day, for I heard nothing from my children. Some months passed then a glimpse of some communication found its way to California. Word of my children's safety reached my ears, but so did the venom of Naomi's intentions, via my mother. She didn't return my baby girl because she was holding a grudge from when I took Mika out of her so-called care in Sacramento, California. My ex-wife never once showed concern for her child's welfare, for she thought only of herself, and didn't care that she was living in poverty or squalor and filth at that time.

"Payback" was her word, and her only concern. It was all a morbid game in her eyes, and as long as she obtained her revenge upon me, she was satisfied in the situation of doom for our children's understanding of how life truly is.

Now she had all the cards to my heart in her hands, and for years she willed them mercilessly at my expense. All torturous events concerning Naomi's hold on me were too many to name, but from her scam, I cursed my Creator in ignorance, be it good or bad. I stood guilty! Falling into pity for one's self is not pretty, but an unforeseeable lie waged upon one's self, and is very hard to overcome, so as to see truth of one's self. The true feeling of being alone is suffocating even when you're around others, and surrounded by all. Nothing can relieve the agony and pain of losing your children, even when they live, and then I knew its endless sorrow without compare.

For they live but not with their father, and without the love I had to give, having no contact or means of retrieving them, I suffered. That fucking Bitch! That fuck'n bitch taught me what it really means to hate another human-being, so much as to kill, in which I knew nothing, even when I stood as a so-called gangsta in the midst of bodily harm or in the presence of evil spirits and poverty without hope. The Creator of the Universe and Most High of all creation showed pity upon me once again. Months had passed since that horrible day, and then I received another call, but it wasn't from my children's mother, but from my own mother, once more. All of a sudden, my son was in the hands of my mother. The mother of my children had fully condemned herself in condemning me. She was immersed in the gang-banging culture we both fled as pups, hooked on drugs and out roaming the dangerous streets of Gary, Indiana once again, but this time, my daughter was alongside her crazy ass. As my heart dropped from the news, my hope was restored on one front!

My son was in the hands of my mother and soon so would be my daughter, for logic dictates that the universe corrects all errors. Sure enough both of my children were in the loving hands of my mother, and I at last, could sleep peacefully at night.

Yet the longing for my children must continue as is! "Until you fix yourself, you're in no condition to care for another so says the lord." Complacency comes slowly into your day to day life without your children's laughter or presence. Daily, socially driven responsibilities dominated my reality and I began to go with the motions of the herd and believed it was normal. The absence of my children faded away with sorrow of self, and the drinking increased substantially. Life looked gloomy amongst the California sun and rain fell on me daily from the clear sky.

As I go back in retrospect of thought, during the little time I spent with my son, I played the social scene without impunity, involving myself in work outings and after hours socializing with workmates. I soon found myself in need of a babysitter so I could indulge in stress free depravity, so I employed one of my co-workers for the task. In time, she grew on me and we became "familiar" so to speak. With no real feelings for Lori, I placed her on the back burner of my emotional development, or concerns after showing some sexual interest. Because of the unusual work situation I created due to selfishness, pride and the sense of ungodliness and improprieties on both sides of the isle, I broke off any relationship with my ex co-worker after my son's departure. But like the old saying goes, "What comes around goes around" and my unprofessional dealings with her would come back to bite me in the ass. With life looking somewhat bleak, after a long semi-legal battle with my now about to be ex-employer, picking up an agreed upon bi-weekly check at the facility I was formally assigned to, I noticed a shine emanating from the young woman I once engaged face.

Without restraint or reason I turned to her and blurted out these words within the facilities private office, "You're pregnant." I shocked all who were present within the office and she had no response, only a look of "…how…what do you mean?" as she continued her paperwork. She looked up at me once more with a look of perplexity as I walked out of the facility knowing the not so obvious and thinking, "Well, here comes another problem amongst many!"

Overwhelmed with self-imposed and unnecessary problems I inflected upon myself, I felt as if I were fighting the world on all fronts from personal flaws to the social and professional imperfections I uncovered within myself. Fully submersed into the society that we all willfully engage, I felt so lost with the spiritual guidance I once cherished. Though I did not fall victim to the overwhelming brilliance and attraction of the blazing city lights that shone in the nights, I fully gave way to the gleam of promiscuous activities without concern or consequences.

I hoped to fill the void of those I'd lost through the years by sleeping my way around town, but that only deepened the pains of loneliness. Yet the Creator chose to test my worthiness of his service and placed me on a path I did not know I would be obliged to partake by way of my sexual self-indulgences. Years prior, I had impregnated a woman or "lost soul" for whom I had no love.

She was an illegal alien from Mexico and I refused to take responsibility for the child; in turn, I inadvertently set myself on a spiritual path that I myself would take in the near future, a path set in flames of passion, and forged in regretful anguish. I had doomed a young innocent soul to a life without a father and a life of pain and poverty in the back streets of Sacramento, California where in no way life could be worth living. I refused to even believe the child was my own out of pride, ignorance, and selfishness. Furthermore, after her birth, I ignored the constant reminders from the Wascally Wabbott of the resemblance of myself and the child. I knew deep inside he was right, yet my mind would not let the matter rest upon the truth of the matter, although it haunted my soul every waking moment. I fully deluded myself of the responsibly so not to care for the child by telling myself, "I'm not going to pay for someone that may very well not be my own because of the behavior of the mother, who was young and wayward, not unlike myself, but worse, an illegal alien and homeless!" I continued to play the field without impunity and showed zero concern for others or their plight, but little did I know that my selfishness and lack of empathy for others would have to change and change rather abruptly.

Chapter XXVI

KARMA

On a sunny, breezy, October morning, a not so surprising revelation appeared, and would change my life for the better and worse. After trying to remedy a Monday morning hangover from a massive weekend bender, I decided to go out for a pack of cigarettes and noticed a hand written note placed under my windshield wiper. It was a letter from Lori, the woman who was my babysitter and co-worker. I didn't even have to open it, for I instinctively knew its contents. Since Lori was either too afraid or ashamed to knock on my front door with her accusations, she chose to inform me in the letter that she was with child and was very surprised. I, on the other hand, was not surprised! From the moment I saw her in the office of my former employer, I knew she was pregnant even if she didn't know, and pregnant with my child!

After I read the letter, I rerouted my destination from the store to her apartment which was located a few blocks down the road and confronted her with no deniability of fault; in fact, I faced her with joy of spirit. While soothing her fears, I claimed fatherhood willingly and without contest which was far removed from the way I handled the earlier accusations from the wayward woman. I saw the first as unfit and unworthy of my honor, yet I had none, for true honor and moreover, grace, was the first accuser's child, and my child all alone. She deserved more, much more than I could ever give, and I knew it.

As I sat alone sobbing in my own little world, the reality of my lack of humanity became more apparent within my soul and spirit, yet I still yearned for material wealth. Because I was so worried about my own financial wellbeing, I disregarded the wellbeing of an innocent baby girl that truly was my own and it still haunts me without fail. Guilt and self-loathing consumed me. I lost all communication with the child's mother and I prayed for forgiveness, but god would not let my spirit free from my criminal sin against the child. Yet he allowed me to have another born out of wedlock, for his plans for the first child was great, and I knew that fact as well. This second time I would step up to the plate and be a good father once more and for all, or so I thought. Although I cared for my so-called legitimate children financially, they were thousands of miles away and slowly growing apart from me. Pursuing riches and the American Dream destroyed all that mattered, and I was determined not to allow ignorance in youth to continue to direct my actions any longer, for seeking out the occult or secret knowledge would be my focus.

Soon, I turned away from the things that trapped so many from learning truth about happiness and what it implies. And as I dove without fear into the unknown, I changed course in my daily actions and turned back towards upholding my morality. I could feel and see the power of unseen forces standing in the way of my emotional, personal, and spiritual progress. Confusion marked the way to clarity, and earnest prayers to the Most High parted the fog of deception that scoured the path to enlightenment, for there is nothing new under the sun and no one living being has firsthand knowledge of the past. I struggled to understand the turmoil I unwittingly brought upon myself by believing in the non-truths of the dogmas of men. Therefore, I vowed to never put trust in the words of others whether written or spoken, not even my own, for no one truly understands heavenly things. Discernment is the key to true knowledge given by the Most High and not taken by lowly watchers; therefore, I searched for knowledge that could be found by those that searched the ancient text and researched before me. Although I understood that sorrow paves the road to knowledge, I cared not. Mental stress, spiritual starvation, compounded by loneliness and loss, makes the journey one seldom ventures, but I took those steps and never looked back. As one door of hidden information revealed itself and answers were of discernment, another secret door opened then closed, then another door revealed itself before closing.

As I learned and gained more secret knowledge, a fire burned from within! A light shined as the tightrope I walked became illuminated across an abyss of darkness. As spirits and demons swirled within the mouth of the endless black

EDGAR FRENCH, JR.

anti-matter, my heart skipped a beat with each encounter. To venture onto the tightrope of knowing the unknown takes a skill of which I was unaware; yet foolishly, I stepped forth, and quickly found out that the tightrope led to madness for those not worthy to venture forth. Desperately, I set out to find proof of what I already knew within my heart: the Creator of all humanity did not put us here for no reason. As time waned, loneliness found comfort in drunkenness. I found myself losing humanity's grip on sanity and alienated myself from family, friends and foe. With speech far from their understanding, they feared what they could not understand or grasp. Comprehension of ancient text broke down walls obstructing the tightrope's sway, only to find out that those who knew the way purposely put up the walls so no other could obtain what was all for humans to gain! It was ours from the beginning. Yahweh allowed me to obtain small morsels of spiritual food, so not to get entangled in the spider's web that led to madness, which trapped so many who went looking for truth before me.

The longer I walked the tightrope, the further I fell from favor within and out of the world. Neglecting ordinary responsibilities, I found myself on the verge of homelessness.

A wild man willingly in the darkness I'd become! Careless on every front as I feverishly searched out the unknown! No longer did I care for things of this world, yet in the world I resided, and alcohol numbed the pain of the spiritual journey of fire. I was drunk most nights, and deep within the thoughts and writings of past deeds of better men most days. The closer I thought I got to god, the further I fell short of his grace. Then came along someone I least expected to encounter, and a ray of hope broke through the dark clouds of drunken madness. Once more, the Creator of Earth and Heaven came to my rescue. It was the mother, Lori, of my last and final child. The young woman who I wisely predicted her pregnancy before she knew it, stood by me when no one else seemed not to care and revealed her goodness in my despair. In time, I grew to love her and began to feel whole once more. With my last child stripping away the cloud of loneliness, and with calmness of family life, Yahweh directed me towards the light of fulfillment, although I did not deserve it.

However, the forces that be control this third dimensional reality and declare war on those who seek the truth of the lie! The first lie. Did you not know?! Nothing worthwhile comes easy for common folk, or for those of little material means. There is a mighty price to pay for understanding all that should not be understood! For the first few years, I thought my life was finally getting back on track, but little did I know that my new found life would diminish within a blink of an eye, and without my own mischievous doing. Daily, I imparted some spiritual knowledge to Lori, changed her outlook on life, and hurled her onto the road less traveled. I uprooted her from all she knew and she quickly withered in faith of darkness and no longer followed old influences, bringing turmoil within our home unaware. In time, verbal abuse, and then senselessness shrouded her irate behavior that became so common. She longed for the things of the past, fornication was her vice, and faithfulness she did lack, but most of all that stood in her way to enlightenment was the unwillingness to let go of the past. She longed for the light of darkness and only sought out material things no matter how much I warned her.

Words of false grandeur and loss of favor amongst peers stifled her growth into spiritual substance. She wanted what the world had to offer and could not see the trap so clearly before her, so unseen forces cleared the way for me to step back on the road less traveled. For I was to be forged in fire! Little did I know!

Michael: The time has come! For he must walk the walk of all lost Children of Light. The walk that leads all coming out of darkness he must travel. They all must walk through fire before they become whole. He's almost ready for smelting says the lord! Prideful boisterousness he still exhibits, but The Most High sees in him something we ourselves cannot yet see; will he himself figure it out my brother?!

Raphael: The diligence of the Children of Darkness know no bounds, for they work continuously throughout the ages of time. And now they have grown in understanding the knowledge of the gates that separate Azazel and his forces from this third dimension and the humans below. This evil work goes on unchecked! Soon they will break through the veil. Yet here we stand on guard for this one; do you not know his worth my brother?!

Michael: Only the God-Head himself knows his worth my brother, and we are obedient to our father. And obedient is what we shall be! To protect this lowly wretch is our charge my brother! And understanding why we are charged to this task is not our concern dear and loyal solider. But dear comrade look there, the forces of evil stand forever in the child's way of passage! The Dragon's force shows much interest in maintaining his delusion of things not known to him. He must not be allowed to become overwhelmed by the power of unknown forces upon him. We must interfere with patience and sharp eyes; see if he overcomes and prevails whatever calamity that may be placed against him by the wicked one's sway with little protection from us over him.

Raphael: I hear his cries in the night my brother, and he seeks what should be known to all. This war has taken its toll on the mortals alongside immortal! Could you my brother weather the suffering of humanity?! Could I my brother?! We know not time nor death by it, for we suffer no more. We feel no pain nor fear. Woe is warranted for our fallen ones, for man bares the brunt of the Dragon's rage! Let the remnant be shielded by the grace granted this lowly soul, and let us see our father's will take place among them. May the poor wretch's love of our father grow without too much woe, but Michael! Michael he is too weak of spirit! Do you not see the road he must travel? He must know that he is not alone, or death may become his fate.

Michael: Fear not brother, he has much to learn before the road is placed before his feet! We'll guide his every waking thought with glimmers of end times won. The Most High has allowed him renewal of dormant sights and thoughts of old. Restore to him the spirit's range, and allow him the keys to see the remnants of memories long lost and once passed and lost to humanity. As the darkness grows so shall his sight of the unknown secrets of creation! For the word of Yahweh shall ring strong amongst his remnants of light granted! May his mercy be poured upon them all for this one's sake! For they may not last through the persecution and horror allotted them, and not far to come. Morn not dear Raphael, our father's light is not easily extinguished, even among mortals.

CHAPTER XXVII
The Forging Process Begins

Like a milky film cloaking one's eyes, my illusions of long lasting happiness without true repentance before my Creator were slowly fading away. My relationship with my new counter-part Lori, and our child began to wane due to outside influences perpetrated by her mother, and a lack of communication between us both. Furthermore, the strain of alcohol abuse and a lack of attention on my part separated us entirely. Foolishly praying without works of faith, and my immature nature bringing on financial hardship amongst legal aggravations brought upon our family by my hands did not help the course of happiness. The more I navigated my way through the occultism lurking in the ranks of every so-called religious order, hopelessness and dismay accompanied the secret information I'd obtained. The more I learned, the more I felt lost and alone in this wicked world. But something within me would not allow me to give up the search for truth about the living Creator. The ancient text only frustrated my efforts in finding out such truths, and without finding answers to mankind's future and our fate, I made life at home more complicated. "I must know the truth about man's history?! I must know why the world is full of evil, death and misery alongside pain, and I must have knowledge of all that is good in the eyes of the Creator! Why would a loving Creator sentence his most beloved, and greatest creation to slavery, pain and death in this world in which we live?!" Searching made me feel hopeful as I drank myself to sleep every weekend I would ask myself, why? Through the pain and loss of what I loved most, my first beloved children, I'd gained a new certain amount of clarity in ancient text and its duplicitous meaning. I'd adopted more qualities of a Child of Light, and began exhibiting much more of a moral compass. I gradually applied Yahweh's universal rules of morality, even in my drunken state and hour of confusion. With great emotional and physical effort of will, I worked hard in my now new family life, and began to go back towards what was truly good in life, according to Yahweh's word, "The Ten Commandments or Edicts." With that, my new found family's relationship began to heal and grow.

An epiphany occurred. Even in a drunken and incoherent state, Yahweh's word worked! "I must follow the principals I had once forsaken in ignorance." There would be no more foul language, suffering the childish emotions, or having the breakdown of communication on both our ends from which most of our problems were brought into fruition.

I thought perhaps I'd go back towards the organization I vowed never to return thinking I was wrong and full of prideful hubris as the reasoning for my departure in the first place, but I was still thinking in ignorance! However, Yahweh had given me a second chance at being a father and a happy life, in which I wanted most, and to refuse my child the best father she no doubt deserved, I felt as if I had to expose her to the true religion. I said to myself, "Let me get this last drink before I start a new!" I was infused with hubris and unconcern for my fellow man and argued with Lori over nothing, but I was filled with anger from the constant bombardment of her verbal abuse and constant nagging! I popped opened the half pint of vodka before I left the house for another drink. I obtained another half pint of vodka and cracked open the bottle before the door of the liquor store closed in back of me. Finishing the bottle in seconds, I blacked out before leaving the parking lot and hit a parked car without knowing as I lay there in a drunken stupor. I was sent to jail for drunk driving for the very first time, and with a slap on the hand, I was out the next day. Mentally, I resigned myself to follow the spirit and turned back towards the safeguards of morality set forth by the Creator to protect all that is sentient throughout creation, but I was weak of spirit and lost in the dark, so I kept drinking as if it were not a big problem.

I started to notice the causation of mishaps and misfortunes as I drew closer to moral action rather than thought, yet I still drank myself to sleep every night. I witnessed firsthand that unseen forces did indeed direct humankind activities within my own short comings. As my mind's eye opened up into understanding the concept of cause and effect, I unwittingly drove myself towards imaginary lines of chance, both spiritual and physical. Invisible spiritual lines must not be crossed between the works of light and the works of darkness, meaning alcohol abuse. Though knowing the effects to both are necessary in existence, unspoken rules must not be corrupted! No lesson is learned secondhand, and most are learned fast, sharp and hard. Finding out true hardship through mistakes made by one's self seems hard, yet mistakes made in defiance of knowing right and not following it is truly hard! For the spirit is negatively affected more than that of the soul (body) when one knows better and takes no action to stop it. Pushing the limits of understanding, I foolishly behaved prideful in boast, continuing my education in technology as if secular education would brighten my horizons. I witnessed in real time the book of "Revelation" coming into view, as the seven scrolls are laid out and prepared for the opening of their seals within the geopolitical sphere.

I gave no mind of mental overload, and I pushed myself both physically and emotionally researching and in search of spiritual truth; ironically, I reverted back towards alcohol even more. Learning nothing from my first DUI, I recklessly acquired a second within months.

This time it was more than a slap on the wrist; personal freedom was restricted, amongst acquiring more financial hardship attached to the punishment given, ultimately causing even more emotional strife within the home and family life. Yet still I refused to give up on morality, and tried to turn back towards goodness and refrain from indulging alcohol. The forces of darkness intensified its grip upon me!

The more I tried to refrain from alcohol and stay sober, the more mishaps would rear their ugly heads.

I learned nothing from my own actions, but I felt as if I did, yet clearly I had not! I continued to go on in life blinded and bounded by the chains of darkness' light, and fought with all might to break free, but had no avail amongst my efforts. I felt the emptiness grow within my heart and loneliness returned by the second. Thinking I knew the way back to the Creator's grace, I called out his name in the night, but it was not enough! "What was I doing wrong?!" I yelled within my mind in the night. "You will know them by the fruits of their labor" so sayeth the lord. As I navigated the roots of darkness in study of ancient text, I recklessly and possibly wittingly risked the paroles of reaction mandated by the state of California. The effects and consequences of bucking the status quo was dangerous, but defying negative and downright immoral behavior that most scholars would seem to prescribe, was much more perilous than first realized. Actually, as I tested how deep the rabbet-hole was, I felt the bog come close to trapping me in the darkness' light! I saw the effects of choosing moral actions over immoral actions in a world where most see no right from wrong, so I truly stretched the invisible spiritual line, and became blind to the un-natural facts of this system in which we are trapped.

"That's it! I'll put ancient text to the test, for no one knows what's what!" If I'm truly free and endued with free will, my Creator will reveal what is true amongst the countless lies. I should freely rely on him, and he shall truly judge me as he sees fit; however, the evil that holds us all has human minions help hide the road to enlightenment which implies no hope for humanity. Success on your spiritual journey to truly understand the world around you, and that of above, must be found within unorthodox methods, for you may find out why all practical search is hampered from your first attempt into religious realms, so outside religion and into mankind's cell is where your spiritual journey starts and all shall truly find answers beyond the veil. Into the world I went on my quest for universal answers and in search of firsthand information on how the spirit of life and creation really works! Why shall we all suffer so much while our Creator stands by as we all perish in prayer?

It is not the Creator who has left us, for it is we who have unwittingly fallen from him because we were deceived from birth by all and from all institutions in which we trust!

All those that are lost think they know what they know, but yet what is known is given to those that are blind by those that work evil without cause, willingly and knowing or without knowledge of such facts. The brainwashing machine in which modern day Scribes and Pharisees feed the masses is beyond criminal, and those who presume to think they are saved are wrong for the very fact that death still looms, and old age marks Adam and Eve's Original Sin! What truths you were given as a child known as facts are spiritual poison; truly what your master has given you is sweet poison to digest in ignorance's bliss in saying, "… that's just the way it is!"

They willfully give over to evil without question, having success in their efforts to the enemies of darkness, for true knowledge only unveils the unseen spider-webs and obstacles holding us back from our Creator's light, and stops mankind from overcoming the monster's grip, never truly understanding for what ancient text is made. Men have been deceived from the moment our ancestors fell in the garden, and we as a people have forgotten how and why. The truth of the matter is that we all are victims of lost and stolen freedom and were taken by our arch enemy, Lucifer and his minions, "The Brotherhood of The Snake," or half-human traitors, children of the snake and their offspring. Corrupted by the love of power over his fellow man, these fallen ones have sold us all out to the one that opposed The Most High and held for ransom knowledge of the true workings of living things, thus blinding us all to history's fruits.

Only those that teach self-derived theology can deceive and distort, so we have no choice but to rely on our Creator for salvation, for all men are liars, and a book is just a book! For no book can ever serve as firsthand information or truth in knowledge when one's life is held in the balance. How could it be if you were not there to witness firsthand events occurring over some two or three millennia ago?! Like high school rumors spreading in a locker room, the story twists and turns like taffy, especially when one's intellect comes into question, which includes one's self-centered logic to explain away important questions and reinforce one's belief system when it comes under fire or scrutiny. When discernment of truth is entangled with lies, confusion holds sway, especially when the source of all informational knowledge or understanding was given to humanity by the enemy himself!

So when untangling pure truth twisted upon countless lies, your goals seem daunting and tedious at best, not to mention dangerous. For when mankinds enemies' love of the sweet fruit's nectar of despair begins dripping from ones own peer's demise brings pleasure or self-worth, only despair and demise is fostered upon both parties. Power to lord over one's brother is all mankind's enemies will ever have. To maintain power is all the thirteen +1 families will ever seek, for they are pure evil! Self-want is their doom, and they know it!

To feed off your fellow man implies death rather than life. No man wants to die, so why do we?! For the death of humanity is not normal. To destroy or put to death another like one's self should be unthinkable, unless you're not human. For they couldn't care less about another's wellbeing since they're not like others! Possession of material wealth may be the only solace in their minds, especially for lost souls. Yes!

Truth in lies is all you will see in an ancient book that has been tampered and distorted over the eons, for men controlled the levers of editing the Bible's very existence! For "The Brotherhood of The Snake" perfected the art of The Hegelian Dialectic, not Hegel himself.

The Brotherhood learned it from the fallen ones and their teachings of theology. What we dream can be true; did you know that?! All mankind has the spark of life, given by Yahweh himself; therefore, other spirits hate us and want us dead, so the obvious is true. When evil forces insist that their words are true, we know it's a lie, and when the powers that be insist the obvious lie to be as truth, we know what is said is deadly more or less, but not always understood at the time. Duplicity is in the Brotherhood's nature. Knowledge of the past is indeed documented, and was given to humanity as a blueprint for the spirit of man, so as to navigate the river of infinity's loop. History must be accurate and given in full transparency in order to traverse the Children of Darkness' synthesis entangled within history's truth that is set before us. Using secondhand information hinders the process of certainty within the soul, but learning true firsthand discernment is one's only hope for understanding the occult knowledge that leads to everlasting life. No matter what my personal opinions are about my faith, or how I feel about the validity of the ancient texts, I knew I couldn't disregard the obvious influence of unseen forces dictating the outcomes of so many important events occurring throughout history. I was baffled and stumped as I inadvertently stepped onto the road of destiny, which is straight and narrow amongst loneliness, for it is less traveled by lowly men. Slowly, I fell back into despair feeling like I would never reach the light of the Creator, so I soothed my loss with alcohol ever more so.

Soon I found myself back into more serious trouble. I was incarcerated with a stretch of six months and had a revoked license. Once I was officially within the system, I began to understand the depths of the evil protruding from the powers that be, or the Princes and Principalities of supernatural puppet-strings that hold us all under damnation. For the first time, I knew how my ancestors must have felt by being in a state of outright slavery, for no single evil is done in secret. When

EDGAR FRENCH, JR.

another man is telling one what to do in every aspect of his life, anger ensues the thought processes, leaving strife within the spirit, yet our own Creator does nothing of the sort within life itself, no matter how flawed our actions may be.

The prison guards tell one when to sleep, when to eat, when to awake, and when to shower and shit. All self-governance is freedom, but when governance is given over to another human, injustice ensues and creates division. In most cases, one's freedom is given over to people with less moral aptitude than that of oneself or even of the least of humanity. As I moved through the prison's intake process, I noticed the differentiated attitudes and respect levels allotted to me, but why? I had never been in jail before, but from both prisoners and guards alike, I was allotted respect without question.

As I walked through the maze of razor wired chained gates leading to the yard and the holding facilities, I noticed the various looks and expressions on the inmate's faces protruding through the small windows on their doorways and buildings of many colored barracks. As I passed by the many dorms, I noticed looks turned my way, and heard the undertone voices of unknown inmates speaking about me under their breath, "There he is!" What or who was I? This was the first time I've ever been incarcerated. Could it be my family's long infamous criminal history in the Midwest reaching across the nation and all the way to Northern California? "What could it be?" I asked myself as I walked past the many mean and ugly faces.

I was moved into the initial processing unit called the "Red Dorm," where only the infamous street gang called the "Bloods" inhabited, and the first stop before moving on to a jail-house job, and or another dorm if not a Blood member. Normally, after processing an inmate, he gets an assigned job and permanent living quarters within thirty days, but for me that process was waved somehow. I never received an assignment, nor did I leave to any other dorm or living quarters. I entered into the Red Dorm from day one, and never left. I was treated like prison royalty, for there were no arguments from competing gang members or guards. I was left to my own affairs without interference the entire time I was incarcerated. I left jail totally perplexed! I didn't deal with any gangs outside on the streets, neither Bloods nor Crips.

The most ironic fact of my stint in the big house was that I actually became healthier and well rested. All the pressure imposed on so-called normal living that everyone engaged in on the outside of incarceration faded away. There was no more worry of mundane responsibilities like paying light, water or gas bills, and no more worries of paying rent, or having enough food for the children. Although the food supplied to us was bland and downright disgusting, it was better for the body than that of the outside cuisine. Small portions three times daily proved healthier and more beneficial than that offered in the grocery store. With the lack of freedom comes appreciation for the little things. No longer does one concern himself with the material rat race outside his prison walls, but finds himself searching even more feverishly for the meaning of life and why we are all here on this planet. Then on a bright and sunny day, out in the yard, huddled against a lonely old oak tree, I had an epiphany once more.

Our plight as humans or station in life is such a terrible obstacle, chaining us all to darkness; why do we pursue what we do in life? It is our blind spot in realizing truth in this three-dimensional universe. Like a lightening flash, the answer came to me. Universal War is the answer! Mankind, as a species, is inherently victimized in this universal conflict. We're here to confirm the validity of a Creator and or Lucifer! Given the ancient guidelines set-out in all folklore, fairytale and ancient text, we are given free-will, and somehow given a choice in making life altering decisions. Not for one's betterment, but rather one's side in which he himself chooses in the battle between light and darkness, ultimately putting to rest the age old question of who has the right to rule creation.

I now truly understood that all I had learned and set out to learn was all drenched in deception. No longer thinking in the box, I understood that to only think outside of the box would open the doors still hidden. I myself held sway to the illusion that my life mattered only under the stigma of status and station given within such life, but I was wrong. The war between darkness and light is not one of good and evil! It is one of universal rulership. Children of Darkness truly believe they themselves are just in their actions, thinking whatever action obtaining whatever sought out goal, justifies the action and it's outcome. Children of Light, on the other hand, continue to stay clueless under the thought of upholding morality while never getting closer to their Creator, and never really understanding their position in the world at large. Children of Light! You are to think like a Soldier, not a sheep! The war is spiritual in nature, but is spilling over into the physical world.

We must understand the nature of the Beast. The world in which we live is the product of revolution, of which Lucifer is the Father and progenitor.

The revolution we are encountering is the revolution started by darkness in this dimension. It is society itself that was created for the destruction of mankind! What most would consider a normal life is actually an illusion created to confuse and delude those who would chose life over comfort and expand their conscience thought process. Children of Light! Are you so arrogant and self-centered to believe that you are the only sentient life form within this unthinkably huge universe? Think again! To find Yahweh our Creator is to think like a Man and not a child, for when we grow into manhood, we let go of childish things and focus on things of substance! We must question everything, thought, and or spoken word by men, especially those of so-called faith, and assume all that is taught by man is based in duplicities and lies. From secular to religious, from social to personal, we must question all that is taught. We have not been given the basic means to understanding the world and universe in which surrounds us, and that is the first step.

Once again, man will see past his celestial yet tiny home amongst the stars, piercing through the veil of space-time and see beyond the Milky Way Galaxy into the void of space-time itself, thus seeing Galaxies beyond measure. Knowing we ourselves are contained on a small and insignificant planet on the outskirts of a small and ordinary galaxy brings much after thought, not even measuring on a small scale of light in which we reside, protruding from the electromagnetic spectrum, making us feel small in scope of life and in deeds, but illuminated in three dimensions of existence.

Secondly, we understand that truth is often masquerading in plain sight and within ancient text and ancient lies. Discerning the truth from falsehood can be frustrating, but seeing light within the darkness shall be our guide-stone to truly understanding the universe that birthed us, thus learning to live past the physical check points and boundaries, and residing within the spiritual domain. Free will shall lead one towards the road only a few shall walk. The road leading to Yahweh is through Yeshua, and his road was one of endurance through trials and tribulations. What makes any of us different in that aspect? As I came to grips with the reality of my self-irrelevance, I understood that most of my peers roaming around the prison yard had no clue of the purpose of their own existence. I knew I had to find a way to inform my fellow man of the clarity of thought and presence that was imparted to me, but how? I must continue my search and verify my own understanding, which ultimately meant obtaining wisdom through trials and tribulations without dying. I just didn't know that at the time.

Morality is not a virtue of goodness; it is a tool and weapon against darkness! It helps strengthen the one in search of clarity and light. It helps to obtain the strength of Yahweh's light in times of need, pain and want.

The ten laws of the Creator are not commandments, in fact, all throughout the universe these edicts are prescribed as tenets. They are there to instruct those who seek out Yahweh! They have passed the test of time! Men have turned these tenets into commandments in order to deceive and enslave their fellow men, and this is a fact. Nevertheless, they are essential in navigating the narrow road that leads to life. I wished to truly be a Child of Light, thus knowing that the world in which I live is a world designed for those living in darkness and loving it.

As my time of incarceration came nearer to an end, the anxiety of understanding unseen knowledge ensued. Fully rested, I began contemplating on my newly found understanding, peeling back the curtain that covers the face of mankind, but I only saw it waning. With Lori proving herself faithful, I felt a new found spirit to continue in my pursuit for occult knowledge. Once I returned back home, I continued my education in electronics and dove deep into ancient text, which opened up doors once hidden to my understanding of historical events, which confirmed long suspected truths and untruths.

In my search, I found that the Children of Darkness ran all aspects of life! The fallen ones have controlled the narrative of history from the beginning of time, and have hidden the nature of life from all that walk the face of the Earth. On the day of my release, I was fully refreshed physically and spiritually, no longer intending to corrupt my body with any drug nor alcohol, I entered Lori's car with a new found spirit. Unemployed and eager to get back to work and school, I re-enrolled back into school, and began looking for work. Within a few weeks, I was employed as a caretaker of the elderly, in a great upscale location. But the tranquility within our home had declined, and outside influences had infiltrated the mindset of Lori. She began listening to her mother on every front of our relationship, which proved to disrupt our ability to communicate with one another.

Determined to put my new found understanding to action, I refused to engage in any negative discourse with Lori. I defused any outside agitations, calming the fuel of dismay, but the constant barrage of verbal abuse did not reside on Lori's end.

Soon I found myself living in the facility in which I worked. My employer was amazing! Proving more than just an employer, he was a substitute father and protected me from turning back towards drug abuse brought on by mental distress. Since I refused to take the bait of chaos, Lori changed her behavior and disposition and did everything in her power to convince me to return back home for the sake of our child. I agreed and began the long journey Yahweh had in store for me. Months passed and our relationship seemed to be back on track, but that too was an illusion of hope and an exercise in deception.

Overwhelmed with the self-imposed responsibility of maintaining a full and productive secular lifestyle, while being constantly monitored by the state of California via ankle bracelet, I strayed back towards alcohol. The toll of emotional stress brought on by Lori's constant complaining, superimposed on top of everything else, was becoming more and more evident as time passed. I slowly gravitated towards the one thing that brought havoc within my life, "Alcohol!" Although I had gained unseen knowledge of the world surrounding us all, I was unable to disconnect the need of religion from obtaining spiritual growth without man's influence, thus thinking I must be reinstated by an organization that I denounced so long ago. I said to myself, "So far the information I obtained from them had proven true up to this point... they must be the only faith that is accurate to the word of god... I must go back if I would have any chance of being saved from my own hands, and have relief of woe within my newly formed family, and not fall victim from the fate of Revelations."

I taught Lori the basic concepts of Orthodox Christian Theology and became very active preforming Yahweh's tenets daily, and it seemingly helped in all facets of our lives. We began communicating better and turned away from drugs and alcohol alike. Soon the outside influences had no sway over Lori's willingness to listen to me. Fueling her natural spirit within herself to know her Creator, she also changed her behavior by leaps and bounds. She'd given up on worldly associations, and focused more on our family. I thought I'd succeeded in getting us all back on track with Yahweh, but that was fanciful at best. I made the conscience steps required to go back toward what I thought was truth for myself and family, and thought that humbling myself before men would benefit my family as a whole, yet I was wrong again in my thought process.

I convinced Lori to agree to an innocent Bible Study with the organization in which I refused to take part ever again, and we even attended one of their most holy of religious ceremonies, "The Passover." The Passover was observed only on the first full moon of the year for that particular Christian faith, somewhat similar to that of the Jewish observance of salvation. Full of hope in the future for my new family, I thought I'd come to know a true and real religion where there was none. Finally there was a true institution with some remnant of moral consciences and clarity within our household, and I felt righteous pride as we all dressed for the ceremony/unknown pagan ritual. In my mind, I had achieved the impossible and began the long hard road back towards the faith I'd forsaken so many years ago with the thought of starting a new with a new family and a new heart to boot.

I was on my way back towards my Creator's grace, or so I thought. As we approached the religious facility, I thought to myself, "Finally I'd turned back towards the Creator that I loved so much!" Then the inconceivable happened within those highly perceived holy walls. We entered into the brightly lit, yet solemn windowless hall, amongst silence and bowing brows, then I noticed the unthinkable; a cross was hanging on the right side entrance wall. Just when you're expecting the familiar sight as you enter the front door, within similar walls once known, a shock to the system slows your walk and increases your heart rate. An idol stood hanging in the very place in which I was taught not to worship any idols, epically the Christian cross! I was under the impression that the organization stood adamantly against any carving images or idols, in accordance with the Ten Commandments' first decree: no true servant should adorn their abode with any images or idols, so I thought. In accordance to their own doctrine, one that serves the true Creator should not have in their possession, or in their home and should be free of any objects, and or items that may harbor any unseen spirits that may attach themselves to inanimate objects within the walls of their home, businesses or especially their place of worship!

Places of worship should always be shielded from demonic forces that may be attached to material objects. Stunned, I timidly shook strangers' hands as my family and I headed towards an open seat. Once seated, I turned to Lori and under my voice said: "This place is not right!"

As the orator began to speak and remind the audience of the importance of the gathering, he proudly pronounced Jesus as God. Now I was shocked not once, but twice! All hope of finding truth within the once revered faith shriveled up and died from that moment onward. Feeling sick from the experience, I slowly grabbed Lori and Tori by the hands and proceeded to the doors that headed outside the facility. I explained to my family the reason behind our sudden disruption of the event and why we exited the building so quickly. The major inconsistencies being taught within that facility had sickened me to the stomach and stunned me spiritually. More than disappointment gripped my every thought, for what I'd always considered to be truth was vastly in confliction with what was being spewed out of that particular podium, thus solidifying the discerning voice within me and proving that all man-made religions were in fact fake! Saddened by that fact, I thought of all mankind searching for truth, yet the blind shall always be led by the blind. So many people with good intentions believe in their faith so whole heartedly, but are blindfolded like myself within their faith. They either were brought up from birth within it, or taught in the search for the Creator by swindlers, charlatans, gold diggers or fool- hearted preachers that willingly go off the edge of a cliff with their blind followers.

I finally understood that the hypocrisy within the church was so profound and pervasive that the reality of that fact dropped me to my knees! I fell to the floor when entering our apartment and asked the Creator, "Why?!" All hope drained from my body as I pondered on how anyone could find real truth when even the last vestige of a naive youthful belief in religion was riddled with lies. Within my mind's eye, all man-made religious organizations were proven to be false, and I was right! Hope in religion disintegrated right before my eyes. Because I knew the original tenets of Christian doctrine were the Ten Commandments, and knew how they worked in repairing family life, deep down inside, I knew that man-made organizations resonate hypocrisy at its core, no matter what denomination, sect or religious tradition many may profoundly know, and or be associated. The truth of our Creator does not exist within the walls of some so-called ancient Church, Mosque or Synagogue; in fact, it doesn't even exist within some ancient text, but yet mankind knows a Creator exists, for His spirit resides within us. So how can one truly find one's Creator? Where could one go to obtain the truth about Him, or even find the answer of why we are here on this planet? Days passed after our attendance of that farce of a ceremony and my mind would not let go of the feeling of doom, doom for not just my children and loved ones, but for all mankind!

Compelled to find out the origins of religion, I dove straight into the nature of the occult knowledge of the church, but I did not know the dangerous path on which I was about to embark.

With careful re-examination of the history of the religion itself, the truth began to become clear. I read the books that were approved and sanctioned by the church alongside those that were not sanctioned, "The Secret Hidden Texts," once removed from those read long ago, and I truly began to have my eyes opened! I saw that every war and conquest, or every tyrannical rule and mistreatment of humanity started and was finished by the church, and religion was always the root of the conflict. Even the destruction of this planet stems from blind obedience and greed within the church. Religion is the mother of all evil within history won by tyrants! You shall know them from the fruit of their labors! Please see the uncountable numbers of souls lost within the fog of war, famine, starvation, abortions, etc...., for it is the Church that is at the center of all of mankind's woes and industries. The Morning Star is truly cunning! He has implemented the very instrument used to enlighten man to deceive him.

All those who know these theocratic and historical facts truly do the works of their father, for evil sits upon the throne and now I know what that means! Come out of her my children!

All those who may be Children of Light, come out of her, for her time of ending is coming quickly. You are to fight against all she teaches and instructs! Put on your armor and shield! But How? With Courage! No longer could I put faith in what another soul told me. No longer would I consider what I thought to be fact as fact! For all information is second hand. None of us were there! And I truly know nothing! From that fact, I began my journey, yet I did not know the cost of the spiritual road less traveled. So be it! Sounds of the royal trumpets roar! For the spirits above were caught within the winds of my intentions. Soon after my epiphany, all hell broke loose once again in my life. With no illusions, my eyes began to open even wider, and the unseen forces created havoc on the initiate, meaning myself. Lori became so uncontrollable by arguing about everything and anything that moved within our household. Anxiety and emotional strife, tripled and quadrupled overnight. I went back to drinking in the night, after class and on the weekends. I prayed more and more with no reply!

Not yet willing to let go of the journey, I buckled down and leaned towards morality even more so in hope of approval from my Creator. I REPENTED, or at least as much as a full blown drunk could bare. Yet turmoil intervened without warning, making life somewhat unbearable as I prayed; however, unseen forces protected me in times of real urgency and peril. Seeing providence work its magic daily, I gave thanks to our Creator ever more. While searching the World Wide Web, I came across a young blond man based out in Texas, who was spewing wild and unpredictable theories that sounded so far-fetched I laughed.

Most would consider his news as fictitious and riddled with unbelievable claims, yet I listened intently every night as he disclosed his unbelievable messages to the public with fiery words and no restraint. He predicted the end of the United States Constitution, and spelled out the slow erosion of our freedoms in this Country by saying something big was in the wind, and something or someone was going to attack the World Trade buildings in New York, New York.

How could another significantly awaken my spiritual awareness, and help me connect the physical with the spiritual more fully? Not knowing the dangerous experience that would be awaiting me in the near future, I had no clue. Days passed and no sense of evil swarmed the air and the nights cooled down with the sunset of Northern California's heat, but the next morning all my physical and spiritual energy spiked with activity! The day began bright and uneventful at first while I was just lying in the bed, then breaking news appeared on the television screen while I lay motionless in bed. The World Trade Center was under attack. The Country was under attack?! The spirit of uncertainty filled the air. Every human's heart in America had been crushed within an instant. Without a doubt, the young, blonde haired, Texas talk show host, was correct!

From that time until now, I've been a faithful listener of the young Texan. From the very beginning, I could see that the information he covered was uniquely cutting edge. The messages relayed were truly profound in future programing of one's soul. In my search for truth, and unlocking of information, once not connected, the talk show host's disclosers would lead me down roads I never thought I would explore! In my search for the meaning of our own existence, the Texan's subject matter guided my trek.

No one source can lead to enlightenment, but with information not once so conveyed, he spoke freely when none would, thus giving me confidence in my own suspicions. As I ventured down new avenues, my family remained on the invisible roller-coaster that most brainwashed idiots ride within the American experience, namely listening to everything said on television and believing it. It was as if I'd started life from the beginning, not fully understanding anything of true value. I was under the illusionary impression of secular success thinking that having a lot of money leads to happiness and true wealth; I was under the spell of brainwashing, but a quickening had begun.

First, the unseen forces struck my home with unstoppable voracity. Emotionally weak and still undisciplined, I got back behind the wheel of destiny, at the behest of an uncontrollable and verbally abusive girlfriend. She insisted I transport our little girl to her work place for some insignificant gathering after I'd consumed a half pint of Vodka, and she knew it. I was tipsy at best, yet Lori cared not! Not yet drunk and physically able to transport the fragile cargo without incident, I said, "What the Hell... Let's go baby!"

But other precarious unseen forces were in play and my radar was dismantled by alcohol. Begrudgingly, I headed out of the apartment with my baby by my side and strapped my daughter in the front passenger seat and off we went. No sooner than we reached the turn way connecting to the driveway of UC Davis University's site to the public street, a wild eyed woman looked me directly in my eyes, then ran me off the road and kept going. Though speeds were under 10 miles per hour, I hit a small pole on the university's grounds which caused the air bags to deploy. In that small instance, I thought only of my child. I quickly checked her person frantically, but found no physical injuries, just a little shock from the experience. Gaining my own bearings, I called the authorities and her mother on my cell phone to explain the event.

EDGAR FRENCH, JR.

With four other drivers on the scene collaborating my side of the event, the police still submitted a Breathalyzer test and I promptly was hauled off to jail for the third time.

This time, I was released that day with an ankle bracelet, and a two hundred a month added expense. Every facet of my life changed for the worst, but it was mostly financially and emotionally. Soon the physical would come my way. Around the same time, Lori's brother and his girlfriend became homeless and moved in without notice which strained our shaky relationship. A couple of weeks had passed before I noticed a change in her brother's attitude towards me. His overall demeanor towards me became belligerent, abrasive and full of angst and disrespect. Sensing I would have to confront him some day, I voiced my concerns to his sister and reminded her of my violent past, vigorously encouraging her to verbally intercede and mediate between us an armistice to soothe tensions that were certainly brewing under the scenes.

Obviously she didn't take my concerns seriously because his attitude did not decease in intensity. After a few days of his amplified Brutus behavior, I had my full! "Lori he must go!" "I'm giving him a day to find another place, and vacate before he sees the real me!" Lori responded, "Well, you're going to have to tell him yourself." Without delay or restraint, I calmly and respectively approached him soon after Lori and I had the discussion. While relaying his current situation and time restraints imposed upon him, I heard him out. Though he protested somewhat, and spewed the usual, "…what am I to do?" speech, it went as well as could be expected with very little feedback on both sides, yet he agreed to depart as soon as possible. However, the unseen forces that involve themselves in all aspects of our lives were not finished with their hold on him. After a week or so had passed from Loris brother's departure, my own uncle called for assistance, for he himself had fallen on hard times and needed a place to stay until he could gather the funds to obtain an another apartment. After arguing with Lori about my favorite uncle's devastating situation, I assured her that my uncle wasn't a Mooch like her brother and that he would leave as soon as possible.

She agreed to let him and his girlfriend and new child stay until they had the funds to leave. Asking nothing from either party on both sides of our families, Lori and I both were very gracious, very understanding and long suffering when it came to helping family. Uncle Leo and family were gone within thirty days, and before he could move his final possessions, another family member was in need. Next came my own little sister and her new husband calling in need of a place to live after losing both their jobs. It was as if the powers that be were testing the emotional waters between both Lori and myself without restraint. In agreement about the amount we were being tested by the spiritual forces, we would test the waters and see if we would be able to endure the onslaught of the unforeseen happenstance, without folding and giving up on our so-called attempt at being a moral and upstanding family.

Sensing the urgency in the face of my little sister and husband, we both knew that they would leave as soon as they could. The only thing hindering their efforts was the fact that they were broke and looking for work without success. Not knowing how long they would be staying with us created a mountain of animosity towards me from my so-called spouse, for kicking her brother out for not contributing and eating up all our food. Our arguments would intensify in seriousness and severity. Lori would disrupt any conversation promoting solutions to our dilemma, and purposely create issues about which to argue. Communication between Lori and I had become almost nonexistent and something had to be done. Depressed over the looming accounts of turmoil inundating our household, I drank even more so, trying to numb the constant verbal abuse. Not only did I notice the ever growing distance between Lori and me, but I also noticed the ever presence of what many would call: "A Slave Mentality" developing within our home. Obvious depression from being out of work was gripping my brother in law daily in addition to the constant arguments.

Constant ridicule emanating out of the mouths of both female grown-ups occupying the apartment did not relieve his concerns, fears and woes. Knowing both my sister and her husband were hard working and full of pride, I knew they would not ask for any more assistance from me. Since they were already ashamed of having to stay with one who had been shunned by their religious affiliates and labeled an "apostate," they held their tongue and searched for work daily. In the span of two months, three families had found their way to our door to escape homelessness and the toll of our humanity and kindness was becoming unbearable and destructive to the harmony of my own household, so something had to be done. Though finances were tight due to my moronic alcoholic indiscretions, the harmony of my home took precedence. So when my brother in law finally found work, I covertly schemed to help my baby sister find a place as soon as possible without their knowledge and put aside money without Lori's awareness and prying eyes.

When a vacancy at a nearby apartment complex opened, my sister and her husband jumped to the opportunity to acquire its occupancy. They were short five hundred dollars and feverishly sought out ways to obtain the funds needed. It was as if the Creator himself guided my thoughts and intensions because I quietly accrued exactly five hundred dollars. The looming emotional crisis within my household became apparent, and the solution had found its way to my hands and with the grace of the Creator, a crisis had been avoided right at a time when Lori and I had begun to resent one another vigorously.

Though my spiritual and emotional strength teetered on the brink of non-existence, I started drinking more than ever as I opened my mind towards more spiritual inspired thoughts. I felt a sense of relief the day my needy family members prepared to depart my home, and contemplated the time when my family needed the same support from my favorite uncle and imagined the hardship and strain our presence must have caused those who sacrificed their time and home. I knew we'd be blessed from the decision to step forth and help those in our family that were in need. Family is truly a blessing, but that very blessing can become a curse; sadly, I would soon become aware of its agonizing sting. OH My God! The ghetto had returned to my place of residence! The walls, the carpets, and floors were filthy! I saw the effects of charity, and the unwillingness to upgrade anything while others occupied the apartment. Lori and I let the place go to waste. In lieu of the impending disaster hovering over our household, I desperately needed a miracle to happen before Lori and I could come to a resolution and repair our lines of communication and continue to grow as a loving family once more.

We both saw the physical and corrosive nature of those harboring a slave mentality. The dirty walls and filthy carpets were just the physical effects of their presence. I knew that the only way we would be successful as a moral and god fearing family we would have to start fresh, and remembered that cleanliness is next to godliness. I explained to Lori the effects of having a filthy home would have on the attitude and disposition of those residing within it. She agreed and we got to work! Immediately, I began bringing in the materials needed to brighten up our abode. With the removal of all broken and dilapidated furniture within the apartment, and cleaning the carpets at least twice, we made sure every spot and stain disappeared. Ultimately, the effects of just cleaning the carpet and clearing out the apartment improved our relationship dramatically. The combative and divisive dynamics, combined with the removal of wicked spirits through prayer, animosity seemed to disappear as soon as the project began. Smiles and great conversation returned, and good fortune resided within our home once more. Amazed at the overall change in our living situation, Lori confessed her skeptical thoughts in the beginning, and revealed how she thought by asking, "How is just cleaning our apartment going to repair our relationship?"

I explained how the human spirit is affected by the way we live, and how the attitude and disposition of a person is connected to the environment and spirit of the person. To live in light is not to reside in filth or darkness. She smiled and resumed her work painting the three bedroom walls.

With reminders of past poverty removed, although the apartment was damn near empty, a filling spirit of a renewed day started to emerge within our living space. The hard work had paid off remarkably as the sunset began, and I proudly looked at our accomplishments with satisfaction. Then a knock at the door interrupted my exuberant delight in the work Lori and I completed. It was Lori's older brother at our front door with a frown on his face. Unannounced and unwanted, with anger in his eyes, he meant to assault me. He said no words as I opened the door. With vindictive vengeance, he looked me in the eye and cocked backed his right arm, hitting me across the right cheek. Weakened by life itself, the strike was like a feather blowing in the wind. I immediately shook it off and looked back at him with a smile filled with ancient rage, driving out all physical energy and strength from his body. He saw the depth of strength instead of fear, then thought twice. But it was too late. The mistake was made! He had unleashed the wrath of god within me. Quickly grabbing both of his arms, I brought him into the recently emptied out apartment, simultaneously grabbing hold of his clothing, twirling him around and around, thus making him lose all comprehension as I physically beat him to a pulp. Realizing his mistake, he tried to escape out of the open front door with all the adjacent neighbors in the courtyard to witness his shame and defeat.

He was holding on to dear life as I attempted to throw his ass over the gates leading to my apartment, one flight off the ground. His energy and strength returned to him, and he began to run for his life. Holding onto the rails as he slowly groveled down the stairs, with his head pointed to the ground, he screamed, "STOP!" He wobbled towards the back of the building slightly uttering out, "I'll be back!" As if he had redeemed his shame before the crowd. I responded, "I'll be waiting on you Nigga!" As I looked out upon the people in the courtyard witnessing the assault and outcome, I saw total shock and confusion written across the faces of those who saw the incident. I slowly turned back into the apartment and closed the front door. My adrenalin spiked through the roof, my mind began swimming through the legal scenarios, and thought it best to call the police. Since I was the one that was assaulted, I called 911. I expected a response of, "Someone will be responding to the assault sir." Contrarily, a male voice responded to my explanation with, "You won didn't you?!" Then he hung up. No police would respond and there was no concern for the public safety if the perpetrator would return, thus the police showed that they were not responsible for my own safety, or even the public's for that matter. As the night progressed, I received a call from Lori's mother voicing her disapproval, then Lori called expressing frantically that her brother had been hospitalized from the event.

I explained to both parties that I felt no remorse and that I warned Lori of his intent and what my reaction would be if he assaulted me. Oddly, when Lori returned home from work, she showed a new found respect for the one she called boyfriend and partner. In no time at all, our home seemed to be coming into its own with new material wealth and a brand new attitude; things were looking better. I reduced my personal debt and communication between the two of us got even better. Lori and I were finally starting to see eye to eye on most things. I even began to spend more time with our child, being a good father and regulating the verbal abuse emanating from Lori's mouth as a form of discipline to our child. I recognized I had learned nothing from the non-violent resolution of conflict myself, from the obvious violent actions some months earlier between myself and her eldest brother. I knew I didn't learn anything from the intensive studies of ancient text, concerning violence. So I contemplated my spiritual adolescence, and willingness to revolt to violence when confronted with violence. I realized how one searching for his Creator and universal truths easily reverts back towards violence without hesitation. Should I exhibit violence when under duress?

Not to say that people with bad intentions may exhibit violence towards me should always restrain from violent tendency, for I knew they wouldn't, yet I still contemplated my response. For it is one of Yahweh's edicts to fight for righteousness' sake, be it spiritual or physical.

But in the case of Lori's brother, I knew how weak minded he truly was, and how much more battle scarred I was from living in total poverty and real violence daily! I didn't need to prove my fighting ability or battle readiness against someone who was not a credible adversary; on the contrary, he was not a viable threat to my safety, and I knew it. For days to come that very thought plagued my conscience.

I prayed for forgiveness so much it became an afterthought, and I was consumed with the thoughts of escape! Escape from the rat race of modern society, escape from trying to balance all that is expected of me and all of mankind such as juggling: the job, the kids, higher education and success. Yet all the while I still felt empty inside. I spoke out in woe, "Oh, my Creator, please help me get closer to you, and please know what it is I seek… I need to know your true will!" Although I tried to stay focused on my day to day responsibilities, the thought of searching for the truth consumed me. Questions of my existence and our creation would not leave my conscious, forcing me to look up ancient occult knowledge on spiritual influence on mankind's everyday interactions with one another, and studying its long term effects changed my outlook on life and the truth of old famous antidotes and fairy tales. I became aware of the unseen forces that control our three-dimensional reality.

Intrigued, I further pushed the envelope and applied spiritual remedies to all manners of physical situations occurring within my own life, and they worked. Consumed with the thoughts of unseen beings influencing all facets of our lives took me on an unforgettable ride. I just didn't know or realize it at the time. With physical proof of the unseen influences that power humanity from unseen realms, obedience to the Creator supersedes most spiritual infractions on human behavior. I was convinced that the universal edicts given to man overrides all effects imposed on the human emotional, and spiritual turmoil that inflicts us all by the ever so prevalent immorality, and was the key to mankind's freedom from unseen forces and their effects. Often most disturbing behavior exhibited by man is brought on by deposed, exiled or demonic spirits, controlling human behavior without their knowledge, and I set out to prove it in most cases of mental illness, emotional imbalance, or physical addictions to drugs and alcohol.

But Yahweh has a very serious sense of humor. And just as I thought that I'd understood the unspoken rules and tactics of overcoming the effects of universal warfare, reality spoke loud, and physical need and want made itself known. I found myself knowing nothing, having no clue of the nature of the Beast and the fight that lie ahead. For all humans are blindfolded from birth and the road to true enlightenment is an uphill and winding narrow one! Full of ridges and cracked edges, one can fall easily off the narrow road, for it swirls around an anomalous and invisible mountain. It's so treacherous that even a humble man finds no quarter on the road that leads to truth.

Full of pride and full of myself, I reveled in my success and happiness at home, but I asked my Creator for knowledge, and the wisdom to use that knowledge for the betterment of his will on this Earth, not mine. Be careful for what you ask. You just might get it! Blinded by the typical lack of real material wealth, I tried to escape my surroundings, but as I looked outside my window, all I could see was poverty surrounding me; however, our once ghettoized apartment was now transformed into a beautiful living space. My and Lori's work brought pride and confidence within me, and that emotion was not warranted in my eyes. I searched for one that mattered more than myself, and I had to be taught that lesson. All is great! All is super! All is going along well in the world of the unknowing and pompous P. Then it happened. Nothing good lasts for long in this world of illusion. Hungry of substance after a pretty good night out with Lori before she headed out for work, I gulped down a couple of swigs of Old English, and set up a pan of oil on the stove to fry some French fried potatoes, but I had to take a leak, so I did. "Hell I'm good; I just got to take a leak and it won't take too long!" As I headed towards the bathroom to relieve myself, I swear I only took less than a minute draining the weasel before I headed back towards the kitchen to check and see if the oil had gained the right temperature to drop the frozen pre-cut fries in the hot pan, only to find an inferno.

"What the Fuck! I just went for a piss! It only took less than a minute!" The flames were reaching the ceiling, burning uncontrollably. Calmed by years of surviving fires, I quickly searched for anything that would suppress the ignition of an oil based fire. Using cornmeal, flour and salt to contain the flames and neutralize the fire, I removed the burned pan off the stove. The danger of a full blown fire was contained within seconds, but the damage was done. I called 911 and alerted the fire department as I waited for the proper authority to respond, then I called Lori with the bad news. I assured her that only the kitchen area was affected, and most if not all of our belongings were intact and not damaged by smoke or water. I'd contained the fire before the fire department even showed up. She was far from understanding, for we had just finished remodeling the entire three bedroom apartment.

We spent thousands of hard earned dollars on the best furniture money could buy, in addition to the physical hands on labor we both undertook for so many months on the place. Although the material possessions were intact, the kitchen was totaled! The apartment owners had warned us that there was no way we could live in so much fire and smoke damage and were ordered by the fire inspector of the state of California. It was the end of my notions of a new family from that moment, although I didn't know that at the time. Once again, "fire" had altered my life! This was not accidental; the powers of the unseen world had in fact played its hand on my trek towards the knowledge of the universe and unseen things.

Under the illusion of providence, I thought everything was going on track for once, thinking I had overcome all obstacles that stood in my way from obtaining happiness, but I was wrong. In seconds, my world was changed unspeakably. Having nowhere to go and no one to rely upon, my thoughts drifted towards the loneliness that still remained. I've helped everyone in my family in so many ways, but I knew within my heart there was no way they would stretch out a helping hand towards me, for they never had in the past. Only the Wascally Wabbott took us all in when we needed a home, and he had just begun to help himself out of homelessness; therefore, he needed peace from others. There was no way I would impose myself upon him again. There was no easy way out of homelessness for me at that point, but Lori's mother was more than happy to receive her daughter with open arms, minus the man she hated, yours truly of course.

With most of the extra financial means I had accrued in ignorance, I comprised a plan to leave California altogether. I spent some twelve years under the sway of hot days and cold nights, and now it was coming to an end. I'd considered California my real first home, for no other place within these United States of America had been so open to one such as myself. It was the first time I'd spread my wings and actually had the chance to fly! No longer did live under the thumb of the powers that be, so to speak. I cared for my family without Government Assistance or control.

I controlled every facet of my life, or so I thought. I said to myself, "At least I'd begun to raise all my children there, and with some success...but it was my home and I was about to leave for good."

Lori agreed to follow the plan I set forth, and join me after I setup shop on the other side of the country, although she was nervous about leaving the only place she had known as home all her life, unlike me who had escaped the true concrete jungle, moving from state to state. She assured me that we would always be a family and reunite in time. She secured our material possessions in a nearby storage unit, and planned to meet within a few months. I kissed my child as she slept in the backseat of Lori's car, outside "Moss-Glenn Street," where we first worked together, and produced a lovely child. I said to my sleeping child, "I'll see you again my beautiful baby," giving one last kiss as well as I climbed in the driver's seat of my Pinkish Chevy Caviler, and turned the ignition key, and headed out towards Reno and I-80 US interstate.

Cell phones had advanced so much so fast over the years; it was 2003, and I had not yet understood how much the country had changed. My car was full of all my close personal possessions, like "Betsy Blue," which was the very first computer I built from head to toe with my very own hands. Let me not forget Chewy, the family dog, who was by my side as my only companion on the lonely road. On the road once again, with a call from Lori daily, made the trip seem not so long. While on the road heading eastwards, my mind wondered towards the future. She assured me of her love, and comforted me as I traveled the country, bolstering my confidence and faith that we would be together as a family once again, but that was not to be; it was the beginning of the end, but I just didn't see. Yahweh had put me on the path of enlightenment and I knew not what was in store for me. I was on the road less traveled and neither my mind nor body was up for the task. The forging process had just begun and I knew not. For the road less traveled started in a circle and the circle always leads back home in completion. The learning of "Ancient Secret Geometry" was the last thing on my mind, but would be the beginning of my enlightenment and understanding. For the keys of the universe are not spoken by man-made words or spells, nor mathematics; they are vibrational matter and energy and nothing more.

This is true! All theology was given to man by the two hundred fallen ones, and all that we see around us belongs to those called the "Children of the Snake," or the offspring of the Fallen Ones.

All civilization was given to women across the ancient globe, and religion or theology was given to men by the two hundred to divide and conquer mankind, so why would man adopt said knowledge from those that hate them? Why should mankind continue to follow such divisive knowledge, knowing the authors and progenitors of such knowledge as duplicitous to enslave and destroy?!

They are brainwashed from birth. They lie to one's self in order to save face. Let loose your chains and throw off ideology and dogma of men, for there are only two ways of thought. Either you're a Child of Light or a Child of Darkness! Choose one! Stop being children of the book and let men be men; go towards your heavenly father and open your eyes to what is true. For time is running out on all, and my road towards real truth was just beginning…

Warning! The Children of Darkness have made their move on all Children of Light, be it Jew, Islam, Christian, Conservatives, Libertarians and/ or those who believe in protecting themselves and their family. They are relentlessly going after the Second Amendment and the right for law abiding citizens to bear arms. This is the first step towards Marshal Law! And the beginning of Civil War! This is the goal of the Illuminati, Globalist and Leftists. They want us disarmed and divided, so their New World Order can fully take control of The American People and the World as a whole!

The fact of the matter is this: As long as Children of Light hold dear to their belief in a Creator, and continue to stay under the umbrella and the concept of theology given by the Two Hundred Fallen Ones, be it Christianity, Judaism or Islam, the powers that be will use your differences to divide and destroy all mankind without impunity!

EDGAR FRENCH, JR.

You must break free from religious ideology and throw away the mantel of religious identity, for the whole world lies in the hands of the wicked ones, including your little church, mosque and synagogue you may attend! Yahweh gives us free will, and putting that will in the hands of a man-made book written over many millennia only shows ignorance and a lack of concern for one's spiritual wellbeing! We must seek knowledge in order to gain light! We must love our Creator in order to understand the nature of that light! If one puts trust in whatever some man tells him without investigation, one deserves what one gets, period! For his name sake! The Name of the Creator is Yahweh and love him! Use his name when communicating with him!

Follow his Ten Commandments and no other thing, and you will see what religious people cannot see or hear! Do that, and mankind wins! Woe to the Jew and Gentile alike, for you have left your first estate, and dwelled with devils and demons, leaving Yahweh's grace and embracing Lucifer's rebellion without turning back. For this is true! You have forsaken your mandate with the living creator, and lied with man, lusting after one another. You kill innocence and sacrifice babies, as if Yahweh will overlook your crimes against humanity. Did you not know your ancestor's folly? To drink blood of any flesh is sacrosanct, yet you drink the blood of your own children. Your crimes are too many to ignore and you shall suffer the fate of Yahweh's enemies forevermore. For you alone have led humanity towards destruction by corrupting the Creator's word. This story of true enlightenment shall continue, but for another time…

CHAPTER XXVIII

The Keys of the Universe

The story I was telling above is unfinished, for time is of the essence, and the nature of the uncertainty that grips the nation may destroy us all before I will be able to finish the story! Most men have no clue of the history they're facing in this time-line, for we are so blessed but so doomed with the lack of time, and I feel it necessary to impart at least the knowledge that may preserve life in such a crucial point in time, but wait! I shall explain! Dimensional warfare is now converging on the planet, and I may not have access to a computer or typewriter to write the whole story at this time. I would be doing an injustice by not revealing the most important information I received from the Creator of the Universe, and not give it to you! The reader of this dystopian nightmare in which we're living, must have a fighting chance! {These words are only a synopsis.}

Did you ever wonder why the symbol of time is shaped like the number eight sideways and not linear? It is because we are in a time loop within this planet, for we are our past, present and future. We are our ancestors and are ancestors are us! Time is looping upon itself, and we are now approaching the crossroads or the "Singularity," where mankind's fate lies in the balance. Lucifer's time is up, and time to go forward is a must! We will prevail! But those that have controlled the past may continue to control the future, and thus never give up power over all mankind without a fight! We must fight! We must fight spiritually! We must fight physically! For we fight Princes and Principalities, darkness in the night, and treachery in the day. In the midst of law makers, they'll be found! In the midst of industry, they steal the food from babes and bring beloved slavery to their fellow man. We have no choice but to fight, for it is the very existence of mankind that lies in the cross-hairs. Those who were and are made in the CREATOR'S IMAGE have forsaken their mandate and have enslaved their fellow man, for they are the princes and principalities of darkness that we must fight for our right to exist, not some invisible force.

It was said that mathematics "...hold the keys to the universe." That is Moronic! Human words and writing of numbers are strictly a man-made phenomenon, not a universal one. The universe is electromagnetic in nature, where all we know is nothing itself! There is no sound or measurements to the vastness of empty space-time, for we live in miracle upon miracle! It is Geometry at its best. Shapes and structures are the nature of Creation, my friend! And these three shapes comprise all things, believe it or not. Yahweh's burden is light. Lucifer makes it complex.

For light is truth and Darkness is lies. $1+1$ must $= 2$ in light and $1+1$ must $= X$ in Darkness! That is simple; is it not? All matter in this verse is comprised of nothing! Vibration and geometry multiplied by the Electromagnetic Spectrum Field of light combined, builds the physical space- time in which creation expands, for Yahweh's word is energy and energy is power. So called "educated" men make complicated what is natural in creation with their math and their limited way of understanding what is not seen, and all knowledge of this three-dimensional realm was given to women without permission and in rebellion by the 200 fallen angels in order to corrupt mankind's path laid out by his Creator. Once mankind understands the importance of these three shapes, they will then know what the Children of Darkness have kept in secret from all, or at least kept secret to most Children of Light. We are trapped in a three-dimensional paradigm.

The Creator only allows us a small visualized experience within the electromagnetic spectrum, for only a fraction of the Electromagnetic Spectrum of Light is shown to us in this third dimensional realm. Lucifer has given his children and or his Comrades in the rebellion against the Creator all elementary understanding of the unseen powers over man. Yet such power is limited, and such information only pertains to this third dimensional realm for the moment. Not all information pertaining to the dimensional realms are given to those that may see us harm. Lucifer does not know that information just yet! He does not know the secret of the other realms or how to overcome the power of the

Creator, so as to obtain the keys of ultimate power, better known as the God Head! What these so-called men of renown know is just nonsense and empty dreams! They have corrupted the knowledge of this realm by hording what's known from the masses, ultimately thinking that their father, Lucifer, imparted universal knowledge only for them, and they will kill, starve and eat their fellow man to preserve and obtain it!

In the attempt to hold back mankind from obtaining these keys for themselves, the powers that be have behaved foolishly at the risk of killing all life, including themselves and their offspring! The very first geometric shape is the "Square." This is the primary structure of stability and the shape of creation itself. Some throughout time have called it the symbol of the Most High. Any spiritual damage to this structure will result in a physical paradox in this three-dimensional reality and realm! I cannot stress how important that fact is to creation, for we are created using the very structural model of the square, hence the phrase: "Men are the salt of the Earth." Salt seen through a microscope looks like tiny little cubed molecules, too tiny to see with the naked eye. Not only are these molecules electromagnetically charged, but they also regulate the physical realm from the spiritual realm, for they must be in total synchronicity to obtain everlasting life.

It is imperative that these particles are activated within all life, for symmetry and symbiosis between intelligent entities is needed to grow. The communication between one sentient being and another must be obtained symbiotically for the universe to contain its structure. Morality fuels the activation of these molecules in all Homosapiens. The destruction of morality will destroy a people and a nation, including a planet! Morality is the absolute key of the Cube, and is needed in the fulfillment and growth of all sentient beings throughout creation. Even creatures in the wild have a code of morality, and are in symbiosis with all life on this planet and must be maintained. Morality is not a product of religion, for religion has been hijacked at its inception.

The concepts of morality are made insignificant in importance by those in power in order to entrap their fellow man into confusion and destruction. This fact was Yeshua's main teaching; did you know that? To disconnect the cubical key of Morality out of the hands of humanity is to disconnect Yeshua's primary teaching. Love is primarily not a noun; it is a verb and if used inappropriately, it can lead to unimaginable consequences for humanity! Love can kill without proper context, for love of what is evil can be presented in light, and love of what is good can come across as foul. Love of oneself can be given over to man-made organizations that are over seen by off world entities which in fact are corrupting Yahweh's mandate. Morality is necessary for universal enlightenment of all mankind and absolutely necessary for the destruction of the illegitimate cornerstone of disinformation that has kept us all slaves to ideology and personal belief based on secondhand information, such as sixty six books written by thirty three men some four thousand years ago. In fact, Yeshua was labeled a heretic by the very institutions that we look to for guidance, and he was known to many as the first Apostate. Now can you see why Devil worshipers look at Christians {Children of Light} as if they were stupid or cattle? To have love for our Creator is a part of mankind's DNA, and they who control us know this.

Yeshua was teaching his fellow man to love the Creator by getting to know him by name and his mandates alone, so we could break free from those who enslave us from birth. Yeshua was succeeding in his mission to enlighten mankind, even by giving up his mortal life to do so. In time, the message began to spread. Constantine, the emperor of Rome, saw the peoples of the Empire falling under the influence of freedom which was taught by Yeshua. He had to do something to stop the spread of freedom! So Constantine commissioned a campaign to infiltrate the natural movement of mankind's free will by bribing influential leaders throughout the provinces, thus usurping trusted written reading manuals read by the free peoples of that time period.

Constantine secretly co-opted the message of freedom and infused pagan religious doctrines that were dictated by the fallen ones eons ago.

Lucifer succeeded in his mission to deceive mankind for almost six millennia. Morality is not a product of religious doctrine! I repeat that statement because knowing that fact is important in freeing ourselves from the illusion of the system. We must break free from the control mechanisms that divide and conquer us by race, economic station or gender! To follow Yeshua is not to be a Christian, Jew or Gentile! Ideology and religious dogma are tools to divide and destroy mankind. All children of the Creator practice and exercise morality as a necessary need for life by proclaiming it in all facets of existence, no matter where they come from in this world, no matter what color, or creed. We all need the stability of the geometric square to exist in this third dimensional realm, or any other within the electromagnetic spectrometric system.

The second key is the geometric shape of the "Triangle" and it is a very important key in the formation of the universe and creation! It is the primary shape of hierarchy within the universe. As so above so shall it be below! Hierarchy is needed for order and prosperity when enforcing the rule of law that regulates all sentient beings throughout the universe; it also is an essential ingredient in the formation of mineral and crystalline matter, thus an important key of life. But when used by sentient entities of the same order in nature, it should always be inverted in stature, never placed up high in stature! Men have no right to impose hierarchy on his fellow man, although the concept is needed for construction and creation of society and material matter. The formation of Kings and Queens within humanity is the primary creation of tyranny over humanity! Distorting the main purpose of hierarchy has been Lucifer's greatest tool of deception amongst men. By corrupting human DNA with that of Children of the Elohim, Lucifer created a hybrid species called Nephillum, not the Fallen Ones. These beings saw themselves superior to humanity and have lorded over all mankind throughout history with a stern grip. Today, their offspring have superimposed themselves over us and our inheritance, hiding themselves in plain view, for they are the true arbiters of woe! Along with human counterparts, these hybrids have held back universal information concerning the proper use of the hierarchy key in order to control their fellow man and dominate the planet!

Through the manipulation of the hierarchy key, Lucifer has deceived the entire Earth, for the world is his. He has disrupted the natural order of the heavens and all creation using the levers of the hierarchy key.

The hierarchy key was part of the original lie brought forth in the Garden of Eden when Lucifer deceived and convinced humanity that they themselves could be like Yahweh in power, and not have to follow the universal mandates set by the Creator, essentially overriding the Creator's rule of law, causing chaos throughout creation that has never been seen before. Controlling the key of hierarchy is the magic of vibration, and the written word can be used to enslave instead of enlighten. Yes the written word and sound of thought is indeed a form of magic!

The vibrations in creation control the levers of understanding, distortion of reason, and the destruction or construction of truth. The written word is in fact creating a spell! That's why it's called SPELLING! The written word preserves the structure of creation itself, for the word was god, and is god. The verbal and written word can in fact destroy or create matter and give power to those of average intelligence and bring destruction to those that love ignorance. The written or spoken spells of words solidify the hierarchy key within creation. We must come to grips with this fact. The powers that be have controlled the implementation of this key, and dished out the amount of information given to the human race in order to destroy it. They control what we hear, what we see, and what we perceive to be reality; ultimately, controlling all symbols given to man throughout history by twisting and perverting reality, manipulating truth with lies and lies with truth. As long as wicked men control the levers of hierarchy on this planet, we shall suffer the effects of their anti-human agenda. We must wake up to the power of words, take back the reins of its power from evil men, and restore the importance of the magical spells of language and the written word!

The English language is a mixture of languages, incorporating angelic script alongside a multitude of bastardized languages given to men by those fallen from grace, those who are in rebellion against their Creator, the Sovereign ruler of the universe, Yahweh. In order for man to obtain their Creator's favor once more, we must understand that we are at war! The structure of hierarchy has been distorted by men and those that control them in order to lord over humanity and destroy Yahweh's creation in battle. The rebellion against our Creator has failed! We now find ourselves caught in the middle of war to stop and turn back time, and we are victims of a Galactic Civil War of Attrition. No written word can be assumed true because of those who control the levers of hierarchy throughout history. We must use discernment when searching for truth and historical facts. Never shall we assume or believe any written word preserved throughout history without rigorous vetting! We were born in the grips of evil, for no man has been given true history. All information is second hand information and should be looked at as such. If we are to overcome the spell of the misinformation we now live under, we are to understand that hierarchy has been hijacked by those with maleficent objectives. The hierarchal spell of the written word and spoken language should never be underestimated, for all men are liars! Assume all written text as suspect, including this one! Yahweh knows I'm a liar and fallen from grace, for I sin. Knowing nothing is new under the sun gives credence to knowledge misunderstood. Yeshua knew this fact and began to enlighten the Jew and Gentile of the Serpent's control of hierarchy on this planet.

The fallen two hundred used their seed to corrupt the second key, and destroy all humanity and this planet in the process. Since the inception of the written word, we have been deceived. When there is more to creation than that of material wealth and physical health, one tends to seek out his Creator. We who have been deceived from birth can only see in this three-dimensional realm; although we possess much more than our souls, we possess a spirit. Our spirits remain eternal even after the demise of our physical bodies. Lucifer knows this and is envious that we have been forgiven for our transgressions, where as he and his have not! Children of Darkness are the most deceived by focusing on the material rather than that of the spiritual, which leaves them vulnerable to the influence of unseen forces. Because of the distortion and manipulation of this universal key (the triangle), we now suffer tremendously under the atrocious whims of evil men. We were made free sentient beings and are under the protection of the Most High. It was sedition that deceived Adam and Eve or us, but the Creator provided a release from our disgrace, and loop of time. Lucifer does not want mankind to receive that grace and redemption and wants to bring all mankind down with him and his legions. All occult information can only be used for nefarious reasons, and those who attempt to withhold information from their fellow man cannot do so without ultimately bringing downfall upon themselves!

We all are at war! We are not sheep! All man-made religion and the very concept of theology were designed to enslave the mind of the masses, for it came from the two hundred fallen ones who want to destroy Yahweh's creation. Yeshua taught men to break free from that flawed philosophy of man-made Hierarchy, and follow the DNA encoding of mankind, to be obedient to their Creator, and not to follow the corrupted belief structure of men. We are to understand that we are at war, war against princes and principalities! We are to exhibit courage against the Children of Darkness in this time of woe. In order to achieve freedom, we must understand what we are breaking free from which is misleading hierarchy: the rules of men lording over other men! These men who made the rules sided with the rebellious Lucifer, their father, literally!

These wicked men withheld knowledge that may help mankind ascend to the stars and beyond, for they have mastered the magic of the written word, and of the spoken language of the fallen ones. They have failed in their attempt to take control of the heavenly hierarchy and failed in taking the God- Head from Yahweh; therefore, they stand accused!

There is no forgiveness for those who wish to unseat our Creator! Do not fall victim to their fate. The ten mandates given to us are more than universal laws, for they serve as a protection against this spiritual insurrection. The third and final geometric universal key, and Yahweh's most treasured possession next to mankind is "The Sphere!" The Sphere is the geometric shape of Life! Yes, life is symbolized by the sphere. Throughout the universe, one will see the sphere in all matter and sub-space, from the small to the grand and to the majestic. From planets to spiral galaxies, one will find the sphere and life giving properties. By looking through a microscope, one will find the geometric sphere of life. Life is robust and abundant throughout this dimension and all others. We ourselves experience a small yet significant part in its creation and existence. We have inherited the ability to create, form and manipulate the material matter of this dimension from our loving heavenly father, Yahweh. Lucifer and his legions are committed to stop us from receiving this inheritance in full. The Spheres of Life are jewels of creation, and in all dimensional realms spiritual beings are in their formation with safety. Mankind was and is made in the likeness of the Elohim, infused with the ability to create on a micro scale, and commissioned to care for this small but majestic blue and green gem situated in an insignificant outer arm of a microscopic spiral galaxy with a dormant and restricted event horizon at its core.

An Angelic rebellion temporally brought a screeching halt to Yahweh's grand design of the propagations of creation throughout this third dimensional realm, ultimately devising a remarkable and brilliant scheme to entrap and expose the disrupters of creation in just. Lo and behold, Yahweh's first beloved and most beautiful creation, Lucifer and his legions were behind the insurrection that inadvertently trapped his newly beloved creation (mankind) in the middle of the dispute, subsequently breaking the Creator's heart in the process! The Seraphim, Lucifer, who sang praises to the Creator with such earnest and loyal admiration, began to question his father's will and saw himself worthy of worship because of his unmatched beauty and fame. Because of his fame and prominence within the house of the Elohim, he was able to argue and spark doubt within the hearts of many Elohim Judges, better known as the sons of god. This was the question Lucifer posed before the council of the Elohim: "Does any sentient being have the right to exist without the influence of his/her Creator, thus allowing creation to live outside natural universal law, and behave counter to one's mandate and purpose according to the Creator's will?" Lucifer's rebellion created a firestorm of controversy throughout the ranks of the Elohim and nearly destroyed the whole of creation. If it were not for Yahweh's awesome power and ability to prove his awe inspiring right to oversee as sovereign of all creation, no life would remain within the heavenly realms, including this one.

The amount of destruction throughout the heavenly realm was unmeasurable. Lucifer and his minions almost unraveled the fabric of time in many realms. Before he and his cohorts were successful in their efforts to overthrow Yahweh and take control of the God-Head or Wholly Spirit, Yahweh's active force took charge and vanquished the offenders. Since they were unable to disrupt and corrupt the high places of the heavens, Yahweh's awesome spiritual force stopped him and exiled him and his legions down to this third realm or dimension called Earth! Lucifer is hell bent on destroying this majestic planet and the inhabitance of it. Despised and hated is the creation of mankind by many. Lucifer's time is short and he knows this; therefore, he works feverishly to reverse time and undo the salvation of mankind to take us down the road of destruction!

This is the main objective of those operating in the dark places of the world. This is the occult knowledge of the malevolent masters and the overseers of this world of darkness that envelops the sentient beings on this planet. As Yahweh reverses the damage unleashed on the heavenly planes by Lucifer and his rebellious brethren, Lucifer enlightens his seed here on Earth with the knowledge of time displacement so he can reverse time and remedy his mistakes in trying to overthrow the Creator of the universe, and retain ownership of the God-Head from this realm of existence. Children of Darkness are aware of the counterparts placed here by Yahweh to stop this from coming to fruition. These facts have been systematically withheld from the general public and jealously guarded by those in control of historical information and artifacts. The Rebellious sons of the Elohim had corrupted life here on this planet and tried to do the same in the heavenly places but failed. Now that time has caught up with them, they prey on the creative nature of Yahweh's Earthly children to help destroy all that is good.

As in the days of Noah, so shall it be in the days of the coming of the son of man! Giants shall walk among mankind once more as evil men grow closer to their ultimate goal of breaking through the dimensional veil using the {CERN} device to augment time.

They are attempting to pierce the veil between our realm and the fourth that separates us from those immortal beings that wish to do us harm, so they can release these monsters from their dimensional prison and bring them back into the third dimensional landscape of this planet. Their aim is to create havoc and fulfill their ancient proclamation to destroy all mankind. We as Children of Light are charged by our Creator to fight against this last desperate act of sedition by continuing to uphold the universal mandates given by the Creator on the mountain. As long as all of mankind stand for the universal laws mandated by the Creator, Lucifer will not be able to succeed in his plans to destroy creation and stop us from inheriting our god-given right to be free from theology and ideology that hinder us from using our creative abilities to explore the universe. We shall be victorious over this seductive and malicious evil.

We now have entered the time marked in history by Yahweh. The time that the Nephillum shall be set loose! What is to come may shake the foundations of the Earth itself! Wicked men bent on our destruction have succeeded in their efforts to corrupt the very microscopic elements of life on this planet by doing the work of their father, Lucifer. They've created Hybrids and Crimea by using a mixture of human and angelic DNA to re-enact the original corruption of the Earth, and destroy life on this planet once and for all. Lucifer and the seeds of the Serpent shall not be successful! Yahweh shall never allow him to destroy what he has made, and will overthrow and put to a halt his wicked plans to destroy us and this planet.

Please! He that can see, See! And he that can hear, Hear! For there is nothing new under the sun my friends. What was here in the past has always been here. What has been in the future has always been. What has been now, has always been here. For this is a clue to the state in which we live on this planet. The time loop in which we live is a blessing for us in our fallen state, and meant to stop the flow of fallen spirits, and hold Lucifer and his forces in limbo until his time is due. We now have come to that time in space which is called the crossroads, where all time and space intersect. Where the past converges with the present and the present converges with the future. Where time is sped up and slowed down to preserve mankind and this planet from destruction, and to guard the doorway of hell or death. Don't fall victim! Learn the name of the Creator and use his name in communion; learn his edicts and apply them in your life! For to apply those things is to love Yahweh who created you.

But how can you know and love him if you do not know his name? That is why the name, Yahweh, was taken out of the ancient text more than six - thousand times. Our enemies do not want us to use his name, for it will surely bring His spirit, and they know that for a fact!

One cannot find salvation without knowing one's Creator and his purpose for him/her! Yeshua knew this as well, for he came to do the work of his father, not to create another form of theology to enslave his fellow man with human dogma and superstitions! Remember that he was accused of that very thing! He was accused of destroying the Hebrew faith, remember? So why would he create another religion in its place? Wouldn't that make him guilty as charged?! We all know he wasn't! Wake up Children of Light, for war is upon you! Wake up for your salvation draws near!

Chapter XXIX
The End of an Era Is upon Mankind

A Call to Action for the Children of Light

It is the year of our Lord, Two Thousand and Nineteen, and the end of the world as we know it has reared its ugly head! The enemy forces from within have succeeded in their strides to open Cern's secrets! He that was before has succeeded in his plans to deliver mankind up for destruction and kill all that is good within this planet. Only the Children of Light may have any means of escape, for they shall have faith in the unseen forces of the Creator, the unseen forces that govern all matter and heavenly bodies that reside in this universe.

With the advent of high technology, we now know of the unseen properties that exist around us. Man has grown leaps and bounds technically within a blink of an eye; less than three hundred years has passed, but time has run its course! It is imperative that this writer must relay his perceived truths before his time is up. For eons, the ancients have warned mankind of great calamity before any written text on cave wall paintings or even in verbal tribal lore. Knowledge of this futuristic cataclysmic change has been spoken. The effect will bring about A New Earth and A New Heaven. This Earth, its Heavens, and its civilizations, have been destroyed time and time again, yet this knowledge has been suppressed by the same entities haunting mankind from man's beginning.

Using systems of control and tyranny, wicked men have been the indecent counterpart of their ongoing demise. A devilishly and brilliantly run program has led mankind to their destructive end without fail, forever keeping all mankind in a constant time loop! Because of time restraints, I will feebly try to convey sensitive and secret information without going through the minutia of the details concerning the information I'm desperately trying to relay. From the beginning of my story, I have been trying to convey to the reader, symbiotic relationships between the physical and spiritual nature of life and how our actions dictate our journey in creation and how our stars may be changed in the course of our lifetime, ultimately meaning that there are universal rules we all must follow!

Universal rules that cannot be trespassed against. For when these primal rules are forsaken, havoc takes root and destruction is left in its wake. For eons, mankind has been under the control of a sadistic, Satanist cabal of ruthless scum that want not only to control but also to destroy all mankind! They themselves are the most blind and controlled, more than the scum that resides under their ruthless boots.

I do not claim or profess to know all that is known of universal truths or to have all the answers to salvation, but I do know what I have found to be true thus far or in other words, factual truths that work, known by trial and error!

It's plain and simple, and I know you all may know this. We have been lied to, and the treacherous rabbit hole goes very, very deep! We have been lied to on a massive grand scale and scope! This lie encompasses every facet of life such as: Education, Religion, Politics, History, Sports, etc.... All have been co-opted by sinister, evil and wicked men. Yahweh forgives them, for they do not know what they have done. If mankind does not learn his/her history, they are doomed to repeat it! So let us contemplate the obvious. Most humans on the planet have been enduring massive pain, suffering, plagues, injustice and death, all by the hands of their fellow man it would seem, yet in fact, that is not just the case.

There are unseen forces that have been manipulating mankind from behind the electromagnetic veil dating back even beyond antiquity and written language itself; a story has been passed down from generation to generation. The story began with the creation of a paradise and a sentient being coming to ruin by a beautiful and powerful being of light, his name is the Morning Star. Entitled and spoiled, this being coveted the power of the God -Head, better said as the Creator's spirit. For the word God, GOD, or god, has indignation attached to its creation as a word, so here is the problem: all knowledge of our past has been void of that fact and the importance of its meaning.

Examine the word "God" carefully, for when spelled backwards, it means dog! Not only does the word "god" imply the nature of an animal, but it also describes the dog-star constellation, Sirius. With that in mind, we now live in a world that has been inverted! Right means wrong and good means evil! Black is white and white is black! What's pure is tainted and what's tainted is pure. All technology made ten years ago is now invalid. We live in a futuristic yet horrific virtual reality world! The whole world in which we live is now unnatural and unreal! It's a nightmare on steroids, scientifically under surveillance and connected across the globe like a spider's-web. It crosses all boarders without impunity, but yet there's no resistance from the masses! This powerful spy-grid has encompassed our world and is implemented by the very off- world and nightmarish entities that went to war with the Creator of this universe and took a third of the heavens with them. The battle was destructive and bloody in all but a small few realms, yet the Creator prevailed in the end! Before this war began, the heavens were in unity, but the seeds of rebellion were cultivated covertly within the very halls of power itself, for no one had a clue of the scope of the treachery.

All sentient beings worship the Creator of the universe, and all beings had faith in his will. But this so-called enlightened being, Lucifer, posed questions about the Creator's methods and means in carrying out his purpose. Many lost faith in all that was decreed by the Creator, and accused Him of tyranny. At all turns, this rebellious being would speak ill -will towards the Creator, his very own father.

Seeds of doubt arose quickly within the ranks, causing questions to spread far and wide about the reasoning of Yahweh's will, and also bred descent amongst the angels throughout the universe regularly. Lucifer knew he had no basis or justification for his argument without proving his point before the Elohim, so he formulated a plan to rebel against his Creator's will amongst the beings placed in a garden called Eden! And that is where our existence comes into play in this universal chess game. Knowing His rebellious son was up to something devious, Yahweh decided to enact His will and quell the dissension amongst those in the higher realms. Yahweh proposed to create a sentient being on a lower plane of existence to flush out the rebels. Before the hierarchy of the Elohim, Yahweh proposed that these new beings should be made in the image of the Elohim to covertly exhibit their likeness and cognitive abilities within this newly made paradise on such a remote planet in the third dimensional realm.

Yahweh is right! Lucifer sieged on his opportunity to disrupt his father's very good creation, so he deceived the new beings into engaging in a rebellious action against their Creator, and in one swell swoop, corrupted the seeds of mankind in an instant, thus causing the beings to lose their position in creation or the right to live an immortal life. The Creator knew his son's wicked nature, so he kept him under surveillance and caught him in the act. Bold and full of pride, Lucifer outright accused the Creator of being a tyrannical dictator before the Great Hall and the Elohim, hence challenging the Creator before all of creation for the right of Sovereignty over the universe and used deception to prove his case. He thus set into motion the events we now endure, but don't fret! The Creator pronounced judgment upon the agitators and their leader, Lucifer, from the start. With so many questions posed on all realms, justified answers must be obtained to restore order throughout the cosmos.

With the heavens split in two, and the Creator obliged by his own rules to set the matter straight. He stood aside and appointed his champion, Yeshua, to do battle for him; therefore, proving to all creation that He, Yahweh, is Just! And He always had the right to rule his creation and to give what He may give or take away what He sees fit! The Creator, Yahweh, knew that the sentient beings were deceived.

He set in motion a series of events that would redeem his very good creation from the foolishness of their actions, for he knew that they were deceived and restored their positional God-given right to live as immortal beings traversing the universe once and for all. Before punishing the one that caused total chaos throughout creation, the Creator had to put to rest all doubt of his justified majesty and greatness! The Creator knew his fallen son had allies, so he set boundaries between the faithful ones and the accuser's followers, hence enmity between the seeds of the woman and the seeds of the serpent began.

The war between Light and Darkness had begun! With heavenly access, the accuser, Lucifer, posed the question before the Elohim about the purpose of all living beings: "Do we, the first of his creation, the first of creation endowed with free will; do men have free will I ask, or does the Creator impose his tyrannical right to rule over all in which he sees fit without any of our consent, and if so, why did he refuse mankind the knowledge of good and evil, keeping them blind to the nature of the universe in which they reside, and safeguarding them from all ill as long as they continue in ignorance?" These questions caused chaos to reign without check until the questions posed were answered throughout creation; we here on Earth would bare the brunt of the fight. The Creator has stated that mankind has been created with love for his Creator built within himself/herself. Mankind is full of the spirit of Yahweh, not only having love for one's self, but also having a great love for his Creator. Lucifer begged to differ, for he has stated that mankind only loved himself/herself and would curse his/her Creator if left un-checked, and only love Yahweh for what He provides. The accuser has been proven to be a liar, and has been found wanting, so his rebellion has been quelled on all fronts and in all dimensions, and he has been thrown down to this realm (Earth) of existence until judgment. The Dragon knows his time is up! The deceiver has placed in motion a plan to rewrite the outcome of this judgment, thus killing his father, and taking over the God -Head or Wholly Spirit of Divine power!

Two Hundred Heavenly Sons of the Creator were assigned to watch over the development of the new sentient beings and were captured by the beauty of women and decided to leave their first estate to interact with the women of the Earth to taste their sweet nectar by having intercourse with all who they may choose and produced offspring of unnatural spirits and wickedness! Having both Earthly and Heavenly origins, these beings caused chaos and blood shed on a massive scale throughout space-time. The Two Hundred loved their wives and taught them the unseen knowledge of this universe and third dimensional realm. They learned all the Social Sciences, Civilizational Technical Sciences, Agriculture and Farming, War, Theology, Physical Sciences, and Music! This disruption of Yahweh's purpose caused all manner of deprived behavior. It also brought great advancement in knowledge, such as what we see in this time of the crossroads. The world in which we live today is made by the Two Hundred Fallen Ones and it belongs to them. Other "Watchers," who were also assigned to watch over mankind, saw the evil taking place and had no choice but to inform the Creator of the damage being propagated upon his brand new creatures. Foul and deprived was the outcome of the two hundred's willful betrayal, so the Creator carried out their sentence swiftly and decisively, forevermore condemning them to darkness for all time until their death, for the immortal can see nothing after they witnessed the destruction of their offspring.

There are two camps at odds in this story: Those who have taken the side of the Creator and those who have taken the side of the accuser, Lucifer! This information has been the subject of many debates over the eons, but one question has not been answered: What role does man play in this cosmic movie and how does it all end? Hopefully, this novel will shed some light on the situation, not saying I have all the answers to the most profound and important questions ever posed within mankind's history, but I have found certain truths to be sound in all the confusion. In order to answer this question, one must look and examine the world at large and open one's eyes to what he/she sees.

First, we are witnessing the total breakdown of society. The family unit has been decimated and almost destroyed! All resources have been corrupted by design, and co-opted by the powers that be, the followers of Lucifer, but who are they? Since the time of the fall in the Garden of Eden, the most sought after resource on the planet has been knowledge, not gold or silver, but only knowledge! For knowledge is power and power trumps all material treasure that could be found. When one tribe or creed of humanity holds back knowledge or information from another tribe, the tribe with knowledge holds leverage over those that have none, ultimately controlling the outcome of the tribe ignorant of certain information. Furthermore, they made themselves rulers or lords over those who don't know how to overcome the lording tribe's advancements in technology. This is the main driver of all man's woes! So who wields power over us all? Since all mankind suffers from the effects of their actions, who are the ones holding the strings of the puppet? Some may think it is the money changers who enslaved us, or the politicians who wield our fate, but in my lifelong investigations, I've found that behind the scenes of it all lie the Clergy! The Clergy controls all Children of Darkness! That's right!

The Church controls all knowledge known to all mankind and civilization, and they only reveal knowledge that furthers their agenda. By manipulating the belief structure of a certain people, the Clergy takes hold of the outcome of their fate, hence dictating their success or failure in life. But how did that fact come to pass? Throughout mankind's history, the creative success of Yahweh's children, and the mistakes of our forefathers have all been documented and passed down throughout the ages. In time, the corrosion of knowledge has stagnated greatly within the ranks of the masses, first by word of mouth and often times lost by natural calamity, but most ancient knowledge has been preserved in secret, yet concealed from the whole of society. When The Two Hundred revealed the hidden secrets of the Elohim to a certain group of peoples, namely the children of Cain, the written word came into existence and even before all forms of writing were revealed to women, The Children of the Snake hoarded off- world information in the attempt to control the outcome of mankind and gave certain men a vessel to maintain and keep tribal continuity and survival of that clan alone in the goal of upholding tribal identity and history.

By hording ancient secrets in the hands of the Elders or Priests, they preserved the people and kept their society intact, thus preserving and maintaining lifesaving or even life threating information over the length and span of time. Certain men knew the true history of our planet, our universe, and ourselves from the beginning of our existence. By jealously guarding this crucial knowledge, evil men exerted power over their fellow man from the beginning of mankind's existence. The truth of the matter is, every form of religion on the planet has been and still is under the explicit control of the Catholic Church. The Pope owns all of mankind! All banks or money changers and all governments and religious institutions on the planet are held captive under the massive grip of the Vatican. No matter what sect, denomination or form: Christianity, Judaism, and/or Islam are all under The Pope's hierarchy! Every person on the planet takes his/her marching orders from the Pope, wittingly or unwittingly!

The religious orders of the past and of our day have deceived the entire world with empty hopes and dreams of a supernatural savior coming out of the skies, so as to take the faithful into the heavens, thus having the masses believing they are already saved from sin. When in fact, the whole of mankind lingers at the edge of the abyss of destruction by their master's hand, hence forsaking their god-given free will to overcome any adversity that may plague them. The masses blindly give over their free will to the pages of an ancient book and to the dictates of the crooked men of the cloth.

By holding back vital information about the origins of the Creator and his creation, evil men have been in control of our destiny. First of all, let me clarify: All of us are slaves, whether we know it or not! Everything we've learned about life is a lie on every level! Math and science, along with physical and spiritual concepts, are all misleading lies mixed with certain truths, for they are duplicitous in nature! We are considered by historians as the people of the "Book; however, The Bible has been tampered with from its inception, for it has truths twisted amongst metaphors, allegories, and hyperbolical theory. Those who control the belief structures of the masses have everyone in physical and spiritual limbo and ignorance! We have been fed a bunch of hogwash from birth! We now have entered into an age of massive deception. We are taught by the church to develop a personal relationship with some nameless god, with all spiritual references linking us back to the Creator, including his name, which has been removed over 6,000 times or falsely translated. All relevant ancient text has been lost, discarded, or held behind armed guards to deceive those searching for truth; therefore, making the journey towards enlightenment almost unobtainable in the search.

Tell me, how can anyone know you without first learning your name? They can't! It is essential to know a person's name before engaging that person in any meaningful dialogue!

This fact remains the same with our relationship with the Creator! It is essential that we know the name of whom we give such reverence, but the powers that be have stunted our growth towards universal awareness by removing the name of the Creator, thus hindering our understanding of what is needed to break free from the evil one and his minions. In these dark times, acknowledgement of creation is essential, and knowing the name of the one who may deliver us from destruction is imperative! Most Christians believe that the "Most High's" name is Jesus, who, in fact, is not the Son of Man who died for our release from the effect of sin, for his name is forever Yeshua of Nazareth! He only came to do the work of his father, Yahweh. His father is the one that holds our salvation or destruction. The name, "Jesus," in definition, is "Zeus" which literally means one is praying to a pagan god when evoking that name, and the worst part of it is, the Clergy knows this and willfully and maliciously conceals this vital information from their parishioners! In order to decipher ancient text without going insane, one must first understand that all text references to the past reside in the hands of the Catholic Church. One must learn what is fact over what is metaphor and what deception is over truth. Knowing real truths will determine whether or not mankind will survive this upcoming "New World Order" master plan and overcome it, which in point of fact, dates back to the very origins of religion and civilization.

The gods of this world have many names, and so does the Creator in religious dogma, but the truth of the matter is, he only has one name and that name was removed from the Bible over six thousand times! So how could we address the one in which we should address? It is almost impossible to find out the proper pronunciation of the Creator's name which was given to us from time passed. We do however have a starting point. Let us start with the name of the Creator given to us from within the Mosaic Law, better known as The Old Testament. {YHWH} was taken out of the Canonized Bible and replaced with the words LORD and GOD and capitalized to signify where the Creator's name would be. YHWH would be Yahweh when the vowels, "A" and "E" are added between the consonants, "Y" and "W." In addition to the spelling, I have come to find out that the way a word sounds is vital when learning the truth behind the word. We live in an Electromagnetic Material Universe that consists of frequencies, and within all frequencies consist harmonics, and within all harmonics exist vibration and geometry pertaining strictly and solely to a specific harmonic of frequency in tune. Saying a word is similar to tuning a radio station to the station you prefer; therefore, speaking the wrong word invokes the wrong vibration and or connection.

How we pronounce a word gives meaning to the word, making the word either true or false! Knowing the Creator's name and how it's pronounced is crucial and imperative to our ability to communicate with he that holds our salvation! With that fact in mind, knowing that the powers that be have purposely removed the name of the Creator out of all reference books throughout history, we must beg the question, "WHY?"

It was to hinder and break mankind's spiritual connection to the Creator! Evil wicked demons and men held back knowledge so they could hinder us from finding out the true name of our Creator and the truth about themselves.

Some say the entire Bible is a book of metaphoric philosophy, but I beg to differ! But who am I? I know nothing! But I know what works in maintaining happiness! After years of searching ancient text, I've come to the conclusion that all men are liars! I myself fall into that same category, no matter how much I try to find out the truth of our existence. So with that in mind, please consider this. The books in which so many people put so much stock and faith, are full of misleading, deceiving, and deceitful lies and are duplicitous in nature! The so-called Holy Bible, Torah, and/or Quran are just that Holy {Full of Holes}!

All are works of man, not WHOLLY which means COMPLETE, thus rendering them invalid, invalid when searching for infallible truth. After searching for so many years, I have found that each of our so-called wholly books have been altered through time, or rendered invalid by interpretation and ideology, Dogma if you will. So how can we truly find out the truth about our history, or more importantly, how could we truly know the history of our Creator if the written word that we use for enlightenment itself has been corrupted? The answer is that we cannot! With such a revelation, I became an alcoholic even more so! I felt that there was no way out of this living hell we all are living through. But hope comes in mysterious ways, just as our salvation is revealed, mysteriously.

About sixteen years ago, I'd come to an all-time low; my mother died a week after my birthday. I was devastated! I dove right back into the belly of the beast ever so, and drank myself unconscious daily. I was depressed, self-loathing and constantly in denial without reason. Homicidal thoughts consumed my very being. After many drunken run- ins with the law, and feeling as if there was no way out of an ever spiraling web of destruction, and trapped by the whims of an ever suffocating and hopeless existence within society, an epiphany gave way. It became clear that my only hope for sanity or peace of mind led with my departure from my family. Instead of comfort, support and understanding, I was ridiculed and scorned. Seemingly demonic influences not only held sway over me, but also over my entire family. They discarded my overwhelming cry for help.

As weakness and insanity took hold of my reason, they stayed away. It was obvious that I had to leave their presence as soon as possible if I were to overcome my mental spiritual affliction.

While I was alone in my mother's home, a voice came to me saying: "It's Time! Finish the circle and learn!" Soon after, I called my ex-wife, and urged her to move her husband and our children into my mother's home. She was having financial problems and I figured I'd help my children with something tangible since I was unable to care for them emotionally and spiritually. So they moved into my mother's home, and I moved out. I moved into a homeless shelter

EDGAR FRENCH, JR.

in Hammond, Indiana and sure enough, within twenty-four hours, I'd begun feeling relief from the burden of being stuck in a place where dreams are destroyed, and hopelessness rules unchecked. Yet there was the ever growing feeling of hopelessness lingering in the back of mind with not a bit of relief. I needed to leave the place where hopelessness ruled! I had to leave the Midwest entirely. I moved from state to state in search of a vestige of relief and peace of mind, not to mention spiritual soundness, yet I found myself under fire once again by cut throats, thugs and gangsters such as the notorious South American gang called "MS13" located in Houston, Texas.

I found myself back on the road once more, but this time by angelic decree and without knowledge of where I would be relocating, mistakenly traveling towards Boston or so I thought. But Yahweh had different plans for me, for I found myself driving into Pittsburgh, Pennsylvania after getting lost on the New Jersey turn pike. Still under the influence and brainwashing of the church and western social norms, I soon found myself in the thick of things once more. Without fail, I found myself drinking alcohol more than ever. "What was I doing wrong?" was the phrase that replayed in my mind daily as I worked odd jobs and went through the regular motions and mindset of most people trying to gain material wealth, which only led to more destructive behavior and bad decisions in life. But as personal and financial problems increased the more my spiritual eyes would open to the obvious, for this time I would learn the most precious lesson in life from homelessness in Pittsburgh than I'd ever learned in the bosom of prosperity in the past. Like magical falling stars entering into our atmosphere, it finally hit me like a ton of bricks. The answer I'd been looking for was right in front of my eyes like most epiphanies! I had spent years searching for universal truths, and only became more confused as I found more answers to questions of the occult. Suddenly, a voice of clarity came into full view as I watched the public run up and down an escalator in Downtown Pittsburgh. They were like little mice trapped on a mad scientist's experimental Ferris wheel but were going nowhere at a fast pace as I stood still riding up the escalator beside them.

All the pieces fell into place! Ironically, while in the search for freedom, I had found that I was already free. By being homeless, I had no worries and I finally understood the genius behind the madness of the bum on the street, for those so-called "bums" had let go of worldly things! They let the things that kept them trapped fade away. The worries of maintaining wealth became irrelevant. A mortgage, bills and worthless material wants became asinine. Which brings to words uttered some two and half thousand years ago by Yeshua himself, "It would be easier for a camel to go through an eye of a needle than for a rich man to enter into the gates of Heaven" (Matthew 19:24).

There is no way mankind can understand the things of the spirit world when they are so busy keeping up with the Jones' and living under man-made rule and law. After numerous divine interventions in which I described in the beginning of this book, I now understand what my destiny is in this world, and what it implies. Still in a drunken state, I yelled out these words: "Men of renown and those of fame, you shall never leave from up under the levers of power, nor ascend from the halls of the White House, for you are slaves of power for power's sake, and your destruction awaits!" From time in memorial, Children of Light shall yell out these words, "Why am I here? I don't belong here on this planet!"

Darkness rules this world, and no good shall come from man ruling over other men! It was the year, Two Thousand and Seventeen, and the summer of Rage was a flop! Most of the morons tapped to create chaos were distracted by the Electoral process going astray in the United States of America, for the corrupt previous Administration was under siege and co-opted by true American patriots, thus faltering the Social Justice Warriors' plans to disrupt the country with racial upheaval. The powers that be sped up their Eugenic program of total Tyrannical Rule while most of the public stayed asleep to the danger, and willingly stood still as their masters set in place a program of total destruction! Search and you shall find! There is no way out of the destruction reserved by the Creator of the universe. This is what is in store for those who would destroy his creation. Prophetic warning now weighs out its meaning in our time, and we must not fall victim to the self-fulfilling prophecy. To all those who do not put hope in mankind's existence, they shall inadvertently put themselves in opposition with the Creator of the Universe.

Combining the physical and spiritual signs in understanding the dangers we must all face, I now see the future of this Country. Obama shall be our first Dictator if he's not STOPPED! Though he is no longer in The Oval Office, he still has minions inside the Deep State, and FEMA will begin rounding up people by the end of this decade if not stopped! We must resist! We must take to heart the words of our Creator, and I don't mean the Bible, Torah or Quran. These are the words of our Creator given to his profit on the Mount, and they are the only "written" words in stone spoken by the Creator in all history:

Thou Shalt Have No Other Gods Before Me (YHWH)

Thou Shalt Not Make Unto Thee Any Graven Image, Or Any Likeness Of Anything That Is In The Heavens Above, Or That Is In The Earth Beneath, Or That Is In The Water Under The Earth

Thou Shalt Not Take The Name Of The Lord Thy God In Vain

Remember The Day of Yahweh's Vindication, To keep It Wholly

Honor Thy Father And Mother: That Thy Days May be Long Upon The Land Which The Lord Thy God Giveth Thee

Thou Shalt Not Kill

Thou Shalt Not Commit Adultery

Thou Shalt Not Steal

Thou Shalt Not Bear False Witness Against Thy Neighbor

Thou Shalt Not Covet Anything

The words above are the only words known to be written by the hand of Yahweh, period. And these were the words passed down to us from generation after generation, by whom some call a figurative and not a historical real person, by the name of Moses. But I tend to differ with that hypotheses. If there's anything I've learned over the years about my unexplained events and numerous interventions with the unknown, I know this with all my heart: The

Creator does indeed exist! With that in mind, one truth stands strong, and that is this statement! All men are liars! Yet one must have faith in the unknown and unseen in order to expand his/ her horizons in faith. Given that fact, I choose to inform the reader of all probable sources of truth in our history no matter what some man of science or holy guru may entertain. On a personal note, some ancient texts such as the Bible, has proven to be a great source of comfort and solace to many lost souls, yet all Scriptural texts written within all the so-called holy books devised throughout history have only proven to be the source of all wars and destruction of human life on this planet! Religion has created a number of infamous "D words" throughout the length of time, words such as: Destruction, Division, Dissension, Desertion, Deception, Dissolution and Devolution! The ancient texts are actually full of holes when explaining actual events, leaving all truth seekers confused with many unanswered questions.

These duplicitous ancient books have also proven to be a great source of power in the hands of those that would lord over their fellow man, thus never providing to be a source of spiritual closure, or being a valid source of fact gathering answers, or understanding of the reality in which we all live. Over the entire history of man, one thing is magnified in antiquity: the only thing organized religion has accomplished has been the number of lost souls from war, greed, control, tribal sacrifice and cultural ritual. No man could ever atone for the horrific nature of death visited upon us by our fellow man within religion by these so-called men of faith, or so-called men of the cloth.

Religious Dogma has destroyed the future of all mankind! Most Christians follow the Dark One without ever knowing so by engaging in pagan ritual! All festivals and customs are based in Pagan ways, forged by the Two Hundred Fallen Angels! Most of the occultic knowledge of the ancients are saturated in the worship of Saturn, for even the "Black Garb" warn by priests finds its origins in the worship of the ringed planet. From the beginning of civilization, we've been guilty of unwittingly worshiping false gods! Please do not blame your parents, for they themselves were deceived from birth. Most fell victim to the great lie by means of heritage, or tribal area.

None knew of the grand scope of deception that held sway over the masses. None knew the span in which false religious doctrine wielded its magic over us!

None knew how far the tentacles of organized religion ran in the ongoing escapades of life and death! All facets of life have been infected by corruption and devoid of integrity, controlled by wizards of Businesses, Work, Play, Belief, Doubt, etc.... The church controls all Prime Ministers, Presidents, Kings and Queens, financial debts, and land, in addition to controlling all peoples and all institutions of learning! The church controls all lawyers, business men, banks and home owners! All politicians and teachers of higher learning follow the will of their masters: The Church! They all do the will of their father, Lucifer, the original serpent and the liar and deceiver of humanity!

All holy books are just that, holy, thus full of holes, and were designed to deceive, divide, control and destroy all mankind! They were designed to confuse and to facilitate the agenda of those in power, the children of the serpent, those that bathe in darkness' light. Even if one does not believe in a devil or a god, those in power do, so one will bode well if he/she understands that fact. For all those of faith, I'm so sorry to tell you these facts, but in all goodness, you should have known these things from the beginning! Hell! When judging the value of a fruit tree, it is always preferred to examine the roots of the tree! But when a person's development is corrupted from birth by those who from their inception are in opposition of the Creator, you'll do best to judge one's fruit by his actions instead of believing a person because of one's status in society or religion!

Furthermore, every mainstream and back door religious organization has been plagued with scandal. They are the harbingers of Eugenics and destruction such as: abortion, homosexuality, child molestation, crime, bigotry and fornication. They are truly guilty, for they do the work of their father, Lucifer! Moreover, in the hood, better known as the inner cities of the world's population, young men and women are dying in record numbers because of their religious organization's belief structure. Their flocks were made for corruption's hand and given over to the god of this world for sacrifice! Every war fought in mankind's history was a sacrifice of innocence to the god of calamity and destruction!

All war was only waged for the ruin of humanity, for the powers that be will pay for this terrible and horrific legacy of genocide. But they are not alone! Truly, those that rule the church identify as the Children of Darkness' portraitures, yet so does the vagabond down the way, the shop keeper and the bar maid at the pub. We only can judge a tree by its fruit, and most of us have been deceived from birth! But now time has run out for those who call themselves Masters! The world has now entered World War III. Yeshua's warnings are now knocking at our door!

The ancient Wormwood is now affecting the entire planet, and the population of this god forsaken land goes on without care in ignorance. There are so many Children of Light trapped into the world at large and find no relief in their daily lives, never free from the troubles of enslavement. Most are unknowingly suffering from mass mind control; they have spent their lives searching for truth only to find lie after lie from the very people in whom they've put their trust. The fact of the matter is, the whole world lies in the hands of the wicked one, and mankind is the soul enemy of him! Mankind will never find his/her way out! Have you ever heard of the term: "The Truth will set you Free?" Free from what?

The teachings of Yeshua were famous for enlightenment over the woes of his day, and the very woes of Yeshua's day have not changed. The poor is still poor and the rich is still rich, and the status quo still reigns free over the masses! He taught us to break free from the rule of men! I learned the hard lesson that the world we live in is a systematically designed death trap. Designed to cripple the race of mankind from the natural way of life, breaking our unity with nature. Artificial work, food, air, and Earth, were all made to stop humanity from reaching its full potential on this planet, ultimately stunting our physical and spiritual selves! The very amenities we take for granted are the very tools used to enslave us. More than 95% of the world population no longer has the tools or knowledge to live outside urban cities and compounds. Most of humanity has no clue of how the very Earth in which they live works! Most are well known slaves of the system, willingly giving themselves over to the beast, and all who may try to break free from the monetary system and life outside the web that traps us all are ostracized!

The Ten Commandments are not only a guideline for healthy good living and good moral values, they are truly essential for true happiness! It is the very air we breathe, for it is a part of us; we were born with its tenets inside us. The tenets supposedly given to us from our Creator have proven themselves to be true over the age of time! Without those very tenets, all civilizations have crumbled, made devastated, and were disintegrated from within. They are the pillars of human life! And when evil men and their father Lucifer remove them from our lives, they knowingly commit a crime against humanity. They know the word of god shall set us all free from their influence, and is very essential to the importance of having a long successful and happy life!

So-called men of God have hijacked the word of Yahweh and defiled its importance and influence! It is now time to take back those tenets and make them the only source of truth in our homes! No Bible! No Torah! No Quran! No Talbot! Understand that hierarchy is an absolute necessary process; it is needed for any social society to grow and strive in security, but it does not mean those who would enforce proper rules and regulations would have total power over their fellow man, for no man has the right to lord over his people! And lord knows a Socialist society breeds corruption in all walks of life, from the top to the bottom, so does the communal idea. But order must be maintained for a righteous society to flourish and prosper to reach the next level in development. No longer shall we as Children of Light allow evil men of the Church, Industry or Politics to rule unconditionally, unchecked and unchallenged.

They shall never make more wealth than the lowliest of our civilization. The prophecy must be fulfilled said those of little faith! "The Meek Shall Inherit the Earth!" I know life seems as if evil controls all destiny and dictates our future, and honestly it does. But the tide is turning, and good is standing strong with its light! Children of Darkness are on the move towards total destruction, and may just succeed in their efforts! But Children of Light are breaking free from their chains as we speak. Yahweh has given us away out from this Eugenics driven onslaught. Have faith in his words, not ancient text! Hold those values dear in your heart, home, work, and you shall survive the storm on the horizon. Men of power fully know that the word of god or Yahweh's ten edicts is part of every human's DNA! It is literally a part of our makeup; the values of Yahweh's tenets were written inside our very code for life! Without it managing our lives, we are subject to any falsities they may manufacture. Without its guidance in our lives, we will fall victim to the fallen ones, and yes, my readers, they do exist! Within all folklore, fairy tale and mythos there is historical truth. As I traversed into the dark abyss of the occult knowledge held captive by the so-called Elite, I finally placed some of the pieces of the universal puzzle in their perspective places. Humanity has gone from horse and buggy to airplanes and electrometric railways within a small course of one hundred years and that makes no sense! Those in power have given themselves over to the Dark Lord, Lucifer, using ancient technology and techniques such as divination and Magic. Magic to allure simple people into believing a blatant lie, thus holding the secret of our inheritance of traversing the universe in life, and in some cases, gaining old technologies given to mankind by the two hundred fallen ones of old, "The Mighty Ones," and to put a new face on the technology of today. For there is nothing new under the sun.

By illusion and delusion, they have deceived the whole planet into thinking that the way of everlasting life for themselves would be achieved by dumbing down the public by having hypnotized the masses with toys and trinkets, while the Earth itself is put to ruin all the while thinking their actions will set them free from death.

They selfishly hoard life extending technology alongside other unbelievable advances in science all for themselves. Men have literally sold out their own offspring for a lie! Yet there is light at the end of the tunnel. There are so many of us suffering around the globe right now that it would be almost useless to turn the tide of fate, but hopefully, some if not all Children of Light may gain knowledge from the words that I have written, and not continue to fall sway of this so-called modern world. Come up from out of it! To those within the inner-cities of the world, I have a special message of love and kinship. But for those black men who suffered so much in life's journey, I directly interject these facts into you! Within your ranks are the Children of Light, sent to Earth to do Yahweh's service. They have been surrounded by minions of our overlords, ruled by our arch enemy, the Children of Darkness! Please understand that you are in a war! A war not only for your lives, but a universal war between the Creator and his accuser, Lucifer! WAKE UP! Know where you come from! Know your history! You may be surprised at what you find. When searching the past, you may find out facts that will change the manner in which you think. Black men are the original slaves spoken so highly within antiquity, and the Hebrews of ancient text of history, not the so-called Jews of today. Within the bloodline of slaves lies the seed of Yeshua Ben Jesse, and to the unwashed seed of King David of old shall come understanding of their plight and true knowledge behind their mistreatment.

I give no facts to this claim, but I urge you to research your heritage for yourself. Be warned this is not to condemn any race or creed; color is not the question. Hebrews came from every walk of life. That is why when they made a covenant with Yahweh, he had them circumcise every male within the tribe, as a mark of ownership. So don't go on a temper tantrum from this book. In fact, search out those that you will know to be Children of Darkness and try to persuade them from their error. Yeshua was a real man; I know nothing of miracles, but I do know that his life was remarkable by the very fact that Billions follow him to this day. With just a small amount of faith, I've come to believe in his message, and the very fact that those who control the world make sure that those who attempt to follow his example may never know their true worth. The powers that be go through every measure to ensure that black men's lives must be a journey in unsurmountable odds and toils. But as Children of Light, we must go across so many obstacles to succeed in life without succumbing to the darkness' light and give credence to the worth of Yahweh's commandments and give proof to the existence of our Creator and God of the universe! Our brother, Yeshua, was a Child of Light and he overcame the test set at his feet.

Will you please understand that you have been brainwashed from birth; the program MK-Ultra, amongst others, have infiltrated the church in your communities as early as antiquity. Our very own so-called leaders have sold us out from the start of their careers; therefore, they must die for the sins of their ways! For generation after generation, the so-called black leaders' bloodlines must never be able to hold office of importance ever again! The innocent blood of millions, maybe even billions of un-born black children cry out for justice. The blood of black youth rings out against those men of color with marginal Earthly powers! Shame and disgrace is their legacy forever, for generation after generation. They have single handedly destroyed their own people, and reveled in the destruction of their very own children! May Yahweh have no mercy on their souls! We have seen the results of cowardly men following ambitious men, and our children have paid the price of their arrogance.

It is time for all Children of Light to come up out of the systems and shadows of men, and begin to uphold their promise to the Creator and follow his will. We have been told that our nature is war-like, but that is far from the truth! We were made very good in the eyes of our Creator. Meek in nature and more loving than all in creation is mankind and happy in our mandate to make this planet a paradise in service to our father, Yahweh. It has been evil men and unseen forces bent on deceiving us into believing that we are just animals and brutes in nature, having no love for the planet and our fellow human-beings, and only concerned with one's individual wellbeing, but they are all lies! We have been tricked into believing that we are war- like. Throughout history, men have been forced to either protect their children, goods and family alongside themselves, or have no concern of death from those who have given themselves over to imprisoned rebellious children of their most high, Lucifer.

All doing their bidding in blindness, inciting men into violent acts over and over again throughout recorded time incarnate who are moved by those infected and influenced by unseen forces of the spiritual realm. Men have been falling ever so and obliviously into the power of the evil ones from our inception. The time has come for us to break free from the disobedient conditioning of the satanic so-called elite! We must understand that we are Children of Light by nature. It has been those corrupted in spirit, and under the influence of the fallen ones controlling our fate by proxy, better known as {The Brotherhood of the Snake} spoken about throughout history, and folklore. It has been those seeds of darkness that the unseen spiritual rulers trapped on this planet have given control over civilization and this world!

So please stop trying to succeed in this matrix of lies! Those who are somewhat within the human family have sided with the original rebel, and he has entrusted ancient technology to those on high so that they may be able to control society from the beginning of time and enslave all Children of Light from the beginning of civilization. They are bent on destroying all that Yahweh has created, including this planet itself. There is a time for all things under the sun; the end of this world is at hand! We are living in a time of great discovery, enlightenment and woe. We must turn away from the distractions of those in power and break free from the massive brainwashing spewing out bullshit that the corporate dickheads, and government propagandist shovel out of their media system. This is an organized death culture and owned by satanic globalist pedophiles. Please understand that the very system we now live under is a trap. From its inception, the very system we have come to rely on for valid information was designed to deceive and destroy the very mechanism of our free

EDGAR FRENCH, JR.

will. We no longer know how to live on this Earth without the amenities so frequently thrust upon us under the disguise of modern convenience. This artificial so-called modern world is the spider web in which we are enslaved. We are slowly being destroyed by our own willingness to cling to comfort, while those in power jealously hold the knowledge of self-preservation for themselves, in essence, keeping us trapped in ignorance's bliss while they systematically control and kill their fellow man indiscriminately. This is well known to those in power, but the words I speak now are forgotten by all who suffer by the hands of these wicked beings.

Amongst the tears of a morning mother's breath, lies the question that all that reside in poverty and hopelessness ask themselves in the darkness, and in the light, as they bend a knee or sit on the benches of the Church, Synagogue or Mosque. Are we cursed? Over and over this question has haunted the minds of all those searching for truth and enlightenment within the inner-cities and beyond. After a loved one died from war or an overdose of drugs, so many Children of Light asked themselves these questions: Why must my child die like this?! Why do I live without hope? Why am I looked upon with distain and lack of respect from those set up on high?! Why must I fear the faces of men? I have come to learn the answer to these questions and much more. To my brothers and sisters in light, the answer to these questions is war, more specifically, a Universal War! You've been cursed by your own hand! Your history has been stolen from you by those who know the trap of time. This message is strictly for you who reside within the ghetto streets of the Americas! In angst and drunkenness, the answer to breaking the curse was given to me as I lay passed out from alcohol poisoning in the streets of East Liberty.

Don't get it wrong! For many years, I've searched for our Creator, and for years, I have overcome many physical and spiritual battles. And by the grace of Yahweh, I live to write this story. You will see within the pages of my book that I didn't become an alcoholic while I was in search of my Creator, but when I found him.

I became an alcoholic once I found out what I had to do in this world. Once I realized the hidden truth of mankind's fate, I was amazed and terrified. I had to make a great choice within my soul, and at that time it seemed unthinkable at best. But I was wrong! For one to follow and submit to the one and only true

Creator, he must first take the road less traveled. The road is full of pitfalls and traps my friend! You will fall on your way to enlightenment, that's a given! But never give up! Your life may be forfeit in the very pursuit of the truth. To know the one and only true Creator is hazardous to say the least, long in understanding the unseen, and painstaking in all time-lines. The journey to enlightenment would take me on a road that only I could walk, and I ultimately lost all those that I loved in the process. But I had made my choice before birth, or so it seemed. I had no choice but to take the road less traveled, and I was beginning to understand the price of the prize set forth. The more I looked into the past, the more I became depressed! It is true that knowledge brings sorrow, and I understood that, or so I thought. But as I grew in knowledge, both known and unknown, I brought the attention of the unseen to myself.

I brought unwanted attention from those that dwelled amongst the light of the Children of Darkness, yet I survived to tell the tale! To those who are all like me: we originally took the road less traveled in the beginning of our history and life was grand and prosperous, but we have fallen from grace and kept unaware of our true blessings and birthright. Most are unaware that the black slaves of America's past are the Children of Abraham, and they are Hexose "Hebrew," not African! They are the children of the lost tribes of Israel! They have been stripped of their very history because of that fact! Once they understand their history, and the curse that weighs them down, they shall be free, finally free! So shall the world! All peoples in all nations shall be freed from those who wish us all harm! First and foremost, they were slaves before and after the Americas. They are the original slaves! Yet they gained freedom with the help of a Great and Powerful Being, Yahweh! He saved us and brought us into our own land. He asked only one thing from us and that was obedience! To be Obedient and keep his laws close to our hearts, and he would be our God and we would be his people forevermore!

But we fell astray! We turned from our agreement with the Creator! He warned us before we entered into the covenant! He told us not to follow the Children of Cain, and hold fast the mandates of his law for our very wellbeing, but we turned towards the light of darkness willingly; consequently, breaking all Yahweh's Commandments over and over again. So we have reaped what we have sown. We are Hebrew and we have forsaken our God as such! Those within the Church may even know of this, but will never reveal the truth. For they know, once this truth comes to pass, their god and their world will be over and done forevermore! Please, Black men and women, turn back towards your Creator, Yahweh! Learn his name and the power that resides within it! The name of the Creator is paramount in understanding the Host of Hosts and what he has in store for mankind! Come from up out of the whore's mouth! Organized religion is the Whore spoken of throughout antiquity, and her time riding the Beast is almost up! She has lied to you from beyond the time of your forbearers.

Those who have joined with the Beast and called themselves our representatives have sealed our fate from birth! Loving ignorance rather than knowledge has been our downfall. For all books that may be looked upon as wholly and faultless, must also carry the stain of man's hands! And our Creator has said: "All Men Are Liars!" Psalm 116:11. Unfortunately, this quote must also apply to the book in which you are now reading!

As long as you listen to men, you are cursed my fellow brethren! As long as you see material wealth as happiness, you shall forever be cursed by its snare! Yahweh only spoke one law, and that was the Ten Commandments. That's it! All other commentary is designed to keep you under the control of the rulers of this world who are Lucifer and his cohorts! You are drunk off the light of darkness! Turn back towards the living Creator, "Yahweh," and use his name! The name of the Creator has been taken out of all ancient text to keep you from communing with him and gaining understanding of his true grace. Organized Religion has tainted and destroyed all that was, all that is, and all that will be true! She must pay for leading Children of Light into darkness, said The Most High! It is the year Two thousand and nineteen, in the month of February, and the day of the fourth. We now know that we have always lived in the time of the great deception. Using the term of the Prophets of old seems so Illuminist, and shows ill will towards those that may follow! To make "Profit" or gain from the innocent carries an awesome and hefty penalty. From generation to generation, those who have misled Yahweh's Children of Light, shall suffer forever lasting to everlasting! Furthermore, they shall be without grace or forgiveness forever and ever!

This warning is for those who suffer last. Obama still covets the White House! Martial Law shall be his legacy! We have lived amongst the "signs and sigils" of the evil ones, and the Children of Darkness forever, but most of mankind has never taken the time to know their meanings. We have broken bread with those of evil will towards us. Those who want to see both mankind and the planet die, smile in our faces while they silently kill us with their wicked ways! Wakeup! Wakeup! You have no more time! Judgment has been placed upon this wayward world. We all have been found guilty in the eyes of The Most High and found wanting. What devastating horrific turn of events shall it take before mankind shall see? Suffer no more for material gain!

Get on your knees and repent to the Creator of the universe, not to men! Ask Yahweh for forgiveness, and sin against him no longer. Let no man stop you from that humble and noble task! Praise his name, for time is no more! Hold fast Yahweh's Ten Commandments, and mankind shall be set free from death!

Free from men of war, free from temptation, free from want, and free from those who lord over us. For the fight that we engage in is one of two dimensions: The first is spiritual! The second is physical! Death and destruction is knocking at mankind's doorstep! We must overcome the great adversity that resides on Earth now and in the near future. Please understand, we now have entered into the great tribulation and woe!

Out of fear of running out of time, I recorded a vision of what was to come in the nearby future. The events recorded here in this book reflect the time in which we are living now. From extensive research, alongside personal trial and error, I know how great and deep the occultist's deception and duplicitous dogma of evil writing within ancient text can confuse and cause dismay, but keep in mind that it all was put in place by design to confuse and distort truth with secondhand and even third-hand information of so-called accounts that may or may not have happened in the most distant past. Knowing the truth of those facts can destroy all hope and faith in what is true or not, but be assured that the purpose of deceptive wording within ancient text devised by evil men and wicked spirits have been found out by the Lord of Hosts!

Know that the Bible and all other ancient texts are able to remain in circulation so as to wage spiritual warfare against the people of the Earth without the people's knowledge or consent by collecting ancient truths with pagan lies, coupled with personal letters of Children of Light. The powers that be have co-opted and even changed certain words of ancient text to fit their narrative of assured Armageddon, ultimately bringing on mankind's destruction

EDGAR FRENCH, JR.

by proxy! These indisputable facts only make my heart weep in disgust and anger over that very nature of criminality.

I wrapped my mind around the fact that most ancient text have historically been altered within the last Two hundred years, and the truth of that fact can relatively be found by a simple search, yet most people here on this god forsaken planet willfully, and some even joyfully walk gleefully into the light of ignorance in which evil takes root and controls their lives without protest even though they are openly shown the evil that traps them without a cry of concern. Consequently, they wittingly or unwittingly love the illusion and despair that binds them to hell's depths! But as the time-line draws closer to the preordained period for the destruction of the rebellious Children of Darkness, Yahweh has allotted an appointed time for those who had not yet chosen to understand the deadly seriousness of the time at hand, and he has given them the opportunity to take a side in this universal war that affects us all.

Understand and remember that we now live in what most "men of science" know as the Infinity Loop, "∞" which is the true understanding of the number of man: "666." Man in his present state numerically is represented by the number 6 because of the events that occurred in the Garden of Eden which led to mankind's expulsion from paradise, and to this present state of imperfection which ultimately leads to death. Mankind is trapped in a time loop and the number, "666," represents our past, present and future. Yahweh has bought back the wages of sin and granted mankind amnesty from his/her shortcomings. He has restored humanity's original station within creation and the universe. Because Yahweh is just, He has allowed us to fight alongside his angelic guard for our freedom, and held back the scourge of off world entities trapped here in this dimension. Yahweh has placed warnings for those in search of him, safeguarding Children of Light from entities that only wish to see our destruction. Yahweh has placed a time loop around our solar system in order to prevent the needless suffering and loss of spiritual life. For Yahweh is merciful and does not wish to see his most precious creation endure the wrath of evil for long and forever which brings light to the fact that we are our ancestors and we are our future selves!

Those who have had that ancient knowledge and have died in the past, now live in the present and are looking to exploit that fact! Lucifer has used his children to build a time displacement /dimensional doorway, (CERN), in the attempt to go back in time and undo Yeshua's sacrifice, and to release his original conspirators known as the {Two Hundred or Fallen Ones} who are stuck in an alternate universe, so they can continue their plans to disrupt, destroy and corrupt Yahweh's creation before their time is up. Some of us may have asked to come back to this realm of existence after death to help stop Lucifer and his legions from succeeding in his plans to destroy the world of mankind and beyond.

We are now headed towards the crossroads of the infinity loop, where the past meets the present and the present meets the past; the very time in which the Creator has designated for Lucifer and his cohort's destruction to take place. With tremendous urgency, the powers that be, frantically devised a despicable plan to open a dimensional doorway, so as to let loose the flesh eating demons and monsters of old. "The Dark Star System" is due to return, and with its return, comes the living Creator, which will disrupt the time loop and confuse all sentient beings on this planet. Subsequently, this arrival will open the veil that divides and conceals dimensions and will unfortunately release powerful and destructive forces that will do battle against the Children of Light.

Those in power wish to release them before their time is up so they can destroy us for all time, and gloat before their own demise occurs. It is imperative that those who have allied themselves with the dark forces of creation be warned! To unravel the threads of time, and ultimately try to re-create "The Golden Age" of your masters shall at first fail to produce fruit and you shall suffer at the hands of your invisible masters. When evil men of renown return and bring into operation that god forsaken man-made machine that will enable those who have fallen from on high to walk the Earth once more, by peeling back the veil of space-time and dimensional spectrums, they will truly regret it! All you with lustful eyes who have set out to create a One World Order where Lucifer controls all of mankind and the entire globe through 5G, in opposition of the creator, while dooming humanity to destruction, will most surely die first at the hands of the Fallen Ones.

For you have sentenced all mankind to a world of complete spiritual and physical slavery, resulting in total entrapment and tyranny of the entire human race until his demise alongside theirs come to pass. Lucifer has controlled the wonderful creating power of humanity from the invention of the wheel, encouraging them to create machinery of war, in order to go to war with the Creator himself! At the time of the Creator's return, man shall go against their very own Creator. From close examination of ancient manuscripts and texts, the book of Revelation confirms the validity of these future events, and stands as fact for the human race. But assuming the Creator wishes nothing but the survival of all mankind, puts doubt in the ancient narrative. We control the narrative! Revelation is nothing more but a self-fulfilling prophecy, but only if we allow it to be! When examining such texts, one must take into account that all men are liars by default, and assume all historical texts should be given secondhand and even third hand status because of the fallen nature of those in control of the levers of literature throughout history. For the "Victors of War" write the history of time past, but not necessarily the factual accounts.

The fact that is paramount is knowing that "...there is nothing new under the sun!" It is no question that discernment is required when investigating so-called written truths! With action of investigation and discernment of thought, instead of blind belief in some well-intended religious doctrine, one might come to understand the real truth of the past. Understanding that I know nothing, I would assume that my Creator does not wish to see me or my kind destroyed, for in my mind, he is loving, merciful, and kind. For He makes a way out of the quagmire of sinful temptation devised by the illusion of freedom, when in truth, we are enslaved by the invisible strings of society; consequently, living daily in willful ignorance amongst prosperity and instant gratification.

The days of instant gratification shall vanish as fast as the day turns into night! Like in the days of Noah, the ancient ones shall do battle amongst us all! Will you be caught up into the storm without spiritual armor or shall you be as still as the summer breeze at midday, amongst the blades of battle and warfare? The troubles to come must take place so sayeth the written text, but I know that we have the ability to affect change if we so desire.

So let us take into account those who walked the Earth in our stead, and stand true as the dawn for we are the "Children of Light," not Christians, Jews nor Gentiles! We are Mankind! For we were made to create change in the narrative of those that wish us harm! Remember my fellow human-beings, it is a fight of the spirit: not Good and Bad, but Dark and Light! "For The Light of

Darkness fights aimlessly against the Light of Truth." Although the battle has begun to amplify its dark influence here on to this dimensional realm and world, we shall collectively grow in the spirit of the Creator and overcome the order of destruction.

Know the duplicitous nature of the enemy; we know that all truth in this world has been inverted! Put no trust in any man. Have no "Trump" card in your quiver, but only carry arrows of truth as your ammunition. Let courage be your light of hope, for the days ahead are dark. The road is narrow and full of pitfalls. Go forth into the world as angels amongst demons! Although we do not remember the brave stance all Children of Light took within the heavenly places outside of time, we must be assured that we have valiantly volunteered to come back to this plane of existence and engage the rebel forces that have been thrown back to this third dimensional realm, the original place of Lucifer's rebellion: Earth.

We are and shall be victorious! For the children of the book have awakened, and no longer will allow secondhand manuscripts of ancient times or places captivate their imagination with lies! Put no faith in men, for men are liars and the liars have control of the printing press, for they always have, be it Christian, Gentile, Jew or Muslim! Your enemy has taken your faith as hostage to evil ways, making you believe and think the opposite of your own beautiful nature, making you think you're beast- like when instead you are loving.

The enemy has us kill one another, so they themselves wouldn't have to do the work of their father, Lucifer. For they knew the day would come when we all will come together as one under the "truth" of the Creator, and band the rule of man over man into asunder! The day has come when we shall break free from sin and death and take our place in the heavenly places with our Creator, Yahweh. We will go forth into the universe as Children of Light, ultimately creating as Yahweh sees fit. For the key of hierarchy shall be placed back into the hands of the Creator. Mankind will flip the key of hierarchy on the Earth, where the people shall be on top and the state shall serve from the bottom, and those that serve shall prosper as much or little as the modest average person on the face of the planet.

I wish I could inform you of how I came to these conclusions but I'll leave the details for another day, and another book, for the journey has just begun. My fellow men and women, please understand that we must physically fight the powers that be! We as a collective body must come together as one people around the world! We can easily defeat those that destroy, rape, murder and steal all that is good in creation, and come back from total destruction. Off world entities, alongside the so-called "Royal Family," and their minions are behind all woes on this planet! If you willingly allow a man to rule over you, you deserve what you get!

These men have no power; WE DO!!!

No person has the right to rule over another person, period! The geometry of hierarchy must be used to enhance society, not be a tool to lord over mankind! No civil servant should ever enrich himself/herself once entering into the service of the "We the People!" The Hierarchical symbol must be inverted when applied to humanity's affairs here on Earth with humanity on top of the hierarchal structure, and civil servants—i.e. "Government" on the bottom of it! No man of service shall have more wealth then that of the least in society. Yahweh's Laws shall be the laws of the planet! Only then shall his kingdom come on Earth as it is in heaven.

Off world entities are in fact on this planet and in charge of it, alongside their evil seed! The Creator is here and the war is at its end! Wormwood and its system that interacts with that of our Solar System is here! Look to the Sky Children of Light, for your salvation is near. Whether you believe my words to be true or false, please take this advice: "If money is the root of all evil, then selfishness is the soil in which the seeds of evil germinate!" For no man wishes to kill his fellow man by nature, for it is and has always been the elite class or rulers, alongside off-world entities, who enslave the mind of mankind that makes us think we are war-like! We all have been lied too from birth, told to be religious, patriotic, and fight for justice and freedom for one's country, but no person can truly be free with the blood of another person on his hands!

Learn to say "No" to those in power when asked to kill your fellow man. Never raise a hand towards your brother for any cause, and war will be no more, for we the people have the freewill to say "Yes" or "No!" Take your side in this universal war my friend and choose either Light or Dark, for there is no middle ground! Standing in the middle of the road in this universal and spiritual war is the most dangerous place to be! The children of the book, meaning the Mosaic Law, have forgotten their way. Religion is your enemy! True Children of Light have no religion, and they know their Creator's words. They know that all men are liars and know that all books written in antiquity must be suspect and examined with discernment. The credibility of the Scribes and Pharisees is in the realm of secondhand information, for truth has only one author, and we must remember this ancient fact; he who controls history controls his brother in conquest!

The word of Yahweh was delivered to man by Moses on two granite stones, so it is said: "The Ten Commandments!" All other texts are stories of men. Some may be of great advice and instruction, but never held as fact or wholly, for most are used by the victor of war to control their victims without a leash! All words are magical and can be made to either enslave or empower.

Yahweh's laws weigh lightly on those that carry them within their hearts, but stings those of darkness like that of a scorpion's tail! Understand the true teachings of Yeshua! No man has the right to rule over his fellow man! Come out of Babylon ye of little faith, for trust in men only leads to death! Search your heart and see that the love of your Creator resides within you. The whole world lies in the hands of the wicked one, not everyone, but your Church, Synagogue or Mosque in Lucifer's temple of deceit. Love your Creator Yahweh! Love your neighbor like you love yourself! For the word "love" is a two-edged sword, for one can love what is fowl and corrupted, so be careful when using that term "love." Know the origins of religion, ideology, theology and history of our civilization. All knowledge was given to mankind by the fallen ones! Good and Evil, and the reins of power over mankind have never left their off-spring's hands! They have controlled all information and knowledge of the universe from the beginning of the heavenly rebellion until now. Understanding that fact alone should be elementary to the common man, yet most are all victims to ideology and personal belief in fairytales spewed by the church. Please judge a tree by its fruit! What has the history of religion and belief proven without fail? It has proven to destroy hope and faith in each other, consequently dividing humanity from its foundations, and made trust in our fellow man unobtainable!

The truth shall set you free! Free from what? Free from tyranny and free from ignorance of our natural inheritance! The truth shall also set one free from death, ultimately never having another human-being or intelligent entity other than one's Creator ruling over this three-dimensional realm! These were, are, and will always be the hidden teachings of the Nazarene, Yeshua, who is known as the first Apostate! Yeshua took the lost and spiritually starved Children of Light out of the hands of the Children of Darkness: The Synagogue of Satan. These wicked rulers did and still do the work of their father, Lucifer! They steal, they lie, and they kill while they destroy mankind's ability to inherit their future. Let thy kingdom come! Let thy will be done here on Earth like it is in Heaven! We as Children of Light are at WAR! And we shall live as such until Yeshua and his Army returns! What enemy lets his foe operate openly within his camp?! How stupid could one be?! We are to love what is good, and hate what is evil, yet who sets the perimeters of what is either?! Surely not men! The right to dictate what is good and what is evil belongs to our Creator who has designed this majestic universe in which we live, and not to his enemy!

Know your surroundings ye Children of Light, for you're on captured ground, and the Serpent has been thrown down to this dimension and planet! It is his to do as he sees fit, ultimately roaring like a hungry lion, ready to devour all of Yahweh's creation. The enemy is jealously envious of our inheritance, and has vowed to destroy us all as he descends into oblivion, alongside his cohorts in rebellion against The Heavenly Host of Hosts!

These are the words of a liar, for all men fall short of truth! Yet witnessing the truth of creation, I cannot stress the importance of the search. I know that I know nothing, but love for my Creator compels me to write these words, in hope that all sentient beings, be it those of darkness or light, understand what is at stake, for it is mankind's inheritance of everlasting life, traversing the stars, and the ultimate destruction of this planet, and the significance of the nature of this test plane of existence in which we live. Adam and Eve were created perfect in the eyes of their Creator, yet deceived by one that coveted our uniqueness, being created in the image of our Creator was like a slap in the face of those created first. Because mankind is made in the image and likeness of our Creator, that most un-wholly being, Lucifer, envied the entire whole of creation on this planet. We were born enslaved by sin, and tricked into believing that death is our only pathway into the heavens! That is the ancient story we all have read and put blind faith in, or allowed hatred within our heart; yet none know firsthand the true story in time! So know you know nothing, and let the truth of the past ring out by practicing the word of the Creator, and you shall see its power within your life day and night.

But ultimately you will find out that there is more than your wellbeing at stake! What is at stake has nothing to do with your wellbeing at all, but rather who has the right to dictate how all sentient beings must behave in all verses and how they shall live their lives throughout eternity! No prophet am I! For who can profit from slavery?! Fear of failing the Creator is enough to write these words with certainty and sincerity. Did you not know that warnings of shunning by the Creator comes to those who proclaim themselves men of god?! The thought of not being known by my Creator's champion, Yeshua, scares me to death! Who am I to tell this story? A tale of truth that I myself did not have the privilege of witnessing stands null. I only speak what comes from the spirit and heart, not from knowing. Full of sin is my track record, yet still I cling to my Creator's words like a vice-grip! As I practice the ten edicts more and more each day, I understand the nature of the unseen, and know nothing of the pain, sorrow and death that awaits those who have forsaken the ten edicts. It has nothing to do with me. For life is stranger than fiction and my words are those of a two-edged sword, for duplicity holds sway over us all. Yet all must choose a side, right or wrong in this spiritual war!

What applies for me, applies for you! We all are of Adam's seed, and none has superiority over the other! So what makes you saved when I am not?! I'm stuck on a prison planet, just like you! This is not a game; this is a nightmare! Children are being sacrificed as I write these words! Some are being beaten and sexually abused before discarded or eaten! Are they saved?! Wake Up! You live on this planet Earth don't you?! Just as they do. We all are trapped on this three-dimensional battlefield, a battle dripping in the blood of the innocent, where darkness controls all information. So who are we to validate the words of ancient text when none of us has access to what actually happened in the past?! Yet we are a species lost in amnesia, for we are the past, present and future spirits of old. Once the secret code of the infinity loop takes hold of the masses, the choice of a side must take place! For our Creator is just, and all sentient-beings are valued and sacred in his eye, so lock-down has been declared! No spirit can escape or enter this realm without the Most High's proclamation! This is a war zone my friend! But look up! For our salvation draws near! The cries of innocence reach up into the heavens, yet the prayers of ignorance never leave the ground. We all have been misled in our eagerness to find truth, putting much faith in men of stature, and social prominence that we cannot see the obvious; all have fallen short! None have the right way, but all have what is right within them.

The powers that rule over this planet are in themselves Gods of Falsehood! The Creator is not a God! He is the rightful ruler of his creation! Those that oppose him, use that term (god) to identify themselves, who are many. Yahweh is one! There is no other. We should know that all information comes from the fallen ones, and those that kill our fellow man, the victor. The very concept of Theology itself comes from the fallen ones! Be sure to know that you and all mankind are inmates on this planet! Inmates who are in the hands of the wicked one! Children of Darkness control the levers of knowledge on this planet, for there is no way the enemies of light would allow any Child of Light access to any truth that will set them free from this existence! Children of Light are hated by those in power on this planet, please wake up! You may be trapped, but you still have free will. Yahweh's law is written within you, so please use it! Be smart! No one can stop you from understanding that no man has the right to rule over you! Yahweh's burden is light, and there are no rituals in his worship. He asks very little of us! He only gave us ten tenets to observe, and all are good for instruction, good for all manners of life, and sufficient for us to regain what we lost in the past. Our heritage is everlasting life, traversing the universe, and taking our place above those who enslave us now! It is one thing knowing the path to walk, but another thing walking it! Long ago, I had to learn to talk the talk and walk the walk, just as you all will one day. But like all things worth having, we must work hard to achieve our goals, and the words I speak now shall come with a price. I had to walk the road less traveled to come to these conclusions.

The road itself is the very definition of peril, but the age old questions must be answered for true salvation such as: Why?! Why are we here?! Why is there so much pain and suffering?! Why is life so hard?! Why is god allowing so much evil to flourish?! Therefore, the time had come for me to walk the lonely walk into understanding the unknown, but the Creator had to wash out the stains of unrighteousness to one born into the belly of the beast. Forged in fire purifies one's journey in life! For the journey takes a lifetime for a mayfly. One must travel down the road of woe to understand one's follies and go back to his/her true birthplace called "home" before one can truly understand Yahweh's purpose.

I had completed the circle that all servants of truth and light must complete. I journeyed from the only home I'd known as a child, to the other side of the country to find my self-worth and the truth of a creator that must exist so as to serve him more then I served myself and all I loved, only to return to the one place I vowed to never return, yet my creator and heavenly father had other plans for me.

I would follow the road he set forth for me instead of the road I'd set forth for myself. The circle of life had been completed, and now the forging process had begun, although I had no clue nor understanding of the process, but believe me when I say, I would soon find out! Tell me black man, how would you like a white man calling you a Nigga? Would you be okay with that? For that is what we do when we call Yeshua, "Jesus." Would that not offend you if you were he? Well, what if your enemy that hunted you down and killed your family, burned your crops, and sacrificed your children by the millions to Moloch began calling those that followed the teachings of Yeshua, "Jesus follower" as an insult; would that be okay? Would you put up with that if you were a true follower of Yeshua or even prefer your assailant to call you by a name you distain or even having the name of insult condoned and accepted?! The name "Jesus" was given in disrespect of Yeshua's sacrifice, so tell me why are Children of Light associating themselves with the name given to them (Christian) by those who conquered their forefathers, namely the Roman Empire or the Catholic Church? What say you Christian, Jew, or Gentile?

For the name of Jesus is Zeus disguised, and Christ is Crisco or grease, and symbolically sexual in nature; did you not know that?! Yeshua is the one who opened the eyes of those who were lost by religious dogma, and took those who were lost and led them towards life, for mankind was under the great deception of theology given by the Two Hundred Watchers of old, just as we are today. Why can't you give him that honor by calling him by his true name, Yeshua, and not calling him Jesus Christ, a so-called phantom? I do!

All mantels or titles of religion must be torn asunder; no longer shall humanity be placed in a block and closed off by ideology and religious dogma. No longer shall humanity shut themselves off from their fellow man, for we all shall follow Yahweh's tenets and finally be free from man's rule.

EDGAR FRENCH, JR.